A Revised Handbook
to the
FLORA OF CEYLON

VOLUME I

AMARANTHACEAE

BOMBACACEAE

CLUSIACEAE

COMPOSITAE

CONNARACEAE

CONVOLVULACEAE

DIPTEROCARPACEAE

ELATINACEAE

FABACEAE

MIMOSACEAE

TT 78–52029/01

A Revised Handbook
to the
FLORA OF CEYLON

VOLUME I

Sponsored jointly by the
University of Peradeniya,
Department of Agriculture, Peradeniya, Sri Lanka,
and the Smithsonian Institution,
Washington, D.C., U.S.A.

General Editor

M.D. DASSANAYAKE

Editorial Board

M.D. DASSANAYAKE and F.R. FOSBERG

Published for the Smithsonian Institution, and the
National Science Foundation, Washington, D.C.,
by Amerind Publishing Co. Pvt. Ltd., New Delhi

February 1980

Published for the Smithsonian Institution, pursuant to
an agreement with the National Science Foundation,
Washington, D.C., by Amerind Publishing Co. Pvt. Ltd.,
66 Janpath, New Delhi 110001

Available from the U.S. Department of Commerce,
National Technical Information Service,
Springfield, Virginia 22161

Printed at Oxonian Press Pvt. Ltd., Faridabad, India

FOREWORD

The Handbook to the Flora of Ceylon, by Henry Trimen, published in 1893–1900, was in its time, one of the most comprehensive and outstanding floras available for any comparable tropical area. In 1931 A.H.G. Alston added a volume of additions, updating, and corrections to the original five volumes. These six volumes for many years served their purpose very well.

However, the original Handbook was published in a very small edition, and the paper on which it was printed, as was usually the case at the time, was very poor and has deteriorated very badly. Hence the Handbook has for years been absolutely unobtainable, and there are very few copies available even in libraries in Ceylon. Furthermore, botanical science has made substantial progress since the Handbook appeared, and many of Trimen's taxonomic and nomenclatural conclusions are now outdated. Also, with more thorough botanical exploration, new plants have been found to be members of the Ceylon flora. Hence, a new edition of this magnificent work was long overdue.

For quite a number of years Professor B.A. Abeywickrama had in mind a revision of Trimen's Handbook. But heavier and heavier administrative duties consumed his time and there was little opportunity for work on the Ceylon flora, though he did produce, in 1959, an updated Checklist of the Ceylon Flora, which has been most useful to botanists.

Fortuitously, in 1967, the Smithsonian Institution initiated a number of research projects in Ceylon, in cooperation with Ceylonese institutions and scientists. These included an investigation of several problems in plant ecology, with which Prof. Abeywickrama was associated as Co-Principal Investigator. These projects were financed by the Smithsonian using U.S. excess foreign currency under the provisions of Public Law 480.

While we were discussing the ecological investigations, Prof. Abeywickrama wondered if it might not be possible to initiate, using PL-480 support, a project for the revision of Trimen's Handbook to the Flora of Ceylon. I offered to work up a cooperative proposal and submit it to the Smithsonian Special Foreign Currency Program.

This was duly done, approved, and a year's tentative budget authorized. The project was started under the joint auspices of the Smithsonian Institution, the Ceylon Department of Agriculture and the University of Ceylon. I was appointed Principal Investigator. Co-Principal Investigators are Prof. B.A. Abeywickrama, Dr. J.W.L. Peiris, Mr. D.M.A. Jayaweera, Prof. M.D. Dassanayake and Mr. K.L.D. Amaratunga. The plan was to enlist the cooperation of botanists, from wherever available, who were preferably experts in particular families represented in the Ceylon flora. These monographers would be given a period of field work in Ceylon, an opportunity to study the specimens in the Ceylon National Herbarium, in the Royal Botanic Gardens, Peradeniya, with expenses met by the Smithsonian Institution. In return, they would provide updated manuscripts of their families for the revised Handbook, which would then be published by the University of Ceylon, with Smithsonian financing.

This enterprise was initiated in February, 1968, and has been continued without interruption since that date. Quarters for the work, herbarium and library, and other facilities have been furnished by the Division of Systematic Botany of the Department of Agriculture, Peradeniya and by the Botany Department, Faculty of Science, University of Ceylon, Peradeniya. We have enjoyed the cooperation of the U.S. Embassy, Colombo, various Ceylon government departments and agencies, especially the Wildlife Department and the Forest Department, and of many plantations and individuals in all parts of Ceylon, too numerous to enumerate.

Special thanks must be offered to Professor Dieter Mueller-Dombois, of the Botany Department, University of Hawaii, who was for two years Principal Field Investigator for the plant ecology project, and who, on top of his duties in that capacity, supervised the activities of the flora project staff, facilitated the work of the visiting botanists, and acted as finance officer of the project. Without his help, the flora project could not have got started.

Special thanks are also offered to Dr. Marie-Hélène Sachet, Research Botanist, Smithsonian Institution, who, though in no official capacity in the Project, has carried much of the administrative burden, at a sacrifice of her own work. The members of the Flora Project staff at Peradeniya directed by Mr. F.H. Popham, Smithsonian Representative in Ceylon, also deserve great credit for their willing and enthusiastic assistance to the visitors, handling and processing of specimens, typing of labels and manuscripts, and keeping the Project's work going.

The materials on which the flora revisions are based are the visiting botanists' own collections, the herbarium at Peradeniya, personal collections of Mr. K.L.D. Amaratunga and the late Mr. Thomas B. Worthington of Kandy, and materials housed in various foreign herbaria, especially those of Kew, British Museum, and the Indian National Herbarium, Calcutta for the use of which we are grateful to those in charge. A large amount of valuable material was amassed as vouchers for the ecological observations mentioned above and has been utilised by the flora project botanists. Sets of the specimens collected under the auspices of the Smithsonian projects are deposited and permanently available in the U.S. National Herbarium and the Ceylon National Herbarium, Peradeniya. Partial sets are also being deposited in several other Ceylon institutions and in a number of herbaria with tropical interests in other parts of the world.

The resulting revised treatments of the families are to be published, as material accumulates, in volumes of convenient size, without regard to the order of families, starting with the present one. Those families, previously published in fascicles 1 and 2, are to be republished, in revised form, in the new format, as manuscripts are received from the authors. An editorial format has been suggested by us, but the content of each revision and the taxonomic conclusions are those of the various authors. An attempt has been made to have the nomenclature in accord with International Code of Botanical Nomenclature, but the application of the Code is, again, the final responsibility of the authors.

A comprehensive index to these volumes will be prepared and published as a separate volume.

It is hoped that, after the Handbook treatments are published, simplified versions can be prepared, suitable for lower school use and for the use of non-botanists.

We also have the hope that the new Handbook will stimulate active interest in the plant resources of Ceylon. Above all, it is hoped that this interest will bring about the establishment of more national parks and nature reserves in all parts of Ceylon, in order that the remarkable Ceylon flora may still have a suitable range of habitats in which to live. By this means, only, the species will be able to survive for the use and pleasure of many future generations of Ceylonese and of visitors from other parts of the world. Without a great increase in such reserves, at the present rate of deforestation and bringing land under agriculture, very many species will surely become extinct in the near future, as some probably already have.

F.R. FOSBERG,
Botanist, Emeritus,
Smithsonian Institution,
Washington, D.C., U.S.A.

CONTENTS

A Revised Handbook
to the
FLORA OF CEYLON

VOLUME I

AMARANTHACEAE

(by C.C. Townsend*)

Nomen conservandum. Type genus: *Amaranthus* L., Sp. Pl. ed. 1.989. 1753.
Lit.: Schinz in Pflanzenfam. ed. 2, 16c: 7–85. 1934.

Annual or perennial herbs or subshrubs, rarely scandent. Leaves simple, alternate or opposite, exstipulate, entire or almost so. Inflorescence a dense head, loose or spike-like thyrse, spike, raceme or panicle, basically cymose, bracteate; bracts hyaline to white or coloured, subtending one or more flowers. Flowers hermaphrodite or unisexual (plants dioecious or monoecious), actinomorphic, usually bibracteolate, frequently in ultimate 3-flowered cymules; lateral flowers of such cymules sometimes modified into scales, spines or hooks. Perianth uniseriate, membranous to firm and finally more or less indurate, usually falling with the ripe fruit included, tepals free or somewhat fused below, frequently more or less pilose or lanate, green to white or variously coloured. Stamens as many as and opposite to the petals, rarely fewer; filaments free or commonly fused into a cup at the base, sometimes almost completely fused and 5-toothed at the apex with entire or deeply lobed teeth, some occasionally anantherous, alternating with variously shaped pseudostaminodes or not; anthers unilocular (bilocellate) or bilocular (4-locellate). Ovary superior, unilocular; ovules 1–many, erect to pendulous, placentation basal; style very short to long and slender; stigmas capitate to long and filiform. Fruit an irregularly rupturing, circumscissile or indehiscent capsule (utricle), usually with thin, membranous walls, rarely a berry or crustaceous. Seeds round to lenticular or ovoid, embryo curved or circular, surrounding the more or less copious endosperm.

A large and almost exclusively tropical family of some 65 genera and over 1000 species, including many cosmopolitan "weeds" and a large number of xerophytic plants.

KEY TO THE GENERA

1 Leaves alternate
  2 Fertile flowers each subtended by 2 lateral sterile modified flowers consisting of antler-like scales..**4. Digera**
  2 Fertile flowers not subtended by modified sterile flowers

---

*Royal Botanic Gardens, Kew.

1

3 Ovary multiovulate, ovules 4–20 or more.............................**1. Celosia**
3 Ovary uniovulate
  4 Pseudo-staminodes present...**7. Aerva**
  4 Pseudo-staminodes absent
    5 Stamens 1–2; tepals villous....................................**8. Nothosaerva**
    5 Stamens 3–5; tepals not villous
      6 Flowers bisexual; seed with a conspicuous, membranous, cupular aril..........
       ....**2. Allmania**
      6 Flowers unisexual; seed with no aril............................**3. Amaranthus**
1 Leaves opposite
  7 Fertile flowers subtended by modified sterile flowers bearing strongly accrescent hooked
    or glochidiate spines, forming a burr in fruit
    8 Pseudo-staminodes present.....................................**5. Cyathula**
    8 Pseudo-staminodes absent......................................**6. Pupalia**
  7 Fertile flowers not subtended by such modified sterile flowers
    9 Flowers unisexual in lax panicles; leaves variegated (green with yellow veins to purplish
      with pink veins), orbicular to ovate-orbicular, commonly emarginate......**15. Iresine**
    9 Flowers bisexual, in dense to lax heads or spikes; leaves rarely variegated, if so the
      leaves narrower and never emarginate
      10 Filaments fused almost to the top, the tube 5-toothed, the teeth deeply bilobed with
        the anthers set between the lobes; bracteoles with a vertical dorsal crest.........
        ....**14. Gomphrena**
      10 Filaments fused at the base only or free, with or without pseudo-staminodes; brac-
        teoles not dorsally cristate
        11 Pseudo-staminodes absent
          12 Stamens 2; perianth 1–1.25 mm long.........................**8. Nothosaerva**
          12 Stamens 5; perianth over 3 mm long..........................**12. Psilotrichum**
        11 Pseudo-staminodes present
          13 Leaves very narrow, linear-filiform; capsule circumscissile, longitudinally split at
            maturity..**9. Trichurus**
          13 Leaves not linear-filiform; capsule indehiscent or irregularly rupturing
            14 Flowers in dense, sessile axillary heads....................**13. Alternanthera**
            14 Flowers in elongate, pedunculate spikes with the flowers increasingly distant
              below in fruit
              15 Bracteoles strongly spinous with the excurrent midrib; tepals only slightly
                unequal...**10. Achyranthes**
              15 Bracteoles orbicular, hyaline, not spinous; tepals distinctly unequal, the outer
                with a sharper, frequently recurved tip....................**11. Centrostachys**

1. CELOSIA

L., Sp. Pl. ed. 1. 205. 1753; Gen. Pl. ed. 5. 96. 1754. Type species: *C. argentéa* L., Sp. Pl. ed. 1. 205. 1753.

Annual or perennial herbs, sometimes rather woody at the base, occasionally scandent. Leaves alternate, simple, entire or somewhat lobed. Flowers small, hermaphrodite, bibracteolate, in bracteate spikes or more generally dense to lax axillary and terminal bracteate thyrses (the uppermost frequently forming a panicle), lateral cymes lax to dense and forming sessile clusters, the inflorescence then spiciform. Perianth segments 5, free, equal. Stamens 5, the filaments fused below into a short sheath, the free portions deltoid below and filiform above or (not in our area) more or less swollen or with teeth projecting on either side of the anther; anthers bilocular (4-locellate). Ovary with few to many, rarely (not in Ceylon) solitary ovules; style elongate to almost obsolete, stigmas usually 2–3. Capsule circumscissile, sometimes thickened above. Seeds black, usually strongly compressed and shining, roundish, feebly to strongly reticulate, grooved or tuberculate.

About 50 species in the warmer regions of both Old and New Worlds, especially Africa.

KEY TO THE SPECIES

1 Style 5–7 mm long; perianth segments 6–10 mm; flowers usually in a stout, silvery or pink spike 1.5–2.2 cm wide...**1. C. argentea**
1 Style at most 0.75 mm long; perianth segments 2–3 mm; flowers in a slender inflorescence up to 0.7 cm wide
  2 Inflorescence axis glabrous or almost so; leaves long-acuminate, much longer than broad...**2. C. pulchella**
  2 Inflorescence axis more or less densely patent-hairy; leaves blunt or sub-acute at the apex, not or scarcely longer than broad.........................**3. C. polygonoides**

1. Celosia argentea L., Sp. Pl. ed. 1. 205. 1753; Moq. in DC., Prod. 13. 2: 242. 1849; Hook. f. in Fl. Br. Ind. 4: 714. 1885; Trimen, Handb. Fl. Ceylon 3: 393. 1895; Gamble, Fl. Pres. Madras 1166. 1925 repr. 816. 1957. Type: Linnean specimen 288/1 (LINN, lectotype).

Annual herb, erect, 0.4–2 m, simple or with many ascending branches. Stem and branches strongly ridged and often sulcate, quite glabrous. Leaves lanceolate-oblong to narrowly linear, acute to obtuse, shortly mucronate with the excurrent midrib, glabrous; lamina of the leaves from the centre of the main stem 2–15 × 0.1–3.2 cm, tapering below into an indistinctly demarcated, slender petiole; upper and branch leaves smaller, markedly reducing; leaf axils often with small-leaved sterile shoots. Inflorescence a dense (rarely laxer below), many-flowered spike, 2.5–20 × 1.5–2.2 cm, silvery to pink, conical at first but becoming cylindrical in full flower, terminal on the stem and branches, on a long, sulcate peduncle up to c. 20 cm long, which often lengthens during flowering. Bracts and bracteoles lanceolate or the lower deltoid, 3–5 mm, hyaline, more or less aristate with the excurrent midrib, persistent after the fall of the flower. Perianth segments 6–10 mm, narrowly elliptic-oblong, acute to rather blunt, shortly mucronate with the excurrent midrib, with 2–4 lateral nerves ascending more than halfway up each segment, margins widely hyaline. Filaments very delicate, free part subequalling or exceeding the staminal sheath, sinuses rounded with no or very minute intermediate teeth; anthers and filaments creamy to magenta. Stigmas 2–3, very short, the filiform style

5–7 mm long; ovary 4–8-ovulate. Capsule 3–4 mm, ovoid to almost globular. Seeds c. 1.25–1.5 mm, lenticular, black, shining, testa very finely reticulate.

D i s t r. A practically pantropical weed.

E c o l. Frequent, and locally abundant, as a weed of cultivated fields, waste ground and roadsides and in dried-up river beds in the drier regions, scarce elsewhere. Often found very abundantly in one or two fields but not seen in others for some distance around.

V e r n. Kiri-henda (S; = "white spoon").

I l l u s t r. Tadulingam & Venkatanarayana, Handb. S. Indian Weeds 256, pl. 106. 1932.

S p e c i m e n s E x a m i n e d. JAFFNA DISTRICT: near Vallipuram, in flooded rice field, 13 Jan. 1970, *Clayton 5219* (K, PDA, US); disturbed ground c. 10 miles along road from Paranthan to Mullaittivu, 22 Feb. 1973, *Townsend 73/86* (K, PDA, US); Elephant Pass, 24 Feb. 1973, *Townsend 73/114* (K, PDA, US). VAVUNIYA DISTRICT: by roadside, 121 miles along road from Kandy to Jaffna, 21 Feb. 1973, *Townsend 73/72* (K, PDA, US). ANU-RADHAPURA DISTRICT: Mihintale, May 1838, *Gardner s.n.* (PDA); bet-ween Yakalla and Muriyakadewala, 10 March 1973, *Townsend 73/200* (K, PDA, US). POLONNARUWA DISTRICT: dry sandy riverbed, Heerati Oya, 2 miles NW of Bakamune, 6 Oct. 1971, *Jayasuriya 321* (K, PDA); by the tank, Minneriya, 13 March 1973, *Townsend 73/219* (K, PDA, US). MATALE DISTRICT: near milepost 36 between Naula and Dambulla, 22 Jan. 1972, *Jayasuriya et al. 564* (K, PDA). TRINCOMALEE DISTRICT: Trincomalee, waste ground under palms, 4 May 1927, *Alston 541* (PDA); Dambulla—Trin-comalee road just E. of Kantalai, nr. milestone 137, 14 March 1973, *Townsend 73/241* (K, PDA, US). BATTICALOA DISTRICT: Batticaloa, *Gardner s.n.* (PDA). MONERAGALA DISTRICT: Uda Walawe area, in irrigated land, 17 Oct. 1971, *Balakrishnan & Jayasuriya NBK 894* (K, PDA). HAMBAN-TOTA DISTRICT: between Siyambalagoda and Tunkama, not common, 14 Sept. 1969, *Cooray 69091413 R* (K, PDA, US).

2. Celosia pulchella Moq. in DC., Prod. 13, 2: 238. 1849; Hook. f. in Fl. Br. Ind. 4: 715. 1885; Trimen, Handb. Fl. Ceylon 3: 393. 1895; Gamble, Fl. Pres. Madras 1166. 1925, repr. 816. 1957. Type: *Wallich 6913* (K, lectotype).

Erect, annual herb, 24–50 cm, branched from the base upwards, stems and branches striate and often angled, glabrous or more commonly thinly pilose with short multicellular hairs about the nodes. Leaves deltoid-ovate to lan-ceolate, usually considerably longer than wide, more or less long-acuminate at the apex, cuneate to truncate at the base, lamina 1.8–11 × 1–5 cm, glabrous or thinly furnished with short hairs especially at the base and along the petiole, which is 0.6–3 cm in length. Inflorescences slender and unbranched, terminal on the stem and branches, 4–19 × 0.4–0.7 cm, spikelike with the flowers distant to more or less approximate, solitary or in 2–4-flowered sessile clusters, the axis glabrous or very sparingly shortly hairy, peduncle 1–2 cm. Bracts and bracteoles lanceolate to deltoid-ovate, 1–1.5 mm, glabrous or ciliate, white, acute, mucronate with the excurrent green midrib. Perianth segments elliptic-oblong, 2.5–3 mm, whitish or pale straw-coloured, mucronate with the shortly excurrent midrib. Free portion of filaments very much longer than the very short basal sheath. Stigmas 2, recurved, subequalling the c. 0.5–0.75 mm style; ovary with numerous (9–14) ovules. Capsule pyriform, the apex slightly (rarely spongy-) incrassate. Seeds c. 0.8 mm, roundish-reniform, compressed, black, reticulate with convex areolae which lengthen towards the margin, rarely uniformly verruculose.

D i s t r. Local as a weed of waste or sandy ground and along roadsides in the centre and south of the island. Also in India.

I l l u s t r. Wight, Ic. Pl. Ind. Or. 5, pl. 1768. 1852.

N o t e s. I have not yet seen *C. pulchella* with 3 stigmas, but it probably varies with 2–3 stigmas as do *C. polygonoides*, *C. trigyna* and other species of this genus.

S p e c i m e n s E x a m i n e d. ANURADHAPURA DISTRICT: Anuradhapura, abundant, 17 Dec. 1884, *s. coll. s.n.* (PDA). MATALE DISTRICT: Lagalla, Sept. 1887, *s. coll. s.n.* (PDA). NUWARA ELIYA DISTRICT: Maturata, see *Thwaites*. MONERAGALA DISTRICT: Wellawaya, roadside, 3 Jan. 1928, *Alston A. 42* (PDA). HAMBANTOTA DISTRICT: Ruhuna National Park, at Rugamtota, upper alluvial forest on humus sand, 24 Feb. 1968, *Mueller-Dombois & Cooray 68022407* (PDA, US).

3. Celosia polygonoides Retz., Obs. 2: 12. 1781; Moq. in DC., Prod. 13. 2: 238. 1849; Hook. f. in Fl. Br. Ind. 4: 715. 1885; Trimen, Handb. Fl. Ceylon 3: 394. 1895; Gamble, Fl. Pres. Madras 1166. 1925, repr. 817. 1957. Type: Tranquebar, *König*, Hb. Retzius (LD, holotype).

Erect perennial herb, somewhat woody at the base, 15–40 cm, branched from about the base upwards, stem and branches striate and often angled, more or less densely furnished with patent, yellowish, multicellular hairs or rarely glabrous. Leaves broadly ovate to deltoid-ovate, usually scarcely longer than wide, obtuse to subacute at the apex, shortly cuneate to truncate or subcordate at the base, lamina 1.3–3.4 × 1.2–3 cm, more or less pilose especially on the lower surface of the principal veins or rarely almost glabrous, decurrent into a slender, 4–20 mm petiole. Inflorescences slender and unbranched, terminal on the stem and branches, 4–17 × 0.4–0.6 cm, spikelike with the flowers in distant to approximate 2–few-flowered sessile clusters, the axis more or less densely patent-hairy, peduncle 1–3 (−6) cm. Bracts and bracteoles glabrous, ovate to deltoid-ovate, 1.5–2 cm, whitish, acute, mucronate with the excurrent green midrib. Perianth segments elliptic-oblong,

2–2.5 mm, white, mucronate with the shortly excurrent green midrib; style, stigmas, anthers and apex of filaments and ovary deep rose-purple. Free portion of filaments c. 3 times as long as the basal sheath. Stigmas 2–3, more or less circinately recurved, subequalling or longer than the c. 0.5–0.75 mm style; ovary with numerous (12–20+) ovules. Capsule 2.5–4 mm, urceolate, the tip spongy-incrassate with the style set in a distinct depression. Seeds c. 0.6 mm, round, compressed, black, uniformly verruculose.

D i s t r. Locally in some quantity as a weed of cultivated and waste land in the dry zone in the north of the island. Also in India.

I l l u s t r. Tadulingam & Venkatanarayana, Handb. S. Indian Weeds 258, pl. 107. 1932.

S p e c i m e n s   E x a m i n e d. JAFFNA DISTRICT: rear garden of the Palm Court Hotel, Jaffna, abundant, 22 Feb. 1973, *Townsend 73/76* (K, PDA, US). MANNAR DISTRICT: Mannar, *Gardner s.n.* (PDA); ibid. on garden soil in the northern outskirts of the town, 23 Feb. 1973, *Townsend 73/103*, (K, PDA, US) and on compacted soil in the St. Saviour's College compound, 23 Feb. 1973, *Townsend 73/104* (K, PDA, US). The unlocalised specimen *C.P. 2240* presumably originated in this district.

The thickening of the capsule apex in this species is similar to that of the African *C. anthelminthica* Aschers. No specimens referable to *C. polygonoides* on the characters of leaf shape and inflorescence indumentum have been seen other than with such a thickened capsule apex and with uniformly verruculose seeds. Unfortunately, one or two specimens (e.g. from Ceylon, *C.P. 2238*) have been seen with the foliage and glabrous inflorescence axis of *C. pulchella* but the capsule and seeds exactly as in *C. polygonoides*. Thus capsule and seed characters, normally very useful in *Celosia*, appear to break down between this pair of species. Although they are closely related, it does not seem possible to postulate hybridity since specimens similar to *C.P. 2238* have been seen from the Nilgiri Hills in S. India, where *C. polygonoides* is not known to occur. Nor do the two species grow together in Ceylon.

2. ALLMANIA

R. Br. ex Wight in Hook. J. Bot. 1: 226, t. 128. 1834.

Annual herb with entire, alternate leaves. Inflorescence terminal or leaf-opposed, capitulate (condensed cymose); cymes usually with ultimate groups of 3 hermaphrodite flowers, the central sessile or subsessile and subtended by a single bract, the laterals pedicellate and subtended by a bract and two bracteoles, the latter subequalling the perianth. Perianth segments 5, persistent. Stamens 5, shortly monadelphous at the base, without alternating pseudo-staminodes; anthers bilocular (4-locellate). Style long and slender, with two short, divergent stigmas. Ovary with a single erect ovule. Fruit a thin-walled utricle, circumscissile. Seed erect, compressed, firm, furnished at the base with a membranous, bilobed, cupular aril.

A monotypic genus.

Allmania nodiflora (L.) R. Br. ex Wight in Hook. J. Bot. 1: 226, t. 128. 1834; Hook. f. in Fl. Br. Ind. 4: 716. 1885; Trimen, Handb. Fl. Ceylon 3: 394. 1895, incl. var. *longipedunculata*; Gamble, Fl. Pres. Madras 1167. 1925, repr. 817. 1957. Type: Ceylon, Herb. Hermann 1: 2. 101 (BM, lectotype).

Celosia nodiflora L., Sp. Pl. ed. 1. 205. 1753.
Chamissoa nodiflora (L.) Mart., Nova Acta Phys. Med. Acad. Caes. Leop. Carol. Nat. Cur. 13: 187. 1826; Moq. in DC., Prod. 13 (2): 249. 1849.
Allmania albida R. Br. ex Hook. f., Fl. Br. Ind. 4: 717. 1885.

Annual, spreading, prostrate or ascending, 0.1–0.9 m, much branched from the base and usually also to about the middle of the stem; stem usually red, often flexuose below, both it and the branches more or less angular, sulcate or striate, glabrous or almost so to moderately pilose with whitish hairs. Leaves very variable in shape and size, linear to elliptic, oblong, obovate or spathulate, lamina 1.2–9 × 0.2–3 cm, rounded or occasionally widely retuse to apiculate or shortly acuminate at the mucronate apex, cuneate to attenuate at the base with an indistinctly demarcated petiole up to c. 1.5 cm long, glabrous or with the lower surface thinly pilose. Inflorescences at first green or reddish, finally stramineous, subsessile to long-pedunculate, terminal and leaf-opposed, globose to ovoid, erect or somewhat cernuous, compact or occasionally laxer, 0.75–2 cm long; bracts membranous, deltoid-ovate, acuminate, aristate with the considerably excurrent darker midrib, c. 3–4 mm; bracteoles longer and narrower, c. 4–5 mm, the arista more or less equalling the lamina in length; bracts and especially the bracteoles scabrid-pubescent along the keel. Tepals narrowly elliptic-lanceolate, 4–5 mm, silvery-membranous with a single reddish or greenish midrib which is excurrent in a very short mucro, glabrous or more or less pilose dorsally. Filaments 3–3.5 mm, subulate. Style long and slender, at first included but finally shortly exserted. Capsule 3–4 mm, ovoid. Seed 2.5–3 mm, lenticular, black, reticulate with the network more or less shining and the areolae dull.

D i s t r. Tropical Asia from India and Ceylon eastwards to Thailand, Malaya, S. China, Indonesia and the Philippines.

E c o l. Frequent in dry, grassy places, on dry ditches and roadsides, along railway track, on sand dunes and areas of loose sand generally, also in rock crevices, ascending to c. 1660 m. When growing in dense grass it is not conspicuous and can easily be overlooked.

V e r n. Kumatiya (S).

I l l u s t r. Wight, Ic. Pl. Ind. Or. 5, pl. 1770. 1852.

Specimens Examined. JAFFNA DISTRICT: Jaffna, *Gardner s.n.* (PDA); between Mulliyan and Chempiyanpattu, c. 32 miles E.S.E. of Jaffna, near narrow arm of lagoon, 24 Feb. 1973, *Townsend 73/113* (K, PDA, US). POLONNARUWA DISTRICT: railway track between Kaduruwela and Welikanda, near road milestone 60 on road from Polonnaruwa to Batticaloa, 15 March 1973, *Townsend 73/257* (K, PDA, US). PUTTALAM DISTRICT: Chilaw, edge of jungle on dunes, 30 May 1931, *Simpson 8141* (PDA); Wilpattu National Park, Kali Villu opposite Bungalow, 1 May 1969, *Cooray & Balakrishnan 69050103R* (PDA, US). NUWARA ELIYA DISTRICT: Sunnyslope Estate, below Hakgala, 1889, *Nock s.n.* (PDA); Hakgala, patana on way to Ambewela (?), 28 Jan. 1928, *J.M. Silva s.n.* (PDA). TRINCOMALEE DISTRICT: Trincomalee, Feb. 1891, *s. coll. s.n.* (PDA); bank of shallow roadside ditch near milestone 137 on road from Dambulla to Trincomalee just E. of Kantalai, 14 March 1973, *Townsend 73/242.* BATTICALOA DISTRICT: Batticaloa, *Gardner s.n.* (PDA). RATNAPURA DISTRICT: Ratnapura, March 1853, *Gardner s.n.* (PDA). MONERAGALA DISTRICT: near Nilgala, Jan. 1888, *s. coll. s.n.* (PDA). HAMBANTOTA DISTRICT: sea shore, Kirinda, Dec. 1882, *s. coll. s.n.* (PDA); Ruhuna National Park, 200 m W. of Karaugaswala junction, open grassy vegetation on sand between shrubs, 10 Dec. 1967, *Mueller-Dombois & Cooray 67121069* (PDA, US) (several other records from the Park area).

3. AMARANTHUS

L., Sp. Pl. ed. 1. 989. 1753; Gen. Pl. ed. 5. 427. 1754. Type species: *A. caudatus* L. Lit.: Aellen in Hegi, Illustr. Fl. Mitteleuropa ed. 2 Bd. 3/2, Lief. 1: 465–516. 1959. The figures of tepals, ovary etc. in this work are invaluable for identification, especially in the absence of reliably determined material.

Annual or more rarely perennial herbs, glabrous or furnished with short and gland-like or multicellular hairs. Leaves alternate, long-petiolate, simple and entire or sinuate. Inflorescence basically cymose, bracteate, consisting entirely of dense to lax axillary clusters or the upper clusters leafless and more or less approximate to form a lax or dense "spike" or panicle. Flowers dioecious or monoecious, bibracteolate; perianth segments (2–) 3–5, free or connate at the base, membranous, those of the female flowers sometimes slightly accrescent in fruit. Stamens free, usually similar in number to the perianth segments; anthers bilocular (4-locellate). Stigmas 2–3. Ovule solitary, erect. Fruit a dry capsule, indehiscent, irregularly rupturing or commonly dehiscing by a circumscissile lid. Seeds usually black and shining, testa thin; embryo annular, endosperm present.

About 50 species, chiefly in the warmer temperate and subtropical regions of the world, about a dozen species being more or less cosmopolitan weeds in the tropics also. A genus of considerable difficulty taxonomically, especially the "grain amaranths" such as *A. caudatus* and *A. hybridus*, which have been cultivated from ancient times. The foliage of several species is eaten as a kind of spinach in numerous parts of the world.

KEY TO THE SPECIES

1 Leaf axils with paired spines...**1. A. spinosus**
1 Leaf axils without paired spines
  2 Upper flower clusters without subtending leaves, forming a spike-like or paniculate inflorescence
    3 Fruit dehiscent, with a circumscissile lid
      4 Terminal inflorescence alone spiciform, the axillary inflorescences forming more or less rounded clusters, or if axillary spikes present these with globose clusters at junction with stem; bracteoles terminating in awns which are fine, flexuose and more or less hair-like above...**5. A. tricolor**
      4 Terminal and at least some (generally most) of the upper axillary inflorescences spiciform, without globose clusters at the junction of stem and peduncle; bracteoles terminating in stout, rigid awns
        5 Terminal spike of inflorescence long and pendulous; perianth segments of female flowers broadly obovate or spathulate, overlapping each other......**4. A. caudatus**
        5 Terminal spike of inflorescence scarcely pendulous, shorter; perianth segments of female flowers lanceolate to narrowly oblong or narrowly spathulate, not imbricate
          6 Male flowers usually confined to a short distance at the end of each spike, rarely scattered among the females; lid of capsule strongly wrinkled near the line of dehiscence; inflorescence green.......................................**2. A. dubius**
          6 Male flowers intermingled with the females along the length of the spikes; lid of capsule smooth or at most slightly longitudinally sulcate below; inflorescence (in Ceylon) commonly red......................................**3. A. hybridus**
    3 Fruit indehiscent
     7 Fruit scarcely exceeding the perianth, strongly muricate, more or less globose; seeds with shallow, scurfy verrucae on the reticulate pattern of the testa......**7. A. viridis**
     7 Fruit distinctly exceeding the perianth, distinctly compressed; seeds without shallow verrucae...**6. A. lividus**
  2 All flowers in axillary clusters, not forming terminal leafless spikes or panicles
    8 Perianth segments, excluding the long, slender, pale-tipped terminal awn, longer than the capsule...**5. A. tricolor**
    8 Perianth segments, excluding the shorter (to c. 0.75 mm) terminal awn, shorter than the capsule...**8. A. graecizans**

1. Amaranthus spinosus L., Sp. Pl. ed. 1. 991. 1753; Moq. in DC., Prod. 13 (2): 260. 1849; Hook. f. in Fl. Br. Ind. 4: 718. 1885; Trimen, Handb. Fl. Ceylon 3: 396. 1895; Gamble, Fl. Pres. Madras 1170. 1925, repr. 819. 1957. Type: Linnean specimen 117/27 (LINN, lectotype).

Annual herb, erect or slightly decumbent, up to c. 1.5 m in height. Stem stout, sometimes reddish, usually branched, angular, glabrous or increasingly furnished above (especially in the inflorescence) with long, multicellular, flocculent hairs. Leaves glabrous, or thinly pilose on the lower surface of the primary nervation, long-petiolate (petioles up to c. 9 cm, sometimes longer than the lamina), the lamina ovate to rhomboid-ovate, elliptic, lanceolate-oblong or lanceolate, c. 1.5–12 × 0.8–6 cm, subacute or more commonly blunt or retuse at the tip with a distinct, fine, colourless mucro, cuneate or attenuate at the base; each leaf-axil bearing a pair of fine and slender to stout and compressed spines up to c. 2.5 cm long. Flowers green, in the lower part of the plant in axillary clusters 6–15 mm in diameter, towards the ends of the stem and branches the clusters leafless and approximated to form simple or (the terminal at least) branched spikes usually up to c. 15 cm long and 1 cm wide. Lower clusters entirely female, as are the lower flowers of the spikes; upper flowers of the spikes male, mostly for the apical $\frac{1}{4}$–$\frac{2}{3}$ of each spike. Bracts and bracteoles deltoid-ovate, pale-membranous, with an erect, pale or reddish awn formed by the excurrent green midrib, bracteoles shorter than, sub-equalling or little exceeding the perianth, commonly smaller than the bracts. Perianth segments 5, those of the female flowers c. 1.5–2.5 mm, narrowly oblong or spathulate-oblong, obtuse or acute, mucronulate, frequently with a greenish dorsal vitta; those of the male flowers broadly lanceolate or lanceolate-oblong, acute or acuminate, only the midrib green. Stigmas (2–)3, flexuose or reflexed, 1–1.5 mm. Capsule ovoid-urceolate with a short inflated neck below the style base, c. 1.5 mm, regularly or irregularly circumscissile or rarely indehiscent, the lid rugulose below the neck. Seed 0.75–1 mm, compressed, black, shining, very faintly reticulate.

D i s t r. Cosmopolitan in the warmer regions of the world, of presumed American origin; casual in temperate regions.

E c o l. Extremely common on waste and disturbed ground, along road-sides, as a garden weed etc., especially in the neighbourhood of towns and villages. Probably the commonest member of the family on the island.

V e r n. Katu-tampala and Katukera (S); Mudkirai (T).

I l l u s t r. Wight, Ic. Pl. Ind. Or. 2, pl. 513. 1840–43.

S p e c i m e n s E x a m i n e d. TRINCOMALEE DISTRICT: Trincomalee Rest House lawn, 13 Jan. 1968, *Comanor 772* (PDA, US). MATALE DISTRICT: Dambulla, 23 June 1967, *Amaratunga 1335* (PDA). KANDY DISTRICT: roadside between Kandy and Peradeniya, 3 Nov. 1967, *Comanor 520* (PDA, US); Central Agricultural Experimental Station, Gannoruwa, 30 Jan. 1973, *Burtt & Townsend 26* (E, K, PDA, US); Gelioya, bank of paddy field, 26 May 1964, *Amaratunga 825* (PDA). COLOMBO DISTRICT: Panna-wala, waste and cultivated ground, 28 June 1967, *Amaratunga 1352* (PDA); Ja-ela/Gampaha road, coconut plantation, 15 Feb. 1968, *Comanor 1019* (PDA, US). BADULLA DISTRICT: c. 1 mile N. of Boralanda on road to Palu-gama, 28 Feb. 1973, *Townsend 73/127* (K, PDA, US). HAMBANTOTA DIS-TRICT: Tissamaharama, roadside, 23 Jan. 1968, *Comanor 840* (PDA, US).

2. Amaranthus dubius Mart., Pl. hort. Acad. Erlang. 197. 1814, nomen nudum, ex Thell., Fl. Adv. Montpellier 203. 1912. Type: "ex horto Erlangensi", ex herb. Schwaegrichen (M, neotype) see Townsend in Kew Bull. 29: 471-2. 1974.

Amaranthus tristis Moq. in DC., Prod. 13 (2): 260. 1849, non L.

Erect annual herb, mostly up to c. 90 cm (rarely to 1.5 m). Stem rather slender to stout, usually branched, angular, glabrous or increasingly furnished upwards (especially in the inflorescence) with short to rather long, multicellular hairs. Leaves glabrous, or thinly and shortly pilose on the lower surface of the primary venation, long-petiolate (petioles up to c. 8.5 cm, sometimes longer than the lamina), lamina ovate or rhomboid-ovate, 1.5–8 (–12) × 0.7–5 (–8) cm, blunt or retuse at the tip with a distinct, fine mucro formed by the excurrent nerve, cuneate (usually shortly so) at the base; leaf axils without spines. Flowers green, in the lower part of the plant in axillary clusters, 4–10 mm in diameter, towards the ends of the stem and branches the leafless clusters approximated to form simple or more rarely branched spikes c. 3–15 (–25) cm long and 6–8 (–10) mm wide. Lower clusters of flowers entirely female, the spikes generally showing a few male flowers at the tips only (rarely in more than c. the apical 1 cm), occasionally with male flowers also scattered among the lower female flowers. Bracts and bracteoles deltoid-ovate, pale-membranous with an erect pale or reddish awn formed by the excurrent green midrib, bracteoles shorter than or subequalling the perianth, rarely slightly exceeding it. Perianth segments (4–) 5, those of the female flowers c. 1.5–2.75 mm, narrowly oblong or spathulate-oblong, obtuse or sometimes (particularly those approaching the male flowers) acute, mucronulate, frequently with a greenish dorsal vitta above; those of the male flowers broadly lanceolate or lanceolate-oblong, generally acuminate, only the thin midrib green. Stigmas 3, flexuose or reflexed, c. 0.75–1 mm. Capsule ovoid-urceolate with a short inflated neck below the style base, c. 1.5–1.75 mm, circumscissile, the lid strongly rugulose below the neck. Seed 1–1.25 mm, compressed, black shining, faintly reticulate.

D i s t r. Practically cosmopolitan in the tropical regions of the world, probably of comparatively recent spread.

E c o l. Roadside and waste places, often in company with *A. viridis* or *A. spinosus*, not uncommon; also cultivated for its foliage and seeds.

U s e s. Enquiries in the Kegalle District locality revealed it to be a highly esteemed green vegetable. At Trinity Farm the Superintendent informed me that it was sown broadcast among other crops (it was collected in a *Vigna* field) as human green vegetable food and as a source of bird seed; it had not been distinguished from *A. viridis*.

V e r n. In common with other *Amaranthus* species, bears the vernacular name of Tampala (S).

I l l u s t r. Willdenow, Hist. Amaranth. t. 5, f. 10. 1790, as *A. tristis*.

N o t e. *A. dubius* is the only known polyploid *Amaranthus*, and is probably an allotetraploid with *A. spinosus* as one parent; *A. hybridus* L. seems the most likely candidate as the other. It has been demonstrated that hybrids between *A. spinosus* and *A. dubius* occur naturally (see Grant in Canadian J. Bot. 37: 1063–70. 1959), the hybrids being said to resemble *A. dubius*. Such hybrids may well occur in Ceylon.

In spite of various characters mentioned in the literature, I have been able to find no infallible means, other than the presence or absence of axillary spines, by which *A. spinosus* and *A. dubius* can be separated in the herbarium—though the generally considerably greater number of terminal male flowers in the spikes of *A. spinosus* is reasonably reliable. In the field, however, both species have a distinct habit, so that with a little familiarity it is possible to pick out colonies of *A. dubius* even from a moving vehicle.

S p e c i m e n s   E x a m i n e d. KANDY DISTRICT: 10 m from Botany Building, University of Ceylon, Peradeniya, in weed canopy, 2 June 1967, *Comanor 341* (PDA, US); roadside, Hatton, 9 Feb. 1973, *Burtt & Townsend 109* (E, K, PDA, US); Trinity Farm, Kundasale, 5 miles E.S.E. of Kandy, cultivated, 25 Feb. 1973, *Townsend 73/118* (K, PDA, US). NUWARA ELIYA DISTRICT: Waste ground close to Talawakele Rest House, 7 Feb. 1973, *Burtt & Townsend 87* (K, PDA, US). RATNAPURA DISTRICT: Karagala Estate between Higgahena and Bopath Ella waterfall, abundant, 12 Feb. 1973, *Townsend 73/60* (K, PDA, US). COLOMBO DISTRICT: Kalagedihena, 24 Sept. 1969, *Amaratunga 1850* (PDA) (p. max. p.—mixed with *A. viridis*). BADULLA DISTRICT: by Nuwara Eliya road just W. of Badulla, 1 March 1973, *Townsend 73/134* (K, PDA, US).

3. Amaranthus hybridus L., Sp. Pl. ed. 1. 990. 1753.

Annual herb, erect or less commonly ascending, up to c. 2 (–3) m in height, not infrequently reddish-tinted throughout. Stems stout, branched, angular, glabrous or thinly to moderately furnished with short or long multicellular hairs (increasingly so above, especially in the inflorescence). Leaves glabrous, or thinly pilose on the lower margins and underside of the primary nervation, long-petiolate (petioles up to 15 cm but even then scarcely exceeding the lamina), lamina broadly lanceolate to rhomboid or ovate, 3–19 (–30) × 1.5–8 (–12) cm, gradually narrowed to the blunt to subacute mucronulate tip, attenuate or shortly cuneate into the petiole below. Flowers in yellowish, green, reddish or purple axillary and terminal spikes formed of cymose clusters, which are increasingly closely approximate upwards, the terminal inflorescence varying from a single spike to a broad, much-branched, panicle up to c. 45 × 25 cm in length and breadth, the ultimate spike not infrequently nodding; male and female flowers intermixed throughout the spikes. Bracts

and bracteoles deltoid-ovate to deltoid-lanceolate, pale-membranous, acuminate and with a long, pale to reddish-tipped, erect arista formed by the stout,
excurrent, yellow or greenish midrib, subequalling to much exceeding the
perianth. Perianth segments 5, 1.5–3.5 mm, lanceolate or oblong, acute-aristate or the inner sometimes blunt in the female flowers, only the midrib at
most greenish. Stigmas (2–) 3, erect, flexuose or recurved, c. 0.75–1.25 mm.
Capsule subglobose to ovoid or ovoid-urceolate, 2–3 mm, circumscissile, with
a moderately distinct to obsolete "neck"; lid smooth, longitudinally sulcate,
or sometimes rugulose below the neck. Seed black and shining or pale, compressed, 0.75–1.25 mm, almost smooth centrally, faintly reticulate around the
margins.

subsp. **hybridus**

Amaranthus frumentaceus Buch.-Ham. in Roxb., Fl. Ind. ed. 2, 3: 609.1832;
    Trimen, Handb. Pl. Ceylon 3: 396. 1895.

Longer bracteoles of the female flowers mostly about 1.5–2 times long as
the perianth. Stigma-bases and upper part of lid of fruit swollen, so that the
fruit has a distinct "neck".

I l l u s t r. Fiori & Paoletti, Ic. Fl. Ital.: 121, f. 1047. 1899, as *A. hypochondriacus*.

1. var. **hybridus.** Type: Linnean specimen 1117/19 (LINN, lectoype).

Amaranthus chlorostachys Willd., Hist. Amaranth. 34, t. X f. 19. 1790.
Amaranthus hybridus L. subsp. *hypochondriacus* (L.) Thell. var. *chlorostachys*
    (Willd.) Thell., Fl. Adv. Montpellier 205. 1912.

Inflorescences green. No material of this variety has been seen from
Ceylon, but it probably occurs; see note under next variety.

2. var. **erythrostachys** Moq. in DC., Prod. 13 (2): 259. 1849. Type: Cultivated
material from Toulouse Botanic Garden (G–DC., holotype, photo).

Amaranthus hypochondriacus L., Sp. Pl. ed. 1. 991. 1753 (*"hypochondriacus"*);
    Trimen, Handb. Fl. Ceylon 3: 396. 1895.

Inflorescences red.

D i s t r. Cultivated only, as a field crop or ornamental.
N o t e. Said by Trimen to be "cultivated for its seeds, forming a grain
known as 'Landesi' ". In the locality south of Kagama where the plant was
gathered, I was informed that the plant is widely grown in the area for the
grain, which is used to make the small savoury cake known as "Aggla"; in this
locality it was seen as a mixed crop with *Sorghum*, and between Maradan-

kadawala and Tirappana with *Sorghum* and *Eleusine*. All the Ceylonese material seen is of the selected pale-seeded form.

Both of these varieties (var. *erythrostachys* more commonly) are grown as garden ornamentals in the tropics, under the English name of "Prince of Wales' Feathers"; and both probably occur as such in gardens in Ceylon.

V e r n. Rana Tampala (S).

S p e c i m e n s E x a m i n e d. ANURADHAPURA DISTRICT: between 60 and 61 miles from Kandy, south of Kagama on the road to Jaffna, 24 Feb. 1973, *Townsend 73/117* (K, PDA, US); west side of road between Maradankadawala and Tirappana, 8 March 1973, *Townsend 73/186* (K, PDA, US). MATALE DISTRICT: Cultivated patch near Sigiriya Wewa, 11 March 1973, *Townsend 73/205* (K, PDA, US). TRINCOMALEE DISTRICT: Trincomalee, cultivated 1860, *s. coll. s.n.* (K).

Subsp. *hybridus* occurs throughout the tropical, subtropical and warmer temperate regions of the world both as a weed and in cultivation as one of the "grain amaranths"; in cooler temperate regions it is found mostly as a casual—e.g. as a common "wool alien" in Europe.

Subsp. *cruentus* (L.) Thellung also occurs in the tropics of the Old World; it seems to be most frequent in the Malay-Indonesian region, the Philippines and Africa, but may also turn up in Ceylon. It differs from subsp. *hybridus* in having the longer bracteoles of the female flowers mostly 1–1.25 times as long as the perianth segments, and the mature stigma-bases and upper part of the lid of the fruit scarcely swollen, so that the fruit has no distinct "neck".

4. Amaranthus caudatus L., Sp. Pl. ed. 1. 990. 1753; Trimen, Handb. Fl. Ceylon 3: 396. 1825. Type: Herb. Hort. Cliff. p. 443 *Amaranthus* (BM, lectotype).

Annual herb, erect, up to c. 1.5 m in height, commonly reddish or purplish throughout. Stem rather stout, not or sparingly branched, glabrous or thinly furnished with rather long, multicellular hairs which are increasingly numerous upwards. Leaves glabrous, or more or less sparingly pilose along the margins and lower surface of the primary venation, long-petiolate (petiole to c. 8 cm but not longer than the lamina), lamina broadly ovate to rhomboid-ovate or ovate-elliptic, 2.5–15 × 1–8 cm, obtuse to subacute at the mucronulate tip, shortly cuneate to attenuate below. Flowers in axillary and terminal red or green spikes formed of increasingly approximated cymose clusters, the terminal inflorescence varying from a single, elongate, tail-like, pendulous spike to 30 cm or more long and c. 1.5 cm wide, to a panicle with the ultimate spike so formed; male and female flowers intermixed throughout the spikes. Bracts and bracteoles deltoid-ovate, pale-membranous, acuminate and with a long, pale or reddish, rigid, erect arista formed by the yellow-green or reddish stout, excurrent midrib, the longest up to twice as long as the perianth. Perianth segments 5; those of the male flowers oblong-elliptic, 2.5–3.5 mm, acute, aristate; those of the female flowers 1.75–2.5 mm, broadly obovate to spathulate, distinctly imbricate, abruptly narrowed to a blunt or sometimes faintly emarginate, mucronate tip. Stigmas 3, c. 0.75 mm, erect or flexuose. Capsule 2–2.5 mm, ovoid-globose, circumscissile, slightly urceolate, the lid smooth or furrowed below, abruptly narrowed to a short, thick neck. Seeds shining, compressed, black, almost smooth and shining, or commonly subspherical with a thick yellowish margin and a translucent centre, c. 0.75–1.25 mm.

D i s t r. said by Trimen to be "common in gardens", but not seen on a recent visit to the island. Probably a cultivated derivative of the American *A. quitensis* H.B.K. (cf. Sauer, Ann. Mo. bot. Gdn. 54: 127. 1967), and unknown wild.

V e r n. According to de Fonseka and Vinasithamby (1971) the vernacular name Rana Tampala (S) is applied to this species. In English it is well-known as "Love Lies Bleeding".

I l l u s t r. Fiori & Paoletti, Ic. Fl. Ital. 120, f. 1045. 1899.

5. Amaranthus tricolor L., Sp. Pl. ed. 1. 989. 1753; Back. in Fl. Mal. Ser. 1, 4 (2): 77. 1949. Type: Linnean specimen 117/7 (LINN, lectotype).

Amaranthus tristis L., Sp. Pl. ed. 1. 989. 1753.
Amaranthus melancholicus L., Sp. Pl. ed. 1. 989. 1753; Moq. in DC., Prod. 13 (2): 262. 1849.
Amaranthus gangeticus L., Syst. Veg. ed. 10. 1268. 1759; Hook. f. in Fl. Br. Ind. 4: 720. 1885; Moq. in DC., Prod. 13 (2): 260. 1849; Trimen, Handb. Fl. Ceylon 3: 396. 1895; Gamble, Fl. Pres. Madras 1171. 1925, repr. 819. 1957.
Amaranthus mangostanus L., Cent. Pl. 1: 32. 1755; Moq. in DC., Prod. 13 (2): 261. 1849; Hook. f. in Fl. Br. Ind. 4: 720. 1885; Trimen. Handb. Fl. Ceylon. 3: 397. 1895; Gamble, Fl. Pres. Madras 1171. 1925, repr. 820. 1959.
Amaranthus polygamus L., Cent. Pl. 1: 32. 1755.

Annual herb, ascending or erect, attaining c. 1.25 m or more in cultivation. Stem stout, usually much-branched, it and the branches angular, glabrous or furnished in the upper parts with sparse (or denser in the inflorescence), more or less crisped hairs. Leaves glabrous, or thinly pilose on the lower surface or the primary venation, green or variably purplish-suffused, very variable in size, long (up to c. 8 cm) petiolate, the lamina broadly ovate, rhomboid-ovate or broadly elliptic to lanceolate-oblong, emarginate to obtuse or acute at the apex, at the base shortly cuneate to attenuate, decurrent along the petiole. Flowers green to crimson in more or less globose clusters c. 4–25 mm in diameter, all or only the lower axillary and distant, the upper often without subtending leaves and increasingly approximate to form a thick terminal spike of variable length, male and female flowers intermixed. Bracts and bracteoles broadly or deltoid-ovate, bracteoles subequalling or shorter than the perianth, pale-membranous, broadest near the base and narrowed upwards to the green midrib, which is excurrent to form a long, pale-tipped awn usually at least half as long as the basal portion and not rarely equalling it. Perianth segments 3, 3–5 mm long, elliptic or oblong-elliptic, narrowed above, pale-membranous, the green midrib excurrent into a long, pale-tipped awn; female flowers with the perianth segments slightly accrescent in fruit. Stigmas 3, erect or recurved, c. 2 mm. Capsule ovoid-urceolate with a short neck below the style-base, 2.25–2.75 mm, circumscissile, membranous, obscurely wrinkled. Seed 1–1.5 mm, black or brown, shining, very faintly reticulate, lenticular.

D i s t r. Asia from Pakistan to China and Japan in the north and Indonesia in the south; also in New Guinea and New Hebrides and smaller Pacific Island groups (Fiji etc.). Native area blurred by cultivation. Introduced and/or cultivated in Africa, West Indies etc.

E c o l. Occurs both wild as a weed of waste and cultivated ground, and also cultivated, chiefly in the lower, drier areas.

U s e s. Grown as a green vegetable akin to spinach, and as such highly esteemed. The forms with very highly purplish-suffused leaves are quite ornamental.

V e r n. Tampala, Sudu-Tampala (S); Araikkirai, Chirukirai (T).

I l l u s t r. Wight, Ic. Pl. Ind. Or. 2, pl. 514. 1840–43, as *A. tristis*.

N o t e. I do not find the infraspecific division of this species employed by Aellen (in Hegi, Illustr. Fl. Mitteleuropa, ed. 2, Bd. 111/2 Lief. 1: 494–496. 1959) to be practicable. All three subspecies recognised in that work are sympatric, and all manner of difficulties arise in attempting to apply to the system to specimens at hand. One finds separate plants of the same gathering with a terminal leafless spike developed or not—or even the spike developed or not on equally robust branches of the same plant. Similarly, plants with a short terminal spike and the lower axillary inflorescences globose are clearly transitional between those otherwise identical but with no terminal spike and others with all the lower inflorescences also terminating in a spike. Special attention was paid to this species in the field in Ceylon, and both colonies found with consistently no terminal spike to the inflorescence (represented by *Townsend 73/101 & 73/109*) were dwarf, quite prostrate forms of heavily-trodden ground. I therefore attempt no infraspecific division of *A. tricolor* and concur with Trimen that from the evidence gleaned in Ceylon, *Amaranthus mangostanus* is "scarcely more than a stunted prostrate form of *A. gangeticus* (i.e., *A. tricolor*)".

S p e c i m e n s E x a m i n e d. JAFFNA DISTRICT: roadside waste in Jaffna town, 24 Feb. 1973, *Townsend 73/109* (K, PDA, US). MANNAR DIS-

TRICT: waste ground almost in the centre of Mannar town, 23 Feb. 1973, *Townsend 73/101* (K, PDA, US). KANDY DISTRICT: edge of ditch just E. of Urugala, 6 March 1973, *Townsend 73/167* (K). TRINCOMALEE DIS-TRICT: Trincomalee, 18 April 1860, *Glenie 2, 9,* (PDA); Trincomalee, 28 July 1951, *Gunaratnam s.n.* (PDA); cultivated in garden on hill by Kantalai Tank, c. 20 miles S.W. of Trincomalee, 14 March 1973, *Townsend 73/239* (K, PDA, US). GALLE DISTRICT: weed in garden between Hiniduma and Tala-gala (on road to Pitabeddara), 14 Feb. 1973, *Townsend 73/56* (K, PDA, US) (disclaimed as cultivated by the owner of the garden).

6. Amaranthus lividus L., Sp. Pl. ed. 1. 990. 1753.

Annual herb, erect, ascending or prostrate, 6–60 (–90) cm. Stem slender to stout, simple or considerably branched from the base or upwards, more or less angular, green to reddish or yellow, quite glabrous or more rarely with 1-few-celled, short hairs above and/or in the inflorescence. Leaves glabrous or more rarely with scattered few-celled hairs near the base on the lower sur-face of the primary venation, long-petiolate (petioles up to c. 10 cm, frequent-ly longer than the lamina), lamina ovate to rhomboid-ovate, 1–8 × 0.6–6 cm, shortly cuneate below, the apex usually broadly and distinctly emarginate, mucronulate. Flowers green, in slender to stout terminal and axillary spikes or rarely panicles, terminal spikes c. 0.6–11 cm long and 0.3–2 cm wide, or the lower axillary inflorescences of dense cymose clusters up to 2 cm in diameter (in small forms the terminal spikes sometimes indistinct); male and female flowers intermixed. Bracts and bracteoles deltoid-ovate to lanceolate, whitish membranous with a short yellow or reddish mucro formed by the excurrent-midrib, bracteoles shorter than or rarely subequalling the perianth. Perianth segments 3 (occasionally 4 or even 5 in cultivated forms), membranous-margined, male and female both varying from lanceolate-oblong, subacute and mucronate to broadly spathulate and obtuse with the thick midrib ceasing below the summit, but the female frequently blunter, 0.75–2 mm. Stigmas 2–3, short, erect or flexuose. Capsule subrotund to shortly pyriform, compressed, exceeding the perianth, 1.25–2.5 mm, usually rather smooth but sometimes wrinkled on drying, indehiscent or rupturing irregularly at maturity. Seeds 1–1.75 mm, round, compressed, dark brown to black, the centre feebly reti-culate and shining, the margin duller, minutely punctate-roughened over the reticulum.

1. subsp. **lividus.** Type: none located, neotype selected as below.

Amaranthus blitum L., Sp. Pl. ed. 1. 990. 1753, nomen confusum; Hook f. in Fl. Br. Ind. 4: 721. 1885 (excl. var. *sylvestris*); Trimen, Handb. Fl. Ceylon 3: 398. 1895.

Amaranthus oleraceus L., Sp. Pl. ed. 2. 1403. 1763.

Plant robust to very robust, with large leaves, generally erect or ascending. Fruit 2 mm or more in length.

N o t e. The species was clearly described by Linnaeus from fresh cultivated material. There are at the British Museum two apparently 18th century specimens of *Amaranthus* labelled "Hort." in identical writing on the reverse side of the sheets. One, labelled "*A. blitum*" is very like the Linnean type of *A. blitum* (Linnean specimen 1118/14); the other, labelled "*A. lividus*", agrees well with Linnaeus's description of *A. lividus*. These two specimens appear to represent plants of early cultivated stock to which Linnaeus could easily have had access, and which came to be known by his names (see Townsend, Kew Bull. 29: 472. 1974). Hence the second specimen has been selected as neotype of *A. lividus*.

As Trimen (p. 398) observed (under the name *oleraceus*) the typical subspecies has not yet been seen in Ceylon. It is widespread in the warmer parts of Europe, east to Middle Asia, China and Japan, N. Africa from Morocco to Egypt, tropical W. & E. Africa south to Malawi, N. America.

I l l u s t r. Willdenow, Hist. Amaranth. t. 5, f. 9. 1790, as *A. oleraceus*.

2. subsp. **polygonoides** (Moq.) Probst, Wolladventivfl. mitteleur. 74. 1949. Type: *Salzmann* 183a (Herb. G—DC., lectotype).

Euxolus viridis (L.) Moq. var. *polygonoides* Moq. in DC., Prod. 13 (2): 274. 1959.
Amaranthus lividus L. var. *polygonoides* (Moq.) Thell. in Rep. Bot. Soc. & Exch. Club 5: 574. 1920.

Plant smaller and neater, with smaller (rarely as much as 4 cm long and usually less) leaves, generally prostrate to decumbent. Fruit 1.25–1.75 mm in length.

D i s t r. Widespread in the warmer temperate regions and tropics of both Old and New Worlds, in Asia from the Caucasus through India to Malaya, Java and New Guinea; Australia; in tropical Africa mostly in the east; Macaronesia, Mascarene Is., S. America from Guyana south to the Argentina. In Europe and N. America often casual.

E c o l. Not uncommon in the central and southern regions of the island, not hitherto observed in the drier regions of the north and east; occurs along roadsides on waste ground, as a garden or plantation weed; also in forest and streams and ditches; alt. 200–1180 m.

N o t e. Apparently confused with *A. graecizans* by Trimen, under the name (incorrect for either species) *A. polygonoides* L.

Opinions will no doubt differ as to whether these two forms should be treated as subspecies or varieties, and true judgment is probably impossible in these weedy species whose country of origin is in doubt. The preponderance of subsp. *polygonoides* in tropical regions (especially uniform in S. America) and the greater frequency of var. *lividus* in the regions of older civilisations (Europe, China), with intermediates frequent only in India and China, led me after some vacillation to choose the former rank.

Specimens Examined. KANDY DISTRICT: Peradeniya, 1860, *s. coll. s.n.* (K); Hatton, 15 May 1906, *Willis s.n.* (PDA); Brunswick Estate, Maskeliya, 16 Nov. 1926, *Wright s.n.* (PDA); sand of river bank below Laksapana Falls, 9 Feb. 1973, *Burtt & Townsend 120* (E, K, PDA, US); roadside, Hunasgiriya, 6 March 1973, *Townsend 73/174* (K, PDA, US): NUWARA ELIYA DISTRICT: roadside, Ambewela, 26 March 1906, *Willis s.n.* (PDA); high forest, Maturata, 8 May 1906, *Willis s.n.* (PDA); near Talawakele, waste ground between road and tea plantation, 9 Feb. 1973, *Burtt & Townsend 107* (E, K, PDA, US). RATNAPURA DISTRICT: Wikiliya Estate, wild in tea, 24 Feb. 1932, *Simpson 9205* (PDA). BADULLA DISTRICT: c. 1 mile N. of Boralanda, waste ground by road to Palugama, 28 Feb. 1973, *Townsend 73/ 126* (K, PDA, US). GALLE DISTRICT: weed in garden at Talagola, on the Hiniduma/Pittabeddara road, 14 Feb. 1973, *Townsend 73/57* (K, PDA, US). HAMBANTOTA DISTRICT: Ruhuna National Park, 200 m S. of bridge in Yala grass flat, 3 May 1968, *Mueller-Dombois 68050321* (PDA, US).

7. **Amaranthus viridis** L., Sp. Pl. ed. 2. 1405. 1763; Hook. f. in Fl. Br. Ind. 4: 720. 1885; Trimen, Handb. Fl. Ceylon 3: 397. 1895; Gamble, Fl. Pres. Madras 1171. 1925, repr. 820. 1957. Type: Linnean specimen 117/15 (LINN, lectotype).

Amaranthus gracilis Desf., Tabl. Ecole Bot. 43. 1804.
Euxolus caudatus (Jacq.) Moq., in DC., Prod. 13 (2): 274. 1849.

Annual herb, erect or more rarely ascending, 10–75 (–100) cm. Stem rather slender, sparingly to considerably branched, angular, glabrous or more frequently increasingly hairy upwards (especially in the inflorescence) with short or longer and rather floccose multicellular hairs. Leaves glabrous or shortly to fairly long-pilose on the lower surface of the primary or most of the venation, long-petiolate (petioles up to c. 10 cm long and the longest commonly longer than the lamina), lamina deltoid-ovate to rhomboid-oblong, 2–7 × 1.5–5.5 cm, the margins occasionally obviously sinuate, shortly cuneate to subtruncate below, obtuse and narrowly to clearly emarginate at the tip, minutely mucronate. Flowers green, in slender, axillary or terminal, often paniculate spikes c. 2.5–12 cm long and 2–5 mm wide, or in the lower part of the stem in dense axillary clusters to c. 7 mm in diameter; male and female flowers intermixed but the latter more numerous. Bracts and bracteoles deltoid-ovate to lanceolate-ovate, whitish-membranous with a very short, pale or reddish awn formed by the excurrent green midrib, bracteoles shorter than the perianth (c. 1 mm). Perianth segments 3, very rarely 4, those of the male flowers oblong-oval, acute, concave, c. 1.5 mm, shortly mucronate; those of the female flowers narrowly oblong to narrowly spathulate, finally 1.25–1.75 mm, the borders white-membranous, minutely mucronate or not, midrib green and often thickened above. Stigmas 2–3, short, erect or almost so. Capsule subglobose, 1.25–1.5 mm, not or slightly exceeding the perianth, indehiscent or rupturing irregularly, very strongly rugose throughout. Seed c. 1–1.25 mm, round, only slightly compressed, dark brown to black with an often paler thick border, more or less shining, reticulate and with shallow scurfy verrucae on the reticulum, the verrucae with the shape of the areolae.

D i s t r. Practically cosmopolitan in the tropical and subtropical regions of the world, penetrating more widely into the temperate regions of the world than many of its allies—e.g. in N. & S. America and in Europe.

E c o l. Almost as common as *A. spinosus* (and locally more so) on waste and disturbed ground, along roadsides, as a garden weed etc., and often associated with it.

U s e s. The leaves of this species, as with others of this genus, are eaten as a kind of spinach.

V e r n. Kura-Tampala (S); Araikkirai (T).

I l l u s t r. Tadulingam & Venkatanarayana, Handb. S. Indian Weeds: 264, pl. 110. 1932.

S p e c i m e n s E x a m i n e d. JAFFNA DISTRICT: c. 10 miles along the road from Paranthan to Mulaittivu, 22 Feb. 1973, *Townsend 73/87* (K, PDA, US). KANDY DISTRICT: weed in Royal Botanic Garden, Peradeniya, 11 April 1927, *Alston 1209* (PDA); Nawalapitiya, waste ground, with *A. spinosus*, 3 Feb. 1973, *Burtt & Townsend 55* (K, PDA, US). COLOMBO DISTRICT: Kalagedihena, 24 Sept. 1969, *Amaratunga 1850* p. min. p. (PDA). KEGALLE DISTRICT: disturbed ground by Colombo road, Kegalle, nr. junction with road from Undugoda, with *A. spinosus*, 12 Feb. 1973, *Townsend 73/44* (K, PDA, US).

8. Amaranthus graecizans L., Sp. Pl. ed. 1. 990. 1753.

Annual herb, branched from the base and usually also above, erect, decumbent or prostrate, mostly up to c. 45 cm (rarely to 70 cm). Stem slender to stout, angular, glabrous or thinly to moderately furnished with short to long, often crisped multicellular hairs which increase upwards, especially in the inflorescence. Leaves glabrous or sometimes sparingly furnished on the lower surface of the principal veins with very short, gland-like hairs, long-petiolate (petiole from 3–4.5 mm, sometimes longer than the lamina), lamina broadly ovate or rhomboid-ovate to narrowly linear-lanceolate, 4–55 × 2.30 mm, acute to obtuse or obscurely retuse at the mucronulate tip, cuneate to long-attenuate at the base. Flowers all in axillary cymose clusters, male and

female intermixed, male commonest in the upper whorls. Bracts and bracteoles narrowly lanceolate-oblong, pale-membranous, acuminate and with a
pale or reddish arista formed by the excurrent green midrib, bracteoles subequalling or usually shorter than the perianth. Perianth segments 3, all 1.5–
2 mm; those of the male flowers lanceolate-oblong, cuspidate, pale-membranous with a narrow green midrib excurrent in a short, pale arista; those of
the female flowers lanceolate-oblong to linear-oblong, gradually to abruptly
narrowed to the variable mucro, the midrib often bordered by a green vitta
above and apparently thickened, the margins pale whitish to greenish. Stigmas 3, slender, usually pale, flexuose, c. 0.5 mm. Capsule subglobose to
shortly ovoid, 2–2.25 mm, usually strongly wrinkled throughout with a very
short, smooth neck, slightly exceeding the perianth, circumscissile or sometimes not, even on the same plant. Seeds shining, compressed, black, 1–1.25
mm, faintly reticulate.

1. subsp. **graecizans**. Type: Linnean specimen 117/3 (LINN, lectotype).

Amaranthus angustifolius Lam., Enc. 1: 115. 1783, nomen illegit.
Amaranthus blitum L. var. *graecizans* (L.) Moq. in DC., Prod. 13 (2): 263.
  1849.

The typical subspecies, with the leaf-blade (in particular of the larger
leaves of the main stem) at least 2.5 times as long as broad, narrowly oblong
to linear-lanceolate, and perianth segments shortly (to c. 0.25 mm) mucronate; it occurs as the dominant form of the species in the warmer parts of
S.W. Asia (Jordan, Arabia, Iraq, S. Iran etc.), in W. tropical and S. Africa
etc., but not in Ceylon. Here the species is represented by the following two
subspecies:

2. subsp. **silvestris** (Vill.) Brenan, Watsonia 4: 273. 1961. Type: Tournefort
specimen 1849 (P, holotype, photo, IDC microfiche neg. 90 no. 19).

Amaranthus silvestris Vill., Cat. Pl. Jard. Strasb. 111. 1807.
Amaranthus blitum L. var. *sylvestris* Moq. in DC., Prod. 13 (2): 263. 1849;
  Hook. f. in Fl. Br. Ind. 4: 263. 1885.

Leaf-blade (particularly of the main stem leaves) broadly to rhomboid-
ovate or elliptic-ovate, less than 2.5 times as long as broad. Perianth segments mucronate, the mucro very short and straight.

D i s t r. Two specimens only have been seen from Ceylon one presumab-
ly wild and the other cultivated (for what purpose is not recorded).
I l l u s t r. Coste, Fl. de la France 3: 173, No. 3066. 1906.
S p e c i m e n s E x a m i n e d. KANDY DISTRICT: cultivated in the
Economic Nursery, Peradeniya, 28 Oct. 1926, *s. coll. s.n.* (PDA). MONER-

AGALA DISTRICT: Kumaradola Estate, Monaragala, 4 March 1928, *Alston 1660* (PDA).

Subsp. *silvestris* occurs in the Old World from the warmer parts of Europe to the cooler regions of western Asia (Caucasus, N. Iran etc.) and north-west India; also in (chiefly east) tropical Africa.

Villars based his species on Tournefort's "Amaranthus sylvestris, & vulgaris Instit. rei herbar". (Hist. pl. env. Paris: 385. 1698), and Tournefort's specimen 1849 is accepted as the holotype. It is beautiful material of subsp. *silvestris* as here understood, and bears the caption "Blitum minus rubens CB". This is clearly a paraphrase of Bauhin's "Blitum rubrum minus" (Pinax 118. 1623), cited by Tournefort in the synonymy of his "*A. sylvestris* etc."

3. subsp. **thellungianus** (Nevski) Gusev in Bot. Zhurn. 57: 462. 1972. Type: Kugitang, Turkmenia, Nevski Pl. Turc. 730 (LE, holotype).

Amaranthus blitum var. *polygonoides* Moq. in DC., Prod. 13 (2): 263. 1849.
Amaranthus polygamus (non L.) Hook. f. in Fl. Br. Ind. 4: 721. 1885, p.p.).
Amaranthus polygonoides (non L.) Trimen, Handb. Fl. Ceylon 3: 397. 1895).
Amaranthus thellungianus Nevski in Act. Inst. Bot. Acad. Sc. U.R.S.S. 1 (4): 311. 1937.

Leaf-blade linear-lanceolate to rhomboid-spathulate; perianth segments long-aristate, awns mostly 0.3–0.75 mm in length and frequently somewhat divergent, bracteoles also long-aristate.

D i s t r. Said by Trimen to be "common" in dry waste places and by roadsides in the dry region, but present-day observations and available herbarium material scarcely bears this out—though it may be common locally. It is also possible that (like J.D. Hooker in the "Flora of British India") Trimen confused the present species with *A. lividus*, which he does not mention. No habitat is given with any of the Ceylon gatherings, but to judge by the situations favoured elsewhere it is to be expected on rather bare, dry, sandy waste ground, in thin turf, etc.

V e r n. Araikkirai (T).

I l l u s t r. Wight, Ic. Pl. Ind. Or. 2, pl. 512. 1840–43.

S p e c i m e n s E x a m i n e d. ANURADHAPURA DISTRICT: Galkulam, Aug. 1885, *s. coll. s.n.* (PDA). TRINCOMALEE DISTRICT: Trincomalee, 1860, *s. coll. s.n.* (PDA). HAMBANTOTA DISTRICT: Tissamaharama, Dec. 1882, *s. coll. s.n.* (PDA); Ruhuna National Park, between Andunoruwa Wewa and Komawa Wewa, 25 March 1970, *Cooray 70032519R* (PDA, US).

Subsp. *thellungianus* occurs almost exclusively in the Indian subcontinent and Middle Asia, where it is the dominant form of the species.

Linnaeus' record of his *Amaranthus polygonoides* for Ceylon, mentioned by Trimen, is clearly an error. The record is not to be found, as might be supposed from Trimen's remarks, accompanying the original description in Amoen. Acad. 5: 409. 1760, but in ed. 2 of the Species Plantarum (p. 1405). *A. polygonoides* is a very different plant from any Ceylonese species, and is confined to the central regions of the American continent and the West Indies.

4. DIGERA

Forssk., Fl. Aeg.-Arab. 65. 1775.

Annual herb with alternate branches and leaves, leaves entire. Flowers small, in long-pedunculate, axillary, spike-like bracteate racemes, each bract subtending a very shortly pedunculate partial inflorescence consisting of a central fertile flower and two highly modified, sterile, unibracteolate lateral flowers. Perianth segments 4–5, the outer pair opposite and sheathing the remaining flower parts, the inner segments much more delicate and hyaline. Stamens 4–5, free, without intermediate staminode-like teeth, filaments fili- form, anthers bilocular (4-locellate). Style filiform; stigmas 2, divergent. Ovary with a single ovule lateral on a curved funicle, radicle descending. Fruit a hard, indehiscent nutlet enclosed by the persistent perianth and falling together with the sterile flowers and bracteoles. Endosperm copious.

A monotypic genus.

1. Digera muricata (L.) Mart. in Nov. Act. Acad. Caes. Leop.-Carol. 13 (1): 285. 1826; Back. in Fl. Males. Ser. 1. 4 (2): 80. 1949. Type: Linnean specimen 287/6 (LINN, lectotype).

Achyranthes muricata L., Sp. Pl. ed. 2. 295. 1762.
Achyranthes alternifolia L., Mant. 50. 1767; Mant. Alt. 344. 1771.
Digera arvensis Forssk., Fl. Aeg.-Arab. 65. 1775; Moq. in DC., Prod. 13 (2): 324. 1849; Hook. f. in Fl. Br. Ind. 4: 717. 1885; Trimen, Handb. Fl. Ceylon 3: 395. 1895; Gamble, Fl. Pres. Madras 1169. 1925, repr. 818. 1957.

Annual herb, (15–) 20–50 (–70) cm, prostrate or ascending to erect, more or less straggling, simple or with ascending branches from near the base; stem and branches glabrous or very sparingly pilose, with pale ridges. Leaf-blade narrowly linear (not in Asia) to broadly ovate or rarely subrotund, (12–) 20–60 (–90) × (2–) 6–30 (–50) mm, glabrous or the petiole and princi- pal veins of the lower surface of the leaf spreading-hairy, acute or acuminate at the apex, longly or (in broader-leaved forms) rapidly narrowed to the base; petiole slender, in the lower leaves up to c. 5 cm, shortening in the upper leaves. Flowers glabrous, white, often tinged with pink to carmine or red, greenish-white after anthesis, in long and slender, or shorter and denser, long-pedunculate axillary racemes, up to c. 30 cm long, laxer below; peduncles slender, the lower up to c. 14 cm in length, both they and the inflorescence axis glabrous or sparingly spreading-hairy; bracts persistent, deltoid-lanceolate, acuminate, 1–2.75 mm, glabrous, membranous with a green or brownish percurrent midrib, each subtending a very shortly pedunculate partial inflorescence of 3 flowers. Central flower fertile, the 2 membranous, navicular outer perianth segments c. 3–4.5 mm long, oval or oblong, 7–12-nerved (in Asia), acute; the 2–3 inner segments slightly shorter, more delicate, blunt or erose, 1–3-nerved, hyaline, with a darker central vitta; stamens subequalling or shorter than the style; style c. 1.5–4 mm, the 2 stigmas finally recurved. Lateral flowers appressed, 1-bracteolate, bracteoles similar in form to the bract, these flowers much reduced and increasingly so in the upper part of the spike (sometimes absent), modified into accrescent, antler-shaped scales, scales with the lateral lobes narrow (in Asia) to broad and wing-like. Fruit subglobose, slightly compressed, 2–2.5 mm, bluntly keeled along each side, surmounted by a thick rim or a corona of short, firm processes, furnished throughout with verrucae or ridges, style persistent.

Distr. Asia from tropical Arabia and the Yemen to Afghanistan, W. Pakistan, India, Malaysia and Indonesia; south, central and east tropical Africa, Madagascar.

Ecol. Dry sandy places, roadsides, as a weed in gardens etc., apparently uncommon generally but locally frequent.

Vern. Toggil (T).

Illustr. Tadulingam & Venkatanarayana, Handb. S. Indian Weeds 260, pl. 108. 1932, as *D. arvensis*.

Specimens Examined. JAFFNA DISTRICT: Jaffna, *Moon s.n.* (PDA); Mulangavil, c. 32 miles N. of Mannar on the road to Pooneryn, 23 Feb. 1973, *Townsend 73/98* (K, PDA, US). MANNAR DISTRICT: Mannar, *Crawford s.n.* (PDA); Mannar Town, garden weed, 23 Feb. 1973, *Townsend 73/105* (K, PDA, US). COLOMBO DISTRICT: Walpita, in Government Farm, Negombo district, 29 June 1944, *Senaratna s.n.* (PDA). HAMBANTOTA DISTRICT: Tissamaharama, Dec. 1883, *s. coll. s.n.* (PDA); Hambantota, roadside 50 yards from shore, 31 Dec. 1926, *Alston s.n.* (PDA); Ruhuna National Park, Block 1, near Yala Bungalow, not common, 5 Jan. 1969, *Cooray 69010505R* (K, PDA, US).

5. CYATHULA

Blume, Bijdr. 548. 1825, nomen conservandum, non Cyathula Lour., Fl. Cochinch. 93, 101. 1790. Type species: *C. prostrata* (L.) Blume, Bidjr. 549. 1825.

Annual or perennial herbs with entire, opposite leaves. Inflorescence terminal on the stem and branches, spiciform, bracteate, the ultimate division basically a triad of fertile flowers, the outer pair bracteolate and each sub-tended on the outer surface by 2 modified bracteolate flowers consisting of a number of sharply hooked (rarely glochidiate or straight) spines, but one or both of the outer fertile pair sometimes absent or modified; bracteoles some-times also with a strongly hooked arista, the bracteoles and spines of the modified flowers at first small, rapidly accrescent, the spines few to many, clustered, the clusters not or very shortly stalked. Bracts persistent, finally more or less deflexed, bracteoles and perianth falling with the fruit. Perianth segments 5, very shortly mucronate or some (especially the outer 2) hooked-aristate, serving with the bracteoles and modified flowers to distribute the fruit. Stamens 5, the filaments delicate, shortly monadelphous at the base, alternating with distinct, commonly toothed or lacerate pseudo-staminodes; anthers bilocular (4-locellate). Style slender, stigma capitate. Ovary with a single pendulous ovule. Fruit a thin-walled utricle, irregularly ruptured by the developing seed. Seed ovoid, slightly compressed. Endosperm copious.

About 25 species in the tropics of both hemispheres.

KEY TO THE SPECIES

1 Inflorescence dense, capitate; spines of modified flowers up to 5 mm long, glochidiate at the apex...**1. C. ceylanica**
1 Inflorescence spicate, elongate in fruit with the lower flowers increasingly distant; spines of modified flowers up to 2 mm long, simply hooked.................**2. C. prostrata**

1. Cyathula ceylanica Hook. f. in Fl. Br. Ind. 4: 723. 1885; Trimen, Handb. Fl. Ceylon 3: 398. 1895 ("zeylanica", sphalm.). Type: Ooma-oya, March 1854, *Thwaites s.n.* (K, holotype; PDA, isotype).

Probably a perennial herb, 0.6–1.2 m, with slender branches; branches terete, striate, yellowish-tomentose when young, older parts glabrescent, somewhat thickened at the nodes. Leaves ovate to broadly elliptic, 2.5–5.5 × 1.8–3 cm, acute and mucronate at the apex, shortly cuneate at the base, short-ly (to c. 3 mm) petiolate, thinly pilose on the upper surface, moderately so and paler green beneath. Inflorescence a globose or ovoid head c. 2 cm in diameter, peduncle to c. 7 mm; bracts 3–3.5 mm, deltoid-ovate, dorsally pilose, shortly aristate with the excurrent midrib. Outer tepals of fertile flowers lanceolate, 3-nerved, 6 mm including the slender, 3–4-hooked glochi-diate arista; inner tepals 5 mm, also 3-nerved, oblong-oval, acute; all tepals pilose dorsally; bracteoles of lateral flowers of ultimate triad deltoid-ovate at the base, 7–8 mm including the glochidiate arista. Modified flowers with several inwardly diminishing glochidiate-awned bracteoliform processes and a few glochidiate spines c. 5–6 mm long at maturity, clusters falling together to form a compound "burr". Filaments c. 3 mm, delicate, the pseudo-staminodes rather short, truncate and fimbriate. Style slender, 2 mm. Fruit short, 2 mm, truncate at the apex with a thick ridged crest around the outer margin. Seed 2 mm, almost spherical, brown, shining, very faintly reticulate.

It is extraordinary that the original description of this species makes no mention of the glochidiate spines of the capitula, which are very uncommon in the genus.

D i s t r. Both the locality and habitat of this plant, of which only the holotype has apparently ever been collected, are unknown at the present time. "Ooma Oya", the locality of many rare species, is described by Thwaites in the "Enumeratio" as "near Kandy" and by Trimen as "on Lower Badulla Road"; the two designations are scarcely compatible. No locality of this name has been traced near Kandy, and the ravine of the Uma Oya near Ettampitiya has been searched without trace of either the present species, *Psilotrichum scleranthum* (also recorded for "Ooma Oya"), or indeed any amaranth; and the altitude of Ettampitiya (c. 760 m) is higher than any other locality in which the *Psilotrichum* has been found. One can only hope that some chance may bring the answer to this problem, and lead to the rediscovery of this most interesting endemic species, whose only close relative in the genus is the E. African *C. braunii* Gilg ex Schinz—curiously also only known from the type gathering.

I l l u s t r. None published.

2. Cyathula prostrata (L.) Blume, Bijdr. 549. 1825; Moq. in DC., Prod. 13 (2): 326. 1849; Hook. f. in Fl. Br. Ind. 4: 723. 1885; Trimen, Handb. Fl. Ceylon 3: 398. 1895; Gamble, Fl. Pres. Madras 1172. 1925, repr. 820. 1957. Type: Linnean specimen 287/13 (LINN, lectotype).

Achyranthes prostrata L., Sp. Pl. ed. 2. 296. 1762.
Pupalia prostrata (L.) Mart. in Nov. Act. Acad. Caes. Leop.-Carol. 13: 321. 1826.
Desmochaeta prostrata (L.) DC., Cat. Hort. Monsp. 102. 1813.

Annual herb (? sometimes short-lived perennial), stems prostrate to ascending or erect, 20–50 cm, simple or branched up to about the middle, more or less swollen at the nodes, lowest branches divaricate and rooting at the nodes, the upper more erect; stem and branches bluntly 4-angled to subterete, striate or sulcate, subglabrous to more or less densely pilose (especially the lower internodes). Leaves 1.5–8 × 1–4.5 cm, mostly rhomboid to rhomboid-ovate, sometimes rhomboid-elliptic to shortly oval or suborbicular, occasionally with the margin outline distinctly excavate below and/or above the middle, shortly acuminate at the apex, acute to rather blunt (more rarely rounded), shortly cuneate to cuneate-attenuate at the base, subglabrous to moderately pilose on both surfaces, subsessile or distinctly (up to 13 mm) petiolate. Spikes terminal on the stem and branches, at first dense, soon considerably elongating to as much as 35 cm with maturing lower flowers increasingly distant, 5–7 mm wide, peduncle up to c. 10 cm; bracts and bracteoles lanceolate-ovate, c. 1.5–2 mm, mucronate with the shortly excurrent midrib, ciliate; flowers in sessile or shortly pedunculate clusters of 1–3 hermaphrodite flowers laterally subtended by modified flowers, or the uppermost of the spike solitary, perfect, bibracteolate. Tepals 2.25–3 mm, elliptic-oblong, 3-nerved, the outer firmer with the lateral nerves more distinct and joining the shortly excurrent midrib just below the apex, also more densely white-pilose than the inner. Hooked spines of modified flowers numerous, glabrous, reddish, c. 2 mm, fasciculate; clusters of flowers falling together to form a "burr" c. 5 mm in diameter. Filaments very slender, c. 1.5 mm, the pseudo-staminodes rectangular-cuneate with a truncate, dentate or excavate apex. Style slender, c. 0.6 mm. Capsule ovoid, c. 1.5 mm. Seed ovoid, c. 1.5 mm, shining, brown, smooth.

D i s t r. The commonest species of the genus, widespread in the tropics of both Old and New Worlds.

E c o l. A weed of dry grassy places; said by Trimen to be "very common", but does not appear to be so now, and only a few specimens have been seen from the island.

V e r n. Bin karal heba, Bin karalsebo (S).

I l l u s t r. Fawcett & Rendle, Fl. Jamaica 3, 1: 134. 1914.

S p e c i m e n s E x a m i n e d. KANDY DISTRICT: Peradeniya, 21 July 1963, *Amaratunga 656, 758* (PDA). COLOMBO DISTRICT: Colombo, *Moon s.n.* (K); Nittambuwa, 9 Jan. 1967, *Amaratunga 1213* (PDA). BADULLA DISTRICT: Ekiriyankumbura, on Kandy/Bibile road, 13 Feb. 1972, *Balasubramanian s.n.* (PDA): MONERAGALA DISTRICT: 137 miles from Colombo to Wellawaya, roadside at edge of teak forest, 2 March 1973, *Townsend 73/151* (K, PDA, US).

6. PUPALIA

Juss., Ann. Mus. Hist. Nat. Paris 2: 132. 1803 nomen conservandum. Type species: *P. lappacea* (L.) Juss. in Ann. Mus. Hist. Nat. Paris 2: 132. 1803. *Pupal* Adans., Fam. Pl. 2: 268, 596. 1763.

Annual or perennial herbs or subshrubs with entire, opposite leaves. Inflorescence a spiciform bracteate thyrse terminal on the stem and branches, each bract subtending a single hermaphrodite flower on each side of which is set a bracteolate modified flower consisting of a number of sharply hooked spines, or, more commonly, each bract containing a hermaphrodite flower subtended by two or more such triads each contained with a large bracteole. Spines of modified flowers at first very small, rapidly accrescent, finally disposed in 3 or occasionally more stalked clusters of 5–20 spines in 1–3 ranks, the clusters stellately or occasionally dendroidly set on a common peduncle, subequalling to much exceeding the perianth and serving as a means of distributing the fruit. Bracts persistent, finally more or less deflexed, entire partial inflorescences falling intact in fruit. Perianth segments 5. Stamens 5, the filaments delicate to rather solid, fused at the extreme base on to a fleshy, lobed, disk-like cup into which the base of the ovary is narrowed; pseudostaminodes absent; anthers bilocular (4-locellate). Style slender, stigma capitate. Ovary with a single pendulous ovule. Fruit a thin-walled utricle, irregularly ruptured below the firm apex by the developing seed. Seed oblong-ovoid or ovoid, slightly compressed. Endosperm copious.

Four species in the tropics (extending to the subtropics) of the Old World from W. Africa to Malaysia and the Philippines.

Pupalia lappacea (L.) Juss., Ann. Mus. Hist. Nat. Paris 2: 132. 1803; Moq. in DC., Prod. 13 (2): 331. 1849; Hook. f. in Fl. Br. Ind. 4: 724. 1885; Gamble, Fl. Pres. Madras 1173. 1925, repr. 821. 1957.

Achyranthes lappacea L., Sp. Pl. ed. 1. 204. 1753.
Achyranthes atropurpurea Lam., Enc. 1: 546. 1785.
Pupalia atropurpurea (Lam.) Moq. in DC., Prod. 13 (2): 331. 1849; Hook. f. in Fl. Br. Ind. 4: 723. 1885; Trimen, Handb. Fl. Ceylon 3: 399. 1895; Gamble, Fl. Pres. Madras 1173. 1925, repr. 821. 1957.
Desmochaeta atropurpurea (Lam.) DC., Cat. Hort. Monsp. 102. 1813.

Annual or perennial herb, more or less erect and c. 0.3–0.9 m tall, or prostrate and sprawling, or subscandent and scrambling to as much as 2.5 m, stem generally much-branched and swollen at the nodes, branches opposite, divaricate or ascending, slender; stems and branches obtusely 4-angled to almost terete, thinly pilose to densely tomentose. Leaves variable in shape and size, from narrowly ovate-elliptic to oblong or orbicular, 2–10 (–14) × 1–5 (–7) cm, acuminate to obtuse-apiculate or retuse at the summit, shortly or more longly cuneate at the base, narrowed to a petiole 2–2.5 (–3.5) cm long; indumentum of lamina varying from sericeous or tomentose to subglabrous with a few hairs running vertically along the lower surface of the primary venation, rarely quite glabrous, commonly moderately pilose with the hairs along the nerves divergent. Inflorescences at first more or less dense, elongating to as much as 0.5 m in fruit with the lower flowers becoming increasingly remote, axis subglabrous to tomentose, peduncle c. 1–10 cm; bracts lanceolate, 1.5–2.5 mm, persistent, more or less deflexed after the fall of the fruit, subglabrous or pilose, sharply mucronate with the percurrent midrib; partial inflorescences mostly of 1 solitary hermaphrodite flower subtended on each side by a triad of 1 hermaphrodite and 2 modified flowers; bracteoles of each triad broadly subcordate-ovate, (2.75–) 3–5 (–6) mm, abruptly narrowed to the stramineous to dark arista formed by the excurrent midrib, membranous with a pale margin, thinly to very densely hairy; bracteoles of sterile flowers ovate-lanceolate, usually more shortly and less densely pilose. Tepals oblong-ovate to lanceolate-ovate, more or less quickly narrowed to a rather obtuse-mucronate apex to gradually narrowed and acute-aristate, the outer two (3–) 4–5 (–6) mm, subglabrous to more or less tomentose dorsally, 3 (–5)-nerved, the midrib and 2 inner nerves confluent just below the apex and excurrent in the mucro or short arista, inner 3 slightly shorter and more densely pilose. Branches of sterile flowers 3, each terminating in (3–) 5–18 (–20+) setae in 1–3 ranks; setae subglabrous to more or less villous in the lower half, yellowish to purple or red, (1.5–) 3–7 mm, the partial inflorescence falling intact to form a burr c. 8–18 cm in diameter. Style short to rather slender, (0.5–) 0.9–2 (–3) mm. Capsule ovoid, 2–2.5 mm. Seed oblong-ovoid with a prominent radicle, 2 mm long, dark brown, shining, testa at first faintly reticulate but finally smooth or punctulate.

D i s t r. Widespread in the tropics of the Old World; throughout tropical Africa N. to Egypt, also in South Africa & Madagascar, Arabia and Asia from India eastwards to Malaya, the Malayan Is. (Java, Celebes etc.), the Philippines and New Guinea. Introduced in Australia etc.

1. var. lappacea. Type: Ceylon, Herb. Hermann 1: 2, larger piece (BM, lectotype).

Plant more or less erect, thinly pilose, upper surface of leaves darker green with scattered hairs, lower surface paler with hairs usually more numerous. Inflorescence slender, spiky in appearance from the tapering, sharply acute tepals. Branches of sterile flowers terminating in (6–) 8–15 commonly purplish setae in (1–) 2–3 ranks. Burrs 8.5–10 (–12) mm in diameter.

D i s t r. S. India, Ceylon, S. & E. Africa.
I l l u s t r. Wood, Natal Plants 6 (2), pl. 544. 1910, as *P. atropurpurea*.
S p e c i m e n s E x a m i n e d. JAFFNA DISTRICT: Jaffna, Feb. 1890, *s. coll. s.n.* (PDA). MATALE DISTRICT: near Dambulla, Aug. 1885, *s. coll. s.n.* (PDA). KANDY DISTRICT: Haragama, 14 Dec. 1971, *Jayasuriya & Balasubramaniam 450* (K, PDA). KURUNEGALA DISTRICT: Kurunegala (see Trimen). HAMBANTOTA DISTRICT: Ruhuna National Park, Block 11, common, 25 Feb. 1968, *Comanor 1035* (PDA, US); ibid., Block 1, near Yala Bungalow, not common, 5 Jan. 1969, *Mueller-Dombois & Cooray 69010504R* (PDA, US); ibid., Talgasmankada, common, 16 Nov. 1969, *Cooray 69111625R* (PDA, US).

2. var. orbiculata (Heyne ex Wall.) C.C. Townsend in Kew Bull. 29 (3): 469. 1974. Type: *Wallich 6936a*, ex herb. Heyne, no details (K, holotype).

Achyranthes orbiculata Heyne ex Wall. in Roxb., Fl. Ind. 2: 507. 1824.

Cyathula orbiculata (Heyne ex Wall.) Moq. in DC., Prod. 13 (2): 330. 1849.

Pupalia orbiculata (Heyne ex Wall.) Wight, Ic. Pl. Ind. Or. 5 (2): 4, t. 1783.
1852; Trimen, Handb. Fl. Ceylon 3: 400. 1895; Gamble, Fl. Pres. Madras
1173. 1925, repr. 821. 1957.

Plant prostrate; leaves shortly but quite closely pilose, rounded, apiculate
or frequently retuse. Inflorescence stouter. Branches of sterile flowers terminating in 5–9 (–11) yellow setae in 1–2 ranks. Burrs (11–) 13–17 mm in diameter.

D i s t r. & E c o l. Sandy places behind the shore line, not uncommon.
Also S. India.

V e r n. Kummidil, Pichu-kodiya (T).

I l l u s t r. Wight, Ic. Pl. Ind. Or. S, pl. 1783. 1852.

S p e c i m e n s E x a m i n e d. JAFFNA DISTRICT: Jaffna, *Gardner s.n.*
(PDA). MANNAR DISTRICT: Mannar Island, Feb. 1890, *s. coll. s.n.* (PDA).
VAVUNIYA DISTRICT: flat sandy area near sea c. 3/4 mile N. of Mullait-
tivu, 22 Feb. 1973, *Townsend 73/95* (K, PDA, US). PUTTALAM DIS-
TRICT: Chilaw, Dec. 1880, *s. coll. s.n.* (PDA). TRINCOMALEE DISTRICT:
Foul Point, 20 May 1932, *Simpson 9676* (PDA), 4 Feb. 1972, *Dassanayake &*
Balasubramaniam 644 (K, PDA). MATARA DISTRICT: near Kirinda, Dec.
1882, *s. coll. s.n.* (PDA). HAMBANTOTA DISTRICT: Ruhuna National
Park, Patanagala Beach, sand pockets in rock in salt spray range, 1 Sept.
1967, *Mueller-Dombois 67090103* (PDA, US). AMPARAI DISTRICT: dunes
just N. of Arugam Bay, Nov. 1970, *Fosberg 53037* (K, PDA, US).

N o t e. Correct typification having demonstrated that the plant hitherto
known as *P. atropurpurea* must be regarded as *P. lappacea* var. *lappacea*, the
plant hitherto known as *P. lappacea* (sensu Moquin et al.) must be called var.
velutina (Moq.) Hook. f. if the two taxa are treated as varieties of a single
species, as the present author believes they should be. The var. *velutina*, which
is much the commonest form of the species throughout its range, has not
been seen from Ceylon, where the division of the species into the above two
varieties is clear-cut.

7. AERVA

Forssk., Fl. Aegypt.-Arab. 170. 1775, nomen conservandum. Type species: *A.*
javanica (Burm. f.) Juss. ex Schult., Syst. Veg. ed. 15, 5: 565. 1819.

Ouret Adans., Fam. Pl. 2: 268, 586. 1763.

Perennial herbs (sometimes flowering in the first year), prostrate to erect
or scandent. Leaves and branches alternate or occasionally (not in Ceylon)
partly opposite, leaves entire. Flowers hermaphrodite or dioecious, some-

times probably polygamous, bibracteolate, in axillary and terminal sessile or pedunculate bracteate spikes, one flower in the axil of each bract. Perianth segments 5, oval or lanceolate-oblong, membranous-margined with a thin to wider green centre, the perianth deciduous with the fruit but bracts and bracteoles persistent. Stamens 5, shortly monadelphous at the base, alternating with subulate or rarely narrowly oblong and truncate or emarginate pseudo-staminodes; anthers bilocular (4-locellate). Ovary with a single pendulous ovule; style very short to slender and distinct; stigmas 2, short to long and filiform (sometimes solitary and capitate, flowers then probably functionally male). Utricle thin-walled, bursting irregularly. Seed compressed-reniform, firm, black.

About 10 species in the tropics, chiefly centred in Africa.

KEY TO THE SPECIES

1 Outer tepals with the midrib ceasing well below the apex; flowers dioecious, either with a well-developed style and stigmas but no anthers, or anthers present but only rudimentary stigmas . . . . .1. A. javanica
1 Outer tepals with the midrib excurrent in a distinct mucro; flowers hermaphrodite. . . .
. . . . .2. A. lanata

1. Aerva javanica (Burm. f.) Juss. ex Schult., Syst. Veg. ed. 15, 5: 565. 1819; Moq. in DC., Prod. 13 (2): 299. 1849; Hook. f. in Fl. Br. Ind. 4: 727. 1885; Trimen, Handb. Fl. Ceylon 3: 402. 1895. Type: in Herb. Burmann (G, holotype).

Celosia lanata L., Sp. Pl. ed. 1: 205. 1753.
Iresine javanica Burm. f., Fl. Ind. 212, t. 65 f. 2. 1768.
Iresine persica Burm. f., Fl. Ind. 212, t. 65 f. 1. 1768.
Illecebrum javanicum (Burm. f.) Murr., Syst. Veg. ed. 13: 206. 1774.
Aerva tomentosa Forssk., Fl. Aeg.-Arab. cxxii, 170. 1775; Gamble, Fl. Pres. Madras 1178. 1925, repr. 824. 1957.
Achyranthes javanica (Burm. f.) Pers., Syn. 1: 259. 1805.
Aerva wallichii Moq. in DC., Prod. 13 (2): 300. 1849.
Aerva persica (Burm. f.) Merr. in Philipp. J. Sci. 19: 348. 1921.

Perennial herb, frequently woody and suffruticose or growing in erect clumps, 0.3–1.5 m, branched from about the base with simple stems or the stems with long ascending branches. Stem and branches terete, striate, more or less densely whitish-or yellowish-tomentose or pannose, when dense the indumentum often appearing tufted. Leaves alternate, very variable in size and form, from narrowly linear to suborbicular, more or less densely whitish-or yellowish-tomentose but usually more thinly so and greener on the upper surface, margins plane or more or less involute (when strongly so the leaves frequently more or less falcate-recurved), sessile or with a short and indistinct petiole or the latter rarely to c. 2 cm in robust plants. Flowers dioecious. Spikes sessile, cylindrical, dense and stout (up to c. 10 × 1 cm), to slender and interrupted with lateral globose clusters of flowers and with some spikes apparently pedunculate by branch reduction; male plants always with more slender spikes (but plants with slender spikes may not be male); upper part of stem and branches leafless, the upper spikes thus forming terminal panicles; bracts 0.75–2.25 mm, broadly deltoid-ovate, hyaline, acute or obtuse with the obscure midrib ceasing below the apex, densely lanate throughout or only about the base or apex, persistent; bracteoles similar, also persistent. Female flowers with outer 2 tepals 2–3 mm, oblong-obovate to obovate-spathulate, lanate, acute to obtuse or apiculate at the tip, the yellowish midrib ceasing well below the apex; inner 3 slightly shorter, elliptic-oblong, more or less densely lanate, acute, with a narrow green vitta along the midrib, which extends for about two-thirds the length of each tepal; style slender, distinct, with the two filiform, flexuose stigmas at least equalling it in length; filaments reduced, anthers absent. Male flowers smaller, the outer tepals 1.5–2.25 mm, ovate; filaments delicate, the anthers about equalling the perianth; ovary small, style very short, stigmas rudimentary. Utricle 1–1.5 mm, rotund, compressed. Seed 0.9–1.25 mm, round, slightly compressed, brown or black, shining and smooth or very faintly reticulate.

D i s t r. Widespread in the drier parts of the tropics and subtropics of the Old World, from Burma, India and Ceylon westwards through S.W. Asia, across N. Africa to Morocco and south to Cape Verde Islands and Cameroun through Uganda and Tanzania to Madagascar. Introduced in Australia and elsewhere.

E c o l. Sandy places near the sea on the west side of the island, rare.

V e r n. Polpala or Pol-kudu-pala (S), as for *A. lanata*; also Sirm-pulai (T).

I l l u s t r. Tadulingam & Venkatanarayana, Handb. S. Indian Weeds 270, pl. 112-A, as *A. tomentosa*.

S p e c i m e n s   E x a m i n e d. JAFFNA DISTRICT: Delft, *Gardner s.n.* (PDA). PUTTALAM DISTRICT: Karativu Island, Sept. 1883, *s. coll. s.n.* (PDA); Kalpitiya, see Trimen; St. Annes, Talawila, 7 Dec. 1961, *Amaratunga 97* (PDA).

2. **Aerva lanata** (L.) Juss. ex Schult., Syst. Veg. ed. 15, 5: 564. 1819; Moq. in DC., Prod. 13 (2): 303. 1849; Hook. f. in Fl. Br. Ind. 4: 728. 1885; Trimen, Handb. Fl. Ceylon 3: 402. 1895; Gamble, Fl. Pres. Madras 1178. 1925, repr. 825. 1957. Type: Linnean specimen 290/6 (LINN, lectotype).

Achyranthes lanata L., Sp. Pl. ed. 1. 204. 1753.
Illecebrum lanatum (L.) L., Mant. 344. 1771.
Aerva elegans Moq. in DC., Prod. 13 (2): 303. 1849.

Perennial herb sometimes flowering in the first year, frequently woody and suffrutescent below, prostrate to decumbent or erect, stiff or weak and straggling, (0.1–) 0.3–2 m, branched from the base and often also above (upper branches short to long and slender even on the same plant), but main basal shoots frequently unbranched. Stem and branches terete, striate, more or less densely lanate with whitish or yellowish, more or less shaggy hairs, more rarely tomentose or canescent. Leaves alternate, suborbicular to lanceolate-elliptic or ovate-elliptic, shortly to longly cuneate at the base, rounded and apiculate to acute at the apex, commonly densely lanate or canescent on the lower surface and more thinly so above, sometimes subglabrous on the upper surface, rarely glabrous throughout, those of the main stem 10–50 × 5–35 mm, those of the branches and upper part of the stem reducing and often becoming very small; petioles from 2 cm down to almost none. Spikes sessile, solitary or usually in axillary clusters on the main stems or on long to very short axillary branches, 0.4–1.5 (–2) × 0.3–0.4 cm, divergent, cylindrical, silky, white to creamy, forming a long inflorescence leafy to the ultimate spikes; bracts 0.75–1 mm, deltoid-ovate to oblong-ovate, membranous with a short arista formed by the excurrent midrib, pilose, persistent; bracteoles similar or slightly smaller, also persistent. Flowers (in Ceylon) hermaphrodite. Outer 2 tepals hyaline, oval-oblong, abruptly contracted at the tip to a distinct mucro formed by the excurrent nerve, 0.75–1.25 mm without the mucro; inner 3 slightly shorter and narrower, acute with a broad central green vitta along the midrib, which extends for about three-quarters of their length (the vitta more or less furnished with a thickened border of 2 lateral nerves); all tepals densely lanate dorsally. Stamens delicate, at anthesis attaining about half the length of the style. Style and two short, divergent stigmas subequalling the ovary in length at anthesis. Utricle c. 1 mm, rotund, compressed. Seed c. 0.6–0.8 mm, reniform, black, shining, the testa almost smooth in the centre, faintly reticulate around the margin.

D i s t r. Widespread in the drier parts of the tropics and subtropics of the Old World—in Africa from Sierra Leone across to Egypt, south to S. Africa (rare) and Madagascar, also in the Seychelles; in Asia from Arabia east to Malaysia, Indonesia, the Philippines and New Guinea.

E c o l. A very common species in the dry regions, on disturbed or waste sandy ground, on sandy flats and in open areas in scrub, rocky slopes etc.

U s e s. Small clumps of this species are frequently grown in gardens for making a kind of medicinal tea (see *Townsend 73/53*, below); such cultivation was also observed near Peradeniya, Kegalla and other places.

V e r n. Polpala or Pol-kudu-pala (S).

I l l u s t r. Tadulingam & Venkatanarayana, Handb. S. Indian Weeds 272, pl. 113. 1932.

N o t e. The description of the perianths given above refers only to this species in the eastern part of its range. In Africa not only the hermaphrodite flowers here described occur, but also female flowers in which the stamens are reduced and bear no anthers. In these the tepals are often but not invariably longer and more gradually narrowed, and the stigmas are longer. Functionally male flowers apparently occur also; these have a perianth similar to the hermaphrodite flowers, but the stigma is subcapitate and scarcely papillose, or the branches very short.

Specimens Examined. VAVUNIYA DISTRICT: 121 miles on the road from Kandy to Jaffna, 21 Feb. 1973, *Townsend 73/71* (K, PDA, US). MANNAR DISTRICT: Landward side of causeway to Mannar Island, c. half mile inland, 23 Feb. 1973, *Townsend 73/106* (K, PDA, US). ANU-RADHAPURA DISTRICT: Wilpattu National Park, Eranapola Motai, 27 April 1969, *Mueller-Dombois et al. 69042730* (PDA, US); ibid., Occapu Kallu, 28 April 1969, *Mueller-Dombois et al. 69042717* (PDA, US); Aukana, 17 Feb. 1973, *Townsend 73/66* (K, PDA, US). MATALE DISTRICT: Dambulla, 30 Oct. 1968, *Amaratunga 650* (PDA). TRINCOMALEE DISTRICT: Kantalai/ Trincomalee Road, milestone 136.2 (A6), 13 Jan. 1968, *Camonor 827* (PDA, US). COLOMBO DISTRICT: Negombo, sandy soil just above beach, 5 Feb. 1970, *Rudd 3068* (PDA, US). MONERAGALA DISTRICT: Bibile, 22 Oct. 1925, *J.M. Silva s.n.* (PDA). HAMBANTOTA DISTRICT: Ruhuna National Park, near Katuwila Ara, 17 June 1967, *Comanor 354* (PDA, US); ibid., main Yala road at mile marker 7, frequent, 23 Jan. 1968, *Comanor 827* (PDA, US); ibid., at Patanagala, common, 13 Dec. 1969, *Cooray 69121304R* (PDA, US). GALLE DISTRICT: grown in garden by roadside c. 6 miles E. of Hiniduma on Pittabeddara road, 14 Feb. 1973, *Townsend 73/53* (K, PDA, US).

8. NOTHOSAERVA

Wight, Ic. Pl. Ind. Or. 6: 1. 1853.

Pseudanthus Wight, Ic. Pl. Ind. Or. 5 (2): 3. 1852, non Sieber ex Spreng., Syst. Veg. ed. 16, 4 (2): 25. 1827.

Annual herb with opposite or alternate branches and leaves. Leaves entire. Flowers small, hermaphrodite, solitary in the axils of scarious bracts, sessile in dense, solitary or clustered spikes. Perianth segments 3–4 (–5), hyaline, perianth subtended by two very small bracteoles. Stamens 1 or 2, the anthers bilocular (4-locellate); filaments filiform, intermediate teeth absent. Style short, stigma capitate. Ovary with a single pendulous ovule, radicle ascending. Capsule delicate, irregularly rupturing, falling with the perianth; bracts and bracteoles persistent. Seed round, laterally compressed, endosperm copious.

A monotypic genus.

Nothosaerva brachiata (L.) Wight, Ic. Pl. Ind. Or. 6: 1. 1853; Hook. f. in Fl. Br. Ind. 4: 726. 1885; Trimen, Handb. Fl. Ceylon 3: 401. 1895; Gamble, Fl.

Pres. Madras 1175. 1925, repr. 823. 1957. Type: Linnean specimen 290/1 (LINN, holotype).

Achyranthes brachiata L., Mant. 50. 1767.
Illecebrum brachiatum (L.) L., Mant. Alt. 213. 1771.
Aerva brachiata (L.) Mart., Nova Acta Phys. Med. Acad. Caes.-Leop. Carol. Nat. Cur. 13 (1): 291. 1826; Moq. in DC., Prod. 13 (2): 304. 1849.
Pseudanthus brachiatus (L.) Wight, Ic. Pl. Ind. Or. 5 (2): 3, t. 1776 bis, B. 1852.

Annual herb, (4–) 10–45 cm, rigidly erect with many spreading branches from about the base upwards; stem and branches subterete, striate, glabrous or thinly hairy. Leaves narrowly to broadly elliptic, elliptic-oblong or ovate, entire, thinly hairy to glabrous or almost so, obtuse to subacute at the tip, gradually or more abruptly narrowed to a petiole about half the length of the lamina, lamina of the lower main stem-leaves c. 10–40 (–50) × 6–20 mm, upper and branch leaves becoming shorter and narrower. Flowers in dense, 3–15 × 2–2.5 mm, white spikes which are clustered in the leaf-axils of the stem and branches, or on very short axillary shoots; spikes sessile, or the terminal spike on the axillary shoots shortly (to c. 3 mm) pedunculate, inflorescence axis thinly to rather densely pilose; bracts hyaline, minutely erose, concave, acute or shortly acuminate, c. 0.5 mm, glabrous or very thinly hairy, nerveless; bracteoles minute, hyaline. Perianth segments broadly oval, c. 1–1.25 mm, subacute to shortly acuminate, villous on the outer surface, with a thick greenish vitta along the midrib, which extends c. 2/3 of the way up each segment. Stamens longer than the ovary and style. Capsule included, c. 0.75 mm, falling with the perianth. Seed c. 0.4 mm, chestnut-brown, smooth and shining.

Distr. S.E. Asia from India to Burma, also reported from Borneo; tropical Africa from Nigeria and the Sudan south to Angola and Rhodesia; Mauritius.

Ecol. Frequent in the dry regions, along ditches, by roadsides, as a weed of cultivation and particularly in damp depressions where water has stood in the wet season.

Vern. Tampala (S); Chirupilai (T).

Illustr. Wight, Ic. Pl. Ind. Or. 5, pl. 1776 bis, B. 1852, as *Pseudanthus brachiatus*.

Specimens Examined. JAFFNA DISTRICT: Jaffna, 12 March 1932, *Simpson 9270* (PDA). VAVUNIYA DISTRICT: 121 miles on the road from Kandy to Jaffna, damp depression in arable field, 21 Feb. 1973, *Townsend 73/70* (K, PDA, US). ANURADHAPURA DISTRICT: 100 miles on the road from Kandy to Jaffna, S. of Punawa, roadside ditch, 24 Feb. 1973, *Townsend 73/115* (K, PDA, US); 60 & 61 miles on road from Kandy to Jaffna, just S. of Kagama, 24 Feb. 1973, *Townsend 73/116* (K, PDA, US); milestone 53, east of the road from Dambulla to Anuradhapura, 8 March 1973, *Townsend 73/181* (K, PDA, US). POLONNARUWA DISTRICT: Polonnaruwa, Govt. Farm, weed in vegetable plots and grassland, 22 June 1943, *Senaratna 3492* (PDA); Minneriya, Ento. Field Station, 19 May 1950, *Nanayakkara s.n.* (PDA); damp depressions in scrub by roadside opposite Minneriya Tank, 13 March 1973, *Townsend 73/217* (K, PDA, US). BATTICALOA DISTRICT: Batticaloa, *Gardner s.n.* (PDA). HAMBANTOTA DISTRICT: Ruhuna National Park, Andronoruwa Vela (Wewa) just W. of Yala Bungalow, 7 Jan. 1969, *Fosberg et al. 51126* (PDA, US); ibid., Block 1, at Kohombagaswala, 3 Dec. 1969, *Cooray 69120310R* (PDA, US).

9. TRICHURUS

C.C. Townsend in Kew Bull. 29 (3): 466. 1974.

Erect perennial herb with opposite or whorled leaves and branches, leaves entire. Flowers bibracteolate, hermaphrodite, in dense axillary and terminal bracteate spikes, each bract subtending a single flower; bracts and bracteoles small, membranous, persistent. Perianth segments 4, lanceolate-subulate, persistent. Stamens 4, shortly monadelphous at the base, alternating with triangular to subquadrate pseudo-staminodes; anthers bilocular (4-locellate). Style very short, with two very short divergent stigmas. Ovary with a single pendulous ovule. Fruit a thin-walled utricle, circumscissile by a minute lid splitting when ripe. Seed ovoid, with a thin-walled area above the radicle which shrinks on drying to form a shallow depression.

A monotypic genus.

Trichurus monsoniae (L. f.) C.C. Townsend in Kew Bull. 29 (3): 466. 1974. Type: Linnean specimen 290/9, ex Koenig (LINN, holotype; isotype in BM).

Illecebrum monsoniae L. f., Suppl. 161. 1781.
Celosia monsoniae Retz., Obs. 2: 13. 1781.
Achyranthes pungens Lam., Enc. 1: 546. 1785.
Achyranthes monsoniae (L. f.) Pers., Syn. 1: 258. 1805.
Achyranthes setacea Roth, Nov. Pl. Sp. Ind. Or. 168. 1821.
Aerva monsoniae (Retz.) Mart. in Nova Acta Phys. Med. Acad. Caes. Leop.-Carol. Nat. Cur. 13 (1): 291. 1826; Moq. in DC., Prod. 13 (2): 305. 1849; Hook. f. in Fl. Br. Ind. 4: 728. 1885; Trimen, Handb. Fl. Ceylon 3: 403. 1895; Gamble, Fl. Pres. Madras 1178. 1925, repr. 825. 1957.

Perennial herb, varying much in habit from densely congested and tufted or taller and simple to much-branched from the base and also above, with short and erect to elongate (up to c. 90 cm) ascending or prostrate stems. Stems wiry and slender with pale, raised, ridges, more or less lanate, with many horizontally spreading opposite or whorled branches (in smaller plants these usually reduced to peduncles). Leaves linear-filiform, up to 2.5 cm long, crowded on the lower internodes, in the upper part of the stem mostly in pairs or whorls subtending the branches. Flowers hermaphrodite, very numerous, in dense spikes 4–5 mm in diameter and (5–) 10–20 (–36) mm in length, terminal on the horizontal peduncles in small forms, in larger forms often some shortly pedunculate at the junction of stem and branches as well as terminal on the stem, branches and opposite branchlets or peduncles. Bracts lanceolate, lanate, c. 2 mm, hyaline with a green midrib; bracteoles similar, smaller. Tepals 4, lanceolate-subulate, hyaline with a green midrib, dorsally lanate, c. 2.5 mm, curving towards the apex of the spike. Androecium delicate, subequalling the basal cup of the utricle. Utricle c. 1 mm, the circumscissile lid much shorter than the base, which is often also longitudinally split at maturity. Seed ovoid, shining, reddish-brown, c. 0.6 mm.

D i s t r. The species also occurs in India and Thailand.

E c o l. Dry, open, sandy places near the sea in the north of Ceylon, apparently very local.

I l l u s t r. Wight, Ic. Pl. Ind. Or. 2, pl. 725. 1840–43, as *Aerva monsoniae*.

S p e c i m e n s   E x a m i n e d. JAFFNA DISTRICT: Jaffna, *Ferguson s.n.* (PDA). VAVUNIYA DISTRICT: Mullaittivu, July 1889, *Nevill s.n.* (PDA); just south of Mullaittivu, Dec. 1970, *Fosberg 53500* (K, PDA, US), *Fosberg & Balakrishnan 53501* (K, PDA, US).

N o t e. It is clear from a specimen sent by Koenig to Sir Joseph Banks and now in BM that the original MS spelling of this specific epithet was "mohnsoniae" (see Rendle, Journal of Botany 71: 181–2, Pl. 601. 1933). This was altered by Retzius and the younger Linnaeus, who both based their descriptions on material sent by Koenig, to "monsonia" and "monsoniae" respectively. The species is dedicated to Lady Anne Monson—a fact perhaps not realised by Retzius whose spelling has been corrected; ignorance of this dedication explains Trimen's footnote: "It is not easy to see in what respect this resembles *Monsonia*, a genus of Geraniaceae".

10. ACHYRANTHES

L., Sp. Pl. ed. 1. 204. 1753; Gen. Pl. ed. 5. 96. 1854. Type species: *A. aspera* L., Sp. Pl. ed. 1. 204. 1753.

Herbs with opposite, petiolate, entire leaves. Inflorescence a more or less slender spike, terminal on the stem and branches, the flowers at first congested and more or less patent, finally laxer and deflexed; bracts deltoid or ovate, the midrib excurrent in a spine. Flowers solitary in the bracts, hermaphrodite. Perianth segments 4–5, 1–3 (–5) nerved, narrowly lanceolate, acuminate, aristate with the excurrent nerve, indurate in fruit especially at the base. Bracteoles 2, spinous, the spine furnished at the base with short and free to longer and adnate membranous wings. Stamens 2–5, filaments filiform, monadelphous, alternating with quadrate to broadly quadrate-spathulate pseudo-staminodes, these simple and dentate or fimbriate, or furnished with a variably developed dorsal scale; anthers bilocular (4-locellate). Style slender, stigma small, truncate-capitate. Ovary with a solitary pendulous ovule, the ovary wall very thin in fruit. Entire flower with bracteoles falling with the ripening of the cylindrical seed, the deflexed bracts persistent.

Six species in the warm temperate and tropical regions of the world.

KEY TO THE SPECIES

1 Stamens 2..**3. A. diandra**
1 Stamens 5
  2 Pseudo-staminodes between the filaments with a narrow, entire or undulate ventral scale and a long, fimbriate dorsal scale; wings on each side of the base of the bracteoles almost entirely adnate to the spine............................**1. A. aspera**
  2 Pseudo-staminodes between the filaments simple, erose or dentate; wings on each side of the base of the bracteoles practically free, somewhat divergent....**2. A. bidentata**

1. Achyranthes aspera L., Sp. Pl. ed. 1. 204. 1753; Moq. in DC., Prod. 13 (2): 314. 1849; Hook. f. in Fl. Br. Ind. 4: 730. 1885; Trimen, Handb. Fl. Ceylon 3: 404. 1895; Gamble, Fl. Pres. Madras 1176. 1925, repr. 823. 1957. Type: Ceylon, Herb. Hermann 2: 69. 105. R.H. specimen (BM, lectotype).

Perennial herb (sometimes woody and somewhat suffrutescent), occasionally flowering in the first year, 0.2–2 m, stiffly erect to subscandent or straggling and more or less prostrate, simple to much-branched, stems stout to very weak, distinctly to obscurely 4-angled, striate or sulcate, subglabrous to densely tomentose, the nodes more or less shrunken when dry. Leaves elliptic, oblong or oval and acute or acuminate to almost round and very obtuse, gradually or abruptly narrowed below, (2–) 3–12 (–16) × 1.3–6 cm, indumentum varying from uniformly subglabrous through subglabrous above and densely appressed-canescent below to more or less densely tomentose on both surfaces; petioles of main stem leaves 3–25 mm, shortening above and below. Inflorescences at first dense, finally elongating to (5–) 8–34 (–40) cm; peduncles (0.6–) 1–6 (–7.5) cm. Bracts lanceolate or narrowly deltoid-lanceolate, pale or brownish-membranous, 1.75–5 (–6) mm, glabrous. Bracteoles 1.5–4.5 (–6) mm, the basal wings 1/3–1/4 the length of the spine and adnate to it, typically tapering off above but not rarely rounded or truncate. Perianth whitish or pale green to red or purple; segments 5, 3–7 (–10) mm, the outer longest, narrowly lanceolate to lanceolate, very acute, with a distinct midrib and 2 obscure to distinct lateral nerves, narrow or moderately pale-margined. Stamens 5, the filaments 1.5–4.5 (–6) mm, alternating with subquadrate pseudo-staminodes. Typically the apex of the latter curves slightly inwards as a narrow, crenate or entire, often very delicate flap, while from the dorsal surface arises a fimbriate-ciliate scale extending across the width of the pseudo-staminode; not rarely, however, this is reduced to a "stag's-horn" process at the centre of the dorsal surface, or even becomes small and filiform—or else subapical or apical so that the pseudo-staminode appears simple (this usually in small forms of var. *sicula*, which has not yet been found in Ceylon). Style slender, 1–4 (–6) mm. Capsule 1–3 (–5) mm. Seed filling the capsule, cylindrical, smooth.

D i s t r. Practically throughout the world in tropical and warmer regions generally. Some forms may have originated in more restricted areas (e.g. var. *sicula* L. in the Mediterranean region and var. *aspera* in India), but this is now a matter of mere conjecture.

E c o l. Very abundant throughout the island except on the highest ground—along roadsides, as a weed of gardens, fields and disturbed ground generally, in dry scrub and along dry forest margins, along streams, in patana, on sandy sea shores etc.

V e r n. Gas-karal-heba, Wel-karal-sebo (S); Nayururi (T).

I l l u s t r. Tadulingam & Venkatanarayana, Handb. S. Indian Weeds: 266, pl. 111. 1932—this represents var. *aspera* (=var. *indica* L.), to which most of the Ceylon material diverges.

S p e c i m e n s E x a m i n e d. JAFFNA DISTRICT: Jaffna, Feb. 1890, *s. coll. s.n.* (PDA). BATTICALOA DISTRICT: Batticaloa, *s. coll. s.n.* (PDA). KANDY DISTRICT: Gundoomalee, Kandy, 14 Nov. 1961, *Amaratunga 4* (PDA); between Hatton and Kotagala Hill, dry ground near school, 7 Feb. 1973, *Burtt & Townsend 81* (E, K, PDA, US). COLOMBO DISTRICT: weedy coconut plantation, Ja-Ela-Gampaha road north of Colombo, 15 Feb. 1968, *Comanor 1020* (PDA, US); Minuwangoda, 3 Nov. 1968, *Amaratunga 1664* (PDA); Uvapola, weed on waste ground, 7 Aug. 1969, *Amaratunga 1974* (PDA); Negombo, on sandy soil near the sea, 18 Sept. 1969, *Amaratunga 1829* (PDA). BADULLA DISTRICT: patana, Fort Macdonald valley, 11 March 1906, *A.M. Silva s.n.* (PDA); by side of railway, Ohiya, 3 May 1906, *A.M. Silva s.n.* (PDA). HAMBANTOTA DISTRICT: Ruhuna National Park, Block 2, near Katuwila Ara, thicket area near stream, 17 June 1967, *Comanor 256* (PDA, US); Patanagala Beach, in sand pockets on rock, 1 Sept. 1967, *Mueller-Dombois 67090104* (PDA, US); Ruhuna National Park, Block 1, 1 mile South of Buttawa at Uraniya Kalapuwa, 10 Dec. 1967, *Mueller-Dombois & Cooray 67121093* (PDA, US).

N o t e. Of the above specimens, *Amaratunga 4* is a very glabrous form which might pass for var. *porphyristachya* (Wall. ex Moq.) Hook. f. but has a more robust inflorescence, and the Batticaloa plant has oblong, acute leaves which bring it into var. *pubescens* (Moq.) C.C. Townsend. Most of the others have roundish leaves more or less tomentose beneath at least on the nerves, have plumper spikelets, and are almost or quite var. *aspera. Burtt & Townsend 81*, however, has plump spikelets and subglabrous, acuminate leaves. For the area involved, Ceylonese populations of *A. aspera* are more difficult to name varietally than most, and here at any rate it may be more expedient to use no formal infraspecific taxa, however useful these may be in various other regions of the world. Moon's Kalatura plant, cited by Trimen as "var. *argentea*", is little different from Linnean specimen 287/2 of var. *indica*, and bears no resemblance to var. *sicula* L. (var. *argentea* (Lam.) Hook. f.).

2. Achyranthes bidentata Blume, Bijdr. 545. 1826; Moq. in DC., Prod. 13 (2): 312. 1849; Hook. f. in Fl. Br. Ind. 4: 730. 1885; Trimen, Handb. Fl. Ceylon 3: 404. 1895; Gamble, Fl. Pres. Madras 1176. 1925, repr. 824. 1957. Type: Mt. Burangrang, Java, *Blume 897.294–84* (L, lectotype).

Erect or straggling herb, 0.6–2 m, much-branched. Stem and branches indistinctly quadrangular, rather flaccid, striate or sulcate, subglabrous to moderately (rarely more densely) hairy, the nodes frequently much shrunken when dry. Leaves elliptic-oblong to broadly oval, rarely to narrowly lanceolate, shortly or longly acuminate, gradually or more abruptly narrowed below, (4.5–) 9–22 (–28) × (1.2–) 2.5–8.5 (–10) cm, usually thinly hairy (or moderately so along the lower surface of the veins), rarely densely appressed-hairy on the lower surface (not in Ceylon); petioles of main stem leaves 3–20 (–30) mm, shortening above and below. Inflorescences at first dense, finally lax and elongating to as much as 20 cm, but commonly about half this length; peduncles 1–4 (–6) cm. Bracts narrowly lanceolate, brownish-membranous, 3–5 mm, glabrous. Bracteoles 3.5–5.5 mm, the basal wings c. 0.5–1.5 mm, almost or quite free from the commonly outwardly curving spine (in eastern Asia, including Ceylon) or variably adnate to it (in northern India, Pakistan and Africa). Perianth segments 5, 4–7 mm, the outer longest, all narrowly lanceolate, very acute, with a distinct midrib and 2 obscure or obvious lateral nerves, narrowly pale-margined. Stamens 5, the filaments 2–3 mm, alternating with subquadrate pseudo-staminodes which are typically simple and shortly dentate or subentire, more rarely (and not in Ceylon) with a much shorter rudimentary tooth—or crest-like, shortly toothed dorsal scale. Style slender, 1–2 mm. Capsule 2–3 mm. Seed filling the capsule, cylindrical, smooth.

D i s t r. Asia from W. Pakistan, India and Ceylon eastwards to China, Japan, Indonesia and the Solomon Islands; east and west Tropical Africa.

E c o l. Described by Thwaites as "very common on waste ground", which is surely incorrect. Trimen is probably more correct as to the habitat, "shady places in grass...especially in the lower montane zone", but the plant is certainly not common today.

S p e c i m e n s E x a m i n e d. MATALE DISTRICT: Kalupahane, La-galla, Sept. 1887, *s. coll. s.n.* (PDA): KANDY DISTRICT: Nitre Cave district, Sept. 1888, *s. coll. s.n.* (PDA); Peradeniya, *Gardner s.n.* (PDA). NUWARA ELIYA DISTRICT: jungle stream at south boundary, Hakgala, 28 Feb. 1906, *Willis s.n.* (PDA).

A. aspera and *A. bidentata* appear to remain quite distinct in Ceylon. For difficulties elsewhere see Townsend in Kew Bull. 28: 145–146. 1973.

3. **Achyranthes diandra** Roxb., Fl. Ind. 2: 504. 1824; Hook. f. in Fl. Br. Ind. 4: 731. 1885; Trimen, Handb. Fl. Ceylon 3: 405. 1895. Type: "Ceylon"; no type specimen having been located, Wight's figure of *Centrostachys diandra* (see below), which is copy of No. 1809 of Roxburgh's unpublished Flora Indica drawings at Kew, is regarded as the type of this species.

Centrostachys diandra (Roxb.) Wall. ex Wight, Ic. Pl. Ind. Or. 2: 7, pl. 722. 1840–1843; Moq. in DC., Prod. 13 (2): 322. 1849; Thw., Enum. Pl. Zeyl. 249. 1861.

Erect annual herb, 30–60 cm, branched from the base upwards. Stem and branches slender and wiry, quadrangular to subterete, striate, rather sparing-ly to moderately appressed-pilose. Leaves linear to linear-lanceolate, gradual-ly narrowed at both ends, acute, 3–10 × 0.3–1.5 cm on the main stem and branches, reducing above, thinly pilose on both surfaces or more densely so along the lower surface of the midrib; petioles of the lower leaves 2–7 mm, upper leaves more or less sessile. Inflorescences long- (mostly 3–5 cm) pe-dunculate, slender, lax and elongating to c. 9–17 cm in fruit, terminal on the stem and branches. Bracts narrowly lanceolate, brownish-membranous, glabrous. Perianth segments (4–) 5, 4–5 mm, the outer longest, all narrowly lanceolate, very acute, obscurely 1-nerved, narrowly pale-margined. Stamens 2, the filaments c. 1.75 mm, alternating with subquadrate pseudo-staminodes which are ciliate-fimbriate at the apex and lacking a dorsal scale. Style slen-der, c. 0.75 mm. Bracteoles about equalling the inner perianth segments, basal wings c. 1 mm, adnate to the straight or outwardly curving spine for c. 3/4 of their length. Capsule c. 2 mm. Seed filling the capsule, cylindrical, smooth.

D i s t r. Endemic. The occurrence of this species was described by Thwaites as "very common", and by Trimen as "common in the dry region", but it does not appear to be common at the present time. Only four herba-rium sheets bearing localities have been seen, and the only sheet giving in-formation on frequency (*Cooray 69011903R*) describes it as "rare".

I l l u s t r. See under "type".

N o t e. The combination *Centrostachys diandra* (Roxb.) Wall. (or even species *Centrostachys diandra* Wall.) has been commonly cited as published in Roxb., Fl. Ind. 2: 504. 1824—the same page has the description of *Achyranthes diandra*. However, not only is no combination legitimately made, but also Wallich makes it clear on p. 497 (in his description of the genus *Centrostachys*) that at the time of writing he is only transferring *Achyranthes aquatica* R. Br. to *Centrostachys*, which he thus regards as a monotypic genus.

Specimens Examined. ANURADHAPURA DISTRICT: Puliyankulam, 18 March 1927, *Alston 1336* (PDA); POLONNARUWA DISTRICT: Topowe, Minneriya, March 1853, *s. coll. s.n.* (PDA). TRINCOMALEE DISTRICT: Trincomalee, *Roettler s.n.* in Wallich Herb. *6929B* (K). HAMBANTOTA DISTRICT: Ruhuna National Park, Block 3, Pilimagala, 19 Jan. 1969, *Cooray 69011903R* (PDA, US).

Achyranthes corymbosa L. = *Polycarpaea corymbosa* (L.) Lam., of the Caryophyllaceae.

11. CENTROSTACHYS

Wall., in Roxb., Fl. Ind. 2: 497. 1824.

Perennial herb with opposite leaves and branches, leaves entire. Flowers hermaphrodite, bibracteolate in shortly pedunculate, elongate, bracteate spikes which are terminal on the stem and branches, each bract subtending a single flower; bracts persistent, hyaline; bracteoles orbicular, hyaline. Perianth segments 5, somewhat spreading at anthesis, later closing together and considerably indurate at the base; upper tepal narrowest and longest, 1–3-nerved, the tip sharper and often recurved, the remaining tepals blunter with up to 7 nerves. Stamens 5, shorter than the perianth, shortly monadelphous at the base, alternating with spathulate pseudo-staminodes furnished with fimbriate dorsal scales; anthers bilocular (4-locellate). Style filiform, stigma capitate. Ovary with a single ovule pendulous on a curved funicle, radicle ascending. Nutlet thin-walled, tightly enclosing the seed, falling together with the persistent perianth and bracteoles. Endosperm copious.

A monotypic genus.

Centrostachys aquatica (R. Br.) Wall. ex Moq. in DC., Prod. 13 (2): 321. 1849; Wight, Ic. Pl. Ind. Or. 5 (2): 4, t. 1780. 1852. Type: Bangkok, Siam, *Koenig s.n.* (BM, holotype).

Achyranthes aquatica R. Br., Prod. Fl. Nov. Holl. 417. 1810; Trimen, Handb. Fl. Ceylon 3: 403. 1895; Gamble, Fl. Pres. Madras 1176. 1925, repr. 823. 1956.

Aquatic or subaquatic perennial 0.5–1.5 m, prostrate to straggling or erect, usually much-branched, considerably rooting at the lower nodes with dense tufts of whitish rhizoids, stem near the base up to 2 cm thick, spongy, hollow. Upper stem and branches sulcate-striate, glabrous for the most part but increasingly appressed-pilose towards the inflorescence. Leaves lanceolate to lanceolate-oblong or oblong-ovate, cuneate or usually attenuate to the base, acute to acuminate at the apex, moderately appressed-pilose on both surfaces (densely so when young), lamina (2.5–) 7–15 × (0.8–) 2–5 cm; petiole 0.4–4 cm. Spike c. 4–12 cm in flower, elongating to 25 cm or occasionally even more in fruit; rhachis moderately to densely appressed-pilose; peduncle short, mostly c. 1.5 cm. Bracts deltoid-lanceolate, 3–4 mm, hyaline (drying pale brownish) with a single midrib, glabrous, finally deflexed below the hard callus left by the fallen perianth; bracteoles orbicular, hyaline, c. 1.5–2 mm, glabrous. Perianth 6–8 mm, the upper (outer) tepal slightly longer than the remainder, with a sharper, often slightly recurved tip, and a somewhat narrower pale border. Filaments stout, 2–3 mm. Style 1.75–2.5 mm. Capsule c. 4 mm, slightly broader at the base but rounded above. Seed smooth, chestnut-brown.

D i s t r. Tropical Asia from India, Burma and Thailand to Java; Norfolk Island; tropical Africa from Nigeria, the Sudan and Ethiopia south to Rhodesia. Several tanks in the Dambulla/Kekirawa area were searched for this species without success in 1973; it may yet exist, for example by the Kala Wewa—but this is a very large tank with several parts of the shore difficult of access.

E c o l. In shallow water by a tank in the dry region, very rare; only one gathering known.

I l l u s t r. Wight, Ic. Pl. Ind. Or. 5, pl. 1780. 1852.

N o t e. Although the authorities for the binomial *Centrostachys aquatica* have been generally accepted as (R. Br.) Wall. in Roxb., Fl. Ind. 2: 497. 1824, such citation is incorrect. The species is listed in that place under *Achyranthes* as "3 A. (*Centrostachys* Wall.) *aquatica*, R." Wallich then describes his new genus *Centrostachys* and states that he proposes detaching "this species" (i.e., *Achyranthes aquatica*) into it. Roxburgh does not appear to have accepted Wallich's genus, as the species reappears as an *Achyranthes* in Carey's edition of the Flora Indica 1: 673. 1832; and Wallich nowhere produces the binomial *Centrostachys aquatica*. Hence this must be dated from Moquin.

S p e c i m e n s   E x a m i n e d. ANURADHAPURA DISTRICT: tank at Kitulatiawa, between Dambulla and Kekirawa ("or Madatugama" added to label in pencil), 4 July 1887, *s. coll. s.n.* (PDA).

12. PSILOTRICHUM

Blume, Bijdr. 1544. 1825. Type species: *Ps. ferrugineum* (Roxb.) Moq. in DC., Prod. 13 (2): 279. 1849.

Perennial herbs or subshrubs, prostrate to scandent, with entire, opposite leaves. Flowers hermaphrodite, in axillary and terminal bracteate heads or spikes, solitary in the axil of each bract and bibracteolate; bracts persistent, finally spreading or deflexed, bracteoles falling with the fruiting perianth. Tepals 5, free, strongly to faintly nerved or ribbed (nerves 3 or more), the outer 2 frequently finally more or less indurate at the base. Stamens 5, shortly monadelphous at the base, without or rarely (not in Ceylon) with alternating pseudo-staminodes; anthers bilocular (4-locellate). Ovary with a single pendulous ovule; style slender but rather short; stigma capitate. Utricle thin-walled, bursting irregularly. Seed compressed-ovoid, brownish.

About 14 species in tropical Asia and Africa, chiefly the latter.

KEY TO THE SPECIES

1 Tepals faintly c. 5-nerved, c. 5 mm long, almost concolorous and shortly pilose.......
....**1. P. scleranthum**
1 Tepals strongly 3-ribbed, c. 3 mm long, green centrally with broad pale borders (especially the outer); outer tepals with more or less patent hairs along the margins; 2 of the 3 inner tepals long-pilose along both margins, the third inner tepal long-pilose along one margin...**2. P. elliotii**

1. Psilotrichum scleranthum Thw., Enum. Pl. Zeyl. 248. 1861; Hook. f. in Fl. Br. Ind. 4: 725. 1885; Trimen, Handb. Fl. Ceylon 3: 400. 1895; Gamble, Fl. Pres. Madras 1174. 1925, repr. 882. 1957. Type: Anuradhapura, *Gardner s.n.* (PDA, holotype, K, isotype).

Psilotrichum africanum Oliv. in Hook. Ic. Pl. 16, t. 1542. 1886.
Psilotrichum trichophyllum Baker in Kew Bull. 1897: 297. 1897.
Psilotrichum concinnum Baker, id. 1897.

Woody perennial herb or small shrub, erect or rooting at the basal nodes, sometimes more or less scandent, 0.6–2 m, much-branched with the branches spreading at 45–90 degrees. Stem and branches in the older parts terete, striate and glabrescent, when young quadrangular and sulcate with pale, thick corners, more or less densely pilose with yellowish, subappressed hairs, slightly swollen at the nodes. Leaves ovate to elliptic or elliptic-oblong, 2–10 × 1–4.2 cm, acute to acuminate at the mucronate apex, shortly to longly cuneate at the base with a 2–5 mm petiole, moderately but finely pubescent on both surfaces (generally more conspicuously so on the lower surface of the primary venation). Inflorescences of rather short spikes, 7–8 mm wide and finally elongating to 2–5 cm, terminal and generally 2 at each node in the axils of the opposite leaves of stem or branches, sessile or on peduncles up to c. 4 cm long; bracts ovate-lanceolate, 2–2.5 mm, more or less densely appressed-pubescent, sharply mucronate with the excurrent midrib, finally spreading

or deflexed; bracteoles whitish, broadly cordate-ovate with the margins slightly overlapping at the base, c. 2 mm with a distinct 0.5 mm mucro formed by
the excurrent midrib, glabrous or slightly pilose along the midrib and/or margins. Tepals white or greenish, very firm, faintly c. 5-nerved with obscure finer
nerves; the 2 outer lanceolate-oblong, acute, 3.5–4.5 mm, finally indurate at
the base, narrowly hyaline-bordered, shortly pilose over the entire dorsal
surface; the 3 inner lanceolate-ovate, acute to acuminate, pilose mainly centrally, the hyaline border widened below. Stamens c. 2.5 mm. Style c. 0.75 mm.
Capsule oblong-ovoid, c. 2.5–3 mm. Seed ovoid, c. 1.75 mm, brown, shining,
faintly reticulate.

D i s t r. S. India (Travancore); widespread in tropical Africa from eastern
Zaire and Angola through Uganda, Kenya and Tanzania to Rhodesia, Zan-
zibar, Mozambique and Madagascar.

E c o l. In dry sandy or loamy scrub and savannah, generally scarce but
locally in some quantity.

I l l u s t r. Hook. Ic. Pl. 16, t. 1542. 1886, as *P. africanum*.

S p e c i m e n s E x a m i n e d. ANURADHAPURA DISTRICT: Anu-
radhapura, *Gardner s.n.* (K, PDA, not seen in 1973). KANDY DISTRICT:
Haragama, Dec. 1881, *s. coll. s.n.* (PDA). HAMBANTOTA DISTRICT:
Tissamaharama, Dec. 1882, *s. coll. s.n.* (PDA); Ruhuna National Park,
Patanagala rocks, in forest and sand, important undergrowth herb, 8 Dec.
1967, *Mueller-Dombois 671208010* (PDA, US); Ruhuna National Park, Block
1, forest patch in plot R. 10, common, 22 Jan. 1968, *Comanor 812* (PDA, US);
Kumbukkan Oya, c. 2 miles above mouth at Migahakanda Meda Duwa,
Block 2, common, 2 Jan. 1969, *Fosberg et al. 51108* (PDA, US); Ruhuna
National Park, Block 1, Rugamtota, 14 Nov. 1969, *Cooray 69111408R* (PDA,
US).

2. **Psilotrichum elliotii** Baker in Thiselton-Dyer (ed.), Fl. Trop. Africa 6 (1):
58. 1909. Type: Uganda, *Scott-Elliot 8062* (K, holotype).

Ptilotus ovatus Moq. in DC., Prod. 13 (2): 281. 1849.
Psilotrichum calceolatum Moq., ibid., 280. 1949, nomen nudum; Hook. f.,
    Fl. Br. Ind. 4: 725. 1885, nomen illegit.; Trimen, Handb. Fl. Ceylon 3: 400.
    1895; Gamble, Fl. Pres. Madras 1174. 1926, repr. 822. 1957.
Psilotrichum ovatum Peter in Feddes Rep. Beih. 40 (2), Anhang. 28. 1932.
Psilotrichum ovatum (Moq. ex Hook.) Haum. in Bull. Jard. Bot. Brux. 18: 11.
    1946.
Psilotrichum peterianum Susseng. in Mitt. bot. Staatss. München Heft 4: 131.
    1952.
Psilotrichum moquinianum Abeywick. in Ceylon J. Sci., Biol. Sci. 2 (2): 158.
    1959.

Perennial herb, somewhat woody at the base, procumbent and forming mats up to c. 1.2 m across or scrambling among low vegetation, considerably branched from the base and often also above. Stem and branches in the older parts terete, striate, finally glabrescent at the base, quadrangular and sulcate when young, densely furnished with long, white hairs, not swollen at the nodes. Leaves ovate to broadly oblong, 1–4.6 × 0.8–2.2 cm, rounded to short-ly acuminate at the mucronate apex, rounded-subtruncate to shortly cuneate at the base, subsessile and semiamplexicaul or with a petiole up to c. 5 mm long, moderately furnished on both surfaces with long, subappressed white hairs, sometimes glabrescent above with age. Inflorescences of rather short spikes, 6–8 mm wide and finally elongating to 1.5–3 cm, terminal and gener-ally 2 at each node in the leaf-axils, sessile or on very slender peduncles up to 2 cm long; bracts deltoid-ovate, 2–2.5 mm, densely white-pilose, finally spreading or deflexed, whitish, the minutely excurrent midrib bordered by a conspicuous green vitta; bracteoles broadly cordate-ovate, 1 mm long and 2 mm wide, colour and indumentum similar to the bracts, similarly shortly mucronate. Tepals membranous, strongly 3-ribbed and greenish centrally with broad pale margins; the 2 outer c. 3 mm with broader, somewhat in-volute pale margins as wide as the ribbed central part, the 3 ribs meeting be-low the apex, which is mucronate with the excurrent midrib, the pale margins uniformly furnished with more or less patent white hairs; the inner 3 similar or more cucullate and indistinctly mucronate above, more narrowly pale-margined, 2 densely long-pilose along both margins and the third along one margin, the second margin with an indumentum similar to that of the outer tepals. Stamens c. 1.75 mm, very delicate. Style c. 0.75 mm. Capsule oblong-ovoid, c. 1.5 mm. Seed ovoid, 1 mm, compressed, brown, shining, faintly reticulate.

D i s t r. S. India; Tropical Africa (Eastern Zaire, Uganda, Kenya, Tanzania).

E c o l. On roadsides, on dry ground with scanty grass cover, in scrub vegetation, on sandy or sandy/clay soils in the dry or intermediate zones of the island, not common but apparently widespread.

I l l u s t r. Feddes Repert. Beih. 40 (2), t. 28. 1932, as *P. ovatum*.

N o t e. The specific epithet *calceolatum*, used by Trimen and others for this species, is rendered illegitimate by the fact that when Hooker published it he cited *Ptilotus ovatus* Moq. as a synonym and thus should have taken up the epithet *ovatus* for the species. Hauman eventually did this, but by that time the name *Psilotrichum ovatum* (Moq.) Haum. was illegitimate as a later homonym. See Verdcourt in Kew Bull. 17: 492–493. 1964. Specimen No. 287/14 in the Linnean Herbarium (LINN), sent to Linnaeus by Koenig but apparently never described, belongs to the present species.

S p e c i m e n s   E x a m i n e d. JAFFNA DISTRICT: Kankasanturai, Feb. 1890, *s. coll. s.n.* (PDA); Mulangavil, c. 32 m N. of Mannar on the road

to Pooneryn, 23 Feb. 1973, *Townsend 73/97* (K, PDA, US). MANNAR DIST-
RICT: Mantai, Feb. 1890, *s. coll. s.n.* (PDA). ANURADHAPURA DIST-
RICT: waste ground in sparse turf near the Bo tree precinct, Anuradhapura,
9 March 1973, *Townsend 73/191* (K, PDA, US). POLONNARUWA DIST-
RICT: Minneriya, March 1858, *Gardner s.n.* (PDA). MATALE DISTRICT:
Sigiriya Rock, 12 Oct. 1966, *Amaratunga 1156* (PDA). .HAMBANTOTA
DISTRICT: Ruhuna National Park, Block 1, mile 11 at Yala Road, 18 Oct.
1968, *Mueller-Dombois 68101837* (PDA, US).

13. ALTERNANTHERA

For·sk., Fl. Aeg.-Arab. 28. 1775. Type species: *A. sessilis* (L.) DC., Cat.
Hort. Monsp. 77. 1813.

Annual or perennial herbs, prostrate or erect to floating or scrambling,
with entire, opposite leaves. Inflorescences of sessile or pedunculate heads or
short spikes, axillary, solitary, or clustered, bracteate. Flowers hermaphrodite, solitary in the axil of a bract, bibracteolate, bracts persistent but the perianth falling with the fruit, bracteoles persistent or not. Perianth segments 5,
free, equal or unequal, glabrous or furnished with smooth or denticulate hairs.
Stamens 2–5, some occasionally without anthers, the filaments distinctly monadelphous at the base into a cup or tube, alternating with large and dentate
or laciniate to very small pseudo-staminodes (rarely these obsolete); anthers
unilocular (bilocellate). Style short, stigma capitate. Ovary with a single pendulous ovule. Fruit an indehiscent utricle, thin-walled or sometimes corky,
seeds more or less lenticular.

A large genus of over 150 species, far the greatest number occurring in the
American tropics and subtropics, from which several have spread to become
widely distributed weeds.

KEY TO THE SPECIES

1 Tepals very dissimilar both in length and form........................**1. A. pungens**
1 Tepals all similar in form, subequal or at most the inner slightly shorter than the outer
  2 Tepals 1-nerved with the prominent midrib only.......................**2. A. sessilis**
  2 Tepals prominently 3-nerved in the lower half
    3 Pseudo-staminodes much shorter than the stamens; plant mat-forming with prostrate
      branches...**3. A. paronychioides**
    3 Pseudo-staminodes as long as the stamens; plant erect or ascending, cultivated only..
    ....**4. A. bettzickiana**

1. Alternanthera pungens Kunth in HBK., Nov. Gen. Sp. 2: 206. 1817. Type:
Maypur Waterfall, R. Orinoco, Colombia, *Humboldt & Bonpland* (P, isotype).

Achyranthes repens L., Sp. Pl. ed. 1. 205. 1753.

Illecebrum achyrantha L., Sp. Pl. ed. 2. 299. 1762.

Alternanthera achyrantha (L.) Sweet, Hort. Suburb. London 48. 1818; Moq. in DC., Prod. 13 (2): 358. 1849.

Alternanthera repens (L.) Link, Enum. Pl. Hort. Berol. alt. 1: 154. 1821, non Gmelin, Syst. Nat. ed. 13, 2 (8): 106. 1791.

Prostrate mat-forming perennial herb with a stout vertical rootstock, also rooting at the lower nodes, much-branched from the base outwards, mats up to c. 1 m across. Branches terete, striate, stout to more slender, more or less densely villous with long, white hairs but frequently glabrescent with age. Leaves broadly rhomboid-ovate to broadly oval or obovate, 1.5–4.5 × 0.3–2.7 cm, rounded to subacute at the apex with a mucro which in the young leaves is often fine and bristle-like, narrowed below to a petiole up to 1 cm long, glabrous or thinly appressed-pilose on both surfaces, especially on the lower surface of the primary venation. Inflorescences sessile, axillary, solitary or more commonly 2–3 together, globose to shortly cylindrical, 0.5–1.5 cm long and 0.5–1 cm wide; bracts membranous, white or stramineous, 4–5 mm, lanceolate-ovate, glabrous or dorsally pilose, distinctly aristate with the excurrent midrib, strongly denticulate around the upper margin; bracteoles similar but smaller, 3–4 mm, falling with the fruit. Tepals extremely dissimilar: the 2 outer (abaxial) deltoid-lanceolate, 5 mm, very rigid, 5-nerved below, the intermediate pair of nerves much shorter and finer, outer 2 nerves meeting above to join the excurrent, pungently mucronate midrib; inner (adaxial) tepal oblong, flat, 3 mm, blunt and strongly dentate at the apex, 3-nerved below but the nerves meeting well below the apex and the apical mucro short and fine; lateral tepals c. 2 mm, sinuate in side view with the two sides of the lamina connivent and denticulate above, sharply mucronate; abaxial and adaxial tepals with small tufts of glochidiate and barbellate whitish bristles about the basal angles, the lateral tepals each with a large tuft about the centre of the midrib. Stamens 5, all with anthers, at anthesis slightly exceeding the ovary and style, the alternating pseudo-staminodes broad, subquadrate, shorter than the filaments, entire to dentate. Ovary compressed, squat, narrowed below; style very short, wider than long. Fruit lenticular, rounded or retuse above, 2 mm. Seed discoid, c. 1.25 mm, brown, shining, faintly reticulate.

Distr. A native of the American continent from the southern U.S.A. to Argentina and Peru, now widespread as a weed in the tropics and subtropics of the Old World.

Ecol. A widespread introduction now frequent in dry sandy places, on disturbed ground, roadsides etc.; appears to endure, and even thrive on, considerably trodden or otherwise compacted soil.

Illustr. Tadulingam & Venkatanarayana, Handb. S. Indian Weeds 274, pl. 114, as *A. echinata*.

Specimens Examined. JAFFNA DISTRICT: by roadside near Palm Court Hotel, Jaffna, 22 Feb. 1973, *Townsend 73/75* (K, PDA, US). MANNAR DISTRICT: Mannar, roadside in town, 23 Feb. 1973, *Townsend 73/102* (K, PDA, US). ANURADHAPURA DISTRICT: grounds of Nuwarawewa Rest House, 9 March 1973, *Townsend 73/190* (K, PDA, US); Kalawewa, 10 July 1965, *Amaratunga 935* (PDA). POLONNARUWA DISTRICT: bare sandy ground near Parakrama Samudra c. 1 mile S. of Polonnaruwa Rest House, 14 March 1973, *Townsend 73/233* (K, PDA, US). TRINCOMALEE DISTRICT: floor of large quarry c. 3 miles past Kantalai on road from Dambulla to Trincomalee, milestone 140, 14 March 1973, *Townsend 73/244* (K, PDA, US). MONERAGALA DISTRICT: trodden roadside in middle of town, Wellawaya, 2 March 1973, *Townsend 73/148* (K, PDA, US). HAMBANTOTA DISTRICT: Tissamaharama, weed, 8 July 1952, *Alwis s.n.* (PDA); Ruhuna National Park, Block near Buttawa Bungalow, 9 Jan. 1969, *Cooray & Balakrishnan 69010915R* (PDA, US).

2. **Alternanthera sessilis** (L.) DC., Cat. Hort. Monsp. 77. 1813; Moq. in DC., Prod. 13 (2): 357. 1849; Hook. f. in Fl. Br. Ind. 4: 731. 1885. Type: Ceylon, Hermann Herbarium 2: 78 (BM, lecto.)

Gomphrena sessilis L., Sp. Pl. ed. 1. 225. 1753.
Illecebrum sessile (L.) L., Sp. Pl. ed. 2. 300. 1762.
Alternanthera triandra Lam., Enc. 1: 95. 1783; Trimen, Handb. Fl. Ceylon 3: 405. 1895; Gamble, Fl. Pres. Madras 1179. 1925, repr. 825. 1957.
Alternanthera repens Gmel., Syst. Nat. ed. 13, 2 (1): 106. 1791.
Achyranthes alternifolia L. f., Sp. Pl. Suppl. 159. 1781, quoad pl. Zeyl., non L., Mant. 50. 1767.

Annual or usually perennial herb; in drier situations with slender, more solid stems, erect, more or less much-branched, to c. 30 cm; in wetter places ascending or commonly prostrate with stems c. 0.1–1 m long, rooting at the nodes, more or less fistular, with numerous lateral branches; when floating very fistular, the stems attaining several metres in length and over 1 cm thick, with long clusters of whitish rootlets at the nodes. Stem and branches green or purplish, with a narrow line of whitish hairs down each side of the stem and tufts of white hairs in the branch and leaf axils, otherwise glabrous, striate, terete. Leaves extremely variable in shape and size, linear-lanceolate to oblong, oval, or obovate-spathulate, 1–9 (–15) × 0.2–2 (–3) cm, blunt to shortly acuminate at the apex, cuneate to attenuate at the base, glabrous or thinly pilose, especially on the lower surface of the midrib; petiole obsolete to c. 5 mm. Inflorescences sessile, axillary, solitary or in clusters of up to c. 5, subglobose or slightly elongate in fruit, c. 5 mm in diameter; bracts scarious, white, deltoid-ovate, mucronate with the excurrent pale midrib, glabrous, c. 0.75–1 mm; bracteoles similar, 1–1.5 mm, also persistent. Tepals oval-elliptic, equal, 1.5–2.5 mm, acuminate to rather blunt, white, glabrous or almost so, shortly but distinctly mucronate with the stout, excurrent midrib, the margins obscurely denticulate. Stamens 5 (2 filaments anantherous), at anthesis subequalling the ovary and style, the alternating pseudo-staminodes resembling the filaments but usually somewhat shorter. Ovary strongly compressed, roundish, style extremely short. Fruit obcordate or cordate-orbicular, 2–2.5 mm long, strongly compressed with a narrow, pale, somewhat thickened margin. Seed discoid, c. 0.75–1 mm, brown, shining, faintly reticulate.

D i s t r. Widespread in the tropics and subtropics of both Old and New Worlds.

E c o l. A very common species in many kinds of habitat from wet paddy and ditches to dry roadside banks, also found as a weed of gardens or other disturbed ground, chiefly lowland but ascending to at least 1180 m.

U s e s. This species is eaten as a vegetable and cultivated as such, being gathered in bundles as watercress is gathered in Europe.

V e r n. Mukunu-wenna (S); Ponankani (T).

I l l u s t r. Wight, Ic. Pl. Ind. Or. 2, pl. 727. 1840–43.

S p e c i m e n s   E x a m i n e d. JAFFNA DISTRICT: Waste ground, Jaffna town, 24 Feb. 1973, *Townsend 73/110* (K, PDA, US). ANURADHA-PURA DISTRICT: Wilpattu National Park, between Magul Illaima and Malimaduwa, along Erige Ela, 13 July 1969, *Wirawan 1113* (PDA, US); Anu-radhapura, waste ground between the New Town and the ruins, 9 March 1973, *Townsend 73/194* (K, PDA, US). KANDY DISTRICT: Peradeniya, in marshy patch, 29 March 1964, *Amaratunga 807* (PDA). NUWARA ELIYA DISTRICT: Talawakele, shallow ditch by roadside near river, 9 Feb. 1973, *Burtt & Townsend 122* (E, K, PDA, US). COLOMBO DISTRICT: Urapola, paddy fields, 24 Jan. 1967, *Amaratunga 1219* (PDA); Minuwangoda, 3 Nov. 1968, *Amaratunga 1668* (PDA); Divulapitya, 24 Sept. 1969, *Amaratunga 1846* (PDA). KEGALLE DISTRICT: roadside bank between Undugoda and Ke-galle, 15 Feb. 1973, *Townsend 73/61* (K, PDA, US). BADULLA DISTRICT: disturbed ground by roadside just west of Badulla on the road to Nuwara Eliya, 1 March 1973, *Townsend 73/135* (K, PDA, US). GALLE DISTRICT: weed in garden by road c. 6 miles east of Hiniduma on road to Pittabeddara, 14 Feb. 1973, *Townsend 73/52* (K, PDA, US). HAMBANTOTA DISTRICT: Tissa Tank, abundant, Dec. 1882, *s. coll. s.n.* (PDA); Mennik Ganga (river) 1 mile above Yala Bungalow, edge of woods in undergrowth on flood plain, 5 Jan. 1969, *Fosberg et al. 51063* (PDA, US); Ruhuna National Park, Block 1, common at Kohombagaswala, 3 Dec. 1969, *Cooray 69120318R* (PDA, US).

3. Alternanthera paronychioides St. Hil., Voy. Distr. Diamans Brésil 2: 439. 1833; Fawcett & Rendle, Fl. Jamaica 3: 140. 1914. Type: roadside near the sea at Rio de Janeiro, *St. Hilaire 223* (P, holotype).

Alternanthera polygonoides sensu Standley, N. Amer. Fl. 21 (2): 136. 1917, non L.

Perennial herb with a stout vertical rootstock, mat-forming with numerous prostrate branches which root at the nodes, mats to c. 80 cm across. Branches more or less white-villous when young (especially at the upper nodes), finally glabrescent and yellowish or reddish, striate. Leaves moderately white-villous when young but finally glabrescent on the upper surface and thinly hairy below, 8–43 × 2–12 mm, the elliptic, oval or obovate lamina obtuse or subacute at the apex, narrowed below into a long, indistinctly demarcated petiole which in the larger leaves almost equals the lamina in length. Inflorescences sessile, axillary, solitary or 2–3 together, more or less globose or finally ovoid, 4–8 mm in diameter; bracts firm, membranous, white, ovate-acuminate, mucronate with the excurrent midrib, c. 2.75 mm; bracteoles similar but smaller and slightly narrower, c. 2.5 mm, falling with the fruit. Tepals white, subequal, oblong-lanceolate, acute, the outer two 4–4.5 mm, the inner three 3.5–4 mm, all prominently 3-nerved to about the middle and darker in the nerved area, mucronate with the excurrent midrib, thinly to moderately pilose in the lower half with patent, white, minutely barbellate hairs. Stamens 5, all fertile, at anthesis slightly exceeding the ovary and style, the alternating pseudo-staminodes much shorter than the filaments, oblong, dentate about the apex. Ovary compressed, narrowed below; style very short, broader than long. Fruit compressed, orbicular-obcordate, c. 1.75–2 mm; seed discoid, c. 1.25 mm, brownish, shining, faintly reticulate.

D i s t r. A native of tropical America (West Indies, Mexico, Panama &c., south to Brazil). Naturalized in the U.S.A.; also in India, Java and other parts of the Old World.

E c o l. Apparently of recent introduction, usually occurring in dry sandy ground with sparse grass cover, frequently where subjected to periodical inundation. Likely to spread with some rapidity in the island.

I l l u s t r. Mart., Fl. Brasil. 5 (1), t. 56. 1875.

N o t e. I entirely concur with Pedersen (Darwiniana 14: 437–439. 1967) that although Linnean specimen 290.21 (LINN) is conspecific with the present species, it cannot be regarded as the type of *Gomphrena polygonoides*, because it is at variance with Linnaeus' ed. 1 description of the latter; also that since Linnaeus' name is impossible to typify satisfactorily, it should be rejected as a nomen confusum. These conclusions I had reached independently before Pedersen's paper came to my notice. The specific epithet was spelt as "paronichyoides" by St. Hilaire, but is used here in the corrected form.

S p e c i m e n s E x a m i n e d. ANURADHAPURA DISTRICT: grounds of Nuwarawewa Rest House, one large plant, 9 March 1973, *Townsend 73/189* (K, PDA, US); by the Abhayagiri Dagaba, Anuradhapura, locally common, 9 March 1973, *Townsend 73/192* (K, PDA, US). MATALE DIST-

RICT: Galewala-Andiyagala, on tank bund, 10 July 1965, *Amaratunga 930* (PDA); Dewahuwa Tank, between Galewala and Andiyagala, on low bund on N. side, 17 Feb. 1973, *Townsend 73/62* (K, PDA, US); near S.W. corner of Kandalama Tank, E. of Dambulla, 11 March 1973, *Townsend 73/216* (K, PDA, US). COLOMBO DISTRICT: Urapola, marshy spot, 27 Sept. 1969, *Amaratunga 1860* (PDA).

4. Alternanthera bettzickiana (Regel) Voss in Vilm., Blumengart. ed. 3. 1: 869. (bettzichiana sphalm); Aschers. & Graebn., Syn. Fl. Mitteleuropas 5 (1): 365. 1920; Bailey, Man. Cult. Pl. ed. 2. 357. 1949. Type: specimen from St. Petersburg Botanic Gardens (LE, holotype).

Telanthera bettzickiana Regel in Index sem. hort. petrop. 1862: 28. 1862 et Gartenflora 11: 178. 1862.

Erect or ascending, bushy perennial herb commonly cultivated as an annual, c. 5–45 cm, stem and branches villous when young but soon glabrescent. Leaves narrowly or more broadly elliptic to oblanceolate or rhomboid-ovate, acute or acuminate at the apex, long-attenuate into an indistinctly demarcated petiole below, often purple-suffused and not rarely variegated. Heads axillary, sessile, usually solitary, globose or ovoid, 5–6 mm in diameter. Tepals white, lanceolate, acute, mucronate with the excurrent midrib, the outer 3 prominently 3-nerved below and darker in the nerved area, with a line of minutely barbellate white hairs along each side of this area, the hairs becoming denser towards the base of the tepal; inner 2 tepals slightly shorter, usually 1–2-nerved. Pseudo-staminodes as long as the filaments, laciniate at the apex.

D i s t r. Said to be a native of tropical America, probably Brazil, but unknown in the wild: probably a cultigen of *A. Flavogrisea* (Urb.) Urb. (= *A. ficoidea avett.*) and now widespread as a bedding plant.

U s e s. Cultivated as a border annual in Peradeniya and Kandy (seen by the author but not collected) and probably elsewhere, leaves eaten as a vegetable as with *A. sessilis*.

I l l u s t r. Makino, Illustr. Fl. Japan ed. 2: 606, f. 1816. 1948.

S p e c i m e n s E x a m i n e d. KANDY DISTRICT: Peradeniya Gardens, 8 Dec. 1926, *Alston 830* (K).

14. GOMPHRENA

L., Sp. Pl. ed. 1. 224. 1753; Gen. Pl. ed. 5. 105. 1754. Type species: *G. globosa* L., Sp. Pl. ed. 1. 224. 1753.

Annual or occasionally perennial herbs with entire, opposite leaves. Inflorescences terminal or axillary, capitate or spicate, solitary or glomerate, often subtended by a pair of sessile leaves, bracteate with the bracts persistent in fruit, the axis frequently thickened. Flowers hermaphrodite, each solitary in the axil of a bract, bibracteolate; bracteoles laterally compressed, carinate, often more or less winged or cristate along the dorsal surface of the midrib, deciduous with the fruit. Tepals 5, erect, free or almost so, more or less lanate dorsally, at least the inner 2 usually more or less indurate at the base in fruit. Stamens 5, monadelphous, the tube shortly 5-dentate with entire to very deeply bilobed teeth, with or without alternating pseudo-staminodes. Style short or long, stigmas 2, suberect or more or less divergent to very short. Ovary with a single pendulous ovule. Fruit a thin-walled, irregularly rupturing utricle. Seed ovoid, compressed.

A rather large genus of about 90 species, centred on tropical America but also with several Australian representatives.

KEY TO THE SPECIES

1 Bracteoles with a small dorsal crest confined to about the upper one-third of the dorsal
surface of the midrib. . . . .**1. G. celosioides**
1 Bracteoles with a large, conspicuous dorsal crest extending from the apex almost to the
extreme base of the midrib
  2 Teeth of the staminal tube deeply bilobed, the lobes blunt and not or scarcely exceeding the anthers which are set between them; leaves broadly lanceolate to broadly oblong
  . . . .**2. G. globosa**
  2 Teeth of the staminal tube deeply bilobed, the lobes long and acute, considerably ex-
  serted beyond the anthers and about equalling them in overall length; leaves narrowly
  oblanceolate to linear-oblong. . . . .**3. G. haageana**

1. Gomphrena celosioides Mart. in Nova Acta Phys.-Med. Acad. Caes. Leop. Carol. Nat. Cur. 13: 301. 1826; Moq. in DC., Prod. 13 (2): 410. 1849; Back. in Fl. Mal. Sér. 1, 4 (2): 96. 1949. Type: Brazil, *Sellow* (K, isotypes).

Gomphrena decumbens sensu Gamble, Fl. Pres. Madras 2 (7): 1179. 1925, repr. 825. 1957, non Jacq.

Annual herb, prostrate and mat-forming to ascending or erect, c. 7–30 cm, much-branched from the base and also above; stem and branches striate, often sulcate, when young usually more or less densely furnished with long, white, lanate hairs, more or less glabrescent with age. Leaves narrowly oblong to oblong-elliptic or oblanceolate, c. 1.5–4.5 × 0.5–1.3 cm, obtuse to subacute at the apex, mucronate, narrowed to a poorly demarcated petiole below, the pair of leaves subtending the terminal inflorescence more abruptly narrowed and sessile, oblong or lanceolate-oblong, all leaves glabrous or thinly pilose above, thinly to densely furnished with long whitish hairs on the margins and lower surface. Inflorescences sessile above the uppermost pair of leaflets, at first subglobose and c. 1.25 cm in diameter, finally elongate and cylindrical, c. 4–7 cm long, axis more or less lanate; bracts deltoid-ovate, 2.5–4 mm, shortly mucronate with excurrent midrib; bracteoles strongly laterally compressed, navicular, c. 5–6 mm, mucronate with the excurrent midrib, furnished along about the upper one-third of the dorsal surface of the midrib with an irregularly dentate or subentire wing. Tepals c. 4.5–5 mm, narrowly lanceolate, 1-nerved, the outer 3 more or less flat, lanate only at the base, nerve thick and greenish below, thinner and excurrent in a short mucro at the tip; inner 2 tepals sigmoid in lateral view at the stronger indurate base, densely lanate almost to the tip, slightly longer than the outer. Staminal tube subequalling the perianth, the 5 teeth deeply bilobed with obtuse lobes subequalling the c. 0.75 mm anthers which are set between them; pseudo-staminodes absent. Style and stigmas together c. 1 mm, style very short, stigmas divergent. Capsule shortly compressed-pyriform, c. 1.75 mm. Seeds compressed-ovoid, c. 1.5 mm, brown, faintly reticulate, shining.

D i s t r. A native of S. America (S. Brazil, Paraguay, Uruguay & Argentina) which has spread rapidly in the present century and is becoming a widely distributed weed in the warmer regions of the world. See Sandwith in Kew Bull. 1946: 29. 1946.

E c o l. This American species, unknown to Trimen, has spread rapidly in Ceylon as elsewhere, and is now one of the commonest species of the family here, occurring along roadsides, in dry rocky and waste places &c., having even accomplished the ascent to the top of Sigiriya Rock.

I l l u s t r. Tadulingam & Venkatanarayana, Handb. S. Indian Weeds 278. Pl. 115. 1932, as "*G. decumbens*?".

S p e c i m e n s E x a m i n e d. JAFFNA DISTRICT: 10 miles along road from Paranthan to Mullaittivu, 22 Feb. 1973, *Townsend 73/88* (K, PDA, US); Mulangavil, c. 32 miles N. of Mannar on road to Pooneryn, 23 Feb. 1973, *Townsend 73/99* (K, PDA, US). VAVUNIYA DISTRICT: 121 miles on road from Kandy to Jaffna, 21 Feb. 1973, *Townsend 73/74* (K, PDA, US). ANURADHAPURA DISTRICT: Aukana, near entrance to site, 17 Feb. 1973, *Townsend 73/66* (K, PDA, US). AMPARAI DISTRICT: 8 miles east of Amparai on road to Karativu, 16 March 1973, *Townsend 73/278* (K, PDA, US). MATALE DISTRICT: summit of Sigiriya Rock, 10 March 1973, *Townsend 73/202* (K, PDA, US); Dambulla-Habarana road, lateritic substrata, 7 May 1968, *Comanor 1210* (PDA, US). KANDY DISTRICT: Peradeniya, by goods shed near new railway station, 24 April 1940, *Senaratna 3030* (PDA); Peradeniya, 17 April 1963, *Amaratunga 590* (PDA). COLOMBO DISTRICT: Roadside, Drieberg's Lane by Maradana railway station, 10 March 1940, *Senaratna 3024* (PDA); Galle Face Green, abundant, 20 Feb. 1973, *Townsend 73/67* (K, PDA, US). MONERAGALA DISTRICT: between Koslanda and Diyaluma Falls, 28 Feb. 1973, *Townsend 73/133* (K, PDA, US); Wellawaya, in middle of town, 2 March 1973, *Townsend 73/149* (K, PDA, US). HAM-

BANTOTA DISTRICT: Ruhuna National Park, Block 1, at Bambewa, 17 Nov. 1969, *Cooray 69111712R* (PDA, US).

2. Gomphrena globosa L., Sp. Pl. ed. 1. 224. 1753; Hook. f. in Fl. Br. Ind. 4: 732. 1885; Backer in Fl. Mal. Sér. 1, 4 (2): 95. 1949. Type: Herb. Hort. Cliffort., specimen *capitulis argenteis*.... (BM, lectotype).

Annual herb, decumbent or erect, branched from the base and also above, c. 15–60 cm; stem and branches striate or sulcate, more or less densely clothed with appressed white hairs at least when young. Leaves broadly lanceolate to oblong or elliptic-oblong, 2.5–12 (–15) × 2–4 (–6) cm, narrowed to an ill-defined petiole below, thinly pilose on both surfaces, the pair of leaves subtending the terminal inflorescence sessile or almost so, broadly to subcor-date-ovate. Inflorescences sessile above the uppermost pair of leaves, usually solitary, globose or depressed-globose, c. 2 cm in diameter, pinkish to deep red; bracts deltoid-ovate, 3–5 mm, mucronate with the shortly excurrent midrib; bracteoles strongly laterally compressed, navicular, c. 8–12 mm, mucronate with the excurrent midrib, furnished from the apex almost to the base of the dorsal surface of the midrib with a broad, irregularly dentate crest. Tepals similar to those of *G. celosioides* but longer (6–6.5 mm), the outer more lanate and the inner less markedly indurate at the base. Staminal tube sub-equalling the perianth, the 5 teeth deeply bilobed with obtuse lobes subequal-ling the anthers; pseudo-staminodes absent. Style and stigmas together c. 2.5 mm, stigmas divergent, subequalling or slightly longer than the style. Capsule oblong-ovoid, compressed, c. 2.5 mm. Seeds compressed-ovoid, c. 2 mm, brown, almost smooth, shining.

D i s t r. A native of tropical America long cultivated in the warmer regions of the world.

E c o l. Commonly cultivated as a garden decorative in Ceylon, and oc-casionally found spontaneously by roadsides and in waste places.

V e r n. Raja-pohottu (S).

S p e c i m e n s E x a m i n e d. JAFFNA DIST.: c. 1 mile before Elephant Pass on the road from Kandy to Jaffna, 2 plants far from human habitation on disturbed ground by roadside, 22 Feb. 1973, *Townsend 73/91* (K, PDA, US); Mulangavil, c. 32 miles N. of Mannar on road to Pooneryn, roadside in village—plant not seen in cultivation here, 23 Feb. 1973, *Townsend 73/100* (K).

3. Gomphrena haageana Klotzsch in Otto & Dietr., Allg. Gartenz. 21: 297. 1853; Backer in Fl. Mal. Sér. 1, 4 (2): 97. 1949. Type: Described from culti-vated material from a British seedsman, grown in the nursery of Adolph Haage junior at Erfurt (B, holotype).

Gomphrena tuberifera Torr., Bot. Mex. Bound. Surv. 181. 1859.

Perennial herb with a tuberous root, erect, c. 20–70 cm, simple to much-branched. Leaves narrowly oblanceolate to linear-oblong, 3–8 × 0.3–1 cm, acute to rather blunt and mucronate at the apex, more or less long-attenuate at the base, rather thinly appressed-pilose on both surfaces, the pair of leaves subtending the terminal inflorescences sessile, lanceolate-ovate, long-acuminate. Inflorescence sessile above the uppermost pair of leaves, globose, 2–2.5 cm in diameter, sometimes finally shortly cylindrical and up to c. 6 cm long; bracts c. 6 cm, narrowly deltoid-ovate, somewhat plicate, mucronate with the shortly excurrent midrib; bracteoles strongly compressed, navicular, c. 10–15 mm, mucronate, with an almost complete crest like that of *G. globosa* but generally even wider and more deeply dentate. Tepals similar to those of *G. celosioides* but the inner even more strongly sigmoid and indurate below. Staminal tube subequalling the perianth, the 5 teeth very deeply bilobed, the subulate, acute lobes much exserted beyond the c. 1.5 mm anthers and subequalling them in overall length; pseudo-staminodes absent. Style and stigmas together c. 2.25 mm, the stigmas about twice as long as the style. Capsule c. 2.15 mm, shortly oblong, compressed. Seed ovoid, compressed, c. 1.75 mm, brown, very faintly reticulate, shining.

Distr. A native of the southern U.S.A. and Mexico, long cultivated in various parts of the tropics.

Ecol. One cultivated specimen only seen, "nursery of the Royal Botanic Garden, Peradeniya, 1899" (PDA). Extent of cultivation at the present time not known.

Illustr. None located.

15. IRESINE

P. Browne, Civ. & Nat. Hist. Jamaica 358. 1756, nomen conservandum. Type species: *I. celosioides* Nutt., Gen. N. Am. Pl. 2: 237. 1818.

Cruicita L., Sp. Pl. ed. 2: 179. 1762.
Xerandra Raf., Fl. Tellur. 3: 43. 1836.
Ireneis Moq. in DC., Prod. 13 (2): 349. 1849.

Annual or perennial herbs, shrubs or subshrubs, sometimes scandent, rarely small trees, with opposite leaves and branches; leaves simple, entire or more or less incised. Flowers hermaphrodite, polygamous or dioecious, bibracteolate, in axillary and terminal bracteate spikes, sometimes condensed to capitula or frequently paniculate; bracts and bracteoles small, membranous. Perianth segments 5, free, frequently pilose or lanate. Stamens 5, shortly monadelphous at the base, pseudo-staminodes occasionally well-developed, more commonly short or obsolete; anthers unilocular (bilocellate). Stigmas 2–3, elongate, or sometimes capitate in functionally male flowers. Ovary with a single pendulous ovule. Capsule membranous, indehiscent. Embryo annular, endosperm present.

About 80 species in the American tropics.

Iresine herbstii Hook. ex Lindl., Gard. Chron. 654. 1864; Dombrain, Floral Mag. 4, Pl. 219. 1865; Standley in N. Amer. Fl. Sér. 1, 21 (2): 167. 1917; Bailey, Man. Cult. Pl. ed. 2. 356. 1949. Type: cultivated material, England, origin R. Plate (K, holotype).

Erect or ascending perennial herb, to c. 1.5 m; stem and branches striate, rather succulent, sulcate when dry, furnished rather sparsely (or more densely in the young parts and about the nodes) with fine, multicellular hairs. Leaves variegated, from purplish with pink veins to green with yellow veins, orbicular to ovate-orbicular, shortly cuneate to truncate at the base, mostly deeply retuse at the apex (sometimes merely rounded), succulent, 2–6 cm long, on the lower surface sparingly furnished with short, frequently golden-glistening hairs; petioles to c. 2 cm. Flowers dioecious, sessile, in many-flowered, much-branched panicles up to c. 20 cm long, panicles leafless or with much reduced leaves subtending the branches. Bracts and bracteoles small, subhyaline, deltoid-ovate, more or less acute, c. 1 mm, glabrous. Perianth segments oblong, blunt or subacute, 1–1.25 mm, 3-nerved, glabrous (but lanate hairs often occurring at the axis between the tepals and the bracteoles). Ovary globose, shorter than the stigmas, style practically obsolete. Capsule not seen.

D i s t r. A native of tropical S. America. Introduced into Europe as a pot plant in the middle of the last century, now widely cultivated in the tropics as an ornamental; naturalized in Mexico, the West Indies and perhaps elsewhere.

E c o l. A decorative species, frequently cultivated in Ceylon as elsewhere in the tropics.

I l l u s t r. Bot. Mag. 91, t. 5499. 1865.

S p e c i m e n s E x a m i n e d. KANDY DISTRICT: Udawattekelle, 13 Nov. 1961, *Amaratunga 16* (PDA). No indication as to whether cultivated or spontaneous.

BOMBACACEAE

(by Andre G. Robyns*)

Type Genus: *Bombax* L., Sp. Pl. 511. 1753 and Gen. Pl., ed. 5. 227. 1754.

Trees, often big, rarely shrubs (not in Ceylon), inermous or aculeate, glabrous or lepidote or with stellate, tufted, or even simple hairs. Leaves alternate, simple or compound-digitate, stipulate, the stipules fugacious. Inflorescences cymose, racemose, paniculiform or fasciculate, or flowers solitary, sometimes ramiflorous. Flowers often large and showy, usually bracteolate, hermaphrodite, actinomorphous, rarely somewhat zygomorphous, usually 5-merous, sometimes subtended by an epicalyx; receptacle glandular or not; calyx valvate, lobate or truncate, caducous, persistent or accrescent; petals usually 5, rarely absent, contorted, usually adnate to the base of the staminal tube; stamens 5-many, usually monadelphous, rarely free; anthers 1- to 2- to many-thecate, free or coherent, sometimes stipitate, hippocrepiform to linear, sometimes anfractuose or more or less globular, usually longitudinally dehiscent, rarely circumscissile or apically poricidal; pollen grains usually 3-treme, porate, colpate or colporate, the sexine reticulate or tegillate and spinulate, sometimes pilate, rarely granulate or smooth; staminodes infrequently present; ovary superior, rarely subinferior (not in Ceylon), 2–5 (–6)- or 10-celled, with (1–) 2-many ovules in each cell, the placentation axile; style simple, the stigma capitate or lobed. Fruit mostly capsular, the pericarp smooth or spinose, loculicidally dehiscent into 3–5 valves, sometimes more or less long-lanate within (kapok), infrequently pulpy and indehiscent; seeds 1-many, glabrous, sometimes alate or arillate, often oleaginous; endosperm generally none or scant; embryo usually curved; cotyledons epigeal, flat or plicate, foliaceous or carnose.

A pantropical family of about 26 genera, particularly well developed in tropical America; two genera, *Cullenia* Wight and *Bombax* L., are native to Ceylon, while two other genera, *Adansonia* L. and *Ceiba* Mill., have been introduced.

The capsules of some genera (*Bombax, Ceiba, Ochroma* Sw.) are filled with woolly fibers, commonly named kapok; *Adansonia, Bombacopsis* Pittier, *Pachira* Aubl. and *Durio* Adans. have edible seeds. *Durio zibethinus* Murr.,

---

*National Botanic Garden, Meise, Belgium.

the durian, is occasionally cultivated in the wetter parts of Ceylon as a fruit-tree. Despite the strong offensive odor, the aril around the seed of the durian is highly valued. The genus *Ochroma*, a neotropical monotypic genus, furnishes the well-known balsa wood, a very lightweight wood which is used for life rafts, insulating, toys, etc. *Ochroma pyramidale* (Cav. ex Lam.) Urban (= *O. lagopus* Sw.) is occasionally planted in the humid zone of the island.

KEY TO THE GENERA

1 Leaves simple, densely lepidote below; flowers ramiflorous, with an epicalyx; corolla absent; staminal tube 5-dentate-lobulate to 5-lobate apically, each lobe with 7–11 stamens along the margins; stamens with very short filaments, the connectives irregularly spherical to club-shaped, covered with numerous stipitate 1-locular circumscissile thecae; capsules spinose, 5-valved; seeds 1-few, completely or incompletely covered by a fleshy aril (native species)...**1. Cullenia**
1 Leaves compound-digitate, the indumentum, when present, of stellate or tufted hairs; flowers without epicalyx; corolla present; stamens longitudinally dehiscent; capsules without spines, dehiscent or not; seeds exarillate.
  2 Stamens numerous, the anthers reniform or hippocrepiform.
    3 Trees to 40 m high or even more, aculeate especially when young; flowers short-pedicellate, bright red; stamens shortly united at the base; anthers hippocrepiform; pollen with reticulate sexine; capsules 5-valved, the valves blackish and glabrous at maturity; seeds embedded in copious kapok (native species).....................**2. Bombax**
    3 Trees to 10 (20) m high, the trunk short, thick and bulging, inermous; flowers long-pendent, white; stamens united for about 1/2 of their length; anthers reniform; pollen with tegillate and spinulate sexine; capsules indehiscent, covered with a dense fulvous velvety tomentum; seeds embedded in a farinaceous pulp (introduced and naturalized in the "arid" zone)...**3. Adansonia**
  2 Staminal tube divided into 5 filaments, each bearing 2–3 anfractuose anthers; capsules 5-valved; kapok copious (introduced, cultivated and naturalized in the wet zone)......
....**4. Ceiba**

1. CULLENIA

Wight, Ic. Pl. Ind. Or. 5: 23. 1852; Masters in Hook. f., Fl. Br. Ind. 1: 350. 1874; Masters, J. Linn. Soc., Bot. 14: 498. 1875; Trimen, Handb. Fl. Ceylon 1: 162. 1893; Kosterm., Comm. For. Res. Inst. Indonesia (Pengumunan Balai Penjelidikan Kehutanan Indonesia) 51: 3. 1956 & Reinwardtia 4: 69. 1956; Raizada, Ind. For. 83: 497. 1957; A. Robyns, Bull. Jard. Bot. Nat. Belg. 40: 244. 1970. Type species: *C. ceylanica* (Gardn.) K. Schum.

Durio Adans.; Bakh., Bull. Jard. Bot. Buitenzong, sér. 3, 6: 224. 1924, pro parte quoad *D. ceylanicus* Gardn.; Alston in Trimen, Handb. Fl. Ceylon 6: 30. 1931.

Trees, tall, evergreen, the branchlets lepidote. Leaves petiolate, simple, entire, the upper surface glabrous, the lower surface covered with numerous overlapping scarious-hyaline peltate scales. Flowers ramiflorous, densely fasciculate on protuberances of the old wood, pedicellate, the pedicels articulate near the middle, densely lepidote; epicalyx irregularly 3–4-lobed at the apex, splitting to the base on one side and deciduous, densely lepidote without; calyx more or less irregularly 5-dentate apically, carnose, deciduous, densely lepidote outside, the scales peltate, scarious-hyaline and overlapping; corolla absent; staminal tube 5-dentate-lobulate to 5-lobate, each lobe with 7–11 stamens along the margins; stamens with short filaments, the connectives irregularly spherical to club-shaped, covered with numerous stipitate 1-locular thecae, the latter more or less globular, densely covered with minute mammiliform deciduous processes, dehiscent by means of an annular transverse median slit (circumscissile); pollen grains more or less spheroidal, 3-colporate, the sexine finely granular to smooth; ovary sessile, densely covered with long-stipitate peltate scales, 5-celled, infrequently 6-celled, with 2–6 superposed ovules in each cell; style longer than the staminal tube, sometimes long-exserted, the stigma capitellate and densely papillate. Capsules more or less globose, densely covered with stout spines, 5-valved; seeds 1 to few in each locule, sometimes reduced to 1 per capsule, completely to incompletely covered by a fleshy aril or exarillate.

A small genus of three species of which two occur in Ceylon, the third one, *C. exarillata* A. Robyns, growing in the rain forests of the western part of the State of Madras, India.

KEY TO THE SPECIES

1 Pedicels 1.5–1.8 cm long; epicalyx 1–1.2 cm long; calyx oblong-tubular, 2.5–3 cm long and 6–9 mm in diam., scarcely swollen at the base; staminal tube 5-dentate-lobulate at the apex, the lobes c. 2–3 mm long; ovary with the cells 2-ovulate; capsules to 10 cm in diam. (spines included), the spines 6–15 cm long; seeds 1–5, to 3.8 cm long; completely surrounded with an orange brown aril..............................**1. C. ceylanica**
1 Pedicels 3.5–4 cm long; epicalyx 2–2.2 cm long; calyx narrowly ovoid, 4–4.5 cm long, markedly swollen and 1.2–1.3 cm in diam. at the base, the apex 5–6 mm in diam.; staminal tube 5-lobate at the apex, the lobes to 10 (14) mm long; ovary with the cells 3–5-ovulate; capsules to 16 cm in diam. (spines included), the spines in 2 distinct tiers, to 4 cm long; seeds 8–19 (1–4 per locule), the lowest ones completely surrounded by a translucid whitish aril, the upper ones incompletely so................**2. C. rosayroana**

1. Cullenia ceylanica (Gardn.) K. Schum. in Pflanzenfam. 3 (6): 68, fig. 35 D. 1890 (as *C. ceylanica* (R. Wight) K. Schum.); Kosterm., Comm. For. Res. Inst. Indonesia 51: 4, fig. 1, 2 a–d. 1956 & Reinwardtia 4: 70, fig. 1, 2 a–d. 1956; Raizada, Ind. For. 83: 498. 1957; Kosterm., Comm. For. Res. Inst. Indonesia 62: 34, fig. 38, 39. 1958 & Reinwardtia 4: 461, fig. 38, 39. 1958; Abeywick., Ceylon J. Sci., Biol. Sci. 2: 193. 1959; A. Robyns, Bull. Jard. Bot. Nat. Belg. 40: 245. 1970. Type: *Gardner 77* (Holo- K).

Durio ceylanicus Gardn., Calcutta J. Nat. Hist. 8: 1. 1847; Bakh., Bull. Jard.
Bot. Buitenzorg, sér. 3, 6: 228. 1924; Alston in Trimen, Handb. Fl. Ceylon
6: 30. 1931; Worthington, Ceylon Trees 79. 1959.
Cullenia excelsa Wight, Ic. Pl. Ind. Or. 5: 23, pl. 1761–62. 1852, pro parte
quoad plantas zeylanicas; Thw., Enum. Pl. Zeyl. 28. 1858; Masters in Hook.
f., Fl. Br. Ind. 1: 350. 1874, pro parte quoad plantas zeylanicas; Masters,
J. Linn. Soc., Bot. 14: 498. 1875, pro parte quoad plantas zeylanicas;
Trimen, Handb. Fl. Ceylon 1: 162. 1893; Willis, Cat. 12. 1911.
Durio zibethinus sensu Moon, Cat. 56. 1824, non Murray (in L., Syst. Veg.
ed. 13. 581. 1774).

Tree to 20–36 m tall, the trunk straight, to 1.8 m GBH and over, the bark
grey, smooth, the crown rather small, rounded-elongated. Leaves with the
petiole 1.2–2.5 cm long, the upper half pulvinate, often somewhat curved to
caudate; blade 8.5–20 cm long and 2.5–5.5 cm wide, narrowly elliptic, infrequently narrowly elliptic-subobovate, rounded at the base, from gradually to
rather abruptly long-acuminate at the apex, with the acumen to 2 cm long and
obtuse to more or less acute, subcoriaceous, the margins somewhat undulated, the upper surface deep green and somewhat shining, the lower surface
olivaceous-lepidote, the scales finely fimbrillate, the costa prominent beneath,
the venation otherwise nearly inconspicuous. Flowers with the pedicels thick
and 1.5–1.8 cm long; epicalyx short-tubular, 1–1.2 cm long, densely tawny-
lepidote without, cinereous-stellate-puberulous within; calyx oblong-tubular,
2.5–3 cm long and 6–9 mm in diam., scarcely swollen and rounded at the
base, the apex 5-dentate with the teeth to 2 mm long, densely covered with
finely fimbrillate tawny scales to 2 mm in diam. without, the lower 2/3 very
densely whitish-lepidote and the upper 1/3 brownish, glabrous and shining
within; staminal tube white at the base and at the apex, reddish in the middle,
longer than the calyx, to 3.5 cm long, the upper part finely and minutely stel-
late-arachnoid, the apex 5-dentate-lobulate, the lobes c. 2–3 mm long, with
7–9 stamens along their margins; stamens with the filaments to 1 mm long,
the connectives c. 1–1.2 mm in diam., the thecae c. 0.4 mm in diam., the stalks
c. 0.2–0.6 mm long; ovary densely white-lepidote, the cells 2-ovulate; style
long-exserted, to 4 cm long, white-arachnoid, the hairs short and fine, the
stigma orange, to 2.3 mm in diam. Capsule globular, to 10 cm in diam.
(spines included), completely dehiscent on the tree, the spines conical, 6–15
mm long, covered with brownish scales, the pericarp (without spines) c. 12
mm thick, snow-white inside; seeds 1–5, chestnut-like, to 3.8 cm long and 2.3
cm thick, completely surrounded with an orange brown aril, the latter laciniate at the apex, the testa brown and shining.

Distr. Endemic in Ceylon, *C. ceylanica* occurs in the dense humid
evergreen forests from sea-level to about 900 m elevation. With *C. rosayroana*, it constitutes "4.5% of the total growing stock of the Wet Evergreen

Forest" (cf. Tisseverasinghe, The Ceylon Forester, n.s. 6: 23. 1963).

U s e s. The wood is light, pale red, rather soft and fairly fine-grained. According to Tisseverasinghe (Commonwealth For. Rev. 42: 144. 1963), it is suitable for furniture making, panelling and for other purposes for which other decorative timbers are normally used. It is also easy to impregnate the wood with preservatives and it can thus conveniently be treated for outdoor use. Presently, however, the timber of *C. ceylanica* is not or very little utilized.

V e r n. Katu-boda, Kata-boda (S).

S p e c i m e n s   E x a m i n e d. KANDY DISTRICT: Hantane (?), alt. 2000–3000 ft, 1847 (leaves & young flowers), *Gardner 77* (holotype K); Peradeniya, Royal Botanic Gardens, 26 Oct. 1922 (leaves & young fruits), *J.M. Silva s.n.* (PDA), 23 March 1969 (leaves, flowers & capsules), *A.G. Robyns 6980* (BR, CANB, E, PDA, US); Murutenne, c. 2 miles W. of Norton Bridge, alt. 750 m, common tree in forest remnant, 3 March 1969 (leaves & young flowers), *Hoogland 11476* (BR, CANB, E, PDA, US). KEGALLE DISTRICT: Kitulgala, forest reserve across Kelani Ganga, rain forest, rather common, alt. 150 m, 26 Feb. 1971 (leaves & flowers), *A.G. Robyns 7239* (BR, PDA, US). RATNAPURA DISTRICT: Gilimale Forest Reserve, rain forest, rather common, 29 Feb. 1971 (leaves & flowers), *A.G. Robyns 7243* (BR, PDA, US); Induruwa, N. of Gilimale, alt. c. 100–120 m, rain forest, 15 Feb. 1969 (leaves & flowers), *A.G. Robyns 6921* (BR, CANB, E, PDA, US). DISTRICT UNKNOWN: *s. coll. C.P. 216* (young fruits) (K); *s. coll. C.P. 734* (leaves & flowers) (BR, K, PDA p.p. [annotated Hantane, *Gardner*; Pasdun Korale, 1868—flowers marked A], US p.p. [US 597121, flowers marked A]); *Walker s.n.* (Herb. R. Wight) (leaves & young flowers) (PDA).

2. Cullenia rosayroana Kosterm. emend. A. Robyns; Kosterm., Comm. For. Res. Inst. Indonesia 51: 4, fig. 2e & 3. 1956 & Reinwardtia 4: 72, fig. 2e & 3. 1956, pro parte exclus. *C. excelsa* Wight et plantis Indiae peninsularis; Raizada, Ind. For. 83: 499. 1957, pro parte exclus. *C. excelsa*; Abeywick., Ceylon J. Sci., Biol. Sci. 2: 193. 1959; A. Robyns, Bull. Jard. Bot. Nat. Belg. 40: 248, fig. 1. 1970. Type: *Kostermans 11110* (holo.-BO, iso.-L).

Tree 24–30 m tall, the trunk straight, c. 90 cm GBH or more, the bark smooth. Leaves with the petiole thick, 1.8–2.5 cm long, usually more or less geniculate; blade 11–22 cm long and 3–5.5 cm wide, narrowly oblong-elliptic, rounded-obtuse at the base, rather abruptly short- to long-acuminate, the acumen to 1 cm long, subcoriaceous to coriaceous, the margins slightly undulated when dry, the upper surface dark green and more or less shining, the lower surface brownish-olivaceous-lepidote, the scales finely fimbrillate, the costa very prominent beneath, the venation otherwise inconspicuous or nearly so. Flowers with the pedicels thick and 3.5–4 cm long; epicalyx tubular-campanulate, 2–2.2 cm long, densely tawny-lepidote without, densely cinereous-pubescent within; calyx narrowly ovoid, 4–4.5 cm long, markedly swollen and 1.2–1.3 cm in diam. at the base, the apex 5–6 mm in diam. and apparently irregularly 2-lobed, the lobes to 5–6 mm long, densely covered with finely fimbrillate tawny scales to 2.5 mm in diam. without, the lower half densely and minutely papillate and the upper half glabrous within; androecium longer than the calyx, to 5.5 cm long, the staminal tube glabrous below, densely whitish-stellate-puberulous above, the apex 5-lobate, the lobes to 10 (14) mm long, whitish-stellate-puberulous, with 9–11 stamens along their margins; stamens with the filaments scarcely 1 mm long, the connectives rather ellipsoid, to 1.5 mm long, the thecae c. 0.2–0.3 mm in diam., the stalks 0.2–0.8 mm long; pollen c. 72–77 micron in diam.; ovary 5–6 mm long, densely appressed-whitish-lepidote, the scales long-stipitate, the stalks to 1.3 mm long, the cells 3–5-ovulate; style long-exserted, to 5.5 cm long, the lower part densely whitish-lepidote, finely arachnoid towards the apex, the exserted part often geniculate, the stigma orange, c. 2 mm in diam. Capsule globular, to 16 cm in diam. (spines included), dehiscent on the tree, with 2 distinct layers of spines, the lower tier with slender spines 0.8–2.5 cm long, the upper tier with thicker spines 2–4 cm long, lepidote below, the pericarp 7–10 mm thick in the middle (without spines), whitish inside; seeds 8–19 per capsule, 1–4 per locule, to 3 cm long and 2.2 cm thick, the lowest ones completely surrounded with a slimy translucid whitish aril, the upper ones incompletely so, the testa dark brown and shining.

D i s t r. Endemic in Ceylon, where it occurs in the dense humid ever-green forests or rain forests.

U s e s. The wood has the same properties as *C. zeylanica*.

V e r n. Katu-boda, Kata-boda (S).

S p e c i m e n s   E x a m i n e d. COLOMBO DISTRICT: Waga, Indakade Forest, alt. c. 60 m, 28 Feb. 1971 (leaves, flowers & capsules), *A.G. Robyns 7257* (BR, PDA, US). GALLE DISTRICT: near Galle, rain forest, alt. 100 m, March 1956 (flowers & leaves), *Kostermans 11110* (holotype BO, not seen; isotype L); Hiyare, c. 15 miles E. of Galle, alt. c. 100 m, remnants of rain forest, 6 April 1969 (leaves & flowers), *A.G. Robyns 6995* (BR, CANB, E, PDA, US), (capsules), *A.G. Robyns 6996* (BR, CANB, E, PDA, US); Hiniduma, Katukitulgalla Gode Kande, alt. 450–480 m, in secondary wet evergreen forest, 2 April 1971 (leaves, flowers & capsules), *A.G. Robyns 7351* (BR, PDA, US). RATNAPURA DISTRICT: Gilimale, alt. 300 m, rain forest, 26 Oct. 1953 (flowers), *Worthington 6488B* (BR). DISTRICT UNKNOWN: *s. coll. C.P. 734* (PDA p.p. [flowers marked B], US p.p. [US 597121, flowers marked B, US 597122 & US 1576837]).

2. BOMBAX

L., Sp. Pl. 511. 1753 & Gen. Pl. ed. 5. 277. 1754; Masters in Hook. f., Fl. Br. Ind. 1: 349. 1874; Trimen, Handb. Fl. Ceylon 1: 159. 1893; A. Robyns, Bull. Jard. Bot. État Brux. 33: 84. 1963. Type species: *B. ceiba* L.

Salmalia Schott & Endl., Melet. Bot.: 35. 1832; Thw. Enum. Pl. Zeyl. 28. 1858.
Gossampinus sensu Bakh., Bull. Jard. Bot. Buitenzorg, sér. 3, 6: 187. 1924, non Schott & Endl. 1832; Alston in Trimen, Handb. Fl. Ceylon 6: 30. 1931.

Trees, deciduous, armed or not, the trunk buttressed or not. Leaves petiolate, compound-digitate, 5–9-foliolate, the leaflets articulate, sessile or petiolulate, entire-margined, glabrous or the indumentum of tufted hairs. Inflorescences fasciculate or flowers solitary generally towards the apex of the branchlets. Flowers precocious, pedicellate, 3-bracteolate, the bracteoles fugacious; receptacle glandular or not; calyx cupuliform or campanulate to tubiform, truncate to more or less deeply lobed, caducous; petals 5, adnate to the base of the staminal tube, carnose, caducous; stamens many, 2-whorled or apparently 1-whorled, the staminal tube short; anthers medifixed, hippocrepiform, extrorse, 1-thecate, longitudinally dehiscent; pollen grains 3-colpate or 3-colporate, the sexine reticulate; ovary sessile, 5-celled, the cells many-ovulate, the ovules inserted on a central columella; style filiform; stigma 5-lobulate. Capsules subligneous to ligneous, loculicidally 5-valvate, the central columella winged and persistent, the valves inside densely covered with silky fibers (kapok); seeds numerous, small, pyriform to subglobose, glabrous, exarillate, embedded in the whitish to brownish kapok; cotyledons epigeal and expanded above the ground level, opposite, petiolate, equal, folded, foliaceous, the primordial leaves simple.

A paleotropical genus of eight species of which only one occurs in Ceylon.

Bombax ceiba L., Sp. Pl. 511. 1753, pro parte quoad plantas asiaticas, exclus. syn. Bauhin; Moon, Cat. 50. 1824; A. Robyns, Taxon 10: 160. 1961 & Bull. Jard. Bot. État Brux. 33: 88, phot. 1 & 7, pl. 3. 1963. Type: Rheede, Hort. Mal. pl. 52. 1682 (lecto; see A.G. Robyns, Taxon 10: 156–160. 1961).

Bombax malabaricum DC., Prod. 1: 479. 1824; Masters in Hook. f., Fl. Br. Ind. 1: 349. 1874; Trimen, Handb. Fl. Ceylon 1: 160. 1893; Willis, Cat. 12. 1911.
Salmalia malabarica (DC.) Schott & Endl., Melet. Bot. 35. 1832; Thwaites, Enum. Pl. Zeyl. 28. 1858; Abeywick., Ceylon J. Sci., Biol. Sci. 2: 193. 1959.
Gossampinus malabarica (DC.) Merril, Lingn. Sci. J. 5: 126. 1927; Alston in Trimen, Handb. Fl. Ceylon 6: 30. 1931; Worthington, Ceylon Trees 75. 1959.

Salmalia insignis sensu Abeywick., l.c., non (Wall.) Schott & Endl. 1832.
Gossampinus insignis sensu Worthington, l.c. 76, non (Wall.) Bakh. 1924.

Tree up to 40 m high or even more, the trunk to 3 m or more in girth, upright, usually buttressed; crown large, the branches spreading, more or less horizontal and more or less whorled; bark greyish, aculeate especially when young, the prickles sharp and conical; branchlets tufted-puberulous or glabrous. Leaves 5–7-foliolate, the petiole to 27 cm long, tufted-puberulous to glabrous; leaflets subsessile to distinctly petiolulate, the petiolule to 2 cm long, minutely puberulous to glabrous; blade elliptic, sometimes narrowly so, or more or less ovate or subobovate, narrowly decurrent at the base, usually long-caudate-acuminate at the apex, the acumen mucronulate, to 23 cm long and 8.5 cm wide, thin and limp when fresh, thin-chartaceous when dry, the upper surface somewhat glossy and minutely tufted-puberulous to glabrous, the lower surface dull, very minutely tufted-puberulous especially along the nerves to glabrous, the costa prominent and the lateral nerves prominulous beneath. Flowers showy, solitary or sometimes geminate, generally towards the apex of the leafless branchlets, 5–12 cm long; pedicel thick, 1–1.5 cm long, glabrous or tufted-puberulous; receptacle c. 0.5 cm long, generally provided with 1 whorl of glands; calyx thick, cupuliform, more or less deeply 2–5-lobed, 1.4–3.5 cm long and 2.2–5.2 cm wide, yellowish green when fresh, glabrous or sparsely puberulous without, sericeous within; petals obovate, sometimes elliptic-obovate to more or less oblong, 4.7–11.5 cm long and 1.7–4.5 cm wide, bright red, tomentellous without, puberulous toward the apex within; stamens 70–110, 3–7 cm long, the filaments reddish towards the apex, connate basally into a short staminal tube; outer whorl with 5 fascicles of 8–20 stamens each, the filaments curved outwards except the 2 inner erect and circumstylar ones, sparsely pubescent below; inner whorl with 10 stamens, each pair of filaments completely united and usually longer than the 10 inner filaments of the outer whorl; anthers blackish; ovary conical, from tomentellous-sericeous to covered with a very minute indumentum; style exceeding the stamens, reddish towards the apex, tomentellous to glabrous basally, the stigma with 5 spreading red lobes. Capsules oblong, cuneate on both ends, dehiscing on the tree (in Ceylon) or not, the valves 9.5–17 cm long and 2.3–3.2 cm wide, blackish and glabrous at maturity, the columella brownish; seeds more or less pyriform, c. 0.5 cm long, the testa dark brown and smooth; kapok white.

D i s t r. Throughout tropical Asia, extending eastwards to New Guinea. The Silk Cotton Tree or Red Cotton Tree is found in Ceylon mainly in the forests of the low and mid-country humid zone, up to an elevation of about 1000 m, but occurs also in the intermediate and dry zones. In Wilpattu National Park, it grows "in scattered groups, close to water, in the Villu area" (cf. C.W. Nicholas, The Ceylon Forester, n.s. 4: 40. 1959). Often planted.

U s e s. The wood is light and soft, and is used in the manufacture of matches or for making tea-boxes. The inner bark yields a good fibre suitable for cordage. The fleshy calyces of the young flowers are sometimes cooked and eaten as a vegetable. The kapok is used for stuffing mattresses and pillows. The seeds are oleaginous. The tree is sometimes planted along roads and streets, especially in India.

V e r n. Katu-imbul (S); Parutti (T), Kaddu-olaga (T) (fide Worthington, Ceylon Trees 75. 1959), Illavu (T) (fide Worthington, loc. cit.).

N o t e. Collections from the intermediate and dry zones are characterized by longer petiolulate leaflets and by somewhat larger flowers.

The bright red flowers of *B. ceiba* are very conspicuous on the bare crowns during the dry season.

S p e c i m e n s E x a m i n e d. ANURADHAPURA DISTRICT: Kalawewa—Galewela road, alt. 500 ft, 2 July 1950 (leaves & flowers), *Worthington 4815* (BM, BR). BADULLA DISTRICT: Ella, roadside, alt. c. 1000 m, 22 March 1971 (leaves & flowers), *A.G. Robyns 7315, 7316* (BR, PDA, US); Wellewela, along road Hali-Ela to Welimada, milestone 69, roadside, alt. c. 1100 m, 24 March 1971 (leaves & flower buds), *A.G. Robyns 7326* (BR, PDA, US). BATTICALOA DISTRICT: Nachivantivu, near coast, alt. 3 m, in scrub-field area near pond, 8 May 1968 (flowers), *Comanor 1227* (BR, US). KANDY DISTRICT: Hillcrest, Kandy, alt. 2120 ft, planted about 1952, 18 Feb. 1963 (flowers), *Worthington 7059* (BR); Kandy, Suisse Hotel, lake side, alt. 1710 ft, probably planted, 30 Dec. 1950 (leaves & flowers), *Worthington 5044* (BR); ibid., roadside, alt. c. 480 m, 16 Feb. 1971 (flowers), *A.G. Robyns 7188* (BR, PDA, US); Hantane, Dec. 1845 (leaves & flowers), *Gardner s.n.* (*C.P. 545*) (PDA, TDC); Peradeniya, close to old golf links, opposite entrance of Royal Botanic Gardens, 7 Feb. 1969 (flowers), *A.G. Robyns 6909* (BR, E, PDA, US), 23 March 1969 (capsules), *A.G. Robyns 6981* (BR, E, PDA, US), 20 April 1969 (leaves), *A.G. Robyns 6999* (BR, E, PDA, US); ibid., Royal Botanic Gardens, 10 Jan. 1908 (leaves & flowers), *Baker 118* (GH, LE, MO, P, PDA, U, US); ibid., along the Mahaweli Ganga, alt. c. 480 m, 24 Feb. 1971 (flowers), *A.G. Robyns 7216* (BR, PDA, US); ibid., Experimental Station, 8 March 1927 (flowers), *Marcovicz s.n.* (LE); ibid., Jan. 1885 (flowers), *Grunow s.n.* (W); Pilimatalawa, along road from Kandy to Colombo, just S. of Peradeniya, alt. c. 480 m, 22 Feb. 1971 (flowers), *A.G. Robyns 7194* (BR, PDA, US); Godawela, edge of paddy field, alt. 300–600 m, 18 Feb. 1971 (leaves & capsules), *A.G. Robyns 7189* (BR, PDA, US); ibid., along the Mahaweli Ganga, alt. 300–600 m, 18 Feb. 1971 (flowers), *A.G. Robyns 7190* (BR, PDA, US). MATALE DISTRICT: between Alawatugoda and Matale, 3 miles S. of Matale, roadside, alt. 300–450 m, 23 Feb. 1971 (leaves & flowers), *A.G. Robyns 7196* (BR, PDA, US), (leaves), *A.G. Robyns 7197* (BR, PDA, US). PUTTALAM DISTRICT: Wilpattu National Park, between Kanjuran and Kumutu Villu, on sand in low stature forest, 26 April 1969 (flowers), *Wirawan, Mueller-Dombois, Cooray & Balakrishnan 69042602* (PDA, US); ibid., on sandy red soil in dry mixed evergreen forest, near sea level, 28 March 1971 (leaves & flowers), *A.G. Robyns 7332* (BR, PDA, US). RATNAPURA DISTRICT: Ratnapura, in disturbed area, alt. 120–160 m, 27 Feb. 1971 (leaves & capsules), *A.G. Robyns 7252* (BR, PDA, US); Belihuloya, alt. 1850 ft, 19 April 1950 (leaves & flowers), *Worthington 4633* (BR).

N o t e. Besides the above cited specimens, I have seen several collections in the private herbarium of T.B. Worthington, Kandy, Ceylon now in (K): *Worthington 455* (Haldummulla, Badulla Distr.), *2953* (below Ella, Badulla Distr.), *3385* (Heneratgoda Botanical Gardens, Colombo Distr.), *4050* (Passara, Badulla Distr.), and *4437* (Haragama-Kandy, Kandy Distr.).

3. ADANSONIA

L., Sp. Pl. 1190. 1753. Type species: *A. digitata* L.

Trees, deciduous, the trunk thick, cylindrical or conical; bark greyish, tender and sometimes provided with prickles. Leaves long-petiolate, compound-digitate, 3–9-foliolate, the folioles articulate, sessile or petiolulate, entire-margined, rarely denticulate along the margins, glabrous or with tufted hairs especially when young; stipules narrow. Flowers large, axillary, solitary, pendent or erect, the indumentum of tufted hairs; pedicel apically 2-bracteolate, the bracteoles caducous; calyx (3) 5-lobed, glabrous to tomentose outside, sericeous inside; petals 5, circular or obovate to narrowly ovate, glabrous or pubescent on both sides; stamens many, united for more or less half of their length into a cylindrical tube adnate to the base of the corolla; anthers reniform or oblong, 1-thecate; pollen grains with tegillate and spinulate sexine; ovary 5- or 10-celled, the cells multi-ovulate; style long, filiform; stigma with 5 or 10 short spreading lobes. Capsules ligneous, globose or oblong, or more or less ovoid, indehiscent, covered with a dense fulvous tomentum; seeds many, reniform or globose or angulate, exarillate, embedded in a farinaceous pulp; seedlings glabrous, the cotyledons epigeal and expanded above the ground level, opposite, entire, plicate, foliaceous.

A paleotropical genus with six species in Madagascar, two species in Australia and one species in tropical Africa, the latter introduced in Ceylon.

Adansonia digitata L., Sp. Pl. 1190. 1753; Moon, Cat. 49. 1824; Thw., Enum. Pl. Zeyl. 28. 1858; Masters in Hook. f., Fl. Br. Ind. 1: 348. 1874; Trimen, Handb. Fl. Ceylon 1: 159. 1893; Willis, Cat. 127. 1911; Abeywick., Ceylon J. Sci., Biol. Sci. 2: 193. 1959; Worthington, Ceylon Trees 74. 1959. Type: *s. coll. 862* in herb. Linnaeus (holo-LINN).

Tree, erect, to 20 m tall, the trunk very thick, up to 10 m in diam., suddenly tapering into thick branches, the bark usually smooth; young branches

843

pubescent. Leaves gathered towards the apex of the branchlets, 5–7-foliolate; petiole to 18 cm long, usually densely pubescent especially when young, sometimes glabrous; leaflets sessile to subsessile, oblong to obovate-oblong to obovate, cuneate and decurrent at the base, gradually acuminate to caudate-acuminate at the apex, to 15 cm long and 7 cm wide, entire-margined, tufted-pubescent when young, sometimes glabrous. Flowers showy, axillary, pendulous, the pedicels long and flexible, up to 90 cm long, tomentose; buds ovoid to globose, acute at the apex; calyx (3) 5-lobed at anthesis, the lobes broadly triangular, acute, to 9 cm long and 3.5 (6) cm wide at the base, tomentellous outside, sericeous inside; petals broadly obovate to flabelliform, shortly unguiculate at the base, rounded at the apex, 7–9 cm long and 6–8 (12) cm wide, white, becoming brown when dry, glabrous or sparsely hairy outside; staminal tube conical, 3–7 cm long, white, becoming brown when dry, glabrous, divided into many slender filaments equalling more or less the tube; anthers reniform, more or less 2 mm long; ovary hirsute-tomentose, 5–10-locular; style exserted c. 1–1.5 cm beyond the anthers, hirsute-tomentose at the base, the stigma 5–10-lobulate. Capsule oblong to oblong-ovoid, sometimes irregular in shape, more or less longitudinally sulcate, acute to rounded at both ends, 25–40 cm long and 8–12 cm in diam., densely covered with a fulvous velvety tomentum; seeds many, dark brown to black, oleaginous, embedded in a farinaceous pulp.

D i s t r. Throughout the drier parts of tropical Africa; introduced in Madagascar and tropical Asia; naturalized in the "arid zone" in Ceylon.

U s e s. The wood is light and spongy. The soft trunk of the tree is hollowed out by the African natives and made into living houses. The fibres of the bark are strong and used, in Africa, for the manufacture of ropes and even for clothing. The young leaves are eaten as a vegetable. The pulp of the capsules contains tartaric acid and makes a refreshing febrifugal drink with water. In India, the dry capsules are used as floats for their nets by fishermen.

V e r n. Perukku-maran. Papparappuli (T).

Monkeys are very fond of the capsules, hence the English vernacular name, Monkey Bread Tree.

N o t e. Native to tropical Africa, *A. digitata* or the Baobab has been introduced long ago in Ceylon by the Arab traders. Remarkable for the excessive thickness of its trunk as compared with its height, the Baobab is found in the "arid zone" (annual rainfall around 1000 mm) and is very conspicuous in the low thorny scrub jungle in the Mannar region (Mannar peninsula and opposite mainland) (cf. G.J. Eriyagama, The Ceylon Forester, n.s. 5: 66–81. 1961; A. Robyns, Les Naturalistes Belges 51: 193, photo 4. 1970). The largest Baobab seen is growing in Mannar: the tree is about 10 m tall with a girth (GBH) of 17.55 m. On the Island of Delft, the Baobabs are growing in Palmyra and Coconut plantations and, according to my local guide, there are about 50 Baobabs on the island.

The leaves of the seedlings are simple, petiolate and narrowly ovate-linear.

S p e c i m e n s   E x a m i n e d. BATTICALOA DISTRICT: Batticaloa?, 1848 (leaves & flowers), *Gardner s.n.* (*C.P.* 1141) (PDA). JAFFNA DIST-RICT: Island of Delft, alt. 0–10 m, isolated trees in Palmyra and Coconut plantations, 18 March 1969 (leaves), *A.G. Robyns 6966* (BR, E, PDA, US). MANNAR DISTRICT: Mantai, alt. 0–10 m, in forest scrub, 19 March 1969 (leaves), *A.G. Robyns 6969* (BR, PDA, US), 12 Feb. 1890 (leaves & capsules), *s. coll. s.n.* (PDA); Tirukketisvaram, sea level, on sandy soil, 29 March 1971 (leaves & capsules), *A.G. Robyns 7339* (BR, PDA, US); ibid., sandy cap on clayey soil, 11 Dec. 1970 (leaves, flowers & young capsules), *Balakrishnan 605* (BR, PDA, US); Mannar, alt. 0–10 m, planted in the city, 19 March 1969 (leaves), *A.G. Robyns 6970* (BR, PDA, US); Vankalai, alt. 0–30 m, open scrub along road, 19 March 1969 (leaves), *A.G. Robyns 6998* (BR, PDA, US). PUT-TALAM DISTRICT: along trail to Kollankanatta, W. of Wilpattu West Sanctuary, on white sand in dry mixed evergreen forest, c. sea level, 30 March 1971 (leaves), *A.G. Robyns 7343* (BR, PDA, US); ibid., in plot W23 close to the beach, low stature forest, 7 March 1969 (leaves), *Wirawan, Cooray & Bala-krishnan 954* (US).

4. CEIBA

Mill., Gard. Dict. Abridg. ed. 4. 1754; Alston in Trimen, Handb. Fl. Ceylon 6: 30. 1931. Type species: *C. pentandra* (L.) Gaertn.

Eriodendron DC., Prod. 1: 479. 1824; Thw., Enum. Pl. Zeyl. 28. 1858; Mast-ers in Hook. f., Fl. Br. Ind. 1: 350. 1874; Trimen, Handb. Fl. Ceylon 1: 161. 1893.

Trees, generally tall, deciduous, armed or unarmed, the trunk buttressed or not. Leaves petiolate, compound-digitate, 5–9-foliolate, the leaflets arti-culate, the blade often denticulate near the apex. Flowers gathered towards the apex of the branchlets, in axillary fascicles, or solitary or geminate, acti-nomorphous or sometimes subzygomorphous, pedicellate, bracteolate, the bracteoles fugacious, the indumentum of tufted hairs; calyx campanulate to more or less tubiform, truncate or irregularly lobed, persistent or accrescent; petals 5, adnate to the base of the staminal tube, carnose; stamens 5, the sta-minal tube conical (in Ceylon), or the lower part cylindrical and thickened and the upper part conical, the filaments short to long, bearing each 1–3 linear to anfractuose anthers; anthers 1- to 2 (4)-thecate, longitudinally de-hiscent; pollen grains 3-colporate, the sexine reticulate; ovary superior to subinferior, sessile, 5-celled, the cells many-ovulate; style filiform or enlarged above the staminal tube, the stigma capitate or 5-lobulate. Capsules coriaceous to ligneous, loculicidally 5-valvate, the central columella winged and persistent, the valves densely covered with silky fibres (kapok) inside; seeds numerous, obovoid or subglobose, glabrous, exarillate, embedded in the kapok; cotyledons epigeal and expanded above the ground level, opposite, petiolate, plicate and foliaceous.

A genus of which all species, but one, are native to tropical America. *Ceiba pentandra*, native in the American tropics and almost certainly also in the African tropics, has been introduced long ago in the Asian tropics, probably by Arab traders (cf. H.G. Baker, Inst. Intern. Stud., Univ. Calif., Berkeley, Res. Ser. 9: 185–216. 1965).

Ceiba pentandra (L.) Gaertn. var. **pentandra**, Fruct. Sem. 2: 244, t. 133. 1791; Alston in Trimen, Handb. Fl. Ceylon 6: 30. 1931; Abeywick., Ceylon J. Sci., Biol. Sci. 2: 193. 1959; H.G. Baker, Inst. Intern. Stud., Univ. Calif., Berkeley, Res. Ser. 9: 208. 1965. Type: no lectotype indicated as yet.

Bombax pentandrum L., Sp. Pl. 511. 1753; Moon, Cat. 50. 1824.

Eriodendron orientale (Spreng.) Kostel., Algem. Med.-Pharm. Fl. 1875. 1831 (fide Bakh., Bull. Jard. Bot. Buitenzorg, sér. 3, 6: 195. 1924), Thw., Enum. Pl. Zeyl.: 28. 1858.

Eriodendron anfractuosum DC., Prod. 1: 479. 1824; Masters in Hook. f., Fl. Br. Ind. 1: 350. 1874; Trimen, Handb. Fl. Ceylon 1: 161. 1893; Willis, Cat. 12. 1911; Worthington, Ceylon Trees 77. 1959.

Tree of moderate height to tall, rarely exceeding 20 m, the trunk straight, seldom more than 50 cm in diam., the bark greenish and mostly unarmed, usually without buttresses; branches more or less horizontal, in whorls of 3. Leaves gathered towards the apex of the branchlets, 5–9-foliolate, glabrous, long-petiolate, the petiole 5–25 cm long; leaflets petiolulate, the petiolule usually c. 5 mm long, the blade from narrowly ovate-oblong to narrowly obovate-oblong, narrowed at the base, acute to acuminate and mucronulate at the apex, to 20 cm long and 4 cm wide, slightly paler beneath, the margins entire or rarely denticulate near the apex (not in Ceylon). Flowers usually grouped towards the apex of the branchlets, few- to many-fasciculate, the pedicels 2.5–3 cm long, glabrous; buds greenish; calyx green, campanulate, 4–5-lobate, 1–1.2 cm long and 0.8–1.2 cm wide, glabrous outside, silky-villous inside, the lobes shallow and more or less rounded apically; petals yellowish white, obovate-spathulate, adnate for about 2.5–3 mm to the base of the staminal tube, rounded at the apex, 2.5–4 cm long and 1–1.5 cm wide, villous to tomentose outside except at the base, pubescent near the apex inside; staminal tube conical, 5–5.5 mm long, glabrous, the filaments about 2.5 cm long, each bearing 2–3 anfractuose 1-thecate anthers; ovary globular, glabrous, the style white, filiform at the base, suddenly obliquely enlarged above the staminal tube, slightly longer than the stamens, the stigma capitate. Capsule green when young, becoming brownish, ellipsoid to fusiform, narrowed at both ends, to 26 cm long and 4 cm in diam., indehiscent (or tardily dehiscent on the tree?); seeds numerous, subglobose, about 5–7 mm in diam., the testa dark brown to blackish; kapok copious, white to greyish, with a silken sheen.

D i s t r. In Ceylon, *C. pentandra* or the Kapok Tree occurs in the humid zone, up to an elevation of about 1000 m. It is always found in circumstances which suggest that the tree has been planted.

U s e s. The silky fibres attached to the inner wall of the capsules are known as kapok. Since the fibres (each one is a single cell, 0.8–3 cm long, with a wide air-filled lumen) are too short to be spun, kapok is exclusively employed for stuffing purposes. According to H.G. Baker (l.c. 186), "it has very good sound and heat insulating properties, and it is so light and re-silient that it requires a smaller quantity to stuff a mattress, a pillow, or a marine life-preserver than would be needed with any other material. Its supe-riority as a filling for life-preservers is further evidenced by its tendency to repel water and by the fact that, even after prolonged immersion, its buoy-ancy is soon restored by drying".

Before World War II, Indonesia was the largest producer of kapok. After the war, Thailand took over the lead, while other exporting countries include Cambodia, Kenya, Tanzania, India and Pakistan (cf. H.G. Baker, l.c. 188; J.W. Purseglove, Tropical Crops: Dicotyledons 1: 39. 1969). I have seen no Kapok Tree plantations in Ceylon.

V e r n. Pulun-imbul (S).

S p e c i m e n s E x a m i n e d. BADULLA DISTRICT: Ella, steep slope along road, alt. c. 1000 m, 22 March 1971 (leaves & flowers), *A.G. Robyns 7317* (BR, PDA, US). KANDY DISTRICT: Peradeniya, 1847 (leaves & flowers), *Gardner s.n. (C.P. 1138)* (PDA); ibid., c. 1 mile N.E. of Teldeniya, alt. c. 600 m, roadsides, usually planted near houses, 8 Feb. 1969 (leaves & flowers), *A.G. Robyns 6910* (BR, CANB, E, PDA, US), (capsules), *A.G. Robyns 6912* (BR); Godawela, edge of paddy field, alt. 300–600 m, 18 Feb. 1971 (leaves & flowers), *A.G. Robyns 7191* (BR, PDA, US). MONERAGALA DISTRICT: c. 4–5 miles W. of Moneragala along road Passara to Moneragala, alt. 150–300 m, very common, usually planted near houses, 2 April 1969 (leaves & capsules), *A.G. Robyns 6991* (BR, E, PDA, US). RATNAPURA DISTRICT: near Gilimale, Elluwa Mallella, Embuldeniya Estate, alt. c. 30 m, common along road, 15 Feb. 1969 (leaves & flowers), *A.G. Robyns 6920* (BR, PDA, US).

CLUSIACEAE (GUTTIFERAE)

(by A.J.G.H. Kostermans*)

Trees, lactiferous or resiniferous. Leaves opposite, entire, without stipules. Flowers regular, hermaphrodite or polygamous—dioecious. Sepals 4–5, imbricate, persistent or caducous. Petals 4–8, imbricate, rarely 0. Stamens indefinite, more or less free or 1–5 adelphous, in female flowers reduced to staminodes, usually fewer than stamens. Anthers dehiscing transversally or vertically. Ovary 1 to many celled with 1–4 erect or axile ovules in each cell. Fruit dehiscent or not with or without scanty endosperm. Seed large, with or without arillode. Embryo of two large, hardly separable cotyledons or 0, replaced by a thick, homogeneous hypocotyl (tigellus). Xanthones with isopentenyl and geranyl substituents are common (Sultanbawa, J. Nat. Sci. Counc. Sri Lanka 1: 123–165. 1973).

D i s t r. Pantropical.

E c o l. In Sri Lanka *Garcinia*, *Calophyllum* and *Mesua* and one naturalized species of American *Clusia*. Altogether 24 species are known, occurring in the dry and wet zones in the lowlands and in the mountains, *Calophyllum walkeri* reaching the highest elevations.

KEY TO THE GENERA (flower)

1 Stigma sessile or almost so. Stamens (in male flowers) connate in different ways. Embryo a homogeneous mass, cotyledons 0. Petiole base with a winged part (foveola)
  2 Outer stamens free, inner forming a consolidated mass...............**4. Clusia rosea**
  2 Stamens in one central column or in 4 phalanges........................**1. Garcinia**
1 Style long, slender. Filaments free, except a small, basal part. Cotyledons large, plan-convex, often difficult to separate. Petiole base without foveola
  3 End bud long, pointed. Sepals caducous. Fruit non-dehiscent........**2. Calophyllum**
  3 End bud globose, inconspicuous. Sepals persistent and enlarged. Fruit dehiscent..
....**3. Mesua**

KEY TO THE GENERA (fruit and leaves)

1 Petiole with a basal foveola
  2 Fruit dehiscent...**4. Clusia rosea**
  2 Fruit non-dehiscent..**1. Garcinia**

---

*Herbarium Bogoriense, Bogor, Indonesia.

1 Petiole without a foveola
  3 Leaves with numerous, very close parallel lateral veins. Sepals caducous. Fruit non-dehiscent...**2. Calophyllum**
  3 Leaves with fewer parallel laterals. Sepals persistent and enlarged under the fruit. Fruit dehiscent..**3. Mesua**

GARCINIA L.

Trees. Bark, branchlets and fruit with white or yellow, thick, sticky latex. Leaves decussate, the successive pairs at maturity in one plane by torsion of the branchlets; petiole with an adaxial foveola with thin, raised margin; lateral nerves rather irregular with in between short, parallel ones. Flowers axillary and pseudoterminal, polygamously dioecious; sepals 4–5, imbricate, petals 4–5 contort. Male flower: Stamens indefinite, filaments connate into one central column or into phalanges as many as petals; anthers 2-celled, dehiscent vertically or transversally; pistil rudiment present or lacking. Female flower often larger than male one and usually solitary; staminodes in a single row, the filaments connate into a ring at the base or staminodes in short phalanges; ovary 2–12-celled with a single axile ovule in each cell; style short or none; stigma peltate with as many lobes as ovary cells, or the lobes forming one mass only incised at the margin. Stigma usually papillate. Fruit fleshy, 1–12-seeded; seeds large, usually enveloped in a juicy arillode (inner part of endocarp); embryo a solid mass (tigellus) representing the hypocotyl; cotyledons none.

Species about 100 in the Asiatic tropics, the American and African *Rheedia* hardly separable. In Ceylon 5 endemic species, 3 also in India, one imported, naturalized and one cultivated species. The bark contains biflavonoids.

KEY TO THE SPECIES (flower)

1 Stamens monadelphous
  2 Ovary covered with spines
    3 Trees without stilt roots. Leaves acuminate with 50–60 pairs of lateral veins........
    ....**5. G. hermonii**
    3 Trees with stilt roots. Leaves obtuse or obscurely, broadly, very shortly acuminate with c. 25 pairs of laterals..**4. G. echinocarpa**
  2 Ovary smooth
    4 Ovary grooved longitudinally
      5 Anthers c. 10..**1. G. quaesita**
      5 Anthers c. 30..**2. G. zeylanica**
    4 Ovary without grooves...**3. G. morella**
1 Stamens in 2, 4 or 5 phalanges
  6 Phalanges very short, broad, spreading..**6. G. terpnophylla**
  6 Phalanges slender, long, erect, incurved
    7 Stigma with 4–5 very long, slender lobes.....................................**9. G. xanthochymus**

7 Stigma of 4–5 short, cuneiform lobes
  8 Leaves obtuse. Flowers in short or very long, raceme like fascicle-bearing inflorescences...**7. G. spicata**
  8 Leaves acuminate. Flowers in axillary fascicles only...................**8. G. thwaitesii**

KEY TO THE SPECIES (fruit)

1 Fruit longitudinally grooved and ribbed
  2 Fruit red to orange red, grooves very deep, reaching the top of the fruit and there incurving into a deep depression, in which centre a large flat-topped mamilla.......
    ....**1. G. quaesita**
  2 Fruit pale yellow, grooves not very deep, not reaching the flat-topped fruit, without mamilla...**2. G. zeylanica**
1 Fruit not sulcate
  3 Fruit covered with short spines
    4 Fruit 4 cm diam. with conical spines (upper part thin). Mamilla longer than 5 mm. Bole with many stilt roots..**4. G. echinocarpa**
    4 Fruit 6 cm diam. with slender spines. Mamilla up to 5 mm long. No stilt roots....
      ....**5. G. hermonii**
  3 Fruit smooth
    5 Fruit with a conical (often oblique) point. Stigma with long lobes.................
      ....**9. G. xanthochymus**
    5 Fruit obtuse
      6 Fruit oblong, often oblique. Stigma undivided with few papillae..**6. G. terpnophylla**
      6 Fruit globose
        7 Fruit sessile. Stigma undivided, consisting of 4 round, confluent, papillate stigmas
          ....**3. G. morella**
        7 Fruit with conspicuous pedicel. Stigma of 4–5 cuneiform rays
          8 Leaves acuminate. Fruit up to 2.5 cm diam....................**8. G. thwaitesii**
          8 Leaves obtuse. Fruit 4 cm diam................................**7. G. spicata**

1. Garcinia quaesita Pierre, Fl. for. Cochinch. XXII, pl. 83 H. 1883 (exclus. syn. *G. affinis* Wight, *G. zeylanica* Choisy et exclus. descr. fruct.); Trimen, Handb. Fl. Ceylon 1: 95. 1893 (as a syn. of *G. cambogia*); Kosterm., Ceylon J. Sci., Biol. Sci. 12 (1): 59. 1976.

Garcinia cambogia Auct., Anderson in Hook. f., Fl. Br. Ind. 1: 262. 1874 (quoad flos masc., p.p. et quoad cit. Thw., Enum. Pl. Zeyl., p.p.); Trimen, Handb. Fl. Ceylon 1: 95. 1893, p.p.; Chandrasena, Chem. & pharm. Ceylon & Ind. pl. 35. 1935; Worthington, Ceylon Trees 24. 1959.
Garcinia cambogia, var. *b.*, *fructu maturo rubro*, Thw., Enum. Pl. Zeyl. 48. 1858.
Garcinia cambogia, var. red (ratu) goraka, Moon, Cat. 37. 1824; Graham in Hooker's Compan. Bot. Mag. 2: 195, in nota. 1836. Type: Thwaites 1172 (P).

    Tree, up to 20 m tall, up to 60 cm diam., glabrous in all its parts. Bark rough, dark rusty to blackish, cracked and peeling off in rectangular 1–1.5

cm wide, 2 mm thick pieces; live bark 5–10 mm thick, outer part brown red, inner one yellowish, with thick, sticky, dark yellow latex. Branchlets slender, cylindrical with a raised, slender ring at the nodes. Leaves chartaceous to firmly chartaceous (dried), oblanceolate to subobovate or elliptic, 3.5 × 12– 1.5 × 6–5 × 10 cm, obtuse or shortly acutish or with a broad, very short acumen, base tapered, acute, slightly decurrent into the slender, 1–1.5 cm long petiole, foveola inconspicuous. Laterals 8–10 pairs with as many, almost as long parallel ones in between, rather erect (narrow leaves) or erect-patent, slender, prominulous both surfaces, reticulation very lax; midrib flat in its basal part on the upper surface, slender, prominent, reddish brown on the lower one. Flowers white, male ones fascicled in the axils of the upper leaves, pedicels up to 2 cm long, slender, slightly thickened at the apex, outer 2 sepals spreading, concave, oblong-orbicular, stiff, thick, 2 mm long; inner two erect, oblong, 3–3.5 mm long. Petals 4–5, fleshy, ovate to elliptic, acutish, 5–7 mm, base often narrowed. Stamens connate into a cylindrical, 1–1.5 mm long column, bearing the c. 10 anthers on 0.5 mm long free part of filaments. Female flowers solitary and pseudo-terminal, pedicel 2–5 mm long, sepals up to 5 mm long (in fruiting stage). Free stamens as many as grooves of ovary, filaments slender, up to 3 mm long, anthers 0.5 mm long; ovary with 6–9 grooves, crowned by a sessile, dome-like stigma with rays of papillae, obscurely separated, only incised at the margin. Fruit globose to sub-ovoid, up to 5 cm diam., red to orange-red, glossy with 6–9 very deep grooves and as many ribs, running to the tip of the fruit and there curving inwards into an up to 1.5 cm deep depression, from which centre arises a thick, cylindrical, up to 2 cm long mamilla, of which the flat top is the obscurely rayed, papillate stigma, 2–4 mm in diam., incised only at the margin, the persistent sepals reflexed under the fruit.

D i s t r. Endemic.

E c o l. Lowlands to c. 1000 m alt., wet and intermediate zone, often cultivated.

V e r n. (Rat) Goraka (S); Korakkaipuli (T; puli = acid).

N o t e. The "rat goraka" (S). or goraka pulli (T) produces an inferior kind of gamboge. The fruits, which are very acid, even at full maturity, are broken into segments and dried in the sun or over a fire and sold in local markets. They are used for making fish curries and also added to brine for fish preservation. The arillode is thin, sweet-acid, edible. At high altitude the primary branches, arranged like the spokes of a wheel, have very short secondary branches and with their dense foliage look like long tails.

Trimen mentioned (l.c. 95) the var. *papilla*, based on *G. papilla* Wight, based on a single collection (Ferguson, Colombo), which might have been a cultivated plant. *G. papilla* is a distinct species from southern India. Trimen might have been misled by an ovoid form of *G. quaesita*.

Specimens Examined. KANDY DISTRICT: Nawalapitiya, mile 24, alt. 600 m, May, fr., *Kostermans 24051* (G, K, L, P, PDA, US); Udawattekelle above Kandy, alt. 450 m, May, fr., *Kostermans 24007 A* (id.); village garden near Kandy, alt. 400 m, May, young fr., *Kostermans 24025* (id.); Menikdiwela, road Kandy to Alagalla, alt. 400 m, May, fl., *Kostermans 24046* (id.); road Laxapana to Maskeliya near Doublecutting, alt. 900 m, May, fr., *Kostermans 24711* (id.); Botanic Garden Peradeniya, alt. 400 m, May, old fl., *Kostermans 24024* (id.); ibid., April, fl., *Hallier s.n.* (L). BADULLA DISTRICT: road Mahyangane to Bibile, alt. low, dry zone, June, fr., *Kostermans 24415* (G, K, L, P, PDA, US). KEGALLE DISTRICT: Kitulgala, near river, alt. 200 m, April, young fr., *Kostermans & Wirawan s.n.* (id.). GALLE DISTRICT: Hiniduma, along road, May, fr., *Kostermans 24711 A* (id.); Godakande near Hiniduma, 200 m alt., Sept., fr., *Kostermans 25564* (id.).

2. Garcinia zeylanica Roxb., Pl. Corom. 3: 94. 1820 (nomen semi nudum); Fl. Ind. 2: 621. 1832; Wight & Arn., Prod. 101. 1834; Anderson in Hook. f., Fl. Br. Ind. 1: 262. 1874 (a as syn. of *G. cambogia*); Planch. & Triana, Ann. Sci. nat. Sér. 4, Bot. 14: 337. 1860 (excl. *G. affinis* W. & A); Thw., Enum. Pl. Zeyl. 406. 1864; Pierre, Fl. for. Cochinch. XXII. 1883 (quoad. descr. Roxb.); Trimen, Handb. Fl. Ceylon 1: 95. 1893 (as a syn. of *G. cambogia*); Kosterm., Ceylon J. Sci., Biol. Sci. 12 (1): 58. 1976.

Garcinia cambogia, var. *zeylanica* (Roxb.) Vesque in DC., Monogr. 8: 427. 1893 (excl. Pierre 3713); Maheshwari, Bull. Bot. Surv. Ind. 6: 129. 1964.

Garcinia morella Desr., var. *fructu maturo flavo* Thw., Enum. Pl. Zeyl. 48. 1858.

Cambogia gutta L., Murray in Comment. Götting. 9: 180. 1789 (quoad *Arbor indica*, etc. Hermann in Rheede, Hort. Mal. 1: 42. 1678).

Arbor indica quam Gummi Guttae fundit, fructu sulcato aureo mali magnitudine Hermann, l.c. Yellow or Ela goraka, Moon, Cat. 37. 1824.

Tree 20 m high, 30 cm diam., glabrous in all its parts. Bark dark brown, fissured, loose, peeling off in 1 cm wide, 1–2 mm thick pieces; live bark reddish with dark yellow, sticky, thick latex. Branchlets slender, subcylindrical, hardly thickened at the nodes. Leaves subcoriaceous, oblanceolate to broadly oblanceolate, 1.5 × 6–4 × 10 cm, sub-acute, base tapered, slightly decurrent into the slender, 1–1.5 cm long pedicel with inconspicuous foveola; midrib flat on upper surface, slender, prominulous on lower one; laterals 5–7 pairs, steep, prominulous both sides, in between some parallel, shorter laterals, reticulation very lax, obscure. Male flowers in axillary and pseudoterminal bundles; pedicel 1–2.5 cm long, slightly thickened at apex. Sepals 4, the outer two concave, orbicular, 2 mm long, inner ones 3 mm. Petals 4, oblong, concave, fleshy, 6–7 mm long. Filaments connate into a very short cylindrical bundle, bearing the c. 30 anthers on extremely short free filament parts.

"Female flowers solitary, axillary and pseudoterminal, subsessile, rather larger than the male ones, sepals and petals as in male. Filaments 6-8 slender, short, each bearing a short abortive anther. Ovary globose with 6-8 grooves, 6-8-celled. Style none. Stigma peltate, verrucous, no evident division into lobes" (Roxburgh). Fruit like a large apple, depressed globose, up to 8 cm diam., glossy pale yellow with 6-9 broad, rounded ribs and as many, not very deep grooves, both ending below the top of the fruit. Stigma of 6-9 hard, papillate rays, 3-4 mm diam., slightly sunk in the centre of the fruit; no mamilla; sepals persistent, reflexed. Seeds oblong, 3 cm long, embedded in a very soft juicy sweet-acid arillode.

D i s t r. Endemic.
E c o l. Wet evergreen lowland forests of S.W. Ceylon, sometimes cultivated.
N o t e. Of this well known, cultivated tree, the female flowers were only known to Roxburgh. I have not indicated a neotype, as a Roxburgh specimen might turn up. In botanical literature the species has been continuously mixed with the red goraka (*G. quaesita*), from which it is easily distinguished by the yellow, more juicy fruit with less deep grooves which do not reach the top of the fruit and the lack of a mamilla. It is used and prepared in the same way as the red goraka. In the leaves there is hardly any difference, in the single collection of fruiting yellow goraka they are slightly thicker and resemble those of *G. affinis*.

It was introduced from Ceylon into the Missionaries' Garden at Tranquebar and from material of that tree Roxburgh's description was made.
S p e c i m e n s E x a m i n e d. GALLE DISTRICT: Godakande near Hiniduma, wet, evergreen, alt. 300 m, Sept. ripe fr., *Kostermans 25567* (A, BO, G, K, L, P, PDA, US). KANDY DISTRICT: Laxapana, road to Maskeliya, alt. 200 m, May, after anthesis, male fl., *Kostermans 24188* (L).

3. **Garcinia morella** (Gaertn.) Desr. in Lam., Enc. 3 (2): 701, t. 405, f. 2. Febr. 1792 (excl. *Carcapuli* Acosta); Thw., Enum. Pl. Zeyl. 1: 49. 1858; Planch. & Triana, Ann. Sci. nat., Sér. 4, Bot. 14 : 350. 1860 (excl. *Guttifera vera* Koen.); Hanbury, Trans. Linn. Soc. 24: 489, t. 50. 1864 (excl. var. *pedicellata*); Beddome, Fl. Sylv. t. 86. 1869; Lanessan, Adansonia 10: 292, 293, fig. XI (12–20). 1873; Anderson in Hook. f., Fl. Br. Ind. 1: 264. 1874; Vesque in DC., Monogr. 8: 472. 1883 (excl. cit. Philippin.); Trimen, Handb. Fl. Ceylon 1 : 96. 1893; Gamble, Man. Ind. Timb. 55. 1902; Talbot, Trees Bombay 1: 93. 1909; Willis & Smith, Ann. R. Bot. Gard. Perad. 5: 180. 1912; Rama Rao, Fl. Pl. Travanc. 29. 1914; Bryan, Nat. Hist. Hawaii 1: 67, f. 8. 1915; Kanjilal, Fl. Assam 1: 107. 1934; Anon., Wealth of India 4: 105, f. 49. 1956; Maheshwari, Bull. Bot. Survey Ind. 6: 132. 1964; Kostermans. Ceylon J. Sci., Biol. Sci. 12 (1): 61. 1976.

Mangostana morella Gaertn., Fruct. 2: 106, t. 101. 1790. Type: Herb. Gaertner (Tübingen, material reportedly lost; BM).

Hebradendron cambogioides Graham in Hooker's Comp. Bot. Mag. 2: 199, t. 27. 1836; Graham, Christison & Wight, Gamboge of Ceylon, London 1836; Thw., l.c. 49; Wight, Ill. Ind. Bot. 1: t. 44, p. 126 & 130. 1840; Guibourt, Hist. Drogues, ed. 4: 557, t. III. 1822.

Stalagmitis cambogioides Murray in Commentat. Göttingens. 9: 173. 1789 (p.p., exclus. descr. flor., exclus. syn.); Vesque, l.c. (quoad syn. Moon, Cat. 73. 1824).

Garcinia cambogioides Royle, Mater. Med., ed. 3: 339, tab. 1832. Type: *Koenig s.n.* (BM).

Garcinia gutta (non L.) Wight, Ill. 1: t. 44. 1840.

Gambogia gutta (non L.) Thw., l.c.; Lindley, Veg. Kingd. 401. 1853.

Guttaefera vera Koenig, Apparat. Medicam. IV: 655. 1789. Kanawa koraka, Kaepnaji koraka, Gohkathu, Ghoraka, Hermann, Mus. Zeyl. 26. 1717.

Arbor indica gummi guttam fundens, fructi dulci rotundo cerasi magnitudine, Burman, Thes. 271. 1737.

Cambogia L., Fl. Zeyl. 87, no. 195. 1748 (p.p., quoad cit. Hermann et Burman).

Tree, up to 20 m tall and 50 cm diam., usually much smaller, glabrous in all its parts. Bole of immature tree smooth, bark brown to dark brown, thin, in very old trees deeply fissured, rusty brown. Live bark 3–10 mm thick, white to straw, with plenty of brilliant dark yellow, sticky, thick latex. Wood yellowish, hard, mottled. Young twigs quadrangular, drying grey. Leaves drying pale green. Leaves thinly coriaceous to very stiffly coriaceous, obovate or oblanceolate, rarely elliptic, base tapered, acute, apex broadly, shortly, obtusely, usually obscurely acuminate, (2 × 5–) 6 × 9–7 × 13 cm, midrib on upper surface not protruding, laterals obscure, lower surface with prominulous, slender midrib and 7–8 pairs of steep, parallel, slender laterals, in between similar ones, almost as long, reticulation very lax. Petiole 5–10 mm long, foveola conspicuous with slightly raised margins. Flowers sessile or nearly so in axils of leaves or fallen leaves. Male flowers 2–3 together, females usually solitary. Sepals 4, greenish white, elliptic, concave, rather thin, 4–6 mm long. Petals 4, white to pink, rather fleshy (drying thin), veined, broadly elliptic, concave, 5–8 mm long. Male flower: Stamens monadelphous, the short filaments grown together into a subquadrangular central column, the apical, very short part of the filaments free, anthers red, dehiscing transversely. Female flowers same size as male ones; ovary greenish, globose, smooth, 4-celled; style none; stigma peltate, first yellow, later brown-red, consisting of 4 almost round stigmas with rather few, low tubercles, mostly completely fused into a circular body, base of ovary surrounded by c. 12 free stamens, connate at base. Fruit globose, smooth, yellowish, up to 2.5 cm diam., base with the not enlarged, spreading sepals, apex crowned by a flat, tuberculate, round stigma, 2–3 mm diam. Exocarp rather thin, pulp (endocarp) sweet-acid, edible. Seeds kidney-shaped, laterally compressed, testa finely mucronulate.

Distr. Southern India.

Ecol. Dry and wet zone.

Uses. The brilliant yellow latex is an excellent gamboge or gummigut, but only used locally for painting and dyeing. The juice of *Feronia* is used as a mordant. Trees can be tapped when they are 10 years old by making a spiral incision and collecting in small bamboo containers.

Vern. Kanna goraka, Gokatu, Kokatiya.

Note. The leaves of the wet zone trees are sometimes more fleshy than those of the dry zone; in dry zone and in the Uva patanas the trees are stunted, stiff with divaricate branches and thick nodes. The petals are fleshy. The S. Indian plant seems to differ in the female flower which has the staminodes in bundles and hence was kept separate by Beddome.

Specimens Examined. KANDY DISTRICT: Madugoda, March, fl., *Kostermans s.n.* (L); Udawattekele above Kandy, alt. 450 m, Apr., fl., *Kostermans 24007* and *24008* (G, K, L, P, PDA, US); Gannoruwa jungle near Kandy, alt. 400 m, June, fl., *Kostermans 24023* (id.); Moray Estate, Maskeliya, alt. 1500 m, May, fl., *Kostermans 24263* (L, PDA, US); Hantane, 1853, *s. coll. C.P. 322* (PDA). BADULLA DISTRICT: Between Hakgala and Welimada, alt. 500 m, Apr., buds, *Kostermans s.n.* (L, PDA, US); ibid., July, fr., *Subramaniam s.n.* (id.); Madewellegama Pine Nursery above Passera, alt. 1000 m, May, fl., *Kostermans 24856* (id.); ibid., fl., *Kostermans 24436* (id.); ibid., May, fl., *Kostermans 24854* (id.); Talpitikala, Badulla-Passera road, alt. 1000 m, June, fl., *Kostermans 24443* (id.). NUWARA ELIYA DISTRICT: Deltota, May, fl., *s. coll. C.P. 322* (PDA). RATNAPURA DISTRICT: Balangoda, *Gardner C.P. 322* (PDA). GALLE DISTRICT: Hinidumkande (Haycock), May, buds, *Jayasuriya 784* (L, PDA, US). KALUTARA DISTRICT: Morapitiya logging area, wet, evergreen, alt. 100 m, Apr., fr., *Kostermans 24682* (L, PDA, US). LOCALITY UNKNOWN: Herb. Wight propr. (*Walker s.n.*) (PDA).

4. Garcinia echinocarpa Thw. in Hooker's J. Bot. & Kew Gard. Miscell. 6: 71. 1854; Enum. Pl. Zeyl. 1: 49. 1858 (quoad var. *b*); Planch. & Triana, Ann. Sci. nat., Sér. 4, Bot. 14: 348. 1860; Lanessan, Adansonia 10: 286, tab. XI. f. 6. 1870; Pierre, Fl. for. Cochinch. XXIII, t. 80 J. 1883 (quoad var. *b*); Anderson in Hook. f., Fl. Br. Ind. 1: 264. 1874 (quoad var. 2); Beddome, Fl. Sylv. 3: XXI. 1869 (quoad var. *b* Thw.); Vesque in DC., Monogr. 8: 422. 1893 (p.p.); Trimen, Handb. Fl. Ceylon 1: 96. 1893 (quoad mountain species); Brandis, Ind. Trees 51, f. 21. 1907; Rama Rao, Fl. Pl. Trav. 29. 1914; Anon.,

Wealth of India 4: 101. 1956 (fruit red!); Lewis, Veg. Prod. Ceylon 13. 1934; Worthington, Ceylon Trees 25. 1959; Maheshwari, Bull. Bot. Surv. Ind. 6: 126. 1964; Sultanbawa in J. nat. Sci. Counc. Sri Lanka 1: 137. 1973, Kosterm., Ceylon J. Sci. Biol. Sci. 12 (1): 63. 1976.

Garcinia echinocarpa, var. *monticola* Maheshwari, l.c. 126, t. IV. Type: *C.P. 335* (PDA).

Tree, glabrous in all its parts, up to 10 m high and up to 30 cm diam. Bark red-brown, lenticellate, rough, hard, peeling off, 0.5 mm thick; live bark 10 mm, red-brown to dark beefy red with little, white, thick, sticky latex. Bole on rather slender, cylindrical stilt roots, from 50–100 cm from the base, oblique; higher up the bole sometimes small, stiff roots stick out. Branchlets angular. Leaves rigidly coriaceous, obovate to oblanceolate, obtuse, shortly, broadly apiculate, sometimes retuse, base gradually tapered, 1.5×5–6×10 cm; upper surface glossy dark green, midrib flat to impressed, laterals obscure or slender, prominulous, lower surface drying a light chocolate brown, midrib prominent, laterals slender, prominulous, erect-patent, c. 25 pairs, spaced 2–4 mm, no marginal vein, in between laterals often a parallel one, reaching almost the margin. Petiole 1–1.5 cm, stout, red-brown; latex white. Flowers congested in the axils of the two apical leaves (pseudo-terminal), almost sessile (pedicel 0.5 – 1 mm, thick, rectangular with a concave bract at base). Female flowers solitary with 1–3 bracts; buds reddish. Sepals 4, pale green, concave, very thick, suborbicular, 3–4 mm long. Petals pale green, darker green towards tip, thick, elliptic, obtuse, c. 8 mm long, arranged in a spiral. Male flower 1–2 cm diam. in fully opened flower. Stamens 7–10, staminal column short, very thick, the red anthers arranged (on very short free part of filaments) in a round or subquadrangular plane, dehiscent longitudinally. Female flowers slightly larger or as large, darker green. Sterile stamens attached to a 0.5–1 mm high rim around the ovary base, 10–15, two together at the spathulate apex of the 1–2 mm long filament. Ovary globose with numerous tubercles, style short, massive, the upper flat, hardly larger part representing the circular white papillate stigma. Fruit 1–3-seeded, when 3-seeded subglobose with 3 obtuse angles, up to 3.5 cm high, when 2-seeded laterally flattened, covered with pyramidal spines, the upper part thinner, initially spines red-brown. Ripe fruit green to yellowish green, exocarp 1 mm thick; endocarp soft, pulpy, white, sweet, with very little white latex, 2–4 mm thick. Seeds large, oblong, veined, light brown, no arillode. Lesions in the fruit produce rusty red, transparent hard resin droplets. Fruit crowned by the short, massive, cylindrical or conical style, the upper flat part representing the 1–3 tubercled stigmas.

D i s t r. Ceylon, above 1000 m alt., S.W. India?
E c o l. Very common, sub-gregarious, preferring wet places.

V e r n. Madol.

N o t e. In many places this tree is so common that they are named after it (Madulkelle). The stilt roots are always present and become very long in marshy places and on rocks.

The Indian tree, according to Wealth of India, should have red fruit; if this is corroborated, it represents another species.

Timber, 50–55 lbs, splits easily to make roof shingles (Worthington).

S p e c i m e n s   E x a m i n e d. KANDY DISTRICT: Hunasgiriya, April 1851, fr., *C.P. 335* (PDA); Adams Peak, buds, *Gardner* (*C.P. 335*) (PDA); Rangala hill, Sept. 1888, fr., *s. coll. s.n.* (PDA); Madulkelle, young fr., Oct. 1887, *s. coll. s.n.* (PDA); Knuckles, Madulkelle area, alt. 1000 m, June, fl., *Kostermans 25023*, female (A, BO, G, K, L, P, PDA, US); ibid., male fl., *Kostermans 25021* (id.); ibid., June, fr., *Kostermans 25020* (id.); Upper part of Moray Estate, Maskeliya, Adams Peak jungle, alt. 1700 m, May, young fr., *Kostermans 24785* (id.); ibid., June, young fr., *Kostermans 24930* (id.); ibid., May, young fr., *Kostermans 25021* (id.); ibid., May, buds, *Kostermans 24242A, 24274A, 24778* (id.); ibid., June, fr., *Kostermans 24524* (id.); ibid., buds, *Kostermans 24786* (id.); ibid., May, buds, *Kostermans 24782* (id.); ibid., June, buds, *Kostermans 24932* (id.); ibid., May, young fr., *Kostermans 24222* (id.); Rangala, alt. 800 m, March, buds, *Kostermans s.n.* (id.); ibid., Febr., buds, *Balasubramanian 122* (K); ibid., May, young fr., *Kostermans 24224* (id.). GALLE DISTRICT: Enselwatte Estate, above Deniyaya, June, fr., *Kostermans 23653* (id.).

N o t e. Young flower buds are reddish with a whitish tip. The spines on the young fruit are reddish. They are usually pyramidal, sometimes they have a flat or convex basal template with a spine in the centre.

5. Garcinia hermonii Kosterm. in Ceylon J. Sci., Biol. Sci. 12 (1): 64. 1976. Type: *C.P. 2445*, Sinharaja forest, April 1855 (L, PDA).

Garcinia echinocarpa Thw., Enum. Pl. Zeyl. 49. 1858, quoad var. *a* (female); Pierre, Fl. for. Cochinch. XIII. 1883 (quoad *Thwaites 2445*); Anderson in Hook. f., Fl. Br. Ind. 1: 264. 1874, quoad var. 1; Trimen, Handb. Fl. Ceylon 1: 96. 1893 (quoad *Thwaites 2445*).

Tree, up to 20 m high and 50 cm diam., glabrous in all its parts, without stilt roots. Bark smooth to rough, dark rusty, peeling off, 1 mm thick. Live bark 5 mm, beefy to light red, outside dark red, with little, white, thick, sticky latex. Leaves thinly coriaceous to coriaceous, elliptic to lanceolate-elliptic, 3×8–5×10–8×26 cm, conspicuously acuminate with sharp tip, base acute, slightly decurrent; basal part of midrib prominulous on upper surface, midrib prominent on lower one, laterals slender, prominulous on both surfaces, erect-patent, c. 50–60 pairs with a few in between. Petiole 1–2 cm long, foveola with strongly produced margins. Flowers unknown. Sepals of female flower flat, thin, depressed ovate, up to 5–6 mm long and 8 mm wide, stiff, rather thin. Fruit depressed sub-globose, up to 6 cm diam., 2–3-seeded (in 2-seeded fruit laterally flattened), top with a thick mamilla (style), up to 5 mm high, 10 mm diam., consisting at the top of two widely separated, papillate, flat, round stigmas. Seeds 2–3, oblong, 2 cm long, 1.5 cm diam., outside convex, inside formed by two planes forming a very wide angle, brown, glossy; pulp mealy, sweetish.

D i s t r. Endemic.

E c o l. Very wet lowlands of S.W. Sri Lanka (Sinharaja, Hiniduma).

Named in honour of Mr. Maurice A. Hermon, Superintendent of Moray Estate, now of Frotoft Estate.

S p e c i m e n s E x a m i n e d. KALUTARA DISTRICT: Sinharaja forest, April 1855, young fr., *C.P. 2445* (L, PDA); Morapitiya logging area, 14 miles E. of Matugama, low alt., Aug., fr., *Kostermans 25401* (G, K, L, PDA, US); ibid., April, young fr., *Kostermans 24667* (id.); ibid., fr., *Subramanian s.n.* (L); ibid., Aug., fr., *Kostermans s.n.* (id.); along road Kirihembelieh, July, fallen branch, *Meyer 473* (L, PDA, US). GALLE DISTRICT: Hiniduma, March, buds, *Kostermans 11116* (BO, L); Hinidumkande (Haycock) near Hiniduma, alt. 200 m, Aug., fr., *Kostermans 25376* (id.); Godakande near Hiniduma, alt. 300 m, Sept., ripe fr., *Kostermans 25569* (id.); ibid., Sept., young fr., *Kostermans 25565* (id.); Kottawa Arboretum near Galle, Aug., ster., *Kostermans 25467* (G, K, L, PDA, US). KANDY DISTRICT; Ambagamuwa, March, buds, *s. coll. s.n.* (PDA).

6. Garcinia terpnophylla (Thw.) Thw., Enum. Pl. Zeyl., Addend. 406. 1864; Beddome, Fl. Sylv. XXI. 1869; Anderson in Hook. f., Fl. Br. Ind. 1: 268. 1874; Vesque in DC., Monogr. 8: 357. 1893; Trimen, Handb. Fl. Ceylon 1: 97. 1893; Willis & Smith, Ann. R. Bot. Gard. Perad. 5: 180. 1912; Worthington, Ceylon Trees 27. 1959; Kosterm., Ceylon J. Sci., Biol. Sci. 12 (1): 65. 1976; Sultanbawa, J. Nat. Sci. Counc. Sri Lanka 1: 153. 1973.

Terpnophyllum zeylanicum Thw. in Hooker's J. Bot. & Kew Gard. Miscell. 6: 70, tab. 2 C. 1854; Thw., Enum. Pl. Zeyl., l.c. 49. 1858; Planch. & Triana, Ann. Sci. nat., Sér. 4, Bot. 14: 364. 1860 (ceylanicum).
Discostigma zeylanicum (Thw.) Planch. & Triana, l.c. 364 (Mém. 209). Type: *C.P. 2695* (PDA).

Tree, up to 30 m tall and 60 cm diam., glabrous in all its parts. Bole cylindrical or fluted, flutes thick, rounded. Buttresses sometimes up to 2 m high and 1 m out, thin, usually much smaller. Bark smooth or somewhat roughish, reddish brown, soft, 0.5 mm thick. Live bark 3–5 mm, white to yellowish white with very little white or yellowish, thick, sticky latex. Branches horizontal, somewhat pendulous at the ends, slender. Foliage of the flush brownish red. Wood hard, honey coloured. Leaves thinly coriaceous, lanceolate or subovate-lanceolate, gradually acute or acuminate (in the variety subcaudate acuminate with blunt tip), up to 5 × 10 cm (shorter in the variety), base acute; midrib and the slender, numerous erect-patent laterals (with a few in between ones) prominulous or midrib slightly impressed above, strong marginal nerve, reticulation obscure. Petiole slender, 5–12 mm long, channeled above, foveola obscure. Flowers in axillary clusters on strongly reduced, bracteolate shoots. Pedicel slender, cylindrical, up to 5 mm long. Male ones in many-flowered fascicles, up to 8 mm diam. Sepals 4, ovate or ovate-suborbicular, obtuse, sub-coriaceous, up to 2.5 mm long, greenish white. Petals 4, white, thin, oblong, up to 4 mm long. Stamens white, arranged in 4 broad, fleshy, flat, erect or spreading, 2 mm long, 1.5 mm wide obtuse phalanges, bearing the subsessile anthers on both sides (mostly inside) near the apex; base of phalanges adnate to the base of the petals, the bases of the 4 phalanges pairwise united (not in var. *acuminata*). Rudiment of pistil globose, small (lacking in var. *acuminata*). Female flowers solitary or few together, same shape and size as male ones, the globose, 2-celled ovary crowned by a convex hardly incised stigma with smooth, low, round papillae, the base surrounded by 4 short, broad, fleshy phalanges as in the male flower. Fruit reddish brown, smooth, ellipsoid, often oblique, up to 1.5 × 3 cm, one-celled with a single elongate seed with thin, transparent sweet arillode; pericarp rather thin, fleshy, with dark yellow, sticky latex; stigma dome-like, 1–2 mm diam., smoothly pustular. Testa with sulcate sculpture.

1. var. **terpnophylla**

Garcinia terpnophylla var. *lanceolata* Thw., Enum. Pl. Zeyl., l.c. 49. 1858.
Discostigma zeylanicum Planch. & Triana, l.c.

Leaves lanceolate, gradually acute with blunt apex. Staminal phalanges 4, pairwise united at the base. Pistil rudiment present.

D i s t r. Endemic.
E c o l. Mountain rainforest at c. 1000 m alt. I have never found this. The description of the tree and its bark refers to the far more common lowland variety.
S p e c i m e n s E x a m i n e d. NUWARA ELIYA DISTRICT: Watagoda, July 1853, fr., *s. coll. C.P. 2695* (L, PDA); ibid., female fl., leaves up to 5 × 10 cm, *s. coll. C.P. 2695* (L, PDA).

2. var. **acuminata** Thw., l.c. 49. 1858; Anderson l.c.; Trimen l.c. 98.

Discostigma acuminata Planch. & Triana, l.c. 364.
Terpnophyllum acuminatum Thw. ex Planch. & Triana, l.c. Type: *C.P. 3400* (PDA).

Leaves smaller, abruptly caudate acuminate with blunt tip. Male flowers with 4 separate bundles of stamens, no pistil rudiment.

D i s t r. Endemic.

E c o l. Wet lowlands of Sinharaja forest, Ratnapura and Kalutara Distr.

N o t e. Although the variety differs only in minor characters, I have maintained it, because it occurs at a lower altitude and no intermediate leaves with var. *terpnophylla* were found in the material, which I have collected.

S p e c i m e n s E x a m i n e d. KALUTARA DISTRICT: Sinharaja, April 1855, fl., *s. coll. C.P. 3400* (PDA); Kalutara (Caltura), July 1860, fr., *s. coll. C.P. 3400* (PDA). GALLE DISTRICT: Kaneliya forest near Hiniduma, alt. 100 m, near river, June, fr., *Kostermans 25005* (A, BO, G, K, L, P, PDA, US); ibid., near entrance gate along river, May, male fl., *Kostermans 24740* (id.); ibid., May, male fl., *Kostermans 24744* (id.); ibid., Sept., fr., *Kostermans 25600* (id.); ibid., May, male fl., *Kostermans 24725* (id.); Hinidumkande (Haycock), near Hiniduma, 500 m alt., Sept., fr., *Kostermans 25667* (id.). KANDY DISTRICT: cult. in Botanic Garden Peradeniya, April, male fl., *Hallier s.n.* (L).

7. Garcinia spicata (W. & A.) Hook. f., J. Linn. Soc. 14: 486. 1875; Pierre, Fl. for. Cochinch. IV. 1883 (excl. spec. Bombay Ghats); Vesque in DC., Monogr. 8: 309. 1883 (cum vars. *spicata & glomerata*, exclus. vars. *acutifolia & macrantha*); Trimen, Handb. Fl. Ceylon 1: 98. 1893 (exclus. var. *acutifolia* Vesque); Cooke, Fl. Bombay 1: 78. 1901 (exclus. var. *macrantha*); Gamble, Man. Ind. Timb. 50. 1902, p.p.; Fl. Pres. Madras 49. 1907, p.p.; Brandis, Ind. Trees 49. 1907 (excl. var. with larger flowers); Engler in Pflanzenfam. ed. 2, 2: 218. 1925; Kanjilal, Fl. Assam 1: 110. 1934, p.p.; Anon., Wealth of India 4: 107. 1956, p.p.; Worthington, Ceylon Trees 26. 1959; Chowdhury & Ghosh, Ind. For. Rec., N.S., Utiliz. 4: 12, t. III. 1947; Maheshwari, Rec. Bot. Surv. Ind. 6: 112. 1964 (includ. vars. *spicata & glomerata*); Kosterm. Ceylon J. Sci., Biol. Sci. 12 (1): 66. 1976.

Xanthochymus spicatus Wight & Arn., Prod. 1: 102. 1834; Thw., Enum. Pl. Zeyl. l.c. 49, p.p.

Stalagmitis spicata (W. & A.) Walp., Rep. 1: 396. 1842. Type: *Wight* Herb. propr. *138* (CALCUTTA).

Garcinia ovalifolia (Roxb.) Hook. f., Fl. Br. Ind., l.c. 269 (non Oliver 1868).

Xanthochymus ovalifolius Roxb., Hort. Beng. 42. 1814 (nomen); Fl. Ind. 2: 632. 1832; Thw., Enum., l.c. 49 (excl. var. *b*).

Stalagmitis ovalifolius G. Don, Gen. Syst. 1: 621. 1831. Type: Culta in Hort. Calc. from seeds sent by Gen. Hay Macdowall from Ceylon as Ambul Ghoorka.

Garcinia celebica Moon, Cat. 37. 1824.

Stalagmitis cambogioides Murray in Commentat. Gottingens. 9: 175. 1789,
   p.p., quoad male fl. and leaves.
Gummi guttaefera vera Koenig ex Murray, l.c. Type: *Koenig s.n.* (L).

Tree, up to 12 m high, up to 40 cm diam. Bark smooth to slightly hammered, pale brown, hard, 0.5–1 mm thick, obscurely hoop-ringed. Live bark
5–20 mm thick, white to straw, with little white or yellow sticky, thick latex.
Twigs of the flush densely microscopically pubescent. Wood yellowish white,
hard, heavy, 50 lb/cubic ft., liable to split and warp, strong timber for construction purposes. Leaves stiffly coriaceous, elliptic to ovate-elliptic, 3 × 6–9
× 15 cm, obtuse to emarginate, base obtuse, midrib prominulous on both
sides; laterals slender, prominulous on both sides, erect-patent, slightly curved, 15–18 pairs with parallel, half as long in between ones, reticulation very
lax. Petioles 1–1.5 cm long, initially pubescent with strong foveola with
strongly produced margins. Flowers in axils of leaves or fallen leaves. Male
ones in glomerulate many-bracteate fascicles on reduced shoots, sometimes
growing out into 1–10 cm long raceme-like inflorescence, bearing the flowers
in fascicles on reduced shoots. Flowers at base surrounded by minute, pilose
bracts. Pedicel slender, 6–12 mm long. Sepals (4–) 5, pale green, suborbicular, the outer two coriaceous, the inner larger, 2.5–3 mm long, thinner,
margin ciliate, outside pubescent. Petals white, thin, veined, 6–7 × 8.5 mm,
concave. Stamens in 5 erect, incurved, long-clawed, spathulate fascicles of
8–10 each, opposite petals, inserted in bays of the green, glossy, convex torus.
Free part of stamens very short. Pistil none. Female flower same shape and
size. Staminodes in 5 fascicles, bi- or tri-furcate at apex with few, weak
anthers. Ovary globose, 3 (–4)-celled; style 1 mm long; stigma peltate, lobed
to the centre, lobes cuneiform. Fruit subglobose to oblong, depending on the
number of developed seeds, 1–3-seeded (when 2-seeded flattened laterally),
up to 4 cm diam., yellow, bad smell; pulp sweet-acid with bitter after taste,
much sticky yellow latex when young, no arillode. Pedicel c. 1 cm long.
Seeds up to 2.5 cm long, oblong, laterally flattened, testa brown, veined.
Stigma black, 2–3 mm diam. with cuneiform free, smooth lobes.

D i s t r. Southern India.
E c o l. Dry zone.
V e r n. Gokatu, Gonapana (S); Gokottai (T).
N o t e. Roxburgh's description of the fruit does not fit, neither the Cey-
lonese vernacular name.
S p e c i m e n s   E x a m i n e d. JAFFNA DISTRICT: Jaffna anno. 1848,
Gardner C.P. 1173 (PDA); Jaffna, April, fl., *Balasubramaniam s.n.* (L).
BADULLA DISTRICT: Ooma Oya, Sept. 1854, fr., *s. coll. C.P. 1173* (PDA).
ANURADHAPURA DISTRICT: Anuradhapura, male fl., *s. coll. C.P. 1173*
(PDA). MONERAGALA DISTRICT: Bibile, fr., Oct., *de Silva s.n.* (PDA);
Bintenne, July 1853, *s. coll. C.P. 1173* (PDA). AMPARAI DISTRICT: Am-

para-Kandy Rd., mile 18, Divulane forest, alt. 50 m, June, fr., *Kostermans 25175* (A, BO, G, K, L, P, PDA, US); ibid., May, fr., *Kostermans 24843 'A* (id.); Lahugala Tank, July, fr., *Mueller-Dombois & Comanor s.n.* (PDA). MATALE DISTRICT: river near Dambulla, low marshy, May, young fr., *Kostermans 24798* (A, BO, G, K, L, P, PDA, US); ibid., May, fl., *Kostermans 24797* (id.). POLONNARUWA DISTRICT: Polonnaruwa ruin area, low alt., May, fl., *Kostermans 24835* (A, BO, G, K, L, P, PDA, US); ibid., May, fr., *Kostermans 24834* (id.); ster. young shoot, *Kostermans 24305 A* (L); May, fl., *Kostermans 24307* (id.). KANDY DISTRICT: Peradeniya Botanic Garden, April, fl., *Kostermans s.n.* (G, L). HAMBANTOTA DISTRICT: Ruhuna National Park, Aug., buds, *Mueller-Dombois & Comanor s.n.* (PDA); ibid., April, fl., *Fosberg et al. 50159* (PDA). PUTTALAM DISTRICT: Wilpattu National Park, Sept., fr., *Mueller-Dombois et al. s.n.* (PDA).

8. Garcinia thwaitesii Pierre, Fl. for. Cochinch. IV. 1883; Vesque in DC., Monogr. 8: 311. 1893 (sub var. *acutifolia*); Trimen, Handb. Fl. Ceylon 1: 98. 1893 (sub *G. spicata* var. *acutifolia* Anders.); Kosterm. in Ceylon J. Sci., Biol. Sci. 12 (1): 67. 1976. Type: *C.P. 731* (P).

Xanthochymus lanceolatus Thw. ex Pierre, l.c. Type: *Thwaites C.P. 731*.
Xanthochymus ovalifolius var. *b* Thwaites, Enum. Pl. Zeyl. 50. 1858.
Garcinia ovalifolius var. *4 acutifolia* Hook. f., Fl. Br. Ind. 1: 269. 1874.
Garcinia spicata var. *acutifolia* Vesque, l.c. 311; Trimen, l.c.

Tree up to 20 m high and 40 cm diam. Bark smooth, brown with slender, semicircular hoop rings, 0.25 mm thick. Live bark 5 mm, light brown, inside lemon white with little, white, thick, sticky latex. Leaves ovate-elliptic, rarely lanceolate, 1.5 × 4–8 × 15 cm, acuminate, tip obtuse, base acute; laterals 10–12 pairs, united very near the margin, prominulous both surfaces, in between 1–2 parallel, often as long ones, connected by a lax irregular reticulation. Petioles stout, 1–1.5 cm long with large foveola with high rims. Inflorescences completely glabrous. Flowers greenish white in axillary bundles on inconspicuous, 2–4 mm long reduced, bracteate shoots. Pedicel 1.5–5 mm long. Male flower: 5 sepals greenish white, with a little dirty red brown, imbricate, rather thin, orbicular, concave, margin ciliate, outside glabrous, outer ones 1–1.5 mm long, inner pair 3.5 × 4 mm. Petals orbicular, slightly narrowed at base, thin, 4.5–5 mm. Stamens in 5 rather slender, flattened bundles opposite petals and as long as these, erect, incurved, bearing near the apex 6–8 anthers, dehiscent by an apical slit, free part of stamens short. No pistil rudiment. Receptacle convex, glossy, the staminal fascicles inserted in bays. Female flower not seen. Young fruit at base with 4 staminal fascicles. Fruit globose, smooth, 1-seeded, greenish yellow, 1.5–2.5 cm diam. Pedicel 3–10 mm long. Stigma 2 mm diam., sessile, peltate, flat, (3 –) 4 (– 5)-lobed, the lobes cuneiform, separated up to their base, apex rounded.

D i s t r. Endemic.

E c o l. Wet, evergreen lowland forest of S.W. Sri Lanka.

S p e c i m e n s E x a m i n e d. GALLE DISTRICT: Kaneliya forest near Hiniduma, alt. 50 m, May, male fl., *Kostermans 24752* (A, BO, G, K, L, P, PDA, US); ibid., along rivulet, Aug., fl., *Kostermans 24974* (id.); ibid., May, fl., *Kostermans 24752* (id.); ibid., Sept., buds, *Kostermans 25531* (id.). KALU-TARA DISTRICT: Matugama-Morapitiya road, near Morapitiya, along river ravine, June, fl., *Kostermans 24974 A* (id.); ibid., June, fr., *Kostermans 24971* (id.); Morapitiya logging area, 14 miles E. of Matugama, alt. 50 m, April, fr., *Kostermans 24666* (id.).

9. Garcinia xanthochymus Hook. f., Fl. Br. Ind. 1: 269. 1874; Pierre, Fl. for. Cochinch. III, t. 71 A. 1883; Cooke, Fl. Bombay 1: 78. 1901; Rama Rao, Fl. Pl. Travanc. 30. 1914; Burkill, Dict. econ. Pr. 1: 1056. 1935; Sinclair, Bull. Bot. Soc. Bengal 9: 87. 1955; Macmillan, Trop. Pl. & Gard. (ed. 5) 258. 1956; Anon., Wealth of India 4: 108, fig. 50. 1956; Santapau, Rec. Bot. Surv. Ind. (ed. 2) 16: 14. 1960; Maheshwari, Bull. Bot. Surv. Ind. 6: 114. 1960; Kosterm., Ceylon J. Sci., Biol. Sci. 12 (1): 67. 1976.

Xanthochymus pictorius Roxb. Pl. Corom. 2: 51, t. 196. 1789; Fl. Ind. 2: 633. 1832; Lubbock, Contr. knowl. Seedlings 1: 234, fig. 209. 1892.
Stalagmitis pictoria (Roxb.) G. Don, Gen. Syst. 1: 620. 1831.
Xanthochymus tinctorius DC., Prod. 1: 562. 1824 (sphalm. for *pictorius*).
Garcinia tinctoria (DC.) W.F. Wight in U.S. Dept. Agr., Bureau Pl. Industry Bull. 137: 50. 1909; Alston in Trimen, Handb. Fl. Ceylon 6: 20. 1931 (excl. *G. malabarica* Desr.). Type: *Roxburgh*, Circars (Herb. Mart., Brussels).

Tree, up to 15 m high, usually much smaller with a dense, pyramidal crown. Branches patent (upper ones erect-patent), the ends sometimes drooping. Wood yellowish brown, rather hard, moderately heavy. All parts glabrous. Bark blackish or dark grey, peeling off in small pieces. Live bark white with white sticky, thick latex, turning yellowish after exposure. Leaves coriaceous, linear-oblong to oblong-lanceolate (rarely ovate), 4×12–10×35 cm, apex somewhat rounded, and tip sharply apiculate, base rounded to acute, midrib hardly prominent above, prominent on lower surface, laterals conspicuous both sides, 15–20 pairs, irregular, erect-patent, slightly curved towards margin, in between somewhat shorter laterals, reticulation lax, obscure. Petiole stout, 1–2.5 cm long with a large foveola with high margins. Flowers in fascicles of 4–10 in axils of leaves or fallen leaves, on burrs with minute bracts. Pedicel 2–3.5 cm long, thickened towards apex. Male flowers with 5 (rarely 4) greenish white, suborbicular, concave sepals, margin fimbriate, the two outer ones 4–6 mm, inner ones thinner, up to 7 mm long. Petals 5, orbicular, shortly clawed, thin, white, somewhat ciliate, veined, up to 9 mm long. Stamens in 5 rather slender, flattened, up to 13 mm long fascicles, bearing near the forked apices 3–10 anthers on short filaments, the base of the fascicles connate and inserted in bays of the raised torus. Female flower similar. Ovary greenish white, ovoid, pointed, usually 5-celled; style very short, stigma with 5 large, entire, oblong, spreading lobes. Staminodial phalanges 5. Fruit subglobose, pointed (oblique), dark yellow, up to 9 cm diam., the point 2–3 mm, bearing the stigma with long branches. Pericarp with plenty of dark yellow, sticky, thick latex, endocarp forming a sweet, to sweet-acid, pleasant juicy arillode; seeds oblong, brown, testa veined.

D i s t r. India, cultivated in many tropical countries. Planted and semi-naturalized, not common.

V e r n. Rata goraka (rata = foreign).

N o t e. Fruit is used for preserves and jams and are a substitute for tamarind for preparing curries, also used for making vinegar. A decoction of the dried fruit is used as a medicine for billious conditions. The gum of the bark is an inferior kind of gamboge. Seedlings of one year are good for grafting and inarching mangosteen.

10. Garcinia mangostana. CULTIVATED SPECIES. L., Sp. Pl. 443. 1753; Moon, Cat. 27. 1824; Curtis, Bot. Mag. 81: t. 4847. 1855; Hoola v. Nooten, Fleurs, fr. Java, t. 8. 1863; Anderson in Hook. f., Fl. Br. Ind. 1: 260. 1874; Pierre, Fl. for. Cochinch. XXI, t. 54. 1883; Gamble, Man. Ind. Timb. 52. 1902; Fl. Pres. Madras 73. 1915; Popenoe, Man. trop. and subtrop. fruit, t. 24. 1920; Burkill, Dict. 1: 1052. 1935; Hoya & Fukuyama, Formos. Agr. Rev. 1124–28, fig. 1925; Macmillan, Trop. Pl. & Gard. (ed. 5) 237. 1956; Anon., Wealth of India 4: 103, t. 6. 1956; Maheshwari, Bull. Bot. Surv. Ind. 6: 120. 1964.

Mangostana garcinia Gaertn., Fruct. 2: 105. 1790.

Tree up to 20 m tall, glabrous in all its parts, with dense pyramidal crown. Bark dark, smooth. Live bark yellowish with yellow, sticky latex. Wood heavy, hard, red. Leaves elliptic to elliptic-oblong, $6 \times 15–12 \times 25$ cm, acutish to shortly acuminate, very thickly coriaceous, base obtuse or acute, laterals patent, numerous, inarching with double inframarginal vein, rather conspicuous beneath. Petiole stout, 2–2.5 cm long with a strong foveola. Male flowers extremely rare. Hermaphrodite ones 1–2 in the axils of the upper leaves (pseudo-terminal), up to 4 cm diam. Pedicel stout, up to 2 cm long. Sepals 4, rarely 5, concave, thick, persistent, outer ones slightly smaller. Petals 4, purpureous, up to 3 cm long, orbicular, concave, fleshy. Stamens many to few, 1–2-seriate with slender, 4–5 mm long filaments, connate at base; anthers introrse, 2-celled, apex recurved, dehiscent longitudinally. Ovary globose, smooth, 5–8-celled; stigma sessile, punctate, 5–8-lobed, lobes cuneiform. Fruit globose or depressed globose, up to 10 cm diam., glossy purplish black, the enlarged sepals at the base, stigma hard, flat, 5–8-lobed, lobes cuneiform. Pericarp thick, spongy, reddish, with yellow latex, inside light red with slender, longitudinal ribs. Seeds oblong, flattened laterally, enveloped in an opaque, very pleasant, thick, white arillode.

D i s t r. Origin W. Malesia, cultivated in all tropical countries. It prefers a wet soil and wet, hot climate.

E c o l. Cultivated along Colombo—Kandy Rd.; introduced in Ceylon c. 1800.

2. CALOPHYLLUM L.

Trees, usually with quadrangular branchlets and pointed, conspicuous end bud. Bark usually with a yellowish tinge, exudate clear, or milky, little. Leaves opposite, entire, without stipules, lateral veins very numerous, dense, parallel. Flowers hermaphrodite, in axillary or pseudoterminal racemes or in small, raceme-bearing panicles with decussate branching, bracts deciduous. Sepals 4, in two opposite pairs, outer ones concave, enveloping the bud, coloured, inner longer, petaloid. Petals usually 4, sometimes 8, often an irregular number, imbricate, or lacking. Stamens numerous with free filaments or these slightly adnate at the base, and then sometimes in bundles; anthers oblong, dehiscent vertically. Ovary 1-celled with 1 erect ovule; style usually as long as the stamens or longer, often bent, stigma peltate, concave with irregular margin. Fruit with a thin pulp, leathery or with crustaceous endocarp. Seed large with large, flat-convex, shortly petioled cotyledons, often somewhat fused; endosperm sometimes present as a thin, jelly-like layer around the cotyledons. The latter remain in the seed at germination.

D i s t r. Pantropical, more than 150 species, most abundant in tropical Asia. In Lanka 11 species, the coastal *C. inophyllum* known as Domba, the others known as kina (Keena).

N o t e. Kinas belong to the most beautiful group of timber trees, easily recognizable by their glossy leaves with numerous parallel lateral veins and their deeply fissured barks with a boat-like trellis pattern. The timber is in high demand and the trees doomed to become extinct. Some are very rare. The mountain kina is a very beautifully flowering tree and should have been planted in places like Nuwara Eliya, instead of ugly alien trees. The first leaves are smaller and broader, the next pair is usually already much narrower, the next pairs become gradually longer, but are still very narrow.

KEY TO THE SPECIES

1 Leaves cordate at base
  2 Leaves oblong to oblong-elliptic, 5×10–9×20 cm. Inflorescence densely rusty to-mentellous...**11. C. cordato-oblongum**

2 Leaves ovate to obovate to subcoriaceous, 1.5 × 2.5–5 × 6 cm. Inflorescence glabrous
....**10. C. thwaitesii**
1 Leaves at base rounded, acute or cuneate
3 Leaves dimorphic. Inflorescence with large, sub-persistent bracts; they are concealed
between the dangling leaves......................................**5. C. bracteatum**
3 Leaves of one kind. Inflorescences visible
4 Petals 0
5 Leaves very thick, rigidly coriaceous, lanceolate-oblong, 3 × 9–5 × 17 cm. Fruit
whitish green, up to 22 mm long....................................**3. C. moonii**
5 Leaves thinner, coriaceous, elliptic, ovate- or obovate-elliptic, 2 × 3–5 × 9 cm.
Fruit orange yellow, up to 15 mm diam...........................**4. C. calaba**
4 Petals 4–8
6 Fruit with a distinct subconical point
7 Leaves obovate-oval to rhomboid. Inflorescence stout. Flowers 2.5 cm diam......
....**6. C. trapezifolium**
7 Leaves oblong to lanceolate. Inflorescence slender. Flowers less than 2 cm diam.
....**7. C. zeylanicum**
6 Fruit obtuse (sometimes a thin vestige of the style base present)
8 Inflorescence densely tomentose.............................**2. C. tomentosum**
8 Inflorescence glabrous
9 Leaves chartaceous, broadly elliptic, large. Flowers up to 3 cm diam. Fruit pendulous..**1. C. inophyllum**
9 Leaves rigidly coriaceous, small. Flowers much less than 3 cm diam. Fruit upright
10 Leaves obovate-cuneate or spathulate-cuneate, 1 × 2.5–3 × 7 cm.............
....**8. C. cuneifolium**
10 Leaves obovate-rotundate, 1.5 × 2–5 × 6 cm...................**9. C. walkeri**

1. Calophyllum inophyllum. L., Sp. Pl. 1: 513. 1753; Burman f., Fl. Ind. 2: 120.
1768; Wight, Ic. Pl. Ind. Or. 1: t. 77. 1838; Ill. 1: 128. 1840; Thw., Enum. Pl.
Zeyl. 51. 1858 (*C.P. 2764*); Planch. & Triana, Ann. Sci. nat., Sér. 4, Bot. 15:
282. 1861; Anderson in Hook. f., Fl. Br. Ind. 1: 273. 1874; Gamble, Ind.
Timb. 25. 1881; Fl. Pres. Madras 1: 76. 1915; Vesque in DC., Monogr. 8: 544.
1893; Trimen, Handb. Fl. Ceylon 1: 100. 1893; Chandrasena, Chemist. &
Pharmac. Ceylon & Ind. Pl. 33 (Colombo). 1935; Williams, Usef. Pl. Zanzi-
bar 163, tab. 1949; Anon., Wealth of India 2: 18. 1950; Perrier, Fl. Madagasc.,
Guttif. 6. 1951; Henderson & Wyatt Sm., Gard. Bull. 15: 314. 1956; Worthing-
ton, Ceylon Trees 31. 1959; Maheshwari, Bull. Bot. Surv. Ind. 2: 145. 1960;
Robson in Fl. Zambesiaca 1: 394, t. 77. 1961; Sultanbawa, J. Nat. Sci. Counc.
Sri Lanka 1: 147. 1973. Type: Linn. Hort. Cliffort. (BM).

Calophyllum blumii Wight, Ill. 1: 128. 1840.
Calophyllum bintagor Roxb., Fl. Ind. 2: 607. 1832.
Balsamaria inophyllum Lour., Fl. Cochinch. 2: 470. 1790.
Ponna v. Ponna maram, Rheede, Hort. Ind. Malab. 4: 29, t. 38. 1683.
Domba, Doba, Tomba, Hermann, Mus. Zeyl. 15, 28, 66. 1717.
Nux zeylanica rotunda exitiosa, folio rigido glabro splendente, Burm., Thes.
Zeyl. 170. 1737.
Inophyllum flore octifido, Burm., l.c. 131.

Tree, glabrous in all its parts, up to 20 m high and 50 cm diam. Mature trees with deeply fissured, grey to blackish bark. Live bark pink with clear yellow exudate. Wood reddish to reddish brown, heavy. Apical part of branchlets thick, angular. End bud densely, microscopically pilose. Leaves chartaceous to thinly coriaceous, broadly elliptic to obovate-elliptic, 5.5 × 11–6 × 9–9 × 20 cm, rotundate or retuse, base contracted into the petiole, very shortly cuneate, rarely subcordate with acute centre, midrib slender on upper surface, upper half prominulous, lower flat or channeled, on lower surface midrib prominent; laterals filiform, rather patent, prominulous both sides. Petioles 1–3 cm long. Flowers white, up to 3 cm diam., in axillary, white racemes or raceme-bearing panicles, rather few-flowered, up to 16 cm long (usually much shorter). Pedicels slender, 2–6 cm long; main peduncle 1–4 cm long, rather slender. Sepals 4, outer ones 4–6 mm long, concave and like the inner, longer ones, reflexed, petaloid. Petals 4 (rarely up to 8), obovate to elliptic, up to 15 mm long. Stamens 6 mm long, connate at the very base only, obscurely fasciculate. Ovary globose, reddish purple after pollination. Fruit globose, yellow or greenish, up to 4 cm diam. (usually 2–3 cm), pericarp pulpy, astringent, 3–4 mm thick.

D i s t r. Sandy and rocky sea shores of Malaysia, Pacific, E. Africa and India, going as far as Taiwan and Australia, on coral islands often forming a belt parallel to the coast.

E c o l. Lowland, along coast. Inland specimens are planted or spontaneous.

V e r n. Domba (S); Punai, Punnaigam, Dommakottai (T; kottai = seed); Alexandrian laurel; Punnaga (Sanskrit).

N o t e. Ornamental tree. The fruits are the punnai nuts of commerce and were exported to India; they afford a lamp oil and an oil for painting wood work. Mostly produced in the Madras and Kerala States (Domba or Dilo oil, also Punay or Wundi). It supplies the Mariae balsam and a yellowish green resin, known as Tacamahaca (the original one from *C. tacamahaca*, an American tree). The gum of the bark is a purgative and emetic, and applied to wounds and ulcers. The leaves, soaked in water are applied to inflamed eyes. A decoction of the flowers is given to cure syphilis, eczema and even insanity. The timber is used for knees of boats, railway sleepers, etc.

Worthington described the fruit as rough; he produced a photograph with a dried, wrinkled fruit. I saw one specimen from the Philippines with a cordate leaf base.

The type specimen is in the Cliffort Herbarium (BM). It corresponds with copious material in the Van Royen Herbarium at Leiden. A specimen is represented in the Hermann herbarium at Leiden.

S p e c i m e n s   E x a m i n e d. COLOMBO DISTRICT: Colombo, May 1844, *Gardner C.P. 2764* (PDA). BATTICALOA DISTRICT: July, fr., *s. coll.*

s.n. (PDA). BADULLA DISTRICT: Bibile-Mahyangane road, in garden, June, fl., *Kostermans 24409* (A, BO, G, K, L, P, PDA, US). LOCALITY UNKNOWN: July 1857 *s. coll. s.n.* (PDA).

2. **Calophyllum tomentosum** Wight, Ic. Pl. Ind. Or 1: t. 110. 1839; Ill. 1: 128. 1840; Thw., Enum. Pl. Zeyl. 51. 1858; Planch. & Triana, Ann. Sci. nat. Sér. 4, Bot. 15: 269. 1861; Beddome, Fl. Sylv. 1: XXII. 1869; Anderson in Hook. f., Fl. Br. Ind. 1: 274. 1874 (p.p. and excl. *C. elatum* Bedd.); Vesque in DC., Monogr. 8: 552. 1893 (p.p. and excl. *C. elatum* Bedd.); Trimen, Handb. Fl. Ceylon 1: 101. 1893 (includ. *C. elatum* (non Bedd.) Vincent); Chandrasena, Chemist. & Pharmac. Ceylon & Ind. Pl. 34. 1935; Worthington, Ceylon Trees 35. 1959; Maheshwari, Bull. Bot. Surv. Ind. 2: 147, t. IV. 1960. Type: *Walker* in Herb. Wight (CALC.).

Calophyllum elatum (non Bedd.) Vincent in Forest Reports XLIII: 15, 20. 1883; Trimen, l.c., J. of Bot. 23: 142. 1885; Alston, in Trimen, Handb. Fl. Ceylon 6: 21. 1931. Type: *Vincent s.n.* (K, PDA).

Tree, up to 30 m high and 90 cm diam., sometimes with small buttresses. Bark of mature trees greyish yellow to yellowish brown, very deeply fissured (diamond pattern), strips 3–5 cm wide, corky, peeling off, the rifts up to 2 cm deep. Dead bark 3–5 mm thick. Live bark 10 mm, red. Branchlets angular, densely rusty tomentellous, glabrescent. End bud densely rusty tomentellous. Young leaves almost white. Leaves stiffly chartaceous, lanceolate to oblong-lanceolate, rarely narrower, 1×5–2×7–5×15 cm, attenuated both ends, sometimes apex acuminate with blunt tip; midrib on upper surface filiform, prominulous, the lower part channeled, on lower surface slender, tomentellous, prominent. Laterals slender, erect-patent to rather patent, prominent both surfaces. Petiole slender, concave above, glabrescent, 1.5–2.5 cm long. Inflorescences axillary, 8–10-flowered, consisting of simple racemes, or once-branched, 2–5 cm long, densely rusty tomentellous; bracts caducous; peduncles slender. Pedicels very slender, white, 1–1.5 cm long, sparsely to densely tomentellous. Flowers white. Sepals 4, concave, elliptic, outer ones reflexed, half the size of the 7.5 mm long, petaloid inner ones. Petals 4, spathulate, elliptic, thin, veined, initially erect and pressed against each other, early caducous, up to 8 mm long, inner ones smaller. Stamens 4 mm long. Ovary slender, style 2 mm long with peltate, concave, obscurely lobed stigma. Fruit globose, 2.5 cm diam. (young ones apiculate) with thin pericarp. Infructescences c. 2 cm long, fruit pendulous. Pedicel 1–2.5 cm long.

D i s t r. Endemic.

E c o l. Formerly common in the lower hill zone and intermediate zone, now becoming rare.

V e r n. Kina (Keena) or Telkina (tel = oil) (S); Pongu (T).

N o t e. There are several inaccuracies in Worthington's description: the flush is not pinkish, but pure white, the fruit is smaller than described, the bark is wrongly described and the ripe fruit is not tipped. The species has been confused with *C. elatum* Bedd. (called *C. tomentosum* in Troup, Silvicult. Ind. Trees 1: 21. 1921), which does not only differ by the more patent lateral nerves, as stressed by Maheshwari (l.c. 146), but has a pointed fruit.

The sterile shoot, collected by Vincent, originated from the Devulane forest. With the assistance of the beat forest officer, Mr. P.A. Pablis, I found, after a long search a single, large tree in this area (it is the Amparai distr., not Batticoloa) which fits exactly Vincent's collection. Some leaves have a rounded leaf base (exceptionally).

The orange oil (tel) from the fruit of this kina was formerly much used, but because of scarcity of the tree, not any more.

Saplings of 1 m high have the two flush leaves flaccid, drooping, pure white, they thicken, become horizontal, after which they turn green.

The timber is similar to that of the Indian *C. elatum* and much in demand.

S p e c i m e n s   E x a m i n e d. RATNAPURA DISTRICT: Hagalle forest, above Belihuloya, alt. 700 m, May, young fr., *Kostermans 23620* (A, BO, G, K, L, P, PDA, US); Road Belihuloya-Balangoda, June, fl., *Kostermans 25015* (id.); Rakwana, alt. 600 m, June, fr., *Kostermans 25008* (id.); ibid., June, fr., *Balasubramaniam s.n.* (L, PDA); Panilkande, April, young fr., *Worthington 6623* (PDA). MATALE DISTRICT: June, fr., *Kostermans 24494* and *24495* (A, BO, G, K, L, P, PDA, US). AMPARAI DISTRICT: Amparai-Kandy Rd. Divulane forest, low alt., May, fr., fl., *Kostermans 24848* (PDA, L). KANDY DISTRICT: cult. in Botanic Garden Peradeniya, Nov., fl., (this tree has smaller fruit and slightly different leaves and might represent another species), *s. coll. s.n.* (PDA).

3. Calophyllum moonii Wight, Ic. Pl. Ind. Or. 1: t. 111. 1839; Ill. 1: 129. 1846; Thw., Enum. Pl. Zeyl. 32. 1858 (*C.P. 3402*); Planch. & Triana, Ann. Sci. nat. Sér. 4, 15: 269. 1861; Beddome, Fl. Sylv. 1: XXII. 1869; Anderson in Hook. f., Fl. Br. Ind. 1: 271. 1874 (as a syn. of *C. spectabile* W.); Vesque in DC., Monogr. 8: 583. 1893 (id.); Trimen, Handb. Fl. Ceylon 1: 99. 1893 (id.). Type: *Moon s.n.*, between Horana and Nambapane, *C.P. 3402* (CAL, PDA).

Calophyllum spectabile (non Willd.) Anderson, l.c. (quoad syn. *C. moonii*); Trimen, l.c.; Willis & Smith, Ann. R. Bot. Gard. Perad. 5: 180. 1912.
Calophyllum soulattri (non Burm. f.) Alston, in Trimen, Handb. Fl. Ceylon 6: 22. 1931; Worthington, Ceylon trees 33. 1959; Maheshwari, Bull. Bot. Surv. Ind. 2: 142. 1960, p.p.

Tree, up to 20 m high and 25 cm diam. Wood reddish, moderately hard, rather light. Bark smooth, yellowish to dark brown, or finely fissured, strips 2–3 cm wide, peeling off irregularly. Dead bark 1–2 mm thick. Live bark

5 mm, dark beefy red to brown red with little, clear sap. Branchlets angular, stout, densely dark rusty tomentellous. End bud with similar tomentum. Leaves of saplings linear-lanceolate (4 × 22 cm), acute, the flush limp, drooping, pure white, also the end bud pure white, turning dark rusty later. Mature leaves rigidly coriaceous, lanceolate-oblong, rarely ovate-oblong, 3 × 9–5 × 15–5 (–7) × 17 cm, obtuse, the broadest part below the middle, from where the margins go down in straight lines, base very shortly acute. Midrib on upper surface slender, prominulous, densely dark rusty tomentellous, on lower surface stout, prominent, tomentellous; laterals filiform, very close, prominulous on both sides. Petioles stout, concave above, tomentellous, glabrescent, 12–20 mm long. Flowers white in sub-umbellate, few-branched panicles in the axils of the upper leaves; peduncle rather thick, glabrous, 5–10 mm long, bearing 1–3 slender, glabrous, short branches, which in turn bear a few flowers on up to 10 mm long, slender pedicels; bracteoles caducous. Sepals 4, outer ones concave, up to 5 mm long, inner ones up to 7 mm, less concave. Petals 0. Stamens 3 mm long. Ovary globose, style 2–3 mm long. Fruit globose to ellipsoid globose, up to 22 mm long, smooth, with the base of the style persistent. Pedicels rather thick, up to 20 mm long (usually shorter).

D i s t r. Endemic.

E c o l. Wet lowland forests of S.W. Lanka. Usually not common.

V e r n. Domba kina (keena).

N o t e. Differs from *C. soulattri*, with which it has been confused by the much thicker leaves and the shorter flower pedicels. Wight called the leaves linear-lanceolate; this refers to leaves of saplings. The species resembles much more *C. incrassatum* Hend. & Wyatt Sm., than *C. soulattri*.

A form with slightly longer leaves is called napat kina.

The tree occurs mostly in the neighbourhood of rivulets, but also on slopes (Hinidumkande), often in groups.

S p e c i m e n s E x a m i n e d. KALUTARA DISTRICT: Athweltota near Morapitiya, Aug., ster., *Jayasuriya 904* (L, PDA); Morapitiya logging area, 14 miles E. of Matugama, April, fr., *Kostermans 24670 & 24681* (A, BO, G, K, L, P, PDA, US); ibid., April, ster., *Kostermans 24685* (id.); Morapitiya roadside along rivulet, June, fr., *Kostermans 24949* (id.); Mahane Mukalane near Morapitiya, sapling, *Kostermans 24701* (L); Sinharaja, April 1855, ster., *s. coll. C.P. 3402* (PDA); Mandagala Mukalane, Hewesse, March 1887, ster., *s. coll. s.n.* (PDA); Pasdun Korale, Sept. 1865, ster., smaller, oval leaves, *s. coll. C.P. 3402* (PDA). GALLE DISTRICT: Hinidumkande (Haycock) near Hiniduma, Aug., fr., *Kostermans 25560* (L); ibid., sapling, *Kostermans 25545 A* (G, K, L); Kaneliya forest near Hiniduma, alt. 100 m, Sept., fr., *Kostermans 25763* (L); Kottawa Arboretum near Galle, sapling, *Kostermans 24704* (L). COLOMBO DISTRICT: Horana & Nambapane, fl., fr., 13 Dec. 1815, *Moon s.n.* (PDA).

4. Calophyllum calaba L., Sp. Pl., ed. 2, 2: 732. 1762 (excl. cit. Jacquin & Rheede); Burm. f., Fl. Ind. 120. 1768 (*caleba*, excl. cit. Jacquin, Rheede & Stirp. Javan.); Moon, Cat. 41. 1824; Wight, Ill. 1: 129. 1840 (as a syn. of *C. burmanni*); Planch. & Triana, Ann. Sci. nat. Sér. 4, Bot. 15: 262. 1861 (id.); Alston in Trimen, Handb. Fl. Ceylon 6: 21. 1931; Worthington, Ceylon Trees 29. 1959; Sultanbawa, J. Nat. Sci. Counc. Sri Lanka 1: 129. 1973. Type: Hort. Cliffort. (BM).

Calophyllum burmanni Wight, Ill. 1: 129. 1840 (cum var. *parvifolium*, exclus. var. *bracteatum*); Ic. Pl. Ind. Or. 1: t. 107 (var. *parvifolia*) and 108. 1839; Planch. & Triana, l.c.; Thw., Enum. Pl. Zeyl. 52. 1858 (*C.P. 242, 2447*); Beddome, Fl. Sylv. 1: XXII. 1869; Anderson in Hook. f., Fl. Br. Ind. 1: 272. 1874; Vesque in DC., Monogr. 8: 571. 1893; Trimen, Handb. Fl. Ceylon 1: 99. 1893. Type: t. 60, Burman, Thes. Zeyl.
Calophyllum apetalum Willd., in Mag. Ges. naturf. Fr. Berlin 5: 563. 1811 (p.p., quoad spec. Ceylon).
Calophyllum spurium Choisy in DC., Prod. 1: 563. 1824 (p.p.); Vesque, l.c.
Calophyllum retusum Choisy, Guttif. Inde 41 (non Wall.). 1849; Vesque, l.c.
Calophyllum pulcherrimum Auct. (non Wall. ex Choisy) Trimen, J. of Bot. 27: 161. 1889; Handb. Fl. Ceylon 1: 100. 1893; Alston in Trimen, Handb. Fl. Ceyl. 6: 21; Worthington, l.c. 32. Type: *s. coll.*, Mandagala Mukalane, Hewesse, fl., March 1887 (L, PDA).
Hinkina, Kina minor, Hermann, Mus. Zeyl. 46. 1717.
Inophyllum flore quadrifido, Burm., Thes. Zeyl. 130, t. 60. 1737 (excl. syn. Plumier, Rheede, Commelin, Vaillant & Ray).
Calophyllum foliis ovatis obtusis, striis parallelis transversalibus, L., Hort. Cliffort. 206. 1737; Fl. Zeyl. 90. 1747 (excl. Vaillant, Plumier, Ray, Rheede); v. Royen, Hort. Leydens. Prod. 476. 1740.

Tree, up to 10 m high and 90 cm diam. with dense round crown. Bole in young stage bright yellowish orange, smooth, lenticellate, in mature trees very rough, deeply fissured, strips 3–6 cm wide, rifts up to 3 cm deep. Dead bark up to 4 mm thick. Live bark 10–15 mm thick, dark beefy red with little clear sap, contains calabaxanthone. Branchlets rather slender, quadrangular, finely, densely, minutely tomentellous to almost glabrous. End bud densely minutely tomentellous. Leaves initially chartaceous, mature ones rigidly coriaceous, elliptic to ovate or obovate-elliptic, 2×3–6×8–5×9 cm, rotundate or obtusely, obscurely acuminate to emarginate, base very shortly cuneate; upper surface with slender, prominulous midrib, broadened and flattened at the base (or slightly channeled there); lower surface with prominent midrib, initially often pubescent, laterals very slender, erect-patent, prominulous on both surfaces. Petioles densely, minutely tomentellous, glabrescent, or glabrous, 4–12 mm long. Racemes in axils of the upper leaves, 3–6-flowered; main peduncle densely rusty pubescent, 5–10 mm long, slender, sometimes bearing 1 or 2 more slender, erect branches. Pedicels filiform, glabrous or sparsely pubescent, 5–20 mm long, with small deciduous bracts at the base. Sepals 4, oblong, concave, sometimes slightly pilose outside, 3–5 mm long; inner ones thinner, narrower, up to 7 mm long. Petals 0 (rarely 4), spathulate or obovate, up to 7 mm long. Stamens 4 mm long. Ovary globose, style slender, 3 mm long with peltate concave stigma. Fruit ellipsoid to sub-globose, bright orange or yellowish orange, 10×12–14×16 mm, obtuse; pericarp thin, pleasantly sweet-acid, edible. Pedicel slender, up to 25 mm long. Fruit pendulous. Seed ovoid to ellipsoid, testa thin, pale brown. Cotyledons hardly separable.

Distr. Endemic.

Ecol. Common in the coastal parts of the dry zone, and in the talawas (savannahs) of the dry and intermediate zone. In the wet zone a rare variety, the trunk mostly a bright yellow orange. Inland near Kurunegala, Deltota; also near Jaffna. Sometimes planted for its edible fruit.

Vern. Gurukina, Hinkina (S.; Hin = small).

Note. Since I have collected and eaten the fruit of guru kina and of the tree, which Trimen called *C. pulcherrimum*, I assume that the latter is only a young stage of the former. Trimen's type specimen has pubescent inflorescence peduncles and remnants of a tomentum are found on the branchlets. In some material of *C. calaba* from Bibile the branchlets are completely glabrous, hence pubescence cannot be used to separate the two, neither can the dimensions of the sepals be used; they vary considerably in the same specimen. The fruit of both are exactly alike in shape, colour, size and taste.

The type specimen of *C. calaba* in the Cliffort herbarium (BM) corresponds with the numerous sheets of the Van Royen herbarium at Leiden. In the Herbarium of Hermann at Leiden (fol. 1, below) a specimen, marked Nux kina dicta, is represented (cf. also Van Ooststroom in Blumea, Suppl. 1: 191. 1937).

Specimens Examined. AMPARAI DISTRICT: Mile 18, Amparai-Kandy Rd., savannah, May, ripe fr., *Kostermans 24843* (A, BO, G, K, L, P, PDA, US). BATTICALOA DISTRICT: Kalkudah, Febr., fl., *Jayasuriya et al. 890* (PDA, L, US). MONERAGALA DISTRICT: Badernkande, Bibile, alt. 400 m, June, fl., *Kostermans 24406* (PDA, L, US); Bibile, low, dry zone, June, ster., *Kostermans 24385 & 24399 A* (G, L); ibid., April, fl., *Kostermans s.n.* (id.); ibid., June, fr., *Kostermans 24399 & 24404* (id.); ibid., July, fl., *de Silva s.n.* (PDA). KALUTARA DISTRICT: Morapitiya, cult. in garden wet zone, low alt., April, fr., *Kostermans 24669 & 24683* (L); Morapitiya logging area, wet, alt. 100 m, April, ster., *Kostermans 24659* (id.); Kelinkande near Morapitiya, ster., *Balasubramaniam s.n.* (G, K, L); Mahane Mukalane near Morapitiya, alt. 200 m, May, fr., *Kostermans 24699 & 24691* (A, BO, G, K, L, P, PDA, US); side of rocky stream, Mandagale Mukalane, Hewesse, *s. coll.*

s.n. (L, PDA). GALLE DISTRICT: Hinidumkande (Haycock) near Hini-
duma, alt. 500 m, wet, Aug., ster., *Kostermans 25370* (L); Godakande near
Hiniduma, wet, alt. 150 m, May, fr., *Jayasuriya 795* (L, PDA); near Bentota,
March 1887, fl., fr., *s. coll. s.n.* (PDA). KANDY DISTRICT: Elabodakande,
lower Maskeliya Peak wilderness, Elphindale Estate, ster., *s. coll. s.n.* (PDA).
NUWARA ELIYA DISTRICT: Deltota, May 1851, fl., with galls, *s. coll. C.P.
2447* (PDA). KURUNEGALA DISTRICT: Kurunegala, Sept. 1852, *Gardner
C.P. 242* (PDA). JAFFNA DISTRICT: Kodikaman, Aug., buds, *Jayasuriya
s.n.* (L); Jaffna, Sept. 1852, *Gardner C.P. 242* (PDA). COLOMBO DISTRICT:
Colombo, Zool. Gard., Oct., fl., *Worthington 6682* (PDA); Colombo, Sept.,
1852, *Gardner C.P. 242* (PDA). RATNAPURA DISTRICT: Ratnapura,
March 1853, fl., fr., *s. coll. s.n.* (PDA). LOCALITY UNKNOWN: E. Prov.,
seashore, var. fruct. oblongus, *Vincent s.n.* (PDA).

5. Calophyllum bracteatum Thw., Enum. Pl. Zeyl, 51. 1858; Planch. & Triana,
Ann. Sci. nat., Sér. 4, Bot. 15: 280. 1861; Beddome, Fl. Sylv. 1: XXII. 1869;
Anderson in Hook. f., Fl. Br. Ind. 1: 274. 1874; Vesque in DC., Monogr. 8:
554. 1893; Trimen, Handb. Fl. Ceylon 1: 102. 1893; Alston, id. 6: 21. 1931;
Worthington, Ceylon Trees 28. 1959; Sultanbawa, J. Nat. Sci. Counc. Sri
Lanka 1: 136. 1973. Type: *C.P. 2674*, Palaban, Saffragam Prov. (PDA).

Calophyllum acuminatum Moon, Cat. 41. 1824 (nomen, excl. cit. Rumph.).

Tree, up to 20 m high and 45 cm diam. Bark of trees up to 20 cm diam.
smooth, pinkish red-brown, in mature trees very rough, deeply fissured, yellowish, strips 3–6 cm wide, rifts 1 cm deep. Dead bark 5 mm thick, brittle,
hard, scaling off. Live bark 15 mm, beefy red with very little, white, sticky
resin-like sap. Branches slender, pendulous. Branchlets slender, quadrangular, thickened at the nodes, densely rusty tomentellous, glabrescent. End bud
densely rusty tomentellous. Flush whitish, sparsely tomentellous, flaccid,
pendulous. Leaves chartaceous to sub-coriaceous, dimorphic; ordinary ones
lanceolate-oblong to oblong, 2×10–4.5×15–5.5×20 cm, acuminate or long-
acuminate with blunt tip, base gradually tapered, acute or obtuse; upper surface with slender midrib, prominulous in its upper part, narrowly channeled
lower down, on lower surface midrib rusty tomentellous, glabrescent, prominent. Laterals slender, prominulous on both sides, slightly arcuate, rather
patent; margin slightly thickened, often undulate; all nerves reaching the
margin. Petioles slender, often twisted, concave above, glabrescent, 5–10 mm
long. Other leaves much smaller, 2–8 pairs in between the normal leaves,
overlapping, oblong-linear to linear-lanceolate, gradually tapered both ends,
0.5×5–2×8 cm; petiole 1 mm, pilose. Flowers white, 7–12 mm diam. in 4–8-
flowered, axillary, rusty tomentellous, up to 5 cm long racemes. Pedicels
long, slender, pendulous with very hairy, oblong, 5–7.5 mm long bracts at
the base. Sepals 4, greenish white. Petals 4, ovate, obtuse. Fruit pendulous,

smooth, globose to subovoid-globose, up to 2.5 cm diam. (ellipsoid and apiculate when young); exocarp thin, mesocarp pulpy, juicy, acid, 1–2 mm thick. Pedicel 1–2 cm long.

D i s t r. Endemic.

E c o l. Everwet lowland forests in S.W. Lanka, going up to 800 m alt.

V e r n. Walu kina (keena) (walu = bunch of fruit).

N o t e. The seedling has very narrow, linear leaves. Saplings of 2 m have already dimorphic leaves. The leaves are sometimes oblique. Intermediate leaves between the ordinary and the small ones are sometimes present, the leaves gaining in size gradually upwards. Flowers are concealed between the drooping tassels of leaves.

A very ornamental tree, with excellent, heavy timber. Rather common locally, but always scattered.

S p e c i m e n s E x a m i n e d. KALUTARA DISTRICT: Hewesse, ster., March 1887, *s. coll. s.n.* (PDA); Pasdun Korale, Sept., 1885, *s. coll. C.P. 2674* (PDA). RATNAPURA DISTRICT: Palabaddale, Saffragam, March 1853, fl., young fr., *s. coll. C.P. 2674* (PDA); Kukul Korale, March, 1881, fr., *s. coll. s.n.* (PDA); Kalawana-Morapitiya road, low, April, fr., *Kostermans 24641* (A, BO, G, K, L, P, PDA, US); Kuruwita, alt. 500 m, June, fr., *Kostermans 23334* (id.); Tumbagoda, road Balangoda-Rassagalle, alt. 800 m, June, fr., *Kostermans 24464* (id.).

6. Calophyllum trapezifolium Thw., Enum. Pl. Zeyl. 51. 1858; in Hooker's J. Bot. & Kew Gard. Miscell. 6: 72. 1854; Planch. & Triana, Ann. Sci. nat. Sér. 4, Bot. 15: 282. 1861; Anderson in Hook. f., Fl. Br. Ind. 1: 275. 1874; Trimen, Handb. Fl. Ceylon 1: 103. 1893; Vesque in DC., Monogr. 8: 563. 1893; Alston in Trimen, Handb. Fl. Ceylon 6: 21. 1931; Worthington, Ceylon Trees 36. 1959 (?); Sultanbawa, J. Nat. Sci. Counc. Sri Lanka 1: 134. 1973. Type: *C.P. 2446*, Hunasgiriya (PDA).

Tree, up to 10 m high and 20 cm diam., glabrous in all its parts, except the apex of the youngest branchlets and the end bud, which have a dense, microscopical rusty tomentum. Bark rather smooth, finely fissured (strips 3 cm wide), dark orange yellow, 0.5–1 mm thick; contains trapezifolixanthone. Live bark 10 mm, red brown with little, almost clear resin-like sap. Branchlets quadrangular, rather thick. Leaves rigidly coriaceous, obovate-oval to subrhomboid, 3 × 5–5 × 9 cm, rounded or retuse or obscurely, very shortly, broadly acuminate, base tapered, slightly decurrent into the 5–10 mm long petiole, which is concave above; upper surface with filiform midrib prominulous in its upper half, channeled and broader in its lower part, abruptly flattened and broadened at the base; midrib prominent on lower surface. Laterals very slender, erect-patent, prominulous both sides. Racemes axillary of the upper leaves; peduncles stout, angular, 2–5 cm long, sometimes bearing 2 decussate branches. Pedicels up to 25 mm long, stout, basal bracts minute, caducous. Flowers white, up to 2.5 cm diam. Sepals 4, the outer 2 strongly concave, thick, 6–7 mm long; inner ones petaloid, as long as petals. Petals 4, ovate-oblong, narrowed slightly at base, 8–10 mm long, inner pairs shorter. Stamens 6–7 mm long. Ovary globose-ellipsoid, style 7 mm long, stigma peltate, small. Fruit subglobose, towards apex pointed, up to 2 cm long and 17 mm diam. Pericarp thin, mesocarp juicy, acid. Seed surrounded by a thin, jelly-like endosperm.

D i s t r. Endemic.

E c o l. Above c. 1000 m alt. in the Maskeliya Adam's Peak Jungle and in the Knuckles.

V e r n. Kina (Keena).

N o t e. I have never seen this grow out to a tall tree as the related *C. cuneifolium*. Anderson's description is much at variance with ours as to the characters and the size of the flowers, pedicels and fruit. I have not seen a mature fruit myself. I have not seen galls on this species. I suspect Worthington's plate 36 to represent either *C. cuneifolium* or *C. zeylanicum*.

S p e c i m e n s E x a m i n e d. KANDY DISTRICT: Near Gatenne Estate, Maskeliya, April, fl., *de Silva 32* (PDA); upper part of Moray Estate near Fishing hut, alt. 1600 m, May, fl., *Kostermans 24138, 24149 & 24177* (A, BO, G, K, L, P, PDA, US); ibid., June, fl., *Kostermans 24518* (id.); ibid., May, after anthesis, *Kostermans 24780* (id.); ibid., June, fl., *Kostermans 24515* (id.); Hunasgiriya, April 1857, fl., *s. coll. C.P. 2446* (PDA, 3 sheets, one with an extra fr. branch); Knuckles June, fl., *de Silva 9* (PDA); Dolosbage. Sept., ster. *s. coll. s.n.* (PDA).

7. **Calophyllum zeylanicum** Kosterm. in Ceylon J. Sci., Biol. Sci. 12 (1): 70. 1976. Type: *Balasubramaniam W* (L).

Tree, up to 20 m high and 60 cm diam. Bark of mature trees deeply, wavily fissured, yellowish, 3 mm thick; strips 2–4 cm wide, 5 cm thick. Live bark 10 mm, bright red, or pale brownish with red spots, inside white, a little resinous, clear sap. Branchlets slender, the apical part quadrangular and sparsely very minutely pilose or glabrous. End bud slender, densely, microscopically rusty tomentellous. Leaves sub-coriaceous to stiffly coriaceous, oblong to lanceolate to oblanceolate, 1×3–2.5×6–3×8 cm, gradually acute with blunt tip or obscurely, shortly, broadly acuminate; midrib on upper surface filiform, prominulous (upper half), basal part channeled, on lower surface prominent. Laterals very slender, prominulous both sides, erect-patent to rather patent. Petioles slender, 2–7 mm long, showing remnants of pilosity. Inflorescence a raceme or a panicle of few racemes, glabrous; main peduncle slender, 1–3 cm long. Pedicels filiform, 1.5 cm long. Flowers white. Sepals 4, outer ones shorter and more concave. Petals 4, ovate-orbicular, 4–5 mm long. Infructescence with 1-2 cm long slender stiff peduncle; pedicel slender, stiff, up to 1.5-3 cm long. Fruit globose, rusty brown (dried), dull, up to 18 mm diam., apex with a distinct 1-3 mm long sub-conical sharp tip.

D i s t r. Endemic.

E c o l. Adam's Peak Jungle, Knuckles at c. 800 m alt.

V e r n. Kina (Keena).

N o t e. The species is close to *C. cuneifolium*, which differs in steeper lateral nerves and differently shaped leaves. Even in young trees the leaves of *C. cuneifolium* are already cuneiform, which they are not in our species. I do not know, whether the pointed fruits are already mature or not, if so they differ markedly from those of *C. cuneifolium*, which are not pointed and very large.

Specimens Examined. RATNAPURA DISTRICT: Carney-Adam's Peak Rd., alt. 200 m, July, fr., *Balasubramaniam W* (A, BO, G, K, L, P, PDA, US); Rassagalle above Balangoda, alt. 700 m, young tree with typical galls, *Kostermans 23599* (id.). KANDY DISTRICT: Maskeliya valley road from Laxapana to Maskeliya, near Doublecutting, alt. 800 m, sapling, *Kostermans s.n.* (G, L); ibid., May, ster., *Kostermans 24074* (A, BO, G, K, L, P, PDA, US): Knuckles, Madulkelle area, alt. 900 m, June, fr., *Kostermans 25074* (id.); Hunasgiriya, below Madugoda, alt. 700 m, June, fl., *Kostermans 24414* (id.); ibid., June, ster., *Kostermans 25152* A (G, K, L, P, PDA, US).

8. Calophyllum cuneifolium Thw., Enum. Pl. Zeyl. 51. 1858; Planch. & Triana, Ann. Sci. nat. Sér. 4, 15: 289. 1861; Beddome, Fl. Sylv. 3: XXII. 1869; Anderson in Hook. f., Fl. Br. Ind. 1: 275. 1874; Vesque in DC., Monogr. 8: 557. 1893; Trimen, Handb. Fl. Ceylon 1: 103. 1893; Alston in id. 6: 21. 1931; Worthington, Ceylon Trees 30. 1959; Sultanbawa, J. Nat. Sci. Counc. Sri Lanka 1: 148. 1973. Type: *C.P. 2917* (PDA), Medamahanuwera, July 1853 (=*Thwaites 290* (P) and *291* (DC).

Calophyllum trapezifolium (non Thw.) Worthington, Ceylon Trees 36. 1959.

Tree, up to 30 m high and 90 cm diam., glabrous in all its parts, except the scurvy rusty end buds. Bark rough, deeply fissured, hard, yellowish, peeling off in 3-5 cm wide and 5-10 mm thick strips. Live bark beefy red with a little clear resin; contains cuneifolic acid. Branchlets angular, rather slender. Leaves rigidly coriaceous, obovate-cuneate to spathulate-cuneate, $1 \times 2.5-2 \times 4-3 \times 7$ cm (young trees); retuse or obtuse or obtuse with an obscure broad short acumen, base gradually tapered, acute; midrib on upper surface prominulous, the lower part slightly channeled, prominulous on the lower surface. Laterals steep (30-40°), rather coarse on both sides, sometimes inconspicuous. Petioles 8-12 mm long, concave above. Racemes in the axils of the upper leaves, equalling or exceeding the leaves, 4-6-flowered. Peduncles

1–4 cm long, thickish, often with one ramification. Flowers up to 18 mm diam. Sepals 4, outer ones concave, thickish, 6 mm long, greenish white, inner pair as long as the petals, white petaloid, veined, flat. Petals usually 4, obovate to elliptic, narrowed towards base, white, up to 8 mm long, inner smaller and narrower. Stamens 4–5 mm long. Ovary subglobose, style 3–4 mm, stigma peltate, concave. Fruit globose, erect, 2.5 cm diam.; pericarp 2–3 mm thick, pulpy, acid; around the seed a thin jelly-like layer of endosperm.

D i s t r. Endemic.

E c o l. Knuckles, Passera. A very rare species.

V e r n. Kina (Keena).

N o t e. This is certainly one of the largest Kina species (Worthington calls it a small tree). It resembles in its leaf shape strongly *C. ceriferum* from Indochina (which has smaller flowers). Collections from a small tree of 10 cm diam. in the Knuckles show that the leaves have already the cuneiform shape with steep laterals. The tree has become extremely rare.

S p e c i m e n s E x a m i n e d. BADULLA DISTRICT: Talpitigala Pine nursery above Passara, alt. 1000 m, June, fl., fr., *Kostermans 24437* (A, BO, G, K, L, P, PDA, US); Debedde near Badulla, Jan. 1888, ster., *s. coll. s.n.* (PDA). KANDY DISTRICT: Kunckles, Madulkelle area, alt. 800 m, June, fr., *Kostermans 25077* (A, BO, G, K, L, P, PDA, US); ibid., June, fl., fr., *Kostermans 25056* (id.); Madamahanuwera, July 1853 and June 1863, *s. coll. C.P. 2917* (PDA, fl. branches = holotype and one fr. br.).

9. Calophyllum walkeri Wight, Ill. 1: 128, t. 45. 1840 (*walkerii*); Planch. & Triana, Ann. Sci. nat., Sér. 4, Bot. 15: 291. 1861; Beddome, Fl. Sylv. 3: XXII. 1869; Anderson in Hook. f., Fl. Br. Ind. 1: 275. 1874 (excl. cit. *C. decipiens* W.); Trimen, Handb. Fl. Ceylon 1: 104. 1893; Vesque in DC., Monogr. 8: 584. 1893 (excl. *C. decipiens* W.); Alston in Trimen, Handb. Fl. Ceylon 6: 21. 1931; Worthington, Ceylon Trees 37. 1959. Type: *Walker ex Wight* (K, P).

Tree, up to 7 m high and 40 cm diam., glabrous in all its parts, except end bud. Bark yellowish, fissured and cracked rather irregularly; strips 3–4 cm wide, bark itself 1–3 mm thick. Live bark 10–30 mm thick, brownish to light red. Branchlets rather thick, quadrangular. End bud very densely, microscopically rusty pilose. Leaves very rigidly coriaceous, obovate-rotundate, 1.5×2–2×2.5–5×6 cm, top obtuse or retuse or broadly triangular, base cuneate, rarely rounded, midrib flat above, prominent beneath, laterals hardly visible, rather patent, reaching margin. Petiole stout, 3–8 mm long, flat above. Racemes axillary, the top ones forming a terminal panicle by abortion of leaves, up to 10 cm long; peduncle stout. Pedicels thick, up to 2.5 cm long. Flowers numerous, pinkish white or white, up to 2.5 cm diam. Sepals 4, concave, oblong, outer ones 4 mm long, inner up to 8 mm. Petals sub-obovate to spathulate, concave, circa 8, thin; outer ones up to 13 mm long, inner smaller. Stamens up to 4 mm long. Ovary ellipsoid, style as long as the stamens, stigma peltate, fleshy, concave with three obscure lobes. Fruit erect on stiff branches, initially ovoid, acute, at maturity globose, smooth, pale yellow with brown spots, up to 3 cm diam. Pericarp 2 mm thick, fleshy, sweet-acid, edible. Pedicel up to 2.5 cm long, thick. Cotyledons surrounded by a thin layer of firm, jelly-like, clear endosperm.

D i s t r. Endemic.

E c o l. Above 1000 m alt. In some places gregarious.

N o t e. A magnificent tree, when in bloom, entirely covered by the pinkish white flowers (wrongly depicted in Wight as yellow). It does not flower every year.

The terminal, lipped galls, as described by Trimen, do not occur on this tree.

An oil is extracted from the seeds.

S p e c i m e n s   E x a m i n e d. NUWARA ELIYA DISTRICT: Above Frotoft Estate, Ramboda, alt. 2000 m, stunted forest, June, fr., *Kostermans 25100* (A, BO, G, K, L, P, PDA, US); ibid., June, fr., *Kostermans 25087, 25089 et s.n.* (id.); Elk Plains near Ambawela, 1800 m, May, fl., *Kostermans s.n.* (id.); Nuwara Eliya, April 1856, fl., *s. coll. C.P. 1170* (PDA); ibid., anno 1854, fr., *s. coll. s.n.* (PDA); Yalta, Nuwara Eliya, fl., *Plummer s.n.* (PDA). KANDY DISTRICT: Knuckles, Madulkelle area, alt. 1200 m, June, fr., *Kostermans 25083* (A, BO, G, K, L, P, PDA, US); Adam's Peak, March 1856, fl., *s. coll. C.P. 1170* (PDA); Ambagamuwa, March 1852, fl. and July 1863, fl., *s. coll. C.P. 1170* (PDA). RATNAPURA DISTRICT: Gilimale, March, fl., *de Silva s.n.* (PDA). BADULLA DISTRICT: Namunukula, March, fl., *de Silva s.n.* (PDA). LOCALITY UNKNOWN: buds, Col. *Walker s.n.* Herb. Wight (PDA, isotype).

10. Calophyllum thwaitesii Planch. & Triana, Ann. Sci. nat. Sér. 4, Bot. 15: 260. 1861 (cum vars.); Thw., Enum. Pl. Zeyl. 407. 1864; Beddome, Fl. Sylv. 3: XXII. 1869; Anderson in Hook. f., Fl. Br. Ind. 1: 275. 1874; Vesque in DC., Monogr. 8: 556. 1893; Trimen, Handb. Fl. Ceylon 1: 102. 1893; Alston in id. 6: 21. 1931; Worthington, Ceylon Trees 34. 1959; Sultanbawa, J. Nat. Sci. Counc. Sri Lanka 1: 133. 1973. Type: *C.P. 3403*, Ambagamuwa & Nellowa (P).

Calophyllum decipiens (non Wight) Thw., Enum. Pl. Zeyl. 51. 1858 (cum vars.). Type: *C.P. 3403* (PDA).

Tree, up to 30 m high and 40 cm diam., glabrous in all its parts, except the scurvy rusty buds. Bark pinkish to yellowish brown, rough, deeply fissured, strips loose, 3–4 cm wide, 3 mm thick. Live bark brownish red, 10 mm thick, contains thwaitesixanthone. Branchlets quadrangular, thickened at the nodes, the apical part concave at the 4 sides. Leaves rigidly coriaceous, broadly ovate or obovate to suborbicular, 1.5×2.5–3×3–5×6 cm, obtuse to retuse, base cordate; midrib on upper surface slender, prominulous in upper half, channeled in lower one, at base broadly cuneiform, flat, on lower surface prominent. Leterals very slender, erect-patent, slightly arcuate. Saplings with oblong leaves, 2.5×8–4×11 cm. Petiole 0, rarely 1 mm long. Racemes in the axils of the upper leaves, usually much longer than the leaves. Flowers up to 2.5 cm diam., white. Sepals 4, obovate to orbicular-oblong. Petals 4, yellowish white, oblong to obovate-oblong, longer than the sepals. Stamens shorter than petals. Ovary subglobose, style longer, stigma peltate. Pedicel slender. Fruit almost globose, 1.5 cm diam.

D i s t r. Endemic.

E c o l. Lowland, evergreen wet forests in S.W. Sri Lanka, going up to 1500 m altitude.

V e r n. Batu Kina (S).

N o t e. The leaves are always cordate and sessile and the species is in this way distinguishable from C. *walkeri*, a high mountain species. My search for flowering specimens in many years was unsuccessful, apparently it does flower after long periods. The well established name is batu kina (not guru kina, as mentioned by Worthington). In seedlings the leaves are very narrowly lanceolate, becoming gradually broader, until in the sapling stage (1 m and over) they are oblong and three times as long as those of the mature tree. These sapling stages puzzled Thwaites and Planchon. The first created even a variety of the sapling stage. The varieties of Planchon are not the same as those of Thwaites (although they quote the latter); they were based on the length of the racemes.

Saplings have a pure white flush with limpid, pendulous leaves, also the end bud at this stage is pure white.

The tree is one of the larger kinas, contrarily to Worthington's statement, and produces a valuable timber. The fruit is said to be globose, although Worthington's plate gives them as acute.

S p e c i m e n s E x a m i n e d. KANDY DISTRICT: Ambagamuwa, ster., sapling stage, *s. coll. C.P. 3401* (PDA); ibid., March 1835, fl., *s. coll. C.P. 3403* (PDA, 3 fl. branches and 1 fr. one); above Moray Estate, Maskeliya near Fishing Hut, alt. 1600 m, sapling, *Kostermans 24469* (L). GALLE DISTRICT: W. Nelluwa, Hinidon (Hiniduma) Korale, April 1835, *s. coll. C.P. 3403* (PDA, 5 fl. branches): Hiniduma, sapling 4 m, *Kostermans 24723* (G, K, L); Hinidumkande (Haycock) near Hiniduma, alt. 500 m, sapling, *Kostermans 25668* (G, K, L). RATNAPURA DISTRICT: Karawita Korale, March, ster., *de Silva s.n.* (PDA); Tumbagoda, road Tanamawatte-Massenna above Balangoda, 900 m alt., June, ster., *Kostermans 24469 A* and *24474* (A, BO, G, K, L, P, PDA, US); ibid., seedling, *Kostermans 24645* (L). KALUTARA DISTRICT: Sinharaja forest, April 1835, sapling *s. coll. s.n.* (PDA). MATARA

DISTRICT: Morawaka, Panilkande forest, young tree, ster., *Worthington 6624* (PDA).

11. Calophyllum cordato-oblongum Thw., Enum. Pl. Zeyl. 407. 1864; Beddome, Fl. Sylv. 3: XXII. 1869; Anderson in Hook. f., Fl. Br. Ind. 1: 275. 1874; Trimen, Handb. Fl. Ceylon 1: 103. 1893; Vesque in DC., Monogr. 8: 562. 1893; Alston in Trimen, Handb. Fl. Ceylon 6: 21. 1931. Type: *C.P. 3823* (PDA), Hiniduma reserved forest.

Tree, up to 20 m high and 40 cm diam. Bark very dark red brown, fissured, strips 2–3 cm wide, not very deep. Live bark red. Branchlets thick, quadrangular. Young shoots, end bud, pedicel, midrib on lower leaf surface, inflorescences, flower buds and outer sepals densely rusty tomentellous. Wood less hard than that of other local species. Leaves very rigidly coriaceous, oblong to oblong-elliptic (rarely the broader part below the middle), 5 × 10–5.5 × 17–9 × 20 cm (sapling), obtuse, base cordate. Midrib on upper surface slender, prominulous (upper half), lower half broader, narrowly channeled, near base abruptly widened and flattened, on lower surface stout, prominent, densely rusty tomentellous. Laterals very slender, usually rather obscure on both sides, in younger leaves rather broad and conspicuous above. Petiole broad, basal part concave above, 4–8 mm long, tomentellous. Racemes forming a pseudo-terminal, few-branched panicle as long as or shorter than the leaves; peduncles stiff, stout, bracts linear, deciduous. Buds densely tomentellous. Flowers white, 2.5–3 cm diam. Sepals 4 (3), rounded, outer ones 6 mm long, inner petaloid, twice as long with tomentellous midrib. Petals 4 (3), orbicular, up to 15 mm long. Pedicels up to 1 cm long. Infructescence stiff, stout, erect, densely tomentellous, up to 8 cm long with few fruit. Pedicel stout, 5–15 mm long. Fruit globose, smooth, 2 cm diam., erect; pericarp pulpy, 2 mm thick, acid.

D i s t r. Endemic.

E c o l. Wet, evergreen lowland forests of S.W. Sri Lanka, usually near or along rivulets. Not common.

V e r n. Kalu (=black) Kina, because it has the darkest bark of all Ceylonese kinas.

N o t e. Leaves at sapling stage may be 20 cm and over long, in mature trees they are much smaller. Without protective measures this tree will soon be extinct.

S p e c i m e n s E x a m i n e d. GALLE DISTRICT: Kanneliya forest near Hiniduma, alt. 100 m, May, fr., *Kostermans 24771* (A, BO, G, K, L, P, PDA, US); ibid., May, fr., *Kostermans 24769* (id.); ibid., ster., *Kostermans 24764* (id.); Hiniduma forest reserve (Kottawa Arboretum), Aug.–Sept. 1863, fl., *s. coll. C.P. 3823* (L, PDA). There is still one tree in the Kottawa Arb. The species was also observed in sapling stage in the Beriliya forest near Elpitiya.

3. MESUA L.

Type species: *M. ferrea* L.

Trees. Leaves opposite, entire, exstipular, midrib often partially channeled above. Laterals numerous, slender with shorter parallel ones in between. End bud small, rounded. Flowers hermaphrodite, often large, axillary or pseudo-terminal. Sepals 4 in 2 decussate pairs, imbricate, outer ones smaller, thicker, persistent. Petals 4, large, imbricate, alternate with sepals. Stamens numerous, free, or basically slightly connate slender filaments, anthers basifixed, dehiscent by vertical slits. Ovary 1–2-locular with 2 ovules in each cell, erect, anatropous. Style long, stigma peltate, obscurely 3-lobed. Fruit a capsular nut, monolocular, dehiscent into 2–4 valves. Seeds 1–4, erect, without arillode, obtusely angled; testa thin. Embryo exalbuminous, cotyledons large, free, fleshy, radicle minute.

Distr. A genus of about 48 species, mostly in Malesia, occurring in India, Burma, Thailand, Indochina as far as New Guinea. In Ceylon it is represented by 3 species, of which 1 (or 2) endemic.

KEY TO THE SPECIES

1 Leaves ovate or ovate-oblong......................................**1. M. stylosa**
1 Leaves lanceolate, lanceolate-oblong or linear-lanceolate.
  2 Leaves thickly coriaceous, up to 30 cm long. Flowers sessile, over 10 cm diam., each surrounded by 2–3 large, adpressed bracts..........................**2. M. ferrea**
  2 Leaves thinly to rigidly coriaceous, up to 17 cm long. Flowers shortly pedicelled, less than 10 cm diam...**3. M. nagassarium**

1. Mesua stylosa (Thw.) Kosterm., Reinwardtia 7: 430. 1969.

Kayea stylosa Thw., Enum. 50. 1858; Beddome, Fl. Sylv. 1: t. 102. 1869; Anderson in Hook. f., Fl. Br. Ind. 1: 276. 1874; Vesque in DC., Monogr. 8: 618. 1893; Epharm. II, f. 41, 42. 1889; Trimen, Handb. Fl. Ceylon 1: 104. 1893; Worthington, Ceylon Trees 38. 1959; Sultanbawa, J. Nat. Sci. Counc. Sri Lanka 1: 139. 1973. Type: *C.P. 2708* (PDA).
Kayea cuspidata Planch. & Triana in Ann. Sci. nat. Sér. 4, Bot. 15: 296. 1861. Type: *Thwaites 2708* (P).

Tree, up to 5 m high and 40 cm diam., glabrous in all its parts. Bark hard, dark brown, finely cracked, hammered, partially peeling off. Crown dense, ovoid. Branches horizontal. Branchlets slender, stiff, near apex angular. End buds round, inconspicuous. Wood brownish red, finely grained, rather soft. Bark contains kayeaxanthone. Leaves thinly coriaceous, ovate or ovate-oblong, 2.5 × 6–3 × 6–3 × 9 cm, acuminate, more rarely acute or cuspidate, base rounded; midrib very slender above, prominulous, medially channeled, on lower side prominulous. Laterals up to 10 pairs with parallel ones in between, erect-patent, arcuately connected at 1–2 mm from the margin, prominulous on both sides (less above). Petioles slender, 5–8 mm long, channeled above. Flowers c. 1–2 cm diam., in stalked, stiff, erect, axillary, 2–4-flowered racemes, up to 6 cm long, near upper part of branchlets. Pedicels slender, thickened upwards, bracteoles subulate, caducous. Sepals 4, thick, concave, erect, persistent. Petals 4, concave, longer than sepals, obtuse, white. Stamens numerous, shorter than petals. Ovary subglobose, 4-ovuled. Style stout, longer than ovary, stigma small with subulate branches. Fruit for the greater part enveloped by the enlarged, coriaceous, imbricate, depressed-globose, up to 2.5 cm long sepals, tipped by the persistent style base; pericarp coriaceous. Seeds 1–4, large, angular, dark red brown.

D i s t r. Endemic.

E c o l. Moist low country in S.W. Sri Lanka (Kalutara, Pasdun Korale). Very rare.

N o t e. Never recollected. Trimen's vernacular name is meaningless.

S p e c i m e n s E x a m i n e d. KANDY DISTRICT: Botanical Garden Peradeniya, April, young fr., *Kostermans 24553* (A, BO, G, K, L, P, PDA, US).

2. Mesua ferrea L., Sp. Pl. 515. 1753 (exclus. Ray, Rheede). Type: *Hermann* (BM).

Mesua thwaitesii Planch. & Triana, Ann. Sci. nat. Sér. 4, Bot. 15: 305. 1861; Thw., Enum. Pl. Zeyl. 406. 1864; Anderson in Hook. f., Fl. Br. Ind. 1: 278. 1874; Trimen, Handb. Fl. Ceylon 1: 106. 1893; Worthington, Ceylon Trees 41. 1959; Sultanbawa, J. Nat. Sci. Counc. Sri Lanka 1: 144. 1973.

Mesua ferrea, subsp. *thwaitesii* Vesque in DC., Monogr. 8: 632. 1893; Maheshwari, Bull. Bot. Surv. Ind. 5: 339, t. 2. 1963.

Mesua speciosa (non Choisy) Thw., Enum. Pl. Zeyl. 50. 1858 (excl. Choisy, Rheede, Vesque, solum quoad var. *a*). Type: *C.P. 2675* (DC & P).

Naghas, Naghaha, Hermann, Mus. Zeyl. 7. 1717; Van Ooststroom, Blumea, Suppl. 1: 198. 1937.

Mesua foliis lanceolatis, L., Fl. Zeyl. 91, no. 203. 1748 (exclus. Ray, Commelin et Rheede).

Arbor Naghas, Burm., Thes. zeyl. 25. 1737.

Tree, up to 15 m high, glabrous in all its parts. Bark rather smooth, dark brown. Leaves thickly coriaceous, linear-oblong, 3×20–11×30 cm, acuminate or acute, contracted and acute at base. Laterals visible. Lower surface white. Flowers sessile, 1–3 together on a short peduncle in the axils of apical leaves, each surrounded by 2–3 large, adpressed bracts. Flowers 7.5–11.5 cm diam. Sepals sparsely pubescent. Fruit depressed globose, apiculate, surrounded by enlarged sepals and bracts. Seeds 2.

D i s t r. Endemic.

E c o l. Moist low country in S.W. Sri Lanka, always in or near streams or marshy places, rather common.

V e r n. Diya (= water) na (= Mesua) (S).

N o t e. Linnaeus' name *Mesua ferrea* was based on a specimen of Hermann (BM, in Leiden Fol. 19, *Arbor forte duritie zeylanica*), which is not the common Na, but *Mesua thwaitesii*, the Water Na. Linnaeus quoted Naghas or Nagaha of Hermann in his protologue. (Naghas means Na trees; Nagaha is singular hence Arbor Naghas is twice: tree.)

Maheshwari quoted specimens from the Anaimalais and from Travancore, this needs confirmation.

S p e c i m e n s E x a m i n e d. RATNAPURA DISTRICT: Palabadella to Ratnapura, April 1855, buds, *s. coll. s.n.* (PDA).

3. Mesua nagassarium (Burm. f.) Kosterm., Ceylon J. Sci., Biol. Sci. 12 (1): 71. 1976.

Calophyllum nagassarium Burm. f., Fl. Ind. 121. 1768. Type: Rumphius, Herb. Amboin. 7: t. 2.
Mesua ferrea Auct. (non L.) Choisy in DC., Prod. 1: 562. 1824; Roxb., Fl. Ind. 2: 605. 1832; Wight, Ic. Pl. Ind. Or. 1: t. 118. 1839; Ill. 1: 127. 1840; Thw., Enum. Pl. Zeyl. 50. 1858; Planch. & Triana, Ann. Sci. nat. Sér. 4, Bot. 15: 299. 1861; Beddome, Fl. Sylv. 3: XXII. 1869, t. 64. 1871; Anderson in Hook. f., Fl. Br. Ind. 1: 277. 1874; Gamble, Man. Ind. Timb. 27. 1881; Fl. Pres. Madras 1: 77. 1915; Pierre, Fl. for. Cochinch. 7: t. 97. 1885; Vesque in DC., Monogr. 8: 630. 1893; Troup, Sylvicult. Ind. Trees 1: 23, f. 9. 1921; Chandrasena, Chemistr. & Pharmac. Ceylon & Ind. Pl. 36 (Colombo). 1935; MacMillan, Trop. Pl. & Gard., ed. 5: 87. 1956; Anon., Wealth of India 6: 348. 1962; Worthington, Ceylon Trees 39. 1959; Maheshwari, Bull. Bot. Surv. Ind. 5: 336–343. 1963 (excl. subsp. *thwaitesii*).
Nagassarium Rumph., Herb. Amboin. 7: 3, t. 2. 1750.

Tree, up to 30 m high and 70 cm diam.; buttresses sometimes up to 2 m high and 50 cm out, thick, rounded, bole sometimes fluted. Bark ash grey, turning dark brown, rough, peeling off in large flakes, which expose a warty, reddish-brown under surface, coarsely fibrous, red inside, exuding an aromatic, clear resin. Sapwood creamy white to pinkish-brown. Heartwood dark red, very hard, tough and heavy (spec. grav. 1.03). Branchlets very slender, terete; end bud inconspicuous. Leaves very variable, thinly to thickly coriaceous, 1 × 5–5 × 18 cm, usually 3 × 10 cm, linear lanceolate, oblong lanceolate, lanceolate or elliptic oblong, acute, acuminate, base acute or obtuse; midrib slender, prominulous on both sides; laterals very fine, almost invisible, numerous, straight, rather patent, invisible on the white waxy lower surface.

Petioles slender, 5–12 mm long. Flowers usually solitary in the axils of the upper leaves on short peduncles, rarely paired or ternate, diam. 4–10 cm, sweet scented, white. Pedicel short, rather stout, 8–15 mm, densely rusty tomentellous. Sepals 4, orbicular, imbricate, fleshy, concave, 12–15 mm long, densely velvety puberulous outside, persistent. Petals 4, white, thin, cuneate, obovate or obcordate, curled and erose at the margins, very finely brown purplish veined, caducous. Stamens 4–5 mm long, anthers large, linear. Ovary ovoid; style almost as long, often curved, stigma small, peltate. Fruit ovoid to globose with conical point, striate, one-celled, 1–4-seeded. Sepals enlarged, up to 4 cm long, adpressed. Pericarp tough, at least 2-valved. Seeds variously faceted, smooth with glossy, brown, horny testa. Cotyledons fleshy, oily, pale yellow, radicle inferior. Germination with cotyledons remaining within the testa.

D i s t r. Widely distributed in India, going up to 1500 m alt., the Malay Peninsula, Sumatra, Burma, Thailand and Indochina, sometimes gregarious. Cultivated in many tropical countries as avenue trees and often near Buddhist temples.

E c o l. Wetter parts of Sri Lanka, usually in the river valleys, going up to 1000 m.

V e r n. Na (S); Naka, Nagacuram (T).

N o t e. A beautiful tree with bright red limp flush, which turns to pink and all shades of green. Much planted as an ornamental, very variable in leaf size and shape. The timber is not exploited in Sri Lanka (too hard). In India it is used for railway sleepers, bridges, etc; it makes good fire wood. The dried flowers (flores Nagkassar) are used in perfumery and cosmetics and as a medicine; the oil from the flowers is used for soap perfuming. Roots and bark are diaphoretic. Seeds edible. Leaves are used as a poultice for severe colds and headache; a paste of the flowers against bleeding piles, burning feet and a syrup of flowers against dysentery. The dark, thick seed oil for sores, scabies and rheumatism.

KEY TO THE VARIETIES

1 Leaves glaucous white (waxy) underneath
  2 Leaves linear-lanceolate, small....................................2. var. salicina
  2 Leaves broader and longer
    3 Leaves thinly coriaceous, lanceolate to oblong-lanceolate. Calyx densely pubescent
    ....1. var. nagassarium
    3 Leaves thickly coriaceous, lanceolate to oblong-lanceolate. Calyx almost glabrous. Branchlets pendulous...3. var. sclerophylla
1 Leaves green underneath. Branches pendulous.....................4. var. pulchella

1. var. **nagassarium** *Mesua ferrea*, var. *a* leaves lanceolate, Beddome l.c. XXIII.

Mesua ferrea, var. *a* Thw., l.c. 50 & 406.
Mesua ferrea subsp. *ferrea* Maheshwari, l.c. 337 (excl. *M. salicina* & *M. ferrea*, var. *salicina*).
Mesua nagana Gardner, Calcutta J. Nat. Hist. 8: 4. 1847.
Mesua speciosa Choisy in DC., l.c. 562.
Mesua roxburghii Wight, Ill., l.c. 127.
Mesua walkeriana Planch. & Triana, l.c. 301.
Mesua ferrea subsp. *vera* Vesque, l.c. 631. Type: Tab. 2, Rumphius, Herb. Amboin. 7.

Branchlets patent or only slightly pendulous. Leaves lanceolate or lanceolate-oblong, gradually acuminate, base usually acutish; lower epidermis papillate, white. Flowers 8–10 cm diam. Sepals densely, minutely pilose.

Specimens Examined. KALUTARA DISTRICT: Matugama Rest House Garden, June, fr., *Kostermans 24955* (A, BO, G, K, L, P, PDA, US). KANDY DISTRICT: Peradeniya University Campus, May, fl. *Kostermans s.n.* (id.).

2. var. salicina (Pl. & Tr.) Vesque, l.c. 631.

Mesua salicina Planch. & Triana, l.c. 302.
Mesua ferrea var. *b angustifolia* Thw., l.c. 50 & 406.
Mesua ferrea var. *b* leaves linear, Beddome, l.c. XXIII. Type: *Thwaites 602* (P).

Branchlets patent or slightly pendulous. Leaves linear lanceolate, often small; lower surface papillate white. Flowers as in var. *nagassarium*.

Specimens Examined. MATALE DISTRICT: Galegama, May, 1856 *s. coll. s.n.* (PDA). RATNAPURA DISTRICT: road Balangoda to Belihuloya, June, fr., *Kostermans 25012* (A, BO, G, K, L, P, PDA, US).

3. var. sclerophylla (Thw.) Trimen, l.c. 106.

Mesua sclerophylla Thw., Enum. Pl. Zeyl. 407. 1864; Beddome, l.c. XXIII; Anderson, l.c. 277.
Mesua speciosa (non Choisy) Thw., l.c. 50 & 407. Type: *C.P. 603* (PDA), Raigam Korale.

Branchlets pendulous. Leaves rigidly coriaceous, lanceolate to oblong-lanceolate, base rounded, apex acuminate, laterals obscure. Flowers smaller as the preceding.

Specimens Examined. LOCALITY UNKNOWN: *s. coll. C.P. 603* (PDA). Very rare, only a few trees according to Trimen.

4. var. **pulchella** (Planch. & Triana) Trimen, l.c. 106.

Mesua pulchella Planch. & Triana, l.c. 307; Beddome, l.c. XXIII; Anderson, l.c. 277.
Mesua ferrea subsp. *pulchella* Vesque, l.c. 631; Maheshwari, l.c. 339.
Mesua coromandelina (non Wight) Thw., l.c. 50 & 407. Type: *C.P. 3404* (DC, P).

Branchlets pendulous. Leaves green underneath, coriaceous, acuminate, base rounded. Flowers sessile, smaller than preceding.

D i s t r. Wet lowlands in S.W. Sri Lanka.
S p e c i m e n s   E x a m i n e d. GALLE DISTRICT: Hinidumkande (Haycock), ster., *Kostermans 25669* (A, BO, G, K, L, P, PDA, US); also seen in the Kanneliya forest near Hiniduma. KALUTARA DISTRICT: Sinharaja forest, April 1855, *s. coll. C.P. 3404* (PDA).

4. CLUSIA L.

Clusia rosea Jacq., Enum. Pl. Carib. 34. 1860; Fawcett & Rendle, Fl. Jamaica 5: 193. 1926.

Trees or shrubs, up to 20 m high (much smaller, shrubby in Ceylon). Bark smooth. Leaves opposite, thickly coriaceous, obovate, 3.5×8–7×14 cm, rounded and obscurely, broadly, obtusely acuminate, base gradually tapered into the 1–2 cm long petiole; upper surface with hardly visible laterals, lower one drying cinnamon colour, midrib prominulous, laterals filiform, steep, c. 25 pairs, margin slightly thickened. Petiole with distinct foveola. Flowers solitary, axillary or pseudo-terminal and sometimes 2 lateral, 3-flowered cymes. Bracteoles 2–4, smaller than sepals. Sepals 4–6, up to 2 cm long, persistent. Petals 6–8, white or pink, obovate or suborbicular, 3–4 cm long. Male flower (Not collected so far in Sri Lanka) Outer stamens fertile in several whorls, united at base into a cup or ring; inner stamens united into a solid resinous mass. Female flower: Staminodes united into a cup. Ovary globose, stigma sessile, 6–9-rayed. Capsule septicidally dehiscent, green with brown outside, pale inside, the axis angular, winged. Seeds with thin, fleshy, soft, dark red arillode; valves thick, pointed, narrow.

D i s t r. A native of the West Indies.
E c o l. Introduced and naturalized in many places, growing mainly on rocks in open vegetation.
S p e c i m e n s   E x a m i n e d. KANDY DISTRICT: Maskeliya valley, Road Laxapana to Maskeliya, above Double-cutting, alt. 900 m, May, fr., *Kostermans 24082* (A, BO, G, K, L, P, PDA, US); Hantane Ridge, Febr., young fr., *Jayasuriya 114* (G, L); between Geli Oya and Galaha, Dec., fr., *Corner & Wirawan 756* (PDA, US); upper part of Moray Estate, Maskeliya, alt. 1500 m, Aug., female fl., *Kostermans 25409* (A, BO, G, K, L, P, PDA, US).

COMPOSITAE

(by A.J.C. Grierson*)

Giseke, Praelect. Ord. Nat. Pl. 538. 1792, nom. cons. Type: *Aster* L.

Herbs, shrubs or occasionally trees; erect, decumbent, prostrate or twining, glabrous, pubescent or tomentose, often glandular, sometimes lactiferous. Leaves opposite, alternate or radical, simple or pinnately compound, sessile or petiolate, sometimes auriculate or substipulate at the base. Flowers several or numerous, rarely single, actinomorphic or zygomorphic, hermaphrodite, unisexual or neuter, borne on a common receptacle, and surrounded by a common involucre of bracts or phyllaries forming a capitulum. Capitula peduncled, solitary or in clusters, spikes, corymbs or panicles or sessile and sometimes crowded into glomerules and surrounded by an outer series of bracts; homogamous (flowers all of one sex or all hermaphrodite) or heterogamous (marginal flowers female or neuter, central or disc flowers hermaphrodite) or rarely monoecious. Involucre consisting of one or many series of free or connate, often imbricate, green or coloured, herbaceous, indurated, scarious or membranous phyllaries. Flowers either all hermaphrodite, with tubular or infundibuliform corollas, 5- or sometimes 4-toothed at the apex (discoid capitula), or all hermaphrodite and ligulate, i.e. with slender basal tube and strap-shaped ligule formed from 5 corolla lobes, or those of the centre (disc) tubular and hermaphrodite or functionally male and those at the circumference either ligulate (ligules formed from 3 corolla lobes) and female or neuter (radiate capitula) or filiform and female (disciform capitula). Stamens 5 or rarely 3–4, epipetalous, alternating with corolla lobes, anthers usually coherent into a tube, rarely free, linear or oblong, 2-celled, obtuse or sagittate at the base, sometimes caudate or tailed, dehiscence introrse, connective usually with an acute or obtuse appendage at the apex. Style dividing into two spreading branches at the apex and bearing lines of stigmatic papillae within or unbranched or branches failing to separate (then achenes sterile). Style branches of female flowers thin, filiform, those of hermaphrodite flowers usually broader, variously shaped and sometimes appendaged, outer surface of branches often bearing hairs which brush the pollen from the anther tube. Receptacle flat, convex, concave or conical, either paleace-

*Royal Botanic Garden, Edinburgh.

111

ous, i.e. bearing flower-subtending or embracing scales (paleae), or naked (without paleae) or alveolate. Ovary inferior, one-celled, containing one erect basally attached ovule; fruit or achenes dry, indehiscent, terete, angular or compressed, sometimes beaked or rostrate, bearing at the apex a pappus (usually considered as reduced calyx) of hairs, scales, bristles or awns sometimes absent or reduced to a cup-shaped rim.

Members of the Compositae like most plants suffer from distortion when pressed and dried. This is particularly noticeable in the case of the capitulum which may be distinctive in the field but quite changed by the time it reaches the herbarium sheet. Measurements of involucral diameter are particularly distorted on pressing because the phyllaries tend to be squashed laterally and spread out fan-wise from the base. The capitulum which begins as campanulate when fresh may finish almost semicircular in outline. For these reasons I have endeavoured, in the descriptions that follow, to record the shape and size of the fresh involucre, employing the term "diameter" for such measurements but the term "width" (measured across the tips of the phyllaries) when measuring dried material.

The keys have been based as far as possible on readily discernible macroscopic characters. For some genera, however, dissection followed by observation to ascertain details of anther bases and style branches of hermaphrodite flowers is essential (style branches of female flowers are generally filiform and have little diagnostic value). When fresh material is not available dried flowers may generally be restored to a satisfactory state by boiling for a short time in water.

Most of the terms peculiar to the family should be intelligible from the familial description. With respect to the capitulum, however, it should be noted that in addition to homogamous and heterogamous, the terms discoid and disciform have been employed particularly in generic descriptions. Discoid implies that ligulate female ray flowers are lacking and the flowers are all tubular (as in a disc) and therefore of one kind, i.e. homogamous and usually hermaphrodite. Disciform has similar formative origins but with the distinction that although the flowers are all tubular (and may superficially appear to be all alike), the marginal ones are in fact different and female. This is a heterogamous condition.

In the account of the family that follows I have given full descriptions to the 60 genera, containing a total of 133 species, that are found growing in a wild state in Ceylon. In the case of further 23 genera that appear to be commonly cultivated (as given in Macmillan, Tropical Planting and Gardening ed. 5. 1962), and, therefore, liable from time to time to escape, I have been content in addition to including them in the key, to write only short notes on their salient characters.

The Compositae is generally a temperate family, and it is therefore no surprise that the majority of species, about 75%, grow in the montane zones of the island generally above 3000 ft. There are 25 endemic species and, in the case of another five which are also represented in Southern India, the Ceylonese plants are infraspecifically different. 38 species are aliens, mostly from the New World, and out of the total of 60 genera, 25 consist wholly of alien species. The remaining 70 species are indigenous generally to the Indo-Malaysian floristic region though the distribution of some extends more widely throughout the Old World Tropics.

It is also interesting to note that 20 species described here (excluding those described as new or elevated from varietal status) were not recorded by previous authors, e.g. Trimen or Alston. It is also significant that, in the case of 16 species which were included in Trimen's Handbook, there have been no collections since Trimen's time nor, as in the majority of these cases, since Thwaites' time and, in a further 10 species, there has been only one recent gathering.

In the arrangement that follows, which is based on Bentham's System (in Bentham & Hooker, Genera Plantarum 2, 1873) the indigenous and naturalised genera bear a simple consecutive number to distinguish them from those that may only occur in cultivation or as garden-escapes, the numbers of which are followed by a letter, e.g. 55b, 58a, etc.

KEY TO THE TRIBES

(based on Cronquist, Phytogeny and Taxonomy of the Compositae, Amer. Midl. Naturalist 53: 478–511. 1955)

1 Capitula radiate (with 3-toothed ligules), discoid or disciform or with some flowers
  bilabiate but never all ligulate (with 5-toothed ligules)
  2 Capitula chiefly radiate or sometimes disciform or occasionally discoid but, if discoid,
    without long exserted style branches. Flower colour predominantly yellow or white,
    sometimes red, purple or blue
    3 Lower or all leaves tending to be opposite, occasionally all alternate. Phyllaries usu-
      ally herbaceous and several-seriate but sometimes uniseriate and chartaceous or con-
      nate into a burr. Receptacle generally paleaceous or sometimes naked. Pappus
      paleaceous or of a few firm awns or none (except *Tridax*—hair-like plumose bristles)
      ....**5. Heliantheae**
    3 Leaves all alternate. Involucre, receptacle and pappus various but not as above
      4 Phyllaries mostly in several series, imbricate or subequal, rarely equal, and uniseriate
        but then without a calyculus of small bracts at the base
        5 Anthers obtuse to strongly sagittate at the base, rarely subcaudate. Style various
          but not usually truncate
          6 Style branches clearly or widely separating, usually either penicillate or with small
            hairy appendages
            7 Phyllaries herbaceous or somewhat scarious at the margins and tips; receptacle
              naked; style branches appendiculate; pappus capillary. Leaves entire or merely
              toothed, not dissected. Plants mostly inodorous...................**3. Astereae**

7 Phyllaries rather dry, scarcely herbaceous, hyaline or scarious at margin and tips; receptacle paleaceous or naked; style branches mostly truncate and penicillate; pappus none or minute and coroniform; leaves mostly ± dissected. Plants usually strongly aromatic..**6. Anthemideae**

6 Style branches generally connate to near tip, papillate, style gradually thickening and changing in texture slightly below base of branches; pappus scaly or none; receptacle naked or paleaceous..................................**9. Arctoteae**

5 Anthers ± strongly caudate at base, rarely merely sagittate. Style branches narrow, subtruncate or rounded at the tip. Pappus capillary. Receptacle paleaceous or naked. Capitula often disciform or discoid. Phyllaries often scarious or papery, white or coloured..**4. Inuleae**

4 Phyllaries mostly equal and subuniseriate often with a calyculus of small bracts at the base. Receptacle naked. Pappus capillary or none. Style branches truncate, exappendiculate or penicillate

8 Pappus well developed; achenes mostly alike, surface ± smooth......**7. Senecioneae**

8 Pappus absent; achenes mostly heteromorphic, outer ones incurving and strongly warted or tuberculate on the back...............................**8. Calenduleae**

2 Heads discoid or with some corollas bilabiate

9 Anthers obtuse or sagittate at base. Capitula strictly discoid (though *Stokesia* with radiant sterile marginal flowers). Plants not spiny. Flowers predominantly blue, purple or white, rarely creamy but not yellow. Style branches strongly exserted

10 Style branches obtuse, clavate. Anthers generally obtuse at base. Leaves mostly opposite...**2. Eupatorieae**

10 Style branches gradually attenuate. Anthers ± sagittate at base. Leaves nearly always alternate...**1. Vernonieae**

9 Anthers ± strongly caudate at the base. Leaves alternate or radical

11 Capitula strictly discoid; style with a thickened ring below the branches. Leaves usually spiny...**10. Cardueae**

11 Capitula with some or all flowers bilabiate, sometimes flowers tubular 5-lobed. Styles not thickened below branches...........................**11. Mutisieae**

1 Capitula ligulate, flowers all perfect with ligule derived from 5 corolla lobes. Plants often containing latex...**12. Lactuceae**

KEY TO THE GENERA

1 Capitula of two kinds; unisexual: smaller spherical male capitula, terminal, and ovoid female capitula covered with hooked bristles.........................**28. Xanthium**

1 Capitula of one kind only

2 Flowers all ligulate, 5-toothed or lobed at the apex (Subfam. Cichorioideae)

3 Receptacular paleae absent. Pappus of fine simple hairs

4 Pappus hairs of two distinct thicknesses: fine hairs and finer down-like hairs

5 Achenes compressed, narrowed at both ends.......................**59. Sonchus**

5 Achenes almost terete or slightly compressed, narrowed and subrostrate at the apex
....**60. Launaea**

4 Pappus hairs uniform in thickness

6 Plants non-stoloniferous

7 Achenes distinctly rostrate

8 Caulescent herbs bearing numerous capitula. Achenes compressed...**58a. Lactuca**

8 Acaulous herbs. Capitula solitary on leafless scapes. Achenes angular-terete.....
....**58. Taraxacum**

7 Achenes truncate at the apex, erostrate...........................**56. Youngia**
6 Plants bearing long fine stolons. Acaulescent........................**60. Launaea**
3 Receptacular paleae present. Pappus hairs, at least the inner ones, plumose..........
....**57. Hypochoeris**
2 Flowers either all tubular, 3–5 lobed or the outer ones ligulate, entire or 2–3 (but not
5) lobed at the apex (Subfam. Asteroideae)
9 Female and hermaphrodite flowers both tubular 3–5 lobed. Capitula discoid or disciform
10 Capitula consisting of one or several flowers and aggregated into glomerules or compound heads
11 Glomerules of 1-flowered capitula; phyllaries connate into a tubular pseudocalyx..
....**24. Lagascea**
11 Glomerules of 4–25-flowered capitula; phyllaries free
12 Scrambling shrubs. Outer achenes in each capitulum fertile, much compressed,
strongly ciliate...**18. Blepharispermum**
12 Herbs. Achenes otherwise
13 Radical leaves always present. Capitula 4-flowered; corolla lobes secund. Glomerules surrounded by three large carinate bracts..............**3. Elephantopus**
13 Radical leaves not usually present. Capitula more than 4-flowered; corolla lobes
not secund. Glomerules not surrounded by carinate bracts.....**17. Sphaeranthus**
10 Capitula separate though sometimes in tight sessile clusters but not surrounded by
a common whorl of bracts
14 Flowers all hermaphrodite; capitula homogamous, discoid
15 Achenes epappose
16 Receptacular paleae present. Tops of achenes obscured by pouched bases of
corollas...**45a. Santolina**
16 Receptacular paleae absent. Achenes narrowed to a glandular beak at the apex
and not obscured by corolla bases...........................**23. Carpesium**
15 Achenes bearing a pappus though sometimes reduced to a collar-like corona
17 Capitula in tight axillary clusters. Achenes surmounted by a short corona......
....**1. Struchium**
17 Capitula peduncled, solitary or numerous. Achenes bearing a well developed
pappus
18 Pappus of bristles or scales
19 Capitula 5-flowered...**6a. Stevia**
19 Capitula containing more than 5 flowers
20 Marginal flowers radiating, expanded, 5-lobed. Pappus scales deciduous.
Cultivated plants...**2a. Stokesia**
20 Marginal flowers not radiating, similar to those in the centre. Pappus scales
persistent
21 Achenes bearing a pappus of 5 aristate scales...............**5. Ageratum**
21 Achenes bearing 3–4 short gland-tipped bristles..........**4. Adenostemma**
18 Pappus of hairs
22 Phyllaries uniseriate with or without several small calyculate bracts at the base
23 Scandent herbs or shrubs. Capitula few-(4–10) flowered
24 Capitula small; phyllaries 4–5; flowers 4, greenish white........**7. Mikania**
24 Capitula larger; phyllaries 6 or more; flowers 6–10, yellow......**53. Senecio**
23 Erect herbs or shrubs. Capitula many-(more than 10) flowered
25 Involucres with small calyculate bracts at the base
26 Shrubs with simple, entire-margined leaves.................**54. Notonia**
26 Herbs usually with pinnatisect leaves or, if simple, then margins toothed or
lobed

27 Perennials. Leaves mostly basal. Phyllaries about 2 mm broad............**50. Gynura**
27 Annuals. Leaves not confined to the base of stem. Phyllaries about 1 mm broad....
....**51. Crassocephalum**
25 Involucres ecalyculate...**52. Emilia**
22 Phyllaries several-seriate, imbricate
28 Stems and leaf margins spinous.....................................**55 Carduus**
28 Stems and leaf margins unarmed
29 Flowers and pappus 4–5 cm long, both orange-coloured. Cultivated.....**55b. Stifftia**
29 Flowers, white or purplish, and pappus, white or tawny, 1 cm long or less
30 Style branches obtuse or clavate at the apex......................**6. Eupatorium**
30 Style branches acuminate at the apex.............................**2. Vernonia**
14 Flowers dissimilar, marginal ones narrowly tubular or filiform, female; inner ones tubular, hermaphrodite. Capitula heterogamous, disciform
31 Achenes, at least those of hermaphrodite flowers, bearing a pappus
32 Pappus coroniform with a finely ciliate margin......................**9. Grangea**
32 Pappus of distinct bristles or hairs
33 Hermaphrodite flower achenes bearing two short weak bristles; female flower achenes epappose...**8. Dichrocephala**
33 Hermaphrodite and female flower achenes bearing pappus of numerous bristles or hairs
34 Phyllaries scarious
35 Female flowers more numerous than hermaphrodite flowers (6 : 1 or 10 : 1), filiform, with scarcely discernible lobes. Phyllaries yellow or brownish, not white
....**20. Gnaphalium**
35 Female flowers fewer than hermaphrodite flowers (or sometimes 3–4 times more numerous), narrowly tubular with three distinct lobes at the apex. Phyllaries white or yellow
36 Phyllaries yellow (red or white in cultivated forms), ± appressed at the apex..
....**21. Helichrysum**
36 Phyllaries white or sometimes pink when young, ± spreading at their apices....
....**19. Anaphalis**
34 Phyllaries herbaceous
37 Involucre several-seriate, imbricate
38 Corollas of female flowers very short (c. 0.5 mm long)...........**13. Conyza**
38 Corollas of female flowers almost as long as those of hermaphrodite flowers
....**15. Blumea**
37 Involucre uniseriate with a few small calyculate bracts at the base..**49. Erechtites**
31 Achenes completely epappose
39 Weak prostrate or decumbent herbs
40 Leaves pinnately or bipinnately divided..........................**47. Cotula**
40 Leaves simple or dentate lobed................................**44. Centipeda**
39 Erect herbs
41 Low growing annuals. Leaves simple, somewhat fleshy..............**16. Epaltes**
41 Tall perennials. Leaves pinnately divided, aromatic, but not fleshy...**48. Artemisia**
9 Female flowers ligulate, ligules sometimes very short. Hermaphrodite disc flowers tubular, 4–5 lobed. Capitula radiate
42 Receptacle naked, without paleae
43 Achenes bearing a pappus of hairs, bristles, or scales
44 Ray flowers yellow, orange or red
45 Involucre uniseriate; phyllaries fused or coherent sometimes with a few outer shorter calyculate bracts

46 Phyllaries coherent without oil glands. Pappus of numerous silky hairs......**53. Senecio**
46 Phyllaries connate and bearing linear or circular oil glands. Pappus of 5–6 bristles
....**43. Tagetes**
45 Involucre several-seriate, imbricate
47 Low growing or acaulous herbs. Capitula large solitary
48 Pappus of hyaline scales. Disc flowers regularly 5-lobed. Leaves tomentose beneath
....**54c. Gazania**
48 Pappus of hairs. Outer disc flowers bilabiate. Leaves not tomentose beneath. Cultivated..**55a. Gerbera**
47 Tall or medium-sized caulescent herbs or shrubs. Capitula commonly several or numerous
49 Shrubs. Capitula small, in dense corymbs..........................**14. Psiadia**
49 Herbs. Capitula pedunculate or in panicles
50 Pappus paleaceous
51 Leaves decurrent. Pappus of 5–8 short scales. Cultivated.........**43a. Helenium**
51 Leaves not decurrent. Pappus scales 6–10, scarious, terminating in long fine bristles. Cultivated...**43b. Gaillardia**
50 Pappus of hairs
52 Leaves sessile, cordate-auriculate at the base.....................**22. Vicoa**
52 Leaves narrowed or petiolate at the base
53 Capitula in dense, secund, arching branches. Female flowers with obvious yellow ligules. Cultivated.......................................**12e. Solidago**
53 Capitula in open branching panicles. Female flowers tubular or shortly ligulate, not obvious..**13. Conyza**
44 Ray flowers white (or pink in the bud), blue or purple
54 Ligules narrow, 1 mm broad or less, usually numerous...............**12. Erigeron**
54 Ligules broader, c. 2 mm broad, and fewer except in cultivated forms....**12a. Aster**
43 Achenes epappose or pappus present only as a short collar-like corona
55 Base of disc corollas pouched enveloping the tops of the achenes. Margins of phyllaries distinctly scarious
56 Receptacle paleaceous..**45b. Achillea**
56 Receptacle naked
57 Ray achenes alate or subalate, disc achenes terete, angled or winged............
....**45. Chrysanthemum**
57 Ray and disc achenes similar, unwinged....................**45a. Leucanthemum**
55 Base of disc corollas neither pouched nor enveloping the tops of the achenes. Phyllaries herbaceous, not or only slightly scarious
58 Achenes narrowed to a glandular rostrum at the apex
59 Low-growing rhizomatous herbs. Leaves mostly radical. Capitula solitary on scape-like peduncles..**11. Lagenophora**
59 Medium-sized herbs with well developed stems and cauline leaves. Capitula several, pedunculate...**10. Myriactis**
58 Achenes not narrowed to a glandular rostrum at the apex, coronate or epappose
60 Leaves all radical. Capitula solitary on scapose peduncles.............**11a. Bellis**
60 Leaves mostly cauline. Capitula several on branched stems
61 Flowers homochromous, yellow or orange. Ray achenes fertile, inwardly curved, dorsally compressed, muricate; disc achenes sterile, linear.........**54a. Calendula**
61 Flowers heterochromous, ray white, disc yellow. Achenes all alike and fertile, ± straight..**46. Tanacetum**
42 Receptacle paleaceous
62 Styles of disc flowers undivided, disc achenes sterile

63 Capitula ± sessile in the axils of leaves; achenes covered with hooked spines......
....**26. Acanthospermum**
63 Capitula distinctly pedunculate, achenes not spinous
  64 Achenes ellipsoidal, compressed, smooth, black. Ligules deeply trilobed at the apex
....**27. Moonia**
  64 Achenes irregular in outline, sharply trigonous, surface ± reticulate or rugose. Ligules entire or shallowly lobed at the apex...................**25. Melampodium**
62 Styles of disc flowers branched, disc achenes fertile
  65 Ray flower corollas without basal tubes, ligules sessile on the achenes....**28a. Zinnia**
  65 Ray flower corollas with distinct basal tubes, ligules not sessile on the achenes
    66 Mature achenes, at least those of the disc flowers, bearing a pappus of bristles or scales (sometimes weak or deciduous)
      67 Pappus of bristles or awns
        68 Bristles retrorsely barbed
          69 Achenes rostrate...**38. Cosmos**
          69 Achenes erostrate
            70 Annual herbs with leafy stems. Pappus bristles erect...............**39. Bidens**
            70 Perennial herbs, leaves mostly radical, stems almost leafless. Pappus bristles divergent...**40. Glossogyne**
        68 Bristles without retrorse barbs
          71 Ray flowers white or cream coloured
            72 Decumbent herbs. Receptacular paleae linear-lanceolate. Pappus bristles numerous, 4.5–6.5 mm long, plumose...............................**42. Tridax**
            72 Erect herbs. Receptacular paleae oblong, fimbriate at the apex. Pappus bristles 2–3, c. 1 mm long, smooth...............................**31. Blainvillea**
          71 Ray flowers yellow
            73 Capitula ± sessile in leaf axils. Achenes dorsally compressed, margins lacerate; bristles 2, robust...............................**36. Synedrella**
            73 Capitula pedunculate. Achenes laterally compressed, bristles 1–2, weak, caducous
              74 Receptacle conical at least after anthesis; achenes ciliate........**35. Spilanthes**
              74 Receptacle flat or convex; achenes eciliate, puberulous at the apex..**32. Wedelia**
      67 Pappus of ± flattened scales
        75 Scales 2, weak, caducous. Achenes winged......................**37. Coreopsis**
        75 Achenes unwinged; pappus scales several (more than 2) well developed though sometimes deciduous
          76 Tall robust herbs or subshrubs. Rays yellow. Pappus scales ± coherent, 1 or 2 of them longer and aristate
            77 Peduncles hollow. Pappus scales persistent....................**34. Tithonia**
            77 Peduncles solid. Pappus scales deciduous...................**34a. Helianthus**
          76 Small or medium-sized herbs. Rays white. All pappus scales free, subequal in length, fimbriate at the margins............................**41. Galinsoga**
    66 Mature achenes epappose or bearing a pappus of minute horns or scales
      78 Outer involucral bracts usually narrower and reflexed. Cultivated......**38a. Dahlia**
      78 Outer involucral bracts similar to the inner ones, not reflexed
        79 Ray flowers white
          80 Small trees, 2–3 m tall. Leaves pinnately lobed. Paleae broad, ovate, embracing the achenes. Cultivated....................................**30a. Montanoa**
          80 Low growing erect or decumbent herbs. Leaves simple. Paleae narrow, linear..
....**30. Eclipta**
        79 Ray flowers yellow
          81 Capitula axillary, shortly peduncled, ± erect at first, cernuous after anthesis....
....**33. Eleutheranthera**

81 Capitula on relatively long axillary or terminal peduncles
 82 Receptacle elevated, conical, at least after anthesis; achenes strongly compressed
     laterally...**35. Spilanthes**
 82 Receptacle flat or convex; achenes angular or compressed but not strongly so
   83 Outer phyllaries c. 5, elongate-spathulate, patent, covered with stipitate glands....
     ....**29. Sigesbeckia**
   83 Outer phyllaries otherwise, ± erect and eglandular
     84 Leaves bipinnatisect. Achenes ellipsoidal, epappose. Erect herbs......**38. Cosmos**
     84 Leaves simple. Achenes obovoid, somewhat compressed, narrowed to a short un-
       even cup at the apex. Decumbent herbs...........................**32. Wedelia**

Tribe VERNONIEAE

Herbs, shrubs or trees. Leaves basal or cauline, alternate. Capitula homogamous, discoid. Involucral bracts several-seriate, imbricate. Anther bases
obtuse or sagittate. Style branches often elongate, acuminate. Receptacles
naked. Achenes terete or angular, usually 5–10 ribbed. Pappus of hairs or
scales or coroniform.

KEY TO THE GENERA

1 Capitula separate and distinct, not crowded into glomerules and surrounded by bracts.
  Leaves mostly cauline
  2 Marginal flowers radiant, much larger than the inner ones. Capitula large, solitary or
    few...**2a. Stokesia**
  2 Marginal flowers not larger than the inner ones. Capitula small or medium-sized,
    usually numerous sometimes solitary or few
    3 Capitula with distinct peduncles, usually in corymbs. Pappus capillary..**2. Vernonia**
    3 Capitula sessile, axillary, solitary or in small clusters. Pappus a short corona......
      ....**1. Struchium**
1 Capitula compressed 4-flowered, crowded into glomerules and surrounded by three
  stiff folded bracts. Leaves mostly radical, rosulate...................**3. Elephantopus**

1. STRUCHIUM

P. Br., Hist. Jamaica 312 t. 34 fig. 2. 1756. Type species: *S. sparganophorum* (L.) Kuntze.

Sparganophorus Vaill. ex Crantz, Inst, 1: 261. 1766. Type species: *S. vaillantii*
Crantz.

Erect annual herbs. Leaves alternate, petiolate. Capitula 1–6 in sessile
axillary clusters, hemispherical, homogamous, discoid, 20–40 flowered. Phyllaries 3–4 seriate, ovate, membranous with scarious margins. Flowers tubular
at the base, limb campanulate, 3–4 lobed. Anther bases sagittate, auricles acuminate. Style branches subulate, papillose. Receptacle naked. Achenes oblong 3–4-gonous. Pappus a short tubular cartilaginous corona.

Struchium sparganophorum (L.) Kuntze, Rev. Gen. Pl. 366. 1891; Koster, Blumea 1: 370. 1935; Senaratna, Ceylon J. Sci., Sect. A. Bot. 12: 163. 1945; Grierson, Ceylon J. Sci., Biol. Sci. 10: 42. 1972.

Ethulia sparganophora L., Sp. Pl. ed. 2, 1171. 1763. Type: Herb. Vaillant (P).

Stems branched, 25–75 cm tall, erect or somewhat flexuose ± tetragonous, pubescent or glabrescent, glandular. Leaves elliptic-lanceolate or obovate, 5–12 × 2–5 cm, borne on short petioles up to 5–10 mm long, acuminate at the apex, attenuate at the base, margin crenate-serrate, glandular on both surfaces, pubescent especially on the veins beneath. Capitula 4–6 mm diam., 1–6 (–8) in axillary glomerules, phyllaries c. 20, ovate, spinulose, acuminate, 3–4 mm long, 2 mm broad, margins ciliate. Flowers white tinged with mauve, corollas 2 mm long. Achenes c. 1.5 mm long, irregularly 3–4 angular, glandular. Pappus corona whitish, c. 0.5 mm long, oblique and obscurely toothed at the apex.

D i s t r. Trop. America, introduced into Trop. Africa and Asia.

E c o l. In moist ground and ditches in lowland regions in south and west of island, not common. Flowering July–March.

S p e c i m e n s E x a m i n e d. MATARA DISTRICT: Matara, *Senaratna 3199* (PDA). KALUTARA DISTRICT: Kalutara, *Senaratna 1226* (PDA). COLOMBO DISTRICT: Mirigama, *Senaratna 298* (PDA); Negombo, *N.D. Simpson 7922* (PDA, K), *8863* (PDA, K); Ramutugala near Kadawata, *Amaratunga 448* (PDA). PUTTALAM DISTRICT: Punchigangoda, between Madampe and Mahawewa, *Grierson 1136* (E, US, PDA, BR, CANB). KEGALLE DISTRICT: Kegalle, *F.W. de Silva 243* (PDA).

N o t e. This species is a relatively recent introduction as is pointed out by Senaratna (l.c.); it was first collected at Mirigama in November 1931.

2. VERNONIA

Schreber, Gen. 2: 541. 1791, nom. cons. Type species: *V. noveboracensis* (L.) Willd. (Syn. *Serratula noveboracensis* L.) typ. cons.

Annual or perennial herbs, shrubs or trees. Leaves alternate, simple. Capitula homogamous, numerous in corymbs or corymbose panicles, rarely solitary or few. Involucre campanulate, phyllaries pluriseriate, imbricate. Corollas tubular-campanulate, 5-lobed, white or purplish. Anther bases sagittate, apices acute. Style branches elongate, subulate, acute. Receptacle flat, naked. Achenes oblong, terete or angular; 5–10 ribbed, often glandular. Pappus hairs reddish or dirty white, biseriate; outer series often shorter, filiform or scale-like.

KEY TO THE SPECIES

1 Involucre 8–13 mm long, as long as or somewhat shorter than the pappus
  2 Outer phyllaries linear-spathulate, herbaceous....................**1. V. anthelmintica**
  2 Outer phyllaries ovate, lanceolate or linear, acute or acuminate, not spathulate and herbaceous
    3 Corymbs composed of clusters of subsessile capitula. Pappus hairs subequal, shorter outer hairs or scales absent.......................................**7. V. lankana**
    3 Corymbs composed of distinctly stalked capitula, or capitula solitary or few. Outer pappus of shorter hairs or scales present
      4 Inner phyllaries abruptly acuminate into setaceous points c. 1 mm long. Involucres less than 5 mm diam..**11. V. setigera**
      4 Inner phyllaries acute or ± gradually acuminate without setaceous points. Involucres 5 mm diam. or more
        5 Stems much branched. Involucres c. 5 mm diam. when fresh, 0.75–1 cm broad when pressed, inner phyllaries obtuse or subacute...............**5. V. nemoralis**
        5 Stem almost unbranched. Involucres 7–10 mm diam. when fresh, 1.5–2 cm broad when pressed, inner phyllaries acute or acuminate
          6 Outer and intermediate phyllaries acuminate into erect or spreading tips 3–8 mm long. Stems leafy, leaves not aggregated basally nor prominently veined beneath
          ....**3. V. gardneri**
          6 Outer and intermediate phyllaries acute or acuminate, appressed without long tips. Stems almost leafless, leaves mostly basal prominently veined beneath......
          ....**4. V. thwaitesii**
1 Involucres 3–6 mm long, about half, or less, as long as the pappus
  7 Flowers few, 3–8 per capitulum
    8 Trees. Leaves 10–15 cm long, glabrous or brownish pubescent beneath............
    ....**2. V. arborea**
    8 Shrubs. Leaves 3–8 cm long, greyish or silvery pubescent
      9 Leaves pandurate or, if subsessile, ovate, auriculate. Flowers 6–8 per capitulum..
      ....**10. V. zeylanica**
      9 Leaves elliptic, exauriculate. Flowers 3–5 per capitulum............**14. V. elliptica**
  7 Flowers numerous more than 10 per capitulum
    10 Perennial herbs or shrubs, generally (except *V. anceps*) more than 50 cm tall
      11 Inner phyllaries broadly obtuse, mucronate; involucres dark purplish-brown......
      ....**6. V. pectiniformis** subsp. **puncticulata**
      11 Inner phyllaries acute or subacute; involucres green, greyish or white pubescent, not dark brown
        12 Leaves elliptic or oblanceolate. Shrubs
          13 Undersides of leaves white or brownish tomentose, margins ± obscurely denticulate...**8. V. wightiana**
          13 Leaves subglabrous beneath, margins shortly and distantly serrate...........
          ....**9. V. anceps**
        12 Leaves ovate or the uppermost lanceolate. Tall perennial herbs...............
        ....**12. V. hookeriana**
    10 Annual herbs, generally less than 60 (rarely 150) cm tall...........**13. V. cinerea**

1. Vernonia anthelmintica (L.) Willd., Sp. Pl. 3: 1634. 1803; Moon, Cat. 57. 1824; Thw., Enum. Pl. Zeyl. 160. 1859; C.B. Clarke, Comp. Ind. 10. 1876; Hook. f., Fl. Br. Ind. 3: 236. 1881; Trimen, Handb. Fl. Ceylon 3: 9. 1895.

Conyza anthelmintica L., Sp. Pl. ed. 2. 1207. 1763. Type: Herb. Hermann (BM).

Centratherum anthelmintica (L.) Gamble, Fl. Pres. Madras 2: 667. 1921.

Erect annual herbs, 0.5–1.5 m tall. Stems striate, pubescent. Leaves elliptic or oblanceolate, 7–13 × 2–5 cm, attenuate and subpetiolate at the base, acute or acuminate at the apex, margins coarsely and sharply serrate, sparsely appressed pilose above, pubescent especially on the veins beneath. Capitula campanulate, loosely corymbose, sometimes few or solitary. Involucres 1–1.3 cm long, c. 0.75 cm diam. in flower when fresh, 1 cm diam. at maturity, c. 1.5 cm broad when pressed, 4–5-seriate, outer phyllaries linear herbaceous, intermediate ones oblong with long (c. 1 cm) spathulate, herbaceous appendages, inner ones linear-oblong, stiffly membranous, straw coloured, with triangular green apices. Flowers mauve, c. 40 per capitulum, 8–9 mm long. Achenes black, 4–5 mm long, 10-ribbed, pubescent on the ribs, glandular in the grooves between. Pappus tawny-white becoming red with storage; inner pappus hairs 6–7 mm long, deciduous; outer pappus paleaceous, 0.5–0.75 mm long, persistent.

Chromosome number. n = 10 (Mehra *et al.*, Caryologia 18: 37, 1965).

D i s t r. Throughout India.

E c o l. Roadsides and waste ground near houses, possibly not native but naturalised, not common. Flowering Dec.–March.

U s e s. Medicinally, this species is reported to have anthelmintic properties, especially against *Oxyuris* worms. It is also used as a remedy for various skin diseases and, in parts of India, the achenes, ground to a paste with lime juice, are employed for destroying lice of the head and body.

V e r n. Sanni-nayan (S); Kadduchchirakam (T).

S p e c i m e n s   E x a m i n e d. HAMBANTOTA DISTRICT: Ruhuna National Park, Yala flat, *Cooray 70031701* (E, US, PDA). RATNAPURA DISTRICT: Galagama, *(Gardner)*, *C.P. 487* (PDA). MATALE DISTRICT: in Sigiriya Wewa, *Townsend 73/207* (E, K, US, PDA). BADULLA DISTRICT: Lunugala, Jan. 1888, *Trimen s.n.* (PDA). ANURADHAPURA DISTRICT: Anuradhapura, 17 Dec. 1881, *Trimen s.n.* (PDA), *Alston 1057* (PDA, K); Puttalam-Anuradhapura road, *Simpson 9164* (PDA, BM); Mihintale, *Amaratunga 548* (PDA). MANNAR DISTRICT: Illupaikkadavai, *Grierson 1128* (E, US, PDA, BR, CANB). KANDY DISTRICT: Kandy, *Gardner 1215* (BM, K), *Macrae s.n.* (BM, K). WITHOUT LOCALITY: *Moon 102* (BM); *Walker s.n.* (K).

2. Vernonia arborea Ham., in Trans. Linn. Soc. London 14: 218. 1824. Type: In sylvis Nepaliae inferioris et Camrupae, *Hamilton s.n.* (E).

Tree 12 m or more high, bark whitish. Young twigs yellowish tomentose.

Leaves ovate or oblong-elliptic, 10–15 × 3–5 cm, rounded or cuneate at the base into petioles 1–2 cm long, acuminate at the apex, margins entire, glabrous above, uniformly densely pubescent or pubescent only on the veins beneath. Capitula numerous in loose terminal panicles; involucres c. 5 mm long, 4–6 mm broad, 5–6-seriate; phyllaries ovate-oblong, obtuse or subacute, fulvously pubescent at their apices. Flowers 5–6 per capitulum; corollas c. 5 mm long, white or violet. Achenes 3–3.5 mm long, angular, ± distinctly 10-ribbed, glabrous or glandular and sparsely pubescent near the apex. Pappus dingy white, 5–7 mm long, with a few short outer hairs c. 0.5 mm long.

D i s t r . Himalaya south to Java, Borneo and Philippines.

E c o l . In moist forest in the southern part of the island, below 5000 ft, rather common. Flowering July–October.

There are two varieties.

KEY TO THE VARIETIES

1 Leaves oblong-elliptic, suddenly acuminate, ± glabrous except on the veins beneath. .
....**1. var. arborea**
1 Leaves ovate-elliptic, gradually acuminate, uniformly pubescent beneath.............
....**2. var. javanica**

1. var. arborea (see Koster in Blumea 1: 384. 1935); Grierson, Ceylon J. Sci., Biol. Sci. 10: 44. 1972.

Apparently rare and recorded only from one locality.

S p e c i m e n   E x a m i n e d . KEGALLE DISTRICT: Pitawela below Kitulgala, 900 ft, at milestone 57, *Worthington 2087* (K).

2. var. javanica (El.) C.B. Clarke, Comp. Ind. 23. 1876; Koster, Blumea 1: 386. 1935.

Eupatorium javanicum Blume, Bijdr. 903. 1825. Type: in sylvis altioribus Javae insulae, *Blume s.n.* (L).
Vernonia javanica (Blume) DC., Prod. 5: 22. 1836; Thw. Enum. Pl. Zeyl. 160. 1859.
Vernonia arborea Ham. in Hook. f., Fl. Br. Ind. 3: 239. 1881 p.p.; Trimen, Handb. Fl. Ceylon 3: 11. 1895; Worthington, Ceylon Trees 301. 1959.

V e r n . Kobomella (S); Mal Gedumba (S).
S p e c i m e n s   E x a m i n e d . WITHOUT PRECISE LOCALITY: *C.P. 1742* marked G.C. 385 at upper margin and annotated "Rambodde and Adam's Peak, *Gardner*; Hunasgiriya, Aug. 1851; Ambagamuwa and Sittawakke, Sept. 1857" (PDA), unannotated (K). MATALE DISTRICT: Madulkelle, *Worthington 1999* (BM, K. and Herb. Forestry Dept., Colombo).

RATNAPURA DISTRICT: Bambarabotuwa Forest, *Worthington 3204* (K).
KANDY DISTRICT: Kadugannawa, *Gardner 385* (BM, K). KALUTARA
DISTRICT: Kirigalle, Agalawatte, *Balakrishnan NBK 1016* (US, E, PDA).
BADULLA DISTRICT: Ella, Sept. 1890, *Trimen s.n.* (PDA). WITHOUT
LOCALITY: *J.S. MacKenzie s.n.* (K); *Harvey s.n.* (E); *Wight s.n.* (PDA);
Walker 1166 (E); *s.n.* (E-GL, K).

3. Vernonia gardneri Thw., Enum. Pl. Zeyl. 161. 1860. excl. var. *β* (see under
V. thwaitesii); C.B. Clarke, Comp. Ind. 11. 1876; Hook. f., Fl. Br. Ind. 3:
230. 1881; Trimen, Handb. Fl. Ceylon 3: 6. 1895. Type: Ceylon, *Thwaites
C.P. 27, 1745* (PDA, K, BM).

Erect perennial herbs or subshrubs. Stems up to 50 cm tall, appressed
puberulous. Leaves elliptic-lanceolate or linear-lanceolate; 5–15 × 0.7–3 cm,
attenuate and subpetiolate at the base, gradually acuminate at the apex, margins coarsely or finely serrate, flat or somewhat inrolled. Capitula campanulate, in terminal groups of 2–8, sometimes solitary; involucre 12–14 mm long,
0.75–1 cm diam. when fresh, 1.75–2 cm broad when pressed, 6–7 seriate,
subglabrous; outer and intermediate phyllaries ± erect, spreading or squarrose, tapering into long fine subulate points up to 8 mm long; inner phyllaries
oblong, acute or shortly acuminate. Flowers 30–40 per capitulum; corollas
9–10 mm long, pale violet. Achenes 4.5–5.5 mm long, glabrous or sparsely
pubescent, distinctly 10-ribbed. Pappus dirty white or reddish, 6–7 mm long
with a distinct ring of short outer scales 0.75–1 mm long.

Distr. Endemic.
Ecol. In moist shady jungle stream beds among rocks, "rather common"
according to Trimen. Flowering February–May.
There are two varieties.

KEY TO THE VARIETIES

1 Leaves 8–15 × 2–4.5 cm, margins flat, coarsely and acutely dentate. Outer and intermediate phyllaries squarrose, tapering into long fine points c. 8 mm long.............
....1. var. **gardneri**
1 Leaves 5–8 (–11) × 0.7–1.5 cm, margins revolute, finely serrate. Outer and intermediate
phyllaries ± erect, tapering into fine points c. 3 mm long..............2. var. **brevior**

1. var. gardneri

Specimens Examined. WITHOUT PRECISE LOCALITY: "*C.P.
27 and 1745*" annotated "Peradeniya, *Gardner*: Deltota, May 1857; Palagala
(Paragala ?) 1853" (PDA: there are two specimens on this sheet; the one on
the left should be regarded as lectotype, the other is a specimen of var. *brevior*), unannotated (K, BM). WITHOUT LOCALITY: *s. coll. 27* (PDA);

Harvey s.n. (E). KANDY DISTRICT: near Madugoda, *Alston 1667* (PDA, K); Nitre Cave Valley near Rangala, *Simpson 9454* (PDA, BM).

2. var. brevior Grierson, Ceylon J. Sci., Biol. Sci. 10: 43. 1972. Type: *Thwaites* "*C.P. 27* and *1745*" (PDA).

Specimens Examined. WITHOUT EXACT LOCALITY: "*C.P. 27* and *1745*" annotated "Ambagamuwa and Adam's Peak, *Gardner*, 1857" (PDA, holotype). NUWARA ELIYA DISTRICT: Nuwara Eliya, *s. coll. C.P. 27* (PDA, BM). KANDY DISTRICT: Ambagamuwa, Feb. 1846, *s. coll. C.P. 692* (K).

The relationship between these two varieties, which are quite distinct, finds a parallel in that between *V. lankana* var. *lankana* and its variety, var. *crassa*.

4. Vernonia thwaitesii C.B. Clarke, Comp. Ind. 11. 1876; Hook. f., Fl. Br. Ind. 3: 231. 1881; Trimen, Handb. Fl. Ceylon 3: 6. 1895. Type: *Thwaites C.P. 44* (PDA).

Vernonia gardneri var. *nervosa* Thw., Enum. Pl. Zeyl. 161. 1860.

Erect herbs or subshrubs. Stems terete, brownish, up to 60 cm tall, appressed pubescent. Leaves generally more numerous in the lower parts of the stem, ovate, 3–6 × 1–3 cm, rounded or cuneate at the base, subsessile or with short petioles up to 5 mm long, acute at the apex, margins serrate-denticulate, texture thick, subcoriaceous, prominently veined especially beneath, subglabrous above, glandular and sparsely pubescent on the veins beneath. Capitula campanulate, few (2–4) in loose almost leafless corymbs, sometimes solitary. Involucre 1–1.2 cm long, 0.75–1 cm diam. when fresh, 1.5–2 cm broad when pressed, 6-seriate; phyllaries appressed pubescent, outer ones lanceolate, acute or acuminate, intermediate and inner ones oblong or oblanceolate, acute, apiculate and often purplish at the apex. Flowers 30–40 per capitulum; corollas c. 1 cm long, sparsely glandular, bluish-mauve. Achenes c. 3 mm long, glabrous or puberulous, 10-ribbed. Pappus dingy white, 7–8 mm long with a ring of short outer hairs 1 mm long.

Distr. Endemic.

Ecol. On grassy bank and wet rocks, 5000–6000 ft, apparently quite rare. Flowering February–May.

Specimens Examined. WITHOUT EXACT LOCALITY: *C.P. 44* annotated "Ambagamuwa and Adam's Peak, *Gardner*; Horton Plains, May 1856, between Horton Plains and Galagama, Feb. 1857" (PDA), annotated "near Horton Plains" (BM), annotated "Adam's Peak, Mar. 1846" (K). NUWARA ELIYA DISTRICT: Horton Plains, *W. Nock s.n.* (PDA); above Non Pareil Estate, 24 Feb. 1882, *Trimen s.n.* (PDA); Galagama, Feb. 1846, *s. coll. C.P. 62* (K). BADULLA DISTRICT: between Ohiya and Boralanda, 5500 ft, *Grierson 1112* (E, US, PDA, BR, CANB). WITHOUT LOCALITY: *Walker* (Herb. Wight Propr.) *135* (E), *Walker s.n.* (K).

5. Vernonia nemoralis Thw., Enum. Pl. Zeyl. 161. 1860; C.B. Clarke, Comp. Ind. 11. 1876; Hook. f., Fl. Br. Ind. 3: 237. 1881; Trimen, Handb. Fl. Ceylon 3: 9. 1895. Type: *Thwaites C.P. 216* (PDA—holo, BM, K-iso).

Herbs or subshrubs 0.5–1 m tall. Stems purplish, glabrous or puberulous. Leaves ovate-lanceolate, petiolate, petioles 0.5–2 cm long, lamina 5–12 × 1–4.5 cm, rounded or cuneate at the base, acuminate at the apex, margins distantly and sharply serrate, glabrous on both surfaces. Capitula campanulate, few (3–6) in loose corymbs. Involucre 9–12 mm long, c. 5 mm diam. when fresh, 0.75–1 cm broad when pressed, 9–10 seriate, phyllaries whitish pubescent, outer ones lanceolate, intermediate and inner ones oblong or oblanceolate, obtuse or subacute, mucronate, margins ciliate. Flowers 30–40 per capitulum; corollas 10–12 mm long, purple. Achenes c. 3.5 mm long, 10-ribbed, pubescent. Pappus whitish, 6–8 mm long with an outer ring of short hairs c. 1 mm long.

D i s t r. Endemic.
E c o l. By streams and moist tracksides, 1–4000 ft, apparently quite rare. Flowering February–May.
S p e c i m e n s   E x a m i n e d. WITHOUT EXACT LOCALITY: *C.P. 216* annotated "Galagama, *Gardner*, 1856; Singharaja Forest, 1855" (PDA), annotated "Galagama, Feb. 1846" (K), without annotation (BM). RATNAPURA DISTRICT: Galagama, Feb. 1846, *s. coll. C.P. 482* (K); below Non Pareil Estate, Galagama, 25 Feb. 1882, *Trimen s.n.* (PDA); near Balangoda, *Simpson 8441* (BM); above Belihul Oya towards Pusselgolla, *Grierson 1154* (E, US, PDA, BR, CANB). WITHOUT LOCALITY: 13 Apr. 1819, *Moon 696* (BM); *Macrae 744* (BM); *Walker 18* (K), *181* (K).

A form with narrow linear-lanceolate leaves not more than 1 cm broad and narrow inner phyllaries, 1.25 mm broad, was collected by Trimen in Matara Dist., Morowak Korale, N. of Kipa Kande (?) (28 Feb. 1881).

6. Vernonia pectiniformis (DC.) subsp. **puncticulata** (DC.) Grierson, Ceylon J. Sci., Biol. Sci. 10: 45. 1972.

Vernonia puncticulata DC., Prod. 7: 264. 1838; C.B. Clarke, Comp. Ind. 15. 1876. Type: Ceylon, ad alt. 6000 ft. *Walker 255* (E-GL).
Vernonia pectiniformis DC. "var." Arn., Nov. Act. Phys. Med. Acad. Caes. Leop. Card. Nat. Cur. 18: 345. 1836.
Vernonia pectiniformis DC. quoad syn. *V. puncticulata*: Thw., Enum. Pl. Zeyl. 161. 1860; Hook. f., Fl. Br. Ind. 3: 239. 1881; Trimen Handb. Fl. Ceylon 3: 10. 1895.

Erect shrub 1.5–4 m tall. Stems striate, pubescent. Leaves numerous on short (1–1.5 cm) internodes, elliptic-lanceolate or oblanceolate, 5–12 × 2–5 cm, attenuate at the base and subsessile or borne on petioles up to 1 cm long, acute at the apex, margins serrulate, subrevolute, minutely punctate and puberulous on the veins beneath, glabrous and somewhat bullate on the upper surface. Capitula cylindrical-campanulate, in dense terminal corymbs. Involucre 6–7 mm long, c. 4 mm diam. when fresh, 0.75 cm when pressed, 5–6 seriate; phyllaries purplish-brown, shortly pubescent, margins ciliate, outer ones ovate, acute, inner ones oblong, obtuse, 2.5 mm broad, shortly mucronate. Flowers c. 12 per capitulum, corollas c. 9 mm long, purple. Achenes 2.5–3 mm long, faintly 10-ribbed, finely pubescent and glandular. Pappus white at first, becoming yellow or coppery with storage, 6–7.5 mm long with an outer ring of shorter hairs c. 2 mm long.

D i s t r. Endemic subspecies; species also in S. India.

E c o l. In montane forests c. 6000 ft, rather uncommon. Flowering October–April.

S p e c i m e n s E x a m i n e d. WITHOUT EXACT LOCALITY: *C.P. 294* annotated "Nuwara Eliya; Adam's Peak and Pidurutalagala, *Gardner*; Ambagamuwa, Mar. 1852" (PDA), annotated "Pidurutalagala Feb. 1846" (K), unannotated (BM). KANDY DISTRICT: Adam's Peak, *Alston 961* (PDA); ibid., base of cone, 16 May 1906, *Silva s.n.* (PDA). NUWARA ELIYA DISTRICT: Horton Plains, on trail to Little World's End, 2100 m, *Fosberg 50073* (E, US, PDA); Pidurutalagala, 8000 ft, *Grierson 1070* (E, US, PDA, BR, CANB). WITHOUT LOCALITY: *Walker 255* (E-GL), *s.n.* (K).

7. Vernonia lankana Grierson, Ceylon J. Sci., Biol. Sci. 10: 43. 1972. Type: Ceylon, Walker 297 (E-GL).

Vernonia scariosa Arn., Nova Acta Phys. Med. Acad. Caes. Leop. Carol. Nat. Cur. 18: 346. 1836; Thw., Enum. Pl. Zeyl. 161. 1860; Hook. f., Fl. Br. Ind. 3: 236. 1881; Trimen, Handb. Fl. Ceylon 3: 8. 1895. Based on the same type. Non Poir., 1808, nec Baker, 1882.
Decaneurum scariosum DC., Prod. 7: 264. 1838.
Centratherum scariosum C.B. Clarke, Comp. Ind. 4. 1876.

Erect or sprawling subshrubs, 1–2 m tall. Stems striate, glabrous or more usually sparsely or densely brown villous. Leaves ovate, obovate or oblanceolate, 6–12 (–20) × 3–4.5 (–7) cm, attenuate and subpetiolate at the base or on petioles up to 1.5 cm long, acute or shortly acuminate at the apex, ± coarsely and sharply serrate at the margins, brownish villous pubescent on both surfaces, often finely bullate above. Capitula campanulate, usually 10 or more in dense corymbs, individual capitula ± sessile in groups of 2–4. Involucres 10–12 mm long, 4–7.5 mm diam. when fresh, up to 1 cm broad when pressed, 5–6 seriate; phyllaries purplish, pubescent and finely ciliate, outer and intermediate ones ovate or oblong, ± abruptly acuminate into stiff blackish terminal awn, 0.75–4 mm long, inner ones scarious. Flowers 15–25 per capitulum, corollas c. 7 mm long, whitish tinged with mauve. Achenes 3–4 mm long, dark brown, glabrous or sparsely pubescent, distinctly 10-ribbed. Pappus 5–7 mm long, whitish at first, becoming coppery in storage, shorter outer pappus hairs absent.

D i s t r. Endemic.

E c o l. Along jungle streams and in marshy ground around pools, 4000–7000 ft; quite rare. Flowering February–April.

There are two varieties.

KEY TO THE VARIETIES

1 Leaves up to 10 (−12) cm long. Involucre 4–5 mm diam. when fresh, c. 0.75 cm when pressed; phyllaries oblong with terminal awn 0.75–1.5 mm long........1. var. lankana
1 Leaves generally more than 12 cm long. Involucre 7.5 mm diam. when fresh, c. 1 cm broad when pressed; phyllaries ovate with terminal awn 3–4 mm long....2. var. crassa

1. var. lankna

S p e c i m e n s E x a m i n e d. WITHOUT EXACT LOCALITY: *C.P. 389* annotated "Kotmale Oya, *Gardner*; Hunasgiriya, Apr. 1851, Feb. 1852; Halgarama Oya, Elk plains, Apr. 1854; Nuwara Eliya, Feb. 1857" (PDA), annotated, "Kotmale" (K), annotated "6000 ft" (BM). NUWARA ELIYA DISTRICT: Nuwara Eliya, *W. Nock s.n.* (PDA); Hakgala, 28 Feb. 1906, *A.M. Silva s.n.* (PDA); ibid., 23 Feb. 1927, *Alston s.n.* (PDA); ibid., *Grierson 1060* (E, US, PDA, BR, CANB).

2. var. crassa (Thw.) Grierson, Ceylon J. Sci., Biol. Sci. 10: 43. 1972.

Vernonia scariosa var. *crassa* Thw., Enum. Pl. Zeyl. 161. 1860; Trimen, Handb. Fl. Ceylon 3: 8. 1895. Type: *Thwaites C.P. 2825* (PDA).

S p e c i m e n s E x a m i n e d. NUWARA ELIYA DISTRICT: below Horton Plains, Feb. 1857, *s. coll. C.P. 2825* (PDA, BM, K); between Horton Plains and Ohiya, *Simpson 9556* (PDA, BM), *Grierson 1109* (E, US, PDA, BR, CANB). WITHOUT LOCALITY: 12 Apr. 1819, *Moon 685* (BM).

8. Vernonia wightiana Arn., Nova Acta Phys. Med. Acad. Leop. Carol. Nat. Cur. 18: 345. 1836; DC., Prod. 7: 263. 1838; Thw., Enum. Pl. Zeyl. 160. 1859, excl. var. *β*; C.B. Clarke, Comp. Ind. 19. 1876; Hook. f., Fl. Br. Ind. 3: 238. 1881: Trimen, Handb. Fl. Ceylon 3: 9. 1895. Type: Ceylon, ad alt. 1000 hexapod, *Walker s.n.* (E-GL).

Erect or straggling shrubs, 0.25–2.5 m tall. Young branches pale brown tomentose. Leaves elliptic, oblanceolate or spathulate, 1.5–12 × 0.75–4 cm, cuneate and shortly petiolate at the base (petioles up to 1.5 cm long), acute or obtuse, mucronate at the apex, margins denticulate, green and pubescent at first on the upper surface, often becoming blackish on drying, densely greyish brown tomentose beneath. Capitula campanulate, in corymbs of 6–20, pedicels bearing short linear bracts. Involucre 5–6 mm long, 5 mm diam. when fresh, c. 1 cm broad when pressed, 3–4 seriate; phyllaries linear-lanceolate, acuminate, densely tomentose. Flowers 30–40 per capitulum, corollas 7–9 mm long, pubescent, lilac or mauve. Achenes squarish, 4–5 ribbed, brown, 2–3 mm long, sparsely puberulous and glandular. Pappus dingy white, 5–7 mm long, with a ring of short outer scales 0.5 mm long.

D i s t r. Endemic.

E c o l. Patanas, grassy banks and montane forests above 3500 ft; widespread. Flowering November–May (throughout the year, according to Trimen).

V e r n. Konde (S, meaning a knot of hair).

S p e c i m e n s   E x a m i n e d. WITHOUT EXACT LOCALITY: *C.P. 1741* annotated "Horton Plains, Feb. 1857, Pidurutalagala" and bearing gummed labels marked (*Gardner*) "384" and "var. a, b, c, d and e" (PDA) unannotated (K, BM). KANDY DISTRICT: Dolosbage, 3500 ft, *Grierson 1003* (E, US, PDA, BR, CANB). NUWARA ELIYA DISTRICT: On the way to Horton Plains from Pattipola, 6800 ft, 2 May 1906, *Willis s.n.* (PDA); Nuwara Eliya, *Gardner 384 B* (BM); Hakgala Peak, *Simpson 9099* (BM); Single Tree Mount, Nuwara Eliya, *Sinclair 10085* (K); between Horton Plains resthouse and World's End, 2175 m, *Comanor 958* (E, PDA), *Gould & Cooray 13804* (E, US, PDA), *Fosberg 50072* (E, PDA). BADULLA DISTRICT: Top of Namunakula, 12 Mar. 1907, *Silva s.n.* (PDA); Uva Basin, between Palugama and Boralanda (Milestone 4/2), *Fosberg & Mueller-Dombois 50122* (E, US, PDA); below Ohiya Railroad Station, 1690 m, *Mueller-Dombois 67091505* (US, PDA); between Palugama and Boralanda, 1320 m, *Mueller-Dombois & Wirawan 68011414* (US, PDA); Erabedde Arboretum, 4000 ft, *Worthington 5934* (K). RATNAPURA DISTRICT: Kunadiyaparawita, X'mas 1917 *F. Lewis s.n.* (PDA). WITHOUT LOCALITY: "ad alt. 6000 ped." *Walker s.n.* (E-GL), *251* (K); 17 Feb. 1819, *Moon 189* (BM); *Harvey s.n.* (E); *J. Fraser 148* (BM); *Macrae 59* (BM), *402* (BM, K), *s.n.* (K); *Dr. Maxwell s.n.* (K); *G. Thomson s.n.* (K).

N o t e s. This species is variable in height of stem and in size and texture of the leaves but this variation does not appear to be significant. It is in every case an easily recognised species. On the patanas of Horton Plains, a dwarf semiprostrate form occurs, the stems of which never attain a height of more than 30 cm, *Grierson 1097* (E, US, PDA, BR, CANB). At stream sides on Adam's Peak the species appears to hybridise with *V. anceps*, see *Grierson*

1042 (E, US, PDA). The hybrids have the narrower oblanceolate more strongly denticulate leaves which are characteristic of *V. anceps* and the indumentum varies from pubescent to tomentose. The corollas of these plants are less pubescent than they normally are in *V. wightiana* (see Grierson, Ceylon J. Sci., Biol. Sci. 10: 43. 1972).

9. Vernonia anceps C.B. Clarke in Hook. f., Fl. Br. Ind. 3: 233. 1881; Trimen, Handb. Fl. Ceylon 3: 6. 1895. Type: *Thwaites C.P. 164* (PDA, K, BM). *Vernonia wightiana* Arn. var. *β* Thw., Enum. Pl. Zeyl. 160. 1859.

Erect shrubs up to 0.5 m tall. Young stems ± densely leafy, brownish pubescent, later glabrous. Leaves oblanceolate, 4–7 × 0.4–1 (–1.5) cm, attenuate and subpetiolate at the base or with petioles 0.5–0.75 mm long, acute, apiculate at the apex, margins distantly serrate near the apex, somewhat revolute, almost glabrous on both surfaces or pubescent on the veins and punctate beneath. Capitula campanulate, borne in loose corymbs of 4–10 capitula, pedicels bearing narrow linear bracts. Involucres 5–6 mm long, 4–5 mm diam. when fresh, c. 0.75 cm broad when pressed, 4-seriate; phyllaries lanceolate, acute, pubescent. Flowers c. 30 per capitulum; corollas 6.5–7 (–8) mm long, purplish mauve, pubescent at the apex of the lobes, glandular puberulous on the tube. Achenes 2.5–3 mm long, pale brown, 4–5 ribbed, glandular, otherwise glabrous. Pappus dingy white, 5 mm long with a ring of shorter outer scales 0.5 mm long.

D i s t r. Endemic.

E c o l. On river banks among rocks, 4000–6000 ft; uncommon. Flowering December–April.

S p e c i m e n s   E x a m i n e d. WITHOUT EXACT LOCALITY: *C.P. 164* annotated "Adam's Peak, Gardner; Ambagamuwa, Mar. 1852" (PDA), annotated "Adam's Peak, Mar. 1846" (K), unannotated (BM). KANDY DISTRICT: Adam's Peak, Mar. 1846, *s. coll. C.P. 460* (K); N of Laksapana, Simpson 8987 (BM); Maskeliya near Gartmore Estate, 29 Apr. 1926, *Silva s.n.* (PDA); below Gartmore Falls, 4000 ft, *Grierson 1056* (E, US, PDA).

N o t e s. *V. wightiana* and *V. anceps* are closely related and the possibility that hybridisation takes place between them in the neighbourhood of Adam's Peak has already been mentioned (and see Grierson, Ceylon J. Sci., Biol. Sci. 10: 43. 1972). Some of the type material from this locality does not appear to be completely "pure" and specimens from Maskeliya are more distinct. In comparison with *V. wightiana* it would appear that *V. anceps* is always a small shrub of the river banks with narrow almost glabrous leaves which are distantly serrate rather than densely tomentose and denticulate: the involucre is smaller and the phyllaries acute rather than shortly acuminate and pubescent rather than tomentose, the corollas are smaller and pubescent only on the lobes.

10. Vernonia zeylanica (L.) Less., Linnaea 4 (1): 344. 1829; Thw., Enum. Pl.
Zeyl. 160. 1859; C.B. Clarke, Comp. Ind. 20. 1876; Hook. f., Fl. Br. Ind. 3:
238. 1881; Trimen, Handb. Fl. Ceylon 3: 10. 1895; Alston, Kandy Fl. 52,
fig. 274, 1938. *Eupatorium zeylanicum* L., Sp. Pl. 837. 1753; Moon, Cat. 57.
1824. Type: Herb. *Hermann* (BM).

Shrubs (0.5–) 1–2.5 m tall, usually erect or scrambling, occasionally prostrate. Young stems densely pubescent or tomentose, later glabrescent.
Leaves pandurate or ovate, 5–8 × 2–3 cm, attenuate, subsessile and auriculate
at the base or on short petioles 0.5–1 cm long, acute or obtuse at the apex,
margins crenate-dentate, whitish pubescent on both surfaces, sparsely so on
the upper surface and later glabrescent, dense or subtomentose on the under
surface. Capitula campanulate, numerous in terminal corymbs. Involucres 3–
4 mm long, 2–3 mm diam. when fresh, c. 5 mm broad when pressed, 4-seriate;
phyllaries ovate, acute, pubescent and ciliate at the apex. Flowers 6–8 per
capitulum; corollas 5–6 mm long, pale mauve or violet, glandular, otherwise
glabrous. Achenes 2–2.5 mm long, brown, 4–5 ribbed, glandular and puberulous. Pappus dirty white becoming reddish with storage, 4–5 mm long with
a ring of short outer hairs c. 0.5 mm long.

D i s t r. Endemic.
E c o l. Track sides in patanas and on dunes bordering forest scrub at sea
level and up to 3000 ft, common. Flowering June–April.
V e r n. Papula, Hin-botiya (S), Wail-pupula (S, according to Moon);
Kuppilay (T).
S p e c i m e n s   E x a m i n e d. VAVUNIYA DISTRICT: between Meda-
wachchiya and Mannar at milepost 113, *Jayasuriya et al. 591* (US, E, PDA).
TRINCOMALEE DISTRICT: Neighbourhood of Trincomalee, 3 July 1860,
Dubuc s.n. (E); Fort Point, Trincomalee, 19 Aug. 1860, *Dubuc s.n.* (E); Trinco-
malee, *Simpson 8483* (BM); 17 miles N of Trincomalee, *Grierson 1036* (E, US,
PDA). KANDY DISTRICT: Hantane area, Peradeniya 900 m, *Mueller-
Dombois & Cooray 67111328* (US, PDA). KURUNEGALA DISTRICT:
Hettipola, *Amaratunga 673* (PDA). HAMBANTOTA DISTRICT: Hamban-
tota, *Fosberg et al. 51213* (E, US); Ruhuna National Park, Patanagala,
Wirawan 685 (PDA); beach E of Butawa Modera, *Fosberg 50322* (PDA),
Comanor 372 (PDA), *Mueller-Dombois & Cooray 67121039* (US, PDA).
MATALE DISTRICT: Mousekande, *Simpson 8460* (BM). WITHOUT LO-
CALITY: *s. coll. C.P. 1738* annotated "ubique" (PDA); *s. coll., s.n.* "up to
3000 ft" (BM), *s. coll. s.n.* (K); *Walker 1028* (E); *s.n.* (E-GL, K); *Wight 1378/
65* (E, K); *Harvey s.n.* (E); *Brodie s.n.* (E); *Fraser 118* (BM); *G. Thomson s.n.*
(K); *Macrae 453* (BM); *s. coll. 745* (BM).

A prostrate form grows on the beach sand above high tide mark in
Ruhuna National Park—*Grierson 1145* (E, US, PDA, BR).

11. Vernonia setigera Arn., Nova Acta Phys. Med. Acad. Caes. Leop. Carol. Nat. Cur. 18: 345. 1836; C.B. Clarke, Comp. Ind. 18. 1876; Hook. f., Fl. Br. Ind. 3: 235. 1881; Trimen, Handb. Fl. Ceylon 3: 7. 1895. Type: *Walker s.n.* (E-GL).

Vernonia nilgherryensis auct. non. DC.: Thw., Enum. Pl. Zeyl. 160. 1859.

Erect or straggling shrubs or subshrubs, 1–2.5 m tall. Stems densely covered with appressed brown pubescence intermixed with stiffer spreading hairs. Leaves ovate, petiolate, petioles 0.5–2 cm long, laminae 4–10 × 1–5 cm, rounded or cuneate at the base, acute or acuminate at the apex, margins sharply serrate, somewhat harshly pubescent on both surfaces but more densely so beneath, upper surface becoming blackish green on drying. Capitula narrowly campanulate, numerous in dense corymbs. Involucre 6–8 mm long, 2–2.5 mm diam. when fresh, c. 5 mm broad when pressed, 3–4 seriate; phyllaries lanceolate, pubescent, the inner ones rather abruptly acuminate into a setose point c. 1 mm long. Flowers 6–10 per capitulum; corollas 5–6 mm long, glandular, otherwise glabrous. Achenes brown, 1.5–2 mm long, glandular, 5-ribbed. Pappus 5–6 mm long, dirty white, with a ring of short outer hairs c. 0.25 mm long.

D i s t r. Endemic.

E c o l. Jungle paths and montane forests, 5000–6000 ft; common. Flowering December–June.

S p e c i m e n s E x a m i n e d. WITHOUT EXACT LOCALITY: *C.P. 20* annotated "Nuwara Eliya, Feb. 1857; Adam's Peak" (PDA), annotated "Adam's Peak, Mar. 1846" (K), annotated "5000–7000 ft" (BM). NUWARA ELIYA DISTRICT: Nuwara Eliya, *Gardner 386* (PDA, BM, K); *387* (K); ibid., *Amaratunga 415* (PDA); ibid., 6000 ft, *Gamble 27556* (K); Horton Plains, 26 Jan. 1906, *Willis s.n.* (PDA); Hakgala, 2 Mar. 1906, *Willis s.n.* (PDA); Ambawela, 26 Mar. 1906, *Silva s.n.* (PDA); Sita Eliya, *Simpson 9589* (BM); Single Tree Mount, *Sinclair 10083* (E); Kandy—Nuwara Eliya road at Milemarker 43/18, 1870 m, *Comanor 929* (E, US, PDA); Pattipola—Horton Plains road, 2050 m, *Comanor 944* (E, US, PDA); Pidurutalagala, c. 6700 ft, *Grierson 1073* (E, US, PDA, BR, CANB). KANDY DISTRICT: Knuckles, 14 June 1926, *Silva s.n.* (PDA). WITHOUT LOCALITY: *Walker 66* (E), *s. coll. 1698* (E, K), *s. coll., s.n.* (E-GL); *Mackenzie s.n.* (K); *Maxwell s.n.* (K).

12. Vernonia hookeriana Arn., Nova Acta Phys. Med. Acad. Caes. Leop. Carol. Nat. Cur. 18: 346, 1838; C.B. Clarke, Comp. Ind. 19. 1876; Hook. f., Fl. Br. Ind. 3: 235. 1881; Trimen, Handb. Fl. Ceylon 3: 8. 1895; Alston, Kandy Fl. 52. 1938; Bond, Wild Fls. Ceylon Hills 96, t. 48. 1953. Type: In Ceylani montibus alt. 1000 hexapod., *Walker s.n.* (E-GL).

Vernonia conyzoides auct. non. DC.: Thw., Enum. Pl. Zeyl. 160. 1859.

Erect herb or subshrub, 1–2 m tall. Stem striate, softly appressed pubescent. Leaves ovate, petiolate, petioles 1–3 cm long, laminae 7–10 × 2.5–5 cm, truncate or rounded at the base, acuminate at the apex, margins coarsely serrate, sparsely pubescent above, glandular and densely pubescent on the veins beneath. Capitula campanulate, numerous in loose terminal corymbs. Involucre 3–4 mm long, c. 3 mm diam. when fresh, c. 5 mm broad when pressed, 3-seriate; phyllaries densely greyish tomentose, lanceolate or linear oblanceolate, obtuse or subacute. Flowers c. 20 per capitulum; corollas 5.5–6 mm long, mauve, finely and sparsely pubescent. Achenes brown, 2–2.5 mm long, 4–5 ribbed, glandular and sparsely pubescent. Pappus whitish, 4–5 mm long with an outer ring of minute hairs c. 0.1 mm long.

D i s t r. Endemic.

E c o l. Moist shady banks and patanas, 1000–6000 ft; common. Flowering September–April.

S p e c i m e n s   E x a m i n e d. WITHOUT EXACT LOCALITY: *s. coll. 1737,* annotated "Hantane; Ambagamuwa, Feb. 1855" (PDA), annotated "Oonoogal Oya, *Gardner*" (K), unannotated (BM). ANURADHAPURA DISTRICT: Summit of Ritigala, 23 Mar. 1905, *Willis s.n.* (PDA). KANDY DISTRICT: Kandy, 12 Feb. 1819, *Moon 148* (BM); Corbet's Gap near Rangala, *Simpson 9440* (BM); Hantane, 950 m, *Mueller-Dombois & Cooray 68011907* (PDA, US); Makeldeniya, above Teldeniya, 3000 ft, *Grierson 1015* (E, US, PDA, BR, CANB). NUWARA ELIYA DISTRICT: Nuwara Eliya, 6000 ft, *Gardner 387* (BM); Pussellawa-Ramboda road, milemarker 27/10, 1010 m. *Comanor 923* (E, US, PDA); Ramboda Pass, *Simpson 8688* (BM). BADULLA DISTRICT: Welimada—Dikwella Road, 4000 ft., *Simpson 9623* (BM). WITHOUT LOCALITY: "ad alt. 6000 ped.", *Walker s.n.* (E-GL), *248* (K), *1706* (E, K); *Harvey s.n.* (E); *Macrae 384* (BM).

13. Vernonia cinerea (L.) Less., Linnaea 4 (1): 291. 1829; Thw., Enum. Pl. Zeyl. 1859; C.B. Clarke, Comp. Ind. 20. 1876; Hook. f., Fl. Br. Ind. 3: 233. 1881; Trimen, Handb. Fl. Ceylon 3: 7. 1895; Alston, Kandy Fl. 52, fig. 272. 1938.

Conyza cinerea L., Sp. Pl. 862. 1753; Moon, Cat. 58. 1824. Type: Herb. *Hermann* (BM).

Vernonia albicans auct. non DC.: Alston in Trimen, Handb. Fl. Ceylon 6: 159. 1931.

Erect or decumbent annual herbs, (5–) 15–30 cm tall, occasionally up to 1.5 m tall. Stems terete, finely striate, appressed pubescent. Leaves ovate, petiolate or subpetiolate, petioles 0.5–1.5 cm long, laminae 2–5 × 1–2 cm, acute or obtuse at the apex, rounded or attenuate at the base, margins subentire or repand dentate, ± sparsely pubescent above, moderately to densely pubescent and punctate beneath. Capitula few (3–10) or numerous in terminal corymbs. Involucres 3–4 mm long, 2–3 mm diam. when fresh, c. 5 mm broad when pressed, 4–5 seriate, outer phyllaries narrowly lanceolate, inner ones oblong-lanceolate, acute or apiculate, appressed pubescent, purplish-tinged at the apices. Flowers 20–35 per capitulum; corollas 3–4 mm long, bluish mauve, rarely white. Achenes dark brown or blackish, 1.25–1.5 mm long, obscurely 4–5-angular, finely white puberulous. Pappus whitish, 3–4.5 mm long, with an outer ring of shorter hairs c. 0.25–0.5 mm long.

Chromosome number. n = 9 (Mehra *et al.*, Caryologia 18: 37. 1965).

D i s t r. Tropical Asia, Africa, Australia, New Zealand.

E c o l. Common weed of roadsides and waste ground. Flowering throughout the year.

V e r n. Monara-Kudimbiya, Mangul-kumburuvenna, Vatu-pala (S); chitiviyarchenkalainir, Neisudi-Kirai, Neichatti-Kirai, Neichatti-pillu (T). The following Tamil names are also reportedly used for *Conyza floribunda*: Avalangu-pillu, Poom-pillu.

S p e c i m e n s   E x a m i n e d. WITHOUT EXACT LOCALITY: *C.P. 1736* annotated "Jaffna, Ratnapura, *Gardner*; Ambagamuwa, Mar. 1852, (PDA), unannotated (K, BM). KANDY DISTRICT: Peradeniya, Hantane area, 900 m, *Mueller-Dombois & Cooray* 67111305 (PDA), *67110908* (PDA); Peradeniya, 507 m, *Comanor 468* (E, US, PDA); *Comanor 714* (E, US); Galgedera, *Amaratunga 594* (PDA). BADULLA DISTRICT: Haputale Estate, 16 Nov. 1926, *Hyde s.n.* (PDA). MONERAGALA DISTRICT: Bintenne, 26 Apr. 1923, *J.M. Silva s.n.* (PDA). RATNAPURA DISTRICT: Sinharaja Forest, Weddagala, Dec. 1893, *Ferguson s.n.* (PDA); Weddagala, Kehelwatupola near Kudawe, 300 m, *Hoogland 11450* (E, US, PDA, CANB). NUWARA ELIYA DISTRICT: Fort Macdonald Valley, 11 Mar. 1906, *A.M. Smith s.n.* (PDA) Rambodde, *G. Thomson s.n.* (K). KALUTARA DISTRICT: Moragala, *Alston 1657* (PDA). VAVUNIYA DISTRICT: near Vavuniya, *Simpson 8022* (BM). TRINCOMALEE DISTRICT: 12 miles N of Trincomalee, *Grierson 1031* (E, US, PDA, BR, CANB). ANURADHAPURA DISTRICT: Wilpattu National Park, near Eerige Ara confluence with Modegagama Ara, 30 m, *Fosberg et al. 50779* (E, US). HAMBANTOTA DISTRICT: Ruhuna Nat. Park, Situlpahuwa Road, *Cooray 70032703* (US, E, PDA).

N o t e s. Dwarf maritime forms of this species may be found on the sea shore growing with *Spinifex*. The leaves tend to be fleshy and short (c. 1.5 cm long); the capitula in small corymbs of 3–4 with glandular, but otherwise glabrous, involucres; the flowers deep purple crimson. Puttalam Dist., Chilaw, *Simpson 8164* (PDA, BM).

In general the specimens from Ceylon agree with those from Southern India as regards capitulum size, leaf shape and pubescence. There is not, however, the range of variability that Koster (Blumea 1: 408. 1935) found among the Malayan material and, of the varieties which she recognised, the Ceylon plants approach, though are somewhat larger than, var. *parviflora* (Bl.) DC.

14. Vernonia elliptica DC. A straggling scandent shrub with elliptic silvery leaves, small few-flowered capitula borne in axillary corymbs and white flowers which are mauve in the bud and sweet smelling. This species, which is occasionally cultivated (Kandy District: above Teldeniya, *Grierson 1013*), is indigenous to the Nilgiri Hills, S. India, Burma and Siam. It does not at present appear to grow wild in Ceylon but may do so in the future.

Vernonia macrophylla Less., a shrubby Brazilian species, is reported to be cultivated as a foliage plant because of its large ovate leaves which may measure 20–25 cm long and 15 cm broad.

2a. Stokesia laevis (Hill) Greene, another member of the Vernonieae, is cultivated in Ceylon and is known, elsewhere, to escape from time to time. The general aspect of the capitulum resembles that of a *Centaurea* in that the purple marginal flowers are 5-lobed, radiant and larger than the white central ones. The outer phyllaries are fringed with bristles and the pappus consists of 4–5 caducous scales. It is a native of North America.

3. ELEPHANTOPUS

L., Sp. Pl. 814. 1753; Gen. Pl. ed. 5. 355. 1754. Type species: *E. scaber* L.

Stiff perennial herbs bearing large oblanceolate and usually rosulate basal leaves. Stems erect, branched, bearing alternate leaves and terminal glomerules of capitula. Glomerules surrounded by leaf-like bracts and containing several (c. 20) capitula. Capitula homogamous, few (usually 4)-flowered. Involucre oblong, compressed, 2-seriate; phyllaries c. 10 oblong, acute. Corolla tubular, limb deeply cleft into 5 secund lobes. Anther lobes auricled at the base. Achenes 10-ribbed, pubescent. Pappus setae 5, rarely 6 (elsewhere numerous), stiff, uniseriate, becoming dilated and ciliate at the base.

Elephantopus scaber L., Sp. Pl. 814. 1753; Moon, Cat. 59. 1824; DC., Prod. 5: 86. 1836; Thw., Enum. Pl. Zeyl. 161. 1860; Trimen, Handb. Fl. Ceylon 3: 12. 1895; Alston, Kandy Fl. 52. 1938; Koster, Blumea 1: 456. 1935. Type: Habitat in Indiis, Herb. Hort Cliff. (BM).

Rootstock creeping, rhizomatous. Stems (3.5–) 10–50 cm tall, terete, dichotomously branched, appressed whitish strigose. Radical leaves (5.5–)

10–20 × (2.5–) 4–7 cm, petiolate, petioles up to 1.5 cm long, obtuse or acute at the apex, somewhat bullate and sparsely hirsute above (hairs with warty bases), hirsute on the prominent veins beneath and glandular on the intervening areas, margin crenate-serrate, ciliate; cauline leaves shorter, sessile, ovate or oblong, semiamplexicaul at the base. Glomerules surrounded by three carinate, cordate bracts c. 1–1.5 cm long, 1 cm broad at the base. Involucres 8–10 mm long, 2 mm broad, consisting of 8 phyllaries in 2-series, phyllaries whitish hirsute. Flowers lilac or white, corolla tubes 5.5 mm long, lobes linear-lanceolate, 3 mm long. Achenes oblong, 4 mm long, 10-ribbed. Pappus setae 5 mm long.

Chromosome numbers. The following counts have been reported: n = 11, 2n = 22 (Mehra *et al.*, Caryologia 18: 37. 1965).

D i s t r. India northwards to the Himalayas, Burma, Indo China, Malayan Peninsula, W. China, Philippines, Australia, Trop. Africa, but apparently not from Trop. S. America (cf. Trimen).

E c o l. At roadsides, in scrub and plantations, in patanas and short grass and as a weed in lawns. Common in lowland areas and up to 7000 ft.

V e r n. Et-adi (S), Aet-adiya (S—according to Moon); Anichovadi (T).

N o t e s. According to Philipson (J. Bot. 76: 302. 1938) the African plants have 7–10 pappus setae and are separated as subsp. *plurisetus* (O. Hoffm.) Philipson from the typical Asiatic subspecies the pappus of which has 5 (or rarely 6) setae. The roots of this species are apparently used throughout the East in the treatment of dysentry and bowel complaints. Trimen (l.c.) noted that its leaves were used as "an external application".

S p e c i m e n s E x a m i n e d. WITHOUT PRECISE LOCALITY: *s. coll. C.P. 1772* annotated "ubique" (PDA), unannotated (BM). KANDY DISTRICT: Kandy, 1819, *Moon s.n.* (BM); Peradeniya, 23 Apr. 1953 (fls. white), *E.A. Ramanayake s.n.* (PDA); ibid. (fls. white), *Alston 1271* (PDA); ibid., 1610 ft, *Grierson 1039* (E, US, PDA, BR, CANB); *Comanor 709* (E, US, PDA); *Comanor 1169* (US, PDA); ibid., *Fosberg 50660* (E, US); Galagedera, *Amaratunga 593* (PDA). BADULLA DISTRICT: 2 miles S of Welimada, 1225 m, *Mueller-Dombois 67091510* (US, PDA); Fort Macdonald Valley, 11 Mar 1906, *A.M. Silva s.n.* (PDA). POLONNARUWA DISTRICT: Habarane-Polonnaruwa road, 160 m, *Comanor 1213* (US, PDA); A6 road at Marker 110/3, 0–50 m, *Gould & Cooray 13730* (E, US). WITHOUT LOCALITY: *Walker s.n.* (E).

N o t e s. Trimen (l.c.) noted the presence of a dwarf form of this species on Horton Plains. There is only one specimen at Peradeniya of this kind labelled "Horton Plains, 1886, *W. Nock s.n.*". It is a monoglomerulate plant with leaves up to 5.5 cm long, 2.5 cm broad and flowering stems 3.5–8 cm tall. Such a plant has not been recollected nor, indeed, did I find any specimens of *Elephantopus* on Horton Plains in March 1969.

Tribe EUPATORIEAE

Herbs or shrubs. Leaves opposite or the upper ones alternate. Capitula homogamous, discoid, sometimes few-flowered. Phyllaries few or numerous, uniseriate or in several series. Anther bases obtuse. Styles usually much exserted; branches clavate, obtuse. Receptacle naked. Achenes obovoid or oblong, 3–5 ribbed. Pappus of hairs or scales.

KEY TO THE GENERA

1 Flowers few, 4–5 per capitulum. Phyllaries 4–5, uniseriate
  2 Scandent twining herbs. Capitula 4-flowered.........................7. **Mikania**
  2 Erect herbs or subshrubs. Capitula 5-flowered. ....6a. **Stevia**
1 Flowers more than 10 per capitulum. Phyllaries 2 or more seriate
  3 Phyllaries imbricate. Pappus consisting of numerous hairs............6. **Eupatorium**
  3 Phyllaries subequal. Pappus of 3–5 bristles or scales
    4 Capitula in lax corymbs. Pappus of 3–4 thick gland-tipped bristles..4. **Adenostemma**
    4 Capitula in rather dense corymbs. Pappus of 4–5 aristate scales........5. **Ageratum**

4. ADENOSTEMMA

Forst., Char. Gen. 89, t. 45. 1776. Type: *A. lavenia* (L.) Kuntze (=*A. viscosum* Forst.).

Erect or decumbent annual or perennial herbs, usually glandular pubescent. Leaves generally opposite or the upper ones alternate, usually 3-nerved, petiolate or subsessile. Capitula terminal on the branches of lax corymbs, medium sized, homogamous. Involucre campanulate, phyllaries 2-seriate, herbaceous, subequal, connate at the base. Flowers 20–40, hermaphrodite, corollas tubular, glandular and puberulent, 3–5 lobed. Anthers gland-tipped, obtuse or subcordate at the base. Style branches clavate, sometimes much exserted. Receptacle flat or convex, naked, alveolate. Achenes obovoid, 3–5 angular, smooth or glandular-tuberculate, stipitate, borne on minute callose stalks. Pappus of 3 (sometimes 4) thick, clavate, gland-tipped bristles attached to apical ring of achene.

KEY TO THE SPECIES

1 Leaves elliptic-lanceolate, 1–1.5 cm broad, gradually attenuate at the base. Capitula c. 3 cm diam. Corollas 3–5 mm long, glandular near the base, pubescent above. Achenes 3.25 mm long, sparsely verrucose......................1. **A. angustifolium**
1 Leaves ovate, obviously petiolate at the base, generally more than 1.5 cm broad
  2 Capitula c. 3 mm diam. Corollas 1–1.5 mm long, densely tomentose on the upper part. Style branches acarcely exserted.......................2. **A. parviflorum**
  2 Capitula c. 5 mm diam. Corollas 3–4 mm long, glandular and pubescent, but not densely so. Style branches strongly exserted

3 Style branches exserted c. 2.5 mm from corolla mouth. Achenes distinctly verrucose. Leaves ± glabrous, not prominently veined beneath...................**3. A. lavenia**
3 Style branches exserted 3–4 mm from corolla mouth. Achenes smooth or glandular at first. Leaves scabrous on the upper surface, pubescent on the prominent veins beneath...**4. A. macrophyllum**

1. Adenostemma angustifolium Arn., Nova Acta Phys. Med. Acad. Caes. Leop. Carol. Nat. Cur. 18: 347. 1836; Grierson, Ceylon J. Sci., Biol. Sci. 10: 47. 1972.

Adenostemma viscosum Forst. var. *typica* Hook. f., Fl. Br. Ind. 3: 242. 1881, quoad syn.
Adenostemma viscosum Forst.: Trimen, Handb. Fl. Ceylon 3: 13. 1895, quoad syn.
Adenostemma viscosum var. *angustifolium* Edgw. ex C.B. Clarke, Comp. Ind. 29. 1876. Type: In Ceylano, *Walker s.n.* (E-GL).

Stems c. 30 mm tall, glabrous. Leaves elliptic-lanceolate, 5–9 × 0.8–1.5 cm, attenuate at the base, acuminate at the apex, margins bearing a few (c. 4) shallowly serrate teeth in the upper half of the leaf, glabrous on both surfaces, ± distinctly trinerved at the base. Capitula c. 3 mm diam., borne in terminal corymbs, peduncles puberulent. Involucre 4.5 mm long, glabrous or puberulent at the base, phyllaries 2.5–3.5 mm long, linear, obtuse at the apex. Corollas c. 3.25 mm long, 5-lobed, basal tube covered with stalked glands, finely pubescent in the upper part at the base of the lobes. Style branches exserted c. 2 mm beyond mouth of corolla. Achenes brown, 3.25 mm long, sparsely verrucose.

Distr. Also from Sikkim and Western Himalaya.
Specimens Examined. WITHOUT LOCALITY: 17 Mar. 1819, *Moon 542* (BM); *Walker 303* (K) *s.n.* (E-GL type).
Unfortunately there are no localised specimens of this species, which may not now be present on the Island.

2. Adenostemma parviflorum (Blume) DC., Prod. 5: 111. 1836; Grierson, Ceylon J. Sci., Biol. Sci. 10: 47. 1972; Koster, Blumea 1: 476. 1935.

Lavenia parviflora Blume, Bijdr. 906. 1826. Type: "in umbrosis circa Buitenzorg", *Blume s.n.* (L.).
Adenostemma viscosum var. *parviflora* (Blume) Hook. f., Fl. Br. Ind. 3: 242. 1881.

Stems 35 and reputedly up to 70 cm tall, glandular pubescent. Leaves ovate, petiolate (petioles 1–3 cm long), laminae 2–5.5 × 1.5–3 cm, acute or obtuse at the apex, scabrous on both surfaces, glabrescent, margins serrate. Capitula c. 3 mm diam. in loose corymbose panicles on glandular-pubescent peduncles. Involucre pubescent and slightly glandular, 4–5 mm long, phyllaries spathulate, subacute or obtuse, 2–3 mm long. Corollas c. 1.5 mm long, 3–4-lobed, glandular near the base of the tube, tomentose on the lobes. Style branches scarcely exserted from mouth of corolla. Achenes narrowly obovoid, 2.5 mm long, dark brown or black, tuberculate. Pappus bristles c. 0.5 mm long.

D i s t r. Malayan Peninsula and Archipelago, China. Usually found in moist marshy situations.
S p e c i m e n s E x a m i n e d. WITHOUT LOCALITY: "Ceylon Highlands", *Harvey s.n.* (E).

3. Adenostemma lavenia (L.) Kuntze, Rev. Gen. Pl. 1: 304. 1891; Alston in Trimen, Handb. Fl. Ceylon 6: 160. 1931; Koster, Blumea 1: 470. 1935.

Verbesina lavenia L., Sp. Pl. 902. 1753. Type: Herb. *Hermann* (BM).
Lavenia erecta Willd., Sp. Pl. 3: 1724. 1804; Moon, Cat. 57. 1824.
Adenostemma viscosum Forst., Char. Gen. 90. 1776; DC., Prod. 5: 111. 1836; Thw., Enum. Pl. Zeyl. 162. 1860; C.B. Clarke, Comp. Ind. 28. 1876; Hook. f., Fl. Br. Ind. 3: 242. 1881; Trimen, Handb. Fl. Ceylon 3: 13. 1895. Type: Drawing (BM).

Perennial (?) herbs up to 1 m tall. Stems glandular-pubescent with purplish hairs or glabrescent. Leaves ovate, petiolate (petioles 1–5 cm long) or sessile, laminae 5–15 × 1.5–7 cm, cuneate-attenuate at the base, acuminate at the apex, margins ± coarsely serrate-dentate with gland-tipped teeth, strongly 3-nerved at the base, glabrous on both surfaces. Capitula c. 5 mm diam., borne in loose corymbs on glandular-pubescent peduncles. Involucre 6–7 mm tall, pubescent at the base, glabrous above; phyllaries linear-spathulate, 4–5 mm long, 1–1.5 mm broad, ± acute, margins ciliate, Corollas white, 3.5–4 mm long, glandular at the base, sparsely pubescent in the upper part at the base of the lobes. Style branches exserted c. 2.5 mm beyond mouth of corolla. Achenes 4–5 mm long, brown, glandular-tuberculate. Pappus bristles c. 0.75 mm long.
Chromosome number. n = 10 (Mehra *et al.*, Caryologia 18: 37. 1965).

D i s t r. China, Malaya, India, Australia, Tropical Africa, Polynesia.
E c o l. In moist shady upland forests and at track sides, common. Flowers throughout the year.
V e r n. Laveniya (S).
S p e c i m e n s E x a m i n e d. WITHOUT PRECISE LOCALITY: *C.P. 594* annotated "Galle and Bintenne, *Gardner*; Ambagamuwa, *Gardner*; Paragalla, Oct. 1853" (PDA p.p.) annotated "Ambagamuwa, Feb. 1846" (K); unannotated *s.n.* (BM). NUWARA ELIYA DISTRICT: Hakgala, 6 Mar.

1906, *Silva s.n.* (PDA); near St. Coombes, Talawakele, *Simpson 8918* (BM). KANDY DISTRICT: Dolosbage, 3500 ft, *Grierson 1000* (E, US, PDA, BR, CANB). ANURADHAPURA DISTRICT: summit of Ritigala, 24 Mar. 1905, *Willis s.n.* (PDA). RATNAPURA DISTRICT: Yatiantota, *Simpson 8720* (PDA, BM). KEGALLE DISTRICT: Salgala Sanctuary, *Amaratunga 980* (PDA). KALUTARA DISTRICT: Pasdun Korale, Mar. 1887, *Trimen s.n.* (PDA). WITHOUT LOCALITY, *Walker 1233* (E).

4. Adenostemma macrophyllum (Blume) DC., Prod. 5: 113. 1836; Koster, Blumea 1: 480. 1935; Grierson, Ceylon. J. Sci., Biol. Sci. 10: 47. 1972.

Lavenia macrophylla Blume, Bijdr. 905. 1826. Type: Java, "in montanis Gede", *Blume* (L.).
Adenostemma madurense DC. in Wight, Contrib. 9. 1834 et Prod. 5: 113. 1836.
Adenostemma reticulatum DC. in Wight, Contrib. 8. 1834; et Prod. 5: 113. 1836.
Adenostemma viscosum var. *reticulatum* (DC.) C.B. Clarke, Comp. Ind. 30. 1876; Trimen, Handb. Fl. Ceylon 3: 13. 1895.

Perennial (?) herbs, 30–100 cm tall. Stems reddish-brown pubescent or glabrescent in the older parts, leaves ovate, petiolate (petioles 2–8 cm long), laminae 5–20 × 3–12 cm, cuneate-attenuate at the base, acute at the apex, margin coarsely serrate-dentate, teeth gland-tipped, scabrous on the upper surface, pubescent on the prominent veins beneath, ± distinctly 3-nerved at the base. Capitula c. 5 mm diam., in open corymbose panicles, borne on glandular-pubescent peduncles. Involucre 6–7 mm tall, glandular; phyllaries 4–5 mm long, 1–2 mm broad, elliptic-spathulate, acute or obtuse at the apex, margins ciliate. Corollas white, c. 3.5 mm long, 5-lobed, glandular in the lower part, finely pubescent on the lobes. Style branches exserted 3–4 mm beyond mouth of corolla. Achene 4–5 mm long, dark brown or blackish, sparsely glandular or completely smooth and glabrous. Pappus bristles 1–1.5 mm long.

D i s t r. S. India, Himalayas, Assam, Malaya.

E c o l. In moist situations in forests, apparently rare. Flowering throughout the year.

S p e c i m e n s E x a m i n e d. WITHOUT PRECISE LOCALITY: *s. coll. C.P. 594* p.p. (PDA). BADULLA DISTRICT: Haputale, ± 1500 m, *Kostermans 23181* (E). WITHOUT LOCALITY: *Walker 1233* (E).

5. AGERATUM

L., Sp. Pl. 839. 1753; Gen. Pl. ed. 5. 363. 1754. Type species: *A. conyzoides* L.

Erect branching herbs. Leaves opposite, ovate, petiolate, dentate. Capitula small, in dense terminal corymbs, homogamous. Involucres campanulate; phyllaries 2-3 seriate, subequal, linear or oblong-lanceolate. Corollas
tubular, 5-lobed. Anthers ± acutely appendiculate at the apex, obtuse at the
base. Style branches elongate, exserted, obtuse at the tip. Receptacle naked,
convex. Achenes oblong, 4-5 ribbed. Pappus of about 5 aristate scales,
broadening somewhat at the base.

KEY TO THE SPECIES

1 Phyllaries linear-lanceolate, gradually acuminate, entire-margined, glandular........
....2. A. houstonianum
1 Phyllaries oblong-lanceolate, ± abruptly acuminate, margins often dentate or erose,
pubescent or almost glabrous, eglandular..........................1. A. conyzoides

1. Ageratum conyzoides L., Sp. Pl. 839. 1753; Moon, Cat. 57. 1824; Thw.,
Enum. Pl. Zeyl. 161. 1860; C.B. Clarke, Comp. Ind. 30. 1876; Hook. f., Fl.
Br. Ind. 3: 243. 1881; Trimen, Handb. Fl. Ceylon 3: 13. 1895, in nota; Alston
in Trimen., Handb. Fl. Ceylon 6: 160. 1931; Koster, Blumea 1: 484. 1935.
Type: Herb. Hort. Cliff (BM).

Rank smelling annual herbs, 10-100 cm tall. Stems terete, whitish pilose.
Leaves on hirsute petioles up to 5 cm long, lamina 2-8 × 1.5-6 cm, obtuse or
subacute at the apex, truncate, rounded or cuneate at the base, margins
crenate, hirsute on both surfaces with long spreading hairs, lower surface
studded with glistening sessile glands. Capitula 3-4 mm diam. in corymbs of
about 5-15 capitula, borne on pubescent peduncles 0.5-2 cm long which bear
short linear bracts. Phyllaries oblong-lanceolate, 3-4 mm long, 1 mm broad,
acute or rather abruptly acuminate, 2-3 nerved, margins scarious, erose or
dentate in the upper part, subglabrous or with a few pubescent, eglandular
hairs at the margin. Flowers numerous (60-100), white, blue or mauve; corollas 1.75-2 mm long. Styles exserted c. 1 mm beyond corolla mouth. Achenes
narrowly oblong, 1.5-1.75 mm long, black, minutely and sparsely whitish
hirsute on the angles. Pappus scales 5, c. 2 mm long, lanceolate, finely scabrous on the margins, acuminate into a bristle-like point.

Chromosome number. n = 10 has been reported from Indian material
(Mehra et al., Caryologia 18: 37. 1965) but n = 20 from Thailand (Turner in
King, Phytologia 11: 218. 1965) and 2 n = 40 from African material (Harvey,
Taxon 15: 162. 1966). Baker (in Econ. Bot. 26: 37. 1972) also gives n = 20 and
suggests that this species is of hybrid origin with the Central American A.
microcarpum Hemsl. as one of the putative parents.

Distr. American native, now a common weed of all warm countries.

Ecol. Abundant throughout the Island especially on roadsides and
cultivated ground. Flowering during the whole year.

V e r n. "White-weed" or "Goat-weed", Hulan-tala (S); Pumpillu (T).

S p e c i m e n s E x a m i n e d. KANDY DISTRICT: Peradeniya, Royal Botanic Garden (weed), 1887, *s. coll.* (PDA); Gampola-Nawalapitiya road, 800 m, *Comanor 531* (E, US, PDA); Hantane, *Mueller-Dombois & Cooray 67111304* (US, PDA); above Teldeniya, c. 1700 ft, *Grierson 1010* (E, US, PDA, BR, CANB). NUWARA ELIYA DISTRICT: Gorindihela, Hakgala, 27 Feb. 1906, *Silva s.n.* (PDA); St. Coombes near Talawakele, *Simpson 8889*, (BM); Hakgala Gardens, *Simpson 9090* (BM). TRINCOMALEE DISTRICT: Kantalai Tank, 55 m *Comanor 750* (E, US, PDA). ANURADHAPURA DISTRICT: Wilpattu National Park, near Eerige Ara confluence with Modegagama Ara, 30 m, *Fosberg et al. 50791* (E, US, PDA). POLONNARUWA DISTRICT: near Habarane Station, c. 700 ft, *Grierson 1029, a*—white flowered, *b*—blue flowered (E, US, PDA, BR, CANB). HAMBANTOTA DISTRICT: Ruhuna National Park, Rugamtota beside Menik Ganga River, *Fosberg & Mueller-Dombois 50164* (US, PDA); near Yala Camp, *Mueller-Dombois & Cooray 68013016* (US, PDA); Main Yala road, 6–10 m, *Comanor 823* (E, US, PDA). BADULLA DISTRICT: Haputale, 16 Nov. 1926, *J.N. Hyde s.n.* (PDA). KEGALLE DISTRICT: near Mawanella, 210 m, *Comanor 806* (E, US, PDA). WITHOUT LOCALITY: in 1860, *Dubuc s.n.* (E).

2. Ageratum houstonianum Mill., Gard. Dict. ed. 8 n. 2. 1768; Robinson, Proc. Amer. Acad. Arts. 49: 459. 1913 et Contr. Gray Herb. 42: 459. 1913; Koster, Blumea 1: 490. 1935; Grierson, Ceylon J. Sci., Biol. Sci. 10: 47. 1972.

Ageratum mexicanum Sims., Bot. Mag. t. 2524. 1825. Type: (K).
Ageratum conyzoides var. *mexicanum* DC., Prod. 5: 108. 1836. Type: *Houstoun s.n.* (BM).

Herbs up to 1 m tall. Stems erect or decumbent, terete, whitish hirsute and glandular. Leaves on hirsute petioles up to 5 cm long, lamina 2–10 × 1.5–5 cm, acute at the apex, truncate or cordate at the base, margins ± sharply serrate, whitish hirsute on both surfaces, eglandular. Capitula c. 5 mm diam. in dense corymbs of 10–20 capitula, peduncles densely hirsute and glandular pubescent. Phyllaries linear-lanceolate, 4–4.5 mm long, 0.4–0.5 mm broad, gradually acuminate at the apex, 2-nerved, margin entire, pubescent and glandular pubescent. Flowers numerous, c. 65, white, blue or mauve; corollas 2.5–3 mm long, styles exserted c. 2 mm beyond corolla mouth. Achenes linear-oblong, black, 1.75–2 mm long, scabrous on the ribs. Pappus scales 5, c. 2.5 mm long, lanceolate, acuminate into a bristle-like point, margins scabrous. Roadsides and ditches near cultivated ground, apparently not common.

Chromosome number. n = 10 (Mehra *et al.*, Caryologia 18: 37. 1965).

D i s t r. Indigenous to Central America, introduced into tropical Asia and reported from S. India, Assam, Java, Sumatra, Philippines, New Caledonia.

E c o l. Flowering throughout the year.

S p e c i m e n s E x a m i n e d. KANDY DISTRICT: near Maskeliya, c. 3500 ft, *Grierson 1057* (E, US, PDA, BR, CANB); Peradeniya, behind University Botany Building, 508 m, *Comanor 334* p.p. (E, US, PDA); Peradeniya, Lower Hantane road, 535 m, *Comanor 687* (E, US, PDA). NUWARA ELIYA DISTRICT: Nuwara Eliya in 1934?, *W.K. Harris s.n.* (E).

6. EUPATORIUM

L., Gen. Pl. ed. 5. 363. 1754. Type species: *E. cannabinum* L.

Herbs or shrubs. Leaves opposite, dentate, ± distinctly 3-nerved. Capitula in corymbs, homogamous. Involucre oblong-campanulate, phyllaries imbricate. Flowers 10–40 per capitulum, tubular campanulate, 5-lobed, never yellow. Anther bases obtuse. Style branches elongate, exserted, obtuse at the apex. Receptacle naked. Achenes oblong, 4–5 angled. Pappus capillary, uniseriate, hairs numerous, scabrous or finely barbellate.

KEY TO THE SPECIES

1 Capitula cylindrical-campanulate, c. 1 cm long. Flowers pale blue rarely white......
....**1. E. odoratum**
1 Capitula campanulate, c. 0.5 cm long. Flowers white
  2 Leaves ovate, abruptly attenuate into a narrowly cuneate petiole. Corymbs terminal
....**2. E. inulifolium**
  2 Leaves elliptic-lanceolate. Corymbs borne at the ends of short branches from the axils
    of the upper leaves...**3. E. riparium**

1. Eupatorium odoratum L., Syst. ed. 10. 1205. 1759; DC., Prod. 5: 143. 1836; Hook. f., Fl. Br. Ind. 3: 244. 1881; C.B. Clarke, Comp. Ind. 30. 1876; Robinson, Proc. Amer. Acad. Arts. 54 (4): 280. 1918; Contr. Gray Herb. 55: 280. 1918; Senaratna, Ceylon J. Sci., sect. A. Bot. 12: 213. 1947. Type: Herb. Browne (LINN).

Eupatorium conyzoides Vahl, Symb. Bot. 3: 96. 1794. Type: (C).

Erect or sprawling shrub. Stems 1–2.5 m tall, terete, sparsely pubescent. Leaves deltoid-ovate, petiolate, petioles up to 6 cm long, lamina 5–10 × 3–6 cm, cuneate at the base, attenuate, acuminate at the apex, margins bearing a few coarse teeth on either side near the broadest part, pubescent on both surfaces, glandular beneath. Capitula cylindrical-campanulate, 3 mm diam. in dense terminal corymbs c. 10 cm across. Involucre 4–5 seriate, c. 1 mm long, outer phyllaries ovate, inner ones linear, acute, whitish with 3 distinct green lines on each. Flowers 20–35 per capitula, pale bluish-mauve, rarely white, fragrant. Achenes slender, 4 mm long, angular, blackish with 4–5 pale scabrid ribs. Pappus whitish or pale brown when dried, 5 mm long.

Chromosome number. 2n=c. 64. (Mangenot & Mangenot, Rev. Cytol. Biol. Veg. 25: 432. 1962).

D i s t r. Indigenous to Trop. S. America, naturalised in India, Nepal, Burma, Malaya and Thailand.

E c o l. Abundant weed at roadsides, waste ground and forest clearings at lower elevations. Flowering January–July.

N o t e. This species is reputed to be a fish poison.

S p e c i m e n s E x a m i n e d. RATNAPURA DISTRICT: Anguruwela, *Amaratunga 1147* (PDA); Embilipitiya, 26 Jan. 1953, *Kandiah s.n.* (PDA); COLOMBO DISTRICT: Colombo-Kandy road near Pasyala, 140 m, *Comanor 804* (E, US, PDA); KANDY DISTRICT: Royal Botanic Garden, Peradeniya, June 1884, *Trimen* (?) *s.n.* (PDA); Peradeniya, Hantane, 950 m, *Mueller-Dombois & Cooray 68011904* (US, PDA); Peradeniya-Hantane road, 570 m, *Comanor 310* (US, PDA); Peradeniya, University, 535 m, *Comanor 697* (E, US, PDA); above Teldeniya, 1600 ft, *Grierson 1009* (E, US, PDA, BR, CANB); MONERAGALA DISTRICT: E. shore of Senanayake Samudra, 36 m, *Mueller-Dombois & Comanor 67072620* (US, PDA); *Comanor 582* (E, US, PDA). HAMBANTOTA DISTRICT: road between Yala and Gonalabbe, *Comanor 822* (E, US, PDA). WITHOUT LOCALITY: 10 Sept. 1968, *W.L. Weerakoon s.n.* (K).

N o t e s. Hooker (l.c.) noted that *E. odoratum* was "cultivated, but very rarely in India" although Clarke was able to remark as early as 1876 that it had become wild ("efferata") in parts of India and Java. Seneratna in his account of some weeds new to Ceylon (l.c.) wrote that it was first introduced as an ornamental at Peradeniya in 1894 (possibly this is an error for 1884, see above) where it subsequently died out. When it was next introduced is not recorded but between 1937 and 1947 it became naturalised particularly in the Balangoda-Ratnapura area and spread rapidly following the clearance of forests. In the local press it was reported to be a dangerous weed in 1944.

2. Eupatorium inulifolium HBK., Nov. Gen. et Sp. 4: 109. 1820; Robinson, Proc. Amer. Acad. Arts. 54 (4): 291. 1918; Contr. Gray Herb. 55: 291. 1918; Koster, Blumea 1: 496. 1935; Grierson, Ceylon J. Sci., Biol. Sci. 10: 49. 1972. Type: Colombia, Tolima near Mariquita, alt. 850 m, *Humboldt & Bonpland s.n.* (P).

Shrubs 1–2 (–5) m tall. Stems terete, densely and minutely brown pubescent. Leaves deltoid-ovate, petiolate, petioles narrowly cuneate up to 3 cm long, lamina 7–16 × 2.5–7.5 cm, gradually acuminate at the apex, ± abruptly contracted at the base into the petiole, margins shallowly and regularly serrate, glandular and pubescent on both surfaces but more densely so beneath. Capitula campanulate, c. 2–3 mm diam., numerous in large terminal corymbs. Involucre 3–4-seriate, outer phyllaries ovate, obtuse, 2–3 mm long, 1.25 mm broad, inner ones oblong, subacute, 5–6 mm long, stramineous, pubescent, distinctly 2–3 ribbed. Flowers 10–15 per capitulum, creamy white, corollas 4–5 mm long. Achenes oblong, 5-angular, glabrous, 1.5 mm long. Pappus whitish, 4 mm long.

Chromosome number. n = 10 (Powell & King, Amer. J. Bot. 56 (1): 116–121. 1969.

D i s t r. Indigenous to Trop. S. America, introduced in Sumatra and Java.

E c o l. Roadsides at mid elevations, rare? Flowering August.

S p e c i m e n s E x a m i n e d. KANDY DISTRICT: between Pussellawa and Ramboda on Highway A5 at milepost 25, 300 m, *Mueller-Dombois 67082406* (US, PDA); Rozella, *Burtt and Townsend 64* (US, E, K, PDA).

N o t e. This is a new record for the Ceylon flora but it has been known from Java since 1912 where Koster (l.c.) records that it has become relatively common at roadsides and on cultivated ground, e.g. on tea and coffee plantations where it may sometimes assume the proportions of a tree 5 metres tall.

3. Eupatorium riparium Regel, Gartenflora 15: 324 t. 525. 1866; Standley, Contr. U.S. Natl. Herb. 23: 1464. 1926; Koster, Blumea 1: 510. 1935; Bond, Wild Fls. Ceylon Hills 98, fig. 49. 1953; Grierson, Ceylon J. Sci., Biol. Sci. 10: 49. 1972. Type: Cult (LE?).

Ageratina riparia (Regel) King & Robinson, Phytologia 19 (4): 216. 1970.

Erect shrub or subshrub with creeping rootstock. Stems 0.5–1 m tall, pubescent, becoming glabrous near the base. Leaves elliptic-lanceolate, petiolate, petioles 0.5–1.3 cm long, lamina 3.5–7 (–10) × 1–1.5 cm, attenuate at the base, acuminate at the apex, margins ± regularly sharply serrate, subglabrous on the upper surface, sparsely pubescent beneath. Capitula campanulate, 2 mm diam., numerous in small corymbs borne on short branches from the axils of the upper leaves. Involucre 2-seriate, phyllaries c. 12, linear-oblong, obtuse, 4–5 mm long, pubescent, the inner ones scarious with 2–3 prominent ribs. Flowers white, c. 20 per capitulum, corollas 3–3.5 mm long. Achenes black, 1.5–2 mm long, 5-angular, finely white puberulous on the angles. Pappus white, setae finely barbellate, 2.5–3 mm long.

D i s t r. Indigenous to Mexico and West Indies, introduced in India and Java.

E c o l. An abundant and locally dominant weed at track sides, margins of cultivation and in forest clearings above 4000 feet. Flowering December–May and probably throughout the year.

S p e c i m e n s E x a m i n e d. NUWARA ELIYA DISTRICT: Hakgala,

Alston 1556 (PDA); *Amaratunga 416* (PDA); Nuwara Eliya, 1880 m, *Comanor 905* (E, US, PDA); 3 miles N of Horton Plains towards Agrapatana, 1500 m, *Gould 13586* (E, US, PDA). Kandy-Nuwara Eliya road at mile marker 43/18, 1870 m, *Comanor 928* (E, US, PDA). KANDY DISTRICT: Ascent to Adam's Peak from Dalhousie, 4400 ft, *Grierson 1040* (E, US, PDA, BR, CANB). BADULLA DISTRICT: Bogawantalawa-Borolanda road, 1575 m, *Comanor 1056* (E, US, PDA).

N o t e s. This species was and still is grown as an ornamental and was doubtless introduced through garden cultivation (the earliest specimen cited above is from the neighbourhood of Hakgala Botanic Garden collected in 1926). That it has become a troublesome and invasive weed in Ceylon has been officially recognised, for Bond (l.c. 1953) records that a survey of its distribution has been undertaken by the Ministry of Agriculture. It has been used as a source of green material for composting in Java and possibly such a practice would help to curtail its further spread in Ceylon.

6a. Stevia differs from *Eupatorium* in having a paleaceous pappus composed of 5–10 scales and capitula that contain few, usually 5, flowers. Alston (in Trimen, Handb. Fl. Ceylon 6: 160. 1931) reported that a species of *Stevia* (an exclusively American genus) occurred as "an escape at Hakgala". There is no specimen at Peradeniya to substantiate this record nor does the plant appear to have been recollected. Although the identity of the Hakgala *Stevia* is unknown, it should be noted that *S. ovata* Willd. is known to escape from cultivation in Java.

7. MIKANIA

Willd., Sp. Pl. 3: 1742. 1803 nom. cons. Type species: *M. scandens* (L.) Willd. (Syn. *Eupatorium scandens* L.) typ. cons.

Scandent twining herbs. Leaves opposite, petiolate, 3-veined. Capitula small, homogamous, in axillary corymbs, 4-flowered. Involucre of 4 subequal phyllaries, often with a smaller additional bract at the base. Corollas tubular, 5-lobed. Anthers appendiculate, obtuse at the base. Style branches long, slender, subobtuse at the apex, exserted. Receptacle naked. Achenes oblong, 4-angular. Pappus capillary, uniseriate; hairs connate at the base.

Mikania cordata (Burm.) Robinson, Contr. Gray Herb. 104: 65. 1934; Craib, Fl. Siam. Enum. 2: 250. 1936; Koster, Blumea 1: 504. 1935.

Eupatorium cordatum Burm., Fl. Ind. 176, t. 58, fig. 2. 1768. Type: (G?).
Mikania scandens auct. non L.; C.B. Clarke, Comp. Ind. 34. 1876; Hook. f., Fl. Br. Ind. 3: 244. 1881; Alston in Trimen, Handb. Fl. Ceylon 6: 160. 1931; Alston, Kandy Fl. 53, f. 279. 1938; Peradeniya Manual 7 et Ic. 1951.

Mikania volubilis Willd., Sp. Pl. 3: 1743. 1803; Moon, Cat. 57. 1824. Type: Habitat in India Orientali (B).

Stem slightly pubescent or glabrous, up to 7 m long. Leaves deltoid-ovate, petiolate, petioles 2–3 (–5) cm long, lamina 3–10 × 1.5–6 cm, acute or acuminate at the apex, cordate up to the base, margins ± coarsely undulate dentate or sometimes entire, subglabrous or sparsely pubescent on both surfaces, minutely glandular beneath. Capitula cylindrical, 1.5 mm diam., numerous in corymbs borne on short axillary branches. Phyllaries membranous, 2–3 veined, glabrous or sparsely puberulous, 4 mm long. Corolla greenish-white, 4–5 mm long. Achenes narrowly oblong, 2–3 mm long, dark brown, glabrous, glandular. Pappus white at first, becoming reddish-brown on storage, 3 mm long.

Chromosome number. n = 18 (Turner & Lewis, J. Bot. Soc. South Africa 31: 214. 1965).

D i s t r. Trop. Asia, Philippines, New Guinea and Trop. Africa.

E c o l. Weed at margins of forests and roadsides and in secondary forest. Flowering October–March.

V e r n. "Mile-a-minute" (in allusion to its rapid growth) (E); Tuni-Kodi, (T); Loka-palu (S = world ruin), Gam-palu, Vatu-palu, Kehel-palu (S), Mahakihimbiya (S—Moon).

N o t e. Cattle are reputed to browse on the plant especially during the dry season when food is scarce.

S p e c i m e n s   E x a m i n e d. KANDY DISTRICT: Royal Botanic Garden, Peradeniya, Oct. 1887, *Trimen? s.n.* (PDA); Hantane below University Circuit Bungalow, 850 m *Mueller-Dombois & Cooray 67111331* (US, PDA); Nawalapitiya—Ginigathena road, 800 m, *Comanor 533* (E, US, PDA); above Teldeniya, 1700 ft, *Grierson 1014* (E, US, PDA, BR, CANB); MATALE DISTRICT: Dambulla—Trincomalee road near Dambulla, 210 m, *Comanor 732* (E, US, PDA). KEGALLE DISTRICT: Galpitamada, *Amaratunga 1137* (PDA). COLOMBO DISTRICT: *Ramachandra Rao 2* (PDA).

N o t e. This, the only Asiatic species of *Mikania*, was long considered to be conspecific with the North American *M. scandens* until the technical differences that exist between them were pointed out by B.L. Robinson (l.c.).

Tribe A S T E R E A E

Herbs or shrubs with alternate or sometimes basal, rosulate leaves. Capitula heterogamous, radiate or disciform. Involucral bracts several-seriate. Female corollas ligulate or tubular, longer or shorter than the involucre. Anther bases obtuse or sagittate. Style branches complanate, with distinct rounded or triangular appendages at the apex. Receptacle naked. Achenes terete or compressed. Pappus capillary, coroniform or absent.

KEY TO THE GENERA

1 Capitula disciform or with inconspicuous ray flowers ± as long as or scarcely longer than involucre
  2 Leaves toothed or entire, never lobed or pinnatifid. Pappus capillary. Female flowers tubular or with short ligules. Herbs usually with stout ± erect stems......**13. Conyza**
  2 Leaves, at least some of them, pinnatifid. Pappus absent or cupulate or consisting of 2 weak bristles. Female flowers tubular, eligulate. Herbs with weak, decument or prostrate stems
    3 Pappus cupulate, fimbriate. Leaves ± deeply sinuate-pinnatisect.........**9. Grangea**
    3 Pappus absent or consisting of two weak bristles. Leaves generally lyrate-pinnatisect with large terminal lobes, sometimes undivided.................**8. Dichrocephala**
1 Capitula distinctly radiate, ligules clearly longer than involucre
  4 Pappus absent
    5 Low growing herbs with rosulate leaves. Capitula borne on leafless scapes
      6 Achenes truncate at the apex, eglandular. Cultivated plants............**11a. Bellis**
      6 Achenes narrowed into a short glandular beak at the apex. Native grassland plants..**11. Lagenophora**
    5 Medium sized herbs with leafy flowering stems. Achenes bearing a glandular rostrum at the apex...**10. Myriactis**
  4 Pappus of fine hairs present
    7 Small or medium-sized herbaceous plants
      8 Ray flowers yellow. Cultivated plants.............................**12e. Solidago**
      8 Ray flowers white or blue but not yellow
        9 Leaves pinnatisect. Pappus hairs short. Cultivated plants........**12c. Brachycome**
        9 Leaves simple, entire or toothed. Pappus hairs ± as long as disc corollas
          10 Phyllaries narrow, lanceolate or oblanceolate; not conspicuously leafy
            11 Leaves opposite, entire margined. Cultivated plants..............**12d. Felicia**
            11 Leaves alternate, margins toothed
              12 Ligules numerous, generally 1 mm or less broad...............**12. Erigeron**
              12 Ligules fewer, generally more than 1 mm broad. Cultivated plants..........
              ....**12a. Aster**
          10 Phyllaries spathulate, leafy. Cultivated plants...............**12b. Callistephus**
    7 Shrubs up to 3 m tall. Flowers yellow.............................**14. Psiadia**

8. DICHROCEPHALA

DC. in Guill., Arch. Bot. 2: 517. 1833; Prod. 5: 371. 1836. Type species: *Dichrocephala integrifolia* (L. f.) Kuntze.

Annual herbs with erect or decumbent and usually branched stems. Leaves alternate, lyrate-pinnatifid or undivided and coarsely toothed. Capitula small, globose, heterogamous, disciform, borne in loose panicles at the ends of branches. Involucre 1–2 seriate, phyllaries subequal. Female flowers numerous in several series, corollas tubular, 2–3 lobed at the apex. Hermaphrodite flowers fewer, corollas narrowly campanulate, 4–5 lobed. Anthers acute at the apex, minutely sagittate at the base. Style branches (of hermaphrodite flowers) oblong, complanate with minute acuminate appendages. Receptacle naked, elevated, obovoid, flattened at the apex. Achenes of both flower types fertile, compressed, marginally 2-nerved. Pappus absent in female flower achenes but in hermaphrodite flower achenes consisting of two weak bristles.

Dichrocephala integrifolia (L. f.) O. Ktze., Rev. Gen. 1: 333. 1891.

Hippia integrifolia L. f., Suppl. 389. 1781. Type: "Habitat in India" Herb LINN. (1039/1).

Grangea latifolia Lam., Enc. Suppl. 2: 826. 1812; Ill. t. 699 fig. 1. 1823. Type: (P).

Dichrocephala latifolia (Lam.) DC. in Wight, Contrib. 11. 1834; Prod. 5: 372. 1836; Thw., Enum. Pl. Zeyl. 162. 1860; C.B. Clarke, Comp. Ind. 36. 1876; Wight, Ic. Pl. Ind. Or. t. 1096. 1846; Hook. f., Fl. Br. Ind. 3: 245. 1881; Trimen, Handb. Fl. Ceylon 3: 14. 1895; Gamble, Fl. Pres. Madras 2: 679. 1921.

Cotula bicolor Roth, Catalect. 2: 116. 1800; Willd., Sp. Pl. 3: 2171. 1803; Moon, Cat. 58. 1824. Type: Nat. Hist. Mus. Oldenburg, Germany.

Stems whitish villous, much branched, up to about 30 cm tall. Leaves simple, broadly elliptic or subrotund or more usually lyrate-pinnatisect, 2.5–5 cm long, lateral segments 1–2 pairs, oblong-spathulate, 0.3–1.5 cm long, 0.2–1 cm broad, terminal segment broadly ovate or subrotund, 1.5–3 cm long and broad, sparsely villous on both surfaces, margins coarsely serrate dentate. Capitula 3–4 mm diam., 3–10 on divaricately branched axillary peduncles. Phyllaries c. 10, lanceolate, c. 1 mm long. Female flower corollas 2-lobed, 0.5–0.6 mm long, white; hermaphrodite corollas 4-lobed, 0.8–1 mm long, greenish-yellow. Achenes obovate, 1–1.25 mm long, glabrous or minutely glandular at the apex. Pappus bristles of hermaphrodite flower achenes 0.5–1 mm long.

Chromosome number. n=9 (Turner & Lewis, J. Bot. Soc. S. Africa 31: 219. 1965).

D i s t r. Tropical Asia, China and Africa.

E c o l. Common weed of drainage ditches, tea estates and moist waste ground. Flowering throughout the year.

V e r n. Maha-kimbu (S—according to Moon).

S p e c i m e n s   E x a m i n e d. WITHOUT PRECISE LOCALITY: *s. coll. C.P. 3303* marked G.C. 393 at upper margin and annotated "Ratnapura, Mar. 1853, Peradeniya" (PDA), without annotation (BM); s. loc., *s. coll. C.P. 2716* (K), *Walker 250* (K). NUWARA ELIYA DISTRICT: Nuwara Eliya, 30 Dec. 1925, *Alston 1273* (PDA); Nuwara Eliya and Adam's Peak, 6000 ft, *Walker s.n.* (K). KANDY DISTRICT: Slopes of Adam's Peak, 4300 ft, *Grierson 1047* (E, US, PDA, BR, CANB).

N o t e s. Trimen (l.c.) drew attention to what appears to be an erect-growing unbranched variant of this species with undivided leaves which was collected at Kotmale: *C.P. 1766* (PDA, K, BM). Recently (see Grierson, Ceylon J. Sci., Biol. Sci. 10: 49. 1972) it has been shown that *Moon 383* (BM) is a similar specimen. This variant, however, has not been collected again since Thwaites' time and it may no longer be extant.

9. GRANGEA

Adans., Fam. 2: 121. 1763. Type species: *G. maderaspatana* (L.) Poir.

Prostrate or sometimes erect annual herbs. Leaves alternate, sinuate-pinnatifid. Capitula solitary or 2–4, terminal or axillary, heterogamous, disciform. Involucre broadly campanulate; phyllaries 2-seriate, subequal, herbaceous. Marginal female flowers numerous, filiform, outer ones 2 lobed, inner ones 3–4 lobed. Hermaphrodite flowers tubular-campanulate, 4–5 lobed. Anther bases obtuse. Styles with short triangular appendages. Receptacle convex, naked. Achenes ± compressed, 2-ribbed, stipitate, stalks apparently remaining attached to the receptacle at maturity. Pappus cupulate, fimbriate at the margin.

Grangea maderaspatana (L.) Poir., Enc. Suppl. 2: 825. 1811; Thw., Enum. Pl. Zeyl. 163. 1860; C.B. Clarke, Comp. Ind. 37. 1876; Hook. f., Fl. Br. Ind. 3: 247. 1881; Trimen, Handb. Fl. Ceylon 3: 14. 1895.

Artemisia maderaspatana L., Sp. Pl. ed. 2. 1190. 1763; Moon, Cat. 58. 1824.
Type: Herb. Plukenet (BM).

Stems up to 25 cm long, whitish pubescent and glandular. Leaves lyrate-pinnatifid or almost bipinnatifid, up to 10 cm long, bearing 3–5 lobed or pinnatifid lateral segments 0.5–1.5 cm long, 2–10 mm broad, terminal segment oblong or trilobed up to 1 cm long and broad, segments obtuse or subacute at the apex, coarsely pubescent on both surfaces. Capitula (0.5) 0.75–1 cm diam., phyllaries obovate, spathulate, 4.5 mm long, 2 mm broad, coarsely pubescent, margins scarious. Flowers yellow, glandular; female corollas c. 2 mm long, hermaphrodite corollas 2 mm long. Achenes greenish, c. 1.25–1.5 mm long, minutely puberulent and glandular; stipes 0.5 mm long. Pappus whitish, 0.5 mm long.

D i s t r. Egypt, Trop. Africa, India, China, Malaya.

E c o l. On moist ground in the drier northern regions; uncommon. Flowering throughout the year.

S p e c i m e n s E x a m i n e d. WITHOUT PRECISE LOCALITY: *C.P. 1767* annotated "Habarane, July 1846, Gardner; Batticaloa Mar. 1858", (PDA, K, unannotated). WITHOUT LOCALITY: *Gardner* (?) *389* (K). MATALE DISTRICT: Dewahuwa Tank, between Galawela and Andiyagala, *Townsend 73/64* (US, E, K, PDA). TRINCOMALEE DISTRICT: Kantalai, Aug. 1885, *Trimen* (?) *s.n.* (PDA). PUTTALAM DISTRICT: Wirandgoda, Dermalu Pattu, Nov. 1882, *Neville s.n.* (PDA). MONERAGALA DISTRICT: Gal Oya Reservoir, near spillway, 275 m, *Comanor 574* (E, US, PDA).

10. MYRIACTIS

Less., Linnaea 6: 127. 1831. Type species: *M. nepalensis* Less.

Erect annual herbs. Leaves alternate, simple, or subpinnatifid. Capitula solitary or few on long peduncles, heterogamous, radiate. Involucre hemispherical, phyllaries 2-seriate. Ray flowers 2-3 seriate, ligulate. Disc flowers tubular, 5 lobed. Anther bases rounded, obtuse. Style branches with short lanceolate appendages. Receptacle convex, naked. Achenes compressed, 2-ribbed, contracted into a short glandular rostrum at the apex (elsewhere erostrate). Pappus absent.

Myriactis wightii DC. Wight, Contrib. 10. 1834 et Prod. 5: 308. 1836; Wight, Ic. Pl. Ind. Or. t. 1091. 1846; Thw., Enum. Pl. Zeyl. 162. 1860; Hook. f., Fl. Br. Ind. 3: 247. 1881; Trimen, Handb. Fl. Ceylon 3: 15. 1895. Type: Ad Neelgherry, *Wight 1409* (K, E).

Stems 25-50 cm tall, sparsely brownish villous pubescent. Leaves lanceolate or ovate, petiolate, or the uppermost ones sessile, petioles 1-6 cm long, winged, semiamplexicaul, subauriculate; lamina 2-4 × 1-2 cm, cuneate-attenuate at the base, acute and apiculate at the apex, margin coarsely and irregularly serrate, sparsely pubescent on both surfaces. Capitula c. 6 mm diam. in flower, c. 1 cm in fruit. Phyllaries lanceolate, 4-4.5 mm long, 1-1.25 mm broad, acute or obtuse at the apex, margin narrowly scarious, pubescent on the midrib. Ligules linear, white at first, becoming purplish on fading, 2.5-3 mm long, basal tube 0.5-0.75 mm long bearing a few short weak pilose hairs. Disc flowers yellow, 1.5-2 mm long, shortly and weakly pilose at the base of the lobes. Achenes oblanceolate, glabrous, ± abruptly narrowed into a glandular rostrum at the apex, 2-2.5 mm long (including rostrum c. 0.5 mm).

D i s t r. Also in Nilgiri Mountains, S. India.

E c o l. In short grass in montane scrub and forest, common. Flowering September-April and probably throughout the year.

S p e c i m e n s   E x a m i n e d. NUWARA ELIYA DISTRICT: Nuwara Eliya (1851, *Gardner*) *C.P. 1740* (PDA, K, BM); ibid., 7000 ft, *Gardner 390* (BM, K); ibid., *W. Nock s.n.* (PDA); above Hakgala, 4 Apr. 1906, *A.M. Silva* (PDA); ibid. *Simpson 9101* (BM); ibid., c. 6000 ft, *Grierson 1059* (E, US, PDA, BR, CANB); Pidurutalagala, 7500 ft, *Sinclair 10092* (K), Horton Plains, North Entrance, 2100 m, *Fosberg & Mueller-Dombois 50024* (PDA, US).

KANDY DISTRICT: "near Kandy", Sept.–Dec. 1853, *Harvey s.n.* (E). Without locality: *Walker 1709* (E, K); *Wight 515* (E).

11. LAGENOPHORA

Cass. in Bull. Soc. Philom. 34. 1818. Type species: *L. nudicaulis* (Comm. ex Lam.) Dusen.

Small perennial herbs usually with slender rhizomes. Stems scapiform. Leaves simple, mostly radical, rosulate. Capitula small, solitary, heterogamous, radiate. Involucre campanulate-hemispherical, 2–4 seriate. Ray flowers in 2–3 series, ligules revolute, basal tubes very short. Disc flowers tubular, 5-lobed. Anther bases obtuse. Style branches lanceolate. Receptacle flat or convex, naked. Achenes compressed with marginal ribs, narrowed into a short glandular beak at the apex; achenes of disc flowers sometimes sterile, Pappus absent.

Lagenophora gracilis Steetz in Lehmann, Pl. Preiss. 1: 431. 1845; Cabrera, Blumea 14: 300. 1966. Type: Australia, ad sinum regis Georgii III., *Roë* (W).

Lagenophora harveyi Thw., Enum. Pl. Zeyl. 162. 1860. Type: *Thwaites C.P. 21* (513).

Lagenophora billardieri auct. non Cass.; Trimen, Handb. Fl. Ceylon 3: 16, t. 55. 1895.

Lagenophora stipitata auct. non Labill., Druce; Alston in Trimen, Handb. Fl. Ceylon 6: 160. 1931.

Leaves obovate-spathulate, 1.5–5 × 0.75–1.3 cm, obtuse at the apex, attenuate to a short petiole 0.5–1 cm long at the base, margins with 2–3 sinuate-dentate teeth on each side, sparsely pilose on both surfaces. Scapes 7–15 cm tall bearing 1–2 minute bracts, subglabrous. Capitulum 3–4 mm diam. Involucre 3 mm high, phyllaries lanceolate, subacute. Ray flowers white, shading to pinkish purple, basal tubes c. 0.3 mm, ligules 1.5–2 mm long. Disc flowers few, corollas c. 2.5 mm long. Achenes oblanceolate, 2.5 mm long, glabrous, tapering into a short glandular beak, c. 0.5 mm long.

D i s t r. S.E. Asia, Malaysia and Australia.

E c o l. On patana grasslands, 3000–6000 ft, quite rare. Flowering February–May.

S p e c i m e n s E x a m i n e d. WITHOUT PRECISE LOCALITY: on patana land, 3000–4000 ft, "at Rambodde & Galagama, *Gardner*—Hewahetta, W.H. (Harvey) & G.H.T. (Trimen)" (K, annotated thus), *s. coll. s.n.* (PDA, K); *s. coll. C.P. 607* (PDA); "Ceylon Highlands", *Harvey s.n.* (E). NUWARA ELIYA DISTRICT: Galagama, *s. coll. C.P. 513* (PDA, K); near junction of Hakgala and Ambawela roads, *Mueller-Dombois 68051817* (US,

PDA). KANDY DISTRICT: Adam's Peak, *s. coll. C.P. 21* (PDA, BM, K).

11a. Bellis perennis L. is cultivated in upland gardens, especially the double forms with white or pink flowers. The habit of this species is similar to that of *Lagenophora* in having radical leaves and scapose peduncles but is less strongly rhizomatous. The achenes of *Bellis*, however, are truncate at the apex and eglandular.

12. ERIGERON

L., Gen. Pl. ed. 5, 856. 1754. Type species: *E. uniflorus* L.

Annual or perennial herbs, erect or prostrate. Leaves alternate, sessile, entire, dentate or trilobed. Capitula medium-sized, solitary or few in a loose racemose arrangement, heterogamous. Involucre campanulate, phyllaries 2–3 seriate, narrow. Ray flowers numerous in 2 or more series, with prominent ligules, female. Eligulate filiform female flowers (situated between ray and disc flowers) numerous or absent. Disc flowers tubular, 5-lobed bisexual. Anther bases obtuse. Style branches of bisexual flowers complanate with short triangular or obtuse appendages. Receptacle flat or convex, naked. Achenes ellipsoid or narrowly obovoid, compressed. Pappus thin, setose, scabrous.

KEY TO THE SPECIES

1 Erect aromatic annuals; stems densely hirsute; leaves oblong, oblanceolate or spathulate, coarsely toothed; ray flowers purple; eligulate female flowers present (Subgen. Trimorphaea)...**1. E. sublyratus**
2 Sprawling or prostrate non-aromatic perennial herbs; stems glabrous or sparsely pubescent; leaves entire or trilobed; ray flowers white at first becoming purplish on fading; eligulate female flowers absent (Subgen. Erigeron)........**2. E. karvinskianus**

1. Erigeron sublyratus DC. in Wight, Contrib. 9. 1834 et Prod. 5: 292. 1836. Type: in arenosis et apricis provinciae Tanjore, *Wight 1403*.

Erigeron asteroides Roxb., Fl. Ind. 3: 432. 1832; Hook. f., Fl. Br. Ind. 3: 254. 1881; Trimen, Handb. Fl. Ceylon 3: 16. 1895; Gamble, Fl. Pres. Madras 2: 682. 1921, non Link, 1822.
Conyza aegyptiaca auct. non DC.: Thw., Enum. Pl. Zeyl. 163. 1860.
Erigeron hispidus DC. in Wight, Contrib. 9. 1834 et Prod. 5: 292. 1836; C.B. Clarke, Comp. Ind. 54. 1876. Type: *Wight 1404* (K).

Stems up to 45 cm tall, minutely puberulous and hirsute with whitish spreading hairs. Leaves oblanceolate or spathulate, 3–6 × 0.6–2.5 cm, broadly acute or obtuse at the apex, auriculate and semiamplexicaul at the base, margins coarsely toothed or subpinnately lobed, puberulous on both surfaces with stronger spreading hairs along the principal veins beneath. Capitula 4–5 mm diam. (1 cm broad when pressed); solitary on axillary peduncles or several in a loose raceme. Involucre c. 5 mm long, phyllaries linear-lanceolate, acuminate, puberulous along midrib, margins glabrous, subscarious. Ray flowers numerous, pink or purplish, basal tubular portion 2.5 mm long, ligule 2–3 mm long, 0.3–0.4 mm broad. Eligulate female flower corollas 1.5–2 mm long, exserted styles projecting 1.5–2 mm. Disc flowers yellow, 15–20 per capitulum, corolla 3.5–4 mm long. Achenes of ray and eligulate flowers narrowly obovoid, 0.75 mm long, puberulous; those of disc flowers cylindrical, probably infertile. Pappus dirty white, c. 20 setae, 3–4 mm long.

D i s t r. India, Nepal.

E c o l. In sandy and gravelly places at lower elevations near streams and at sea shore; rather uncommon. Flowering September–December and probably later.

V e r n. Narakaramba (T).

S p e c i m e n s E x a m i n e d. WITHOUT PRECISE LOCALITY: *C.P. 1733* (PDA, K, BM) unannotated; annotated "Anuradhapura and Trincomalee, *Gardner*". POLONNARUWA DISTRICT: Mineri, Sept. 1885, *Trimen? s.n.* (PDA); Polonnaruwa, *Seneratna 3498* (PDA). ANURADHAPURA DISTRICT: Anuradhapura, 17 Dec. 1881, *Trimen? s.n.* (PDA). PUTTALAM DISTRICT: near Chilaw, *Simpson 8199* (BM). WITHOUT LOCALITY: 1860, *Dubuc s.n.* (E).

N o t e. This species is sometimes confused with *Blumea obliqua* but the latter may be distinguished by the absence of ray flowers and by its finely dentate leaves.

2. Erigeron karvinskianus DC., Prod. 5: 285, 1836; Grierson, Ceylon J. Sci., Biol. Sci. 10: 52. 1972. Type: Mexico, *Karvinski* (G).

Erigeron mucronatus DC., Prod. 5: 285. 1836; Fyson, Fl. Nilgiri & Pulney 1: 223. 1915; Bond, Wild Fl. Ceylon Hills 100. 1953. Type: Mexico, *Karvinski* (G).

Vittadinia triloba Hort.: Macmillan, Trop. Pl. and Gard. ed. 5. 178. 1962.

Stems prostrate or decumbent, sparsely appressed pubescent, or glabrous, often becoming rooted from the nodes, becoming much branched and bearing up to 3 capitula on peduncles from the upper leaf axils. Leaves narrowly elliptic, entire or oblanceolate and 3 (–5) lobed, 1–2.5 (–5) cm × 3–7 (–15) mm narrowly attenuate and subpetiolate at the base, sharply acute or acuminate at the apex, sparsely appressed-pubescent on both surfaces. Capitula hemispherical, 6–8 mm diam., solitary on ± leafless peduncles 4–10 cm long. Involucre 3.5–4 mm long, phyllaries linear-lanceolate, acuminate, appressed pubescent. Ray flowers 30–50, ligules c. 6 mm long, 0.75 mm broad, white at first turning purplish on fading. Disc flowers yellow, corollas 3 mm long.

Achenes c. 1.2 mm long, sparsely puberulous. Pappus whitish, 2.3 mm long with a few shorter outer setae.

Chromosome number. 2n = 36 (Mehra *et al.*, Caryologia 18: 38. 1965).

D i s t r. Native of Mexico introduced in India, Malaysia and S. Europe.

E c o l. Roadside banks and ditches, common especially near tea estates. Flowering throughout the year.

S p e c i m e n s E x a m i n e d. NUWARA ELIYA DISTRICT: Hakgala Gardens, *Alston 154* (PDA); Hellbodde tea estate, 1000 m, *Mueller-Dombois 67052815* (US, PDA); between Pussellawa and Ramboda, 1060 m, *Comanor 326* (E, US, PDA); Bogawantalawa-Boralanda road, 1575 m, *Comanor 1057* (E, US, PDA). Horton Plains, 2200 m, *Gould 13574* (E, US, PDA.) KANDY DISTRICT: Royal Botanic Garden, Peradeniya, 8 March 1926, *Alstan s.n.* (PDA); Parragala between Gampola and Dolosbage, 3000 ft, *Grierson 1004* (E, US, PDA, BR, CANB).

N o t e. The two earliest specimens at Peradeniya, both from botanic gardens, were collected in 1926, but the species probably did not become widespread for several years afterwards since Alston did not include it in his Supplement to Trimen's Handbook (1931). Its eventual spread was probably to some extent deliberate because Bond (l.c.) records that, because of its mat-forming propensities, it is planted on tea estates "for the protection of drain sides and steep banks". Both the names which De Candolle simultaneously gave to this species have been widely used but *E. mucronatus* appears to have been first treated as a variety of *E. karvinskianus* by Hieronymus (in Bot. Jahrb. 28: 585. 1901). It was later made completely synonymous with the latter by Standley (Contr. U.S. Natl. Herb. 23: 1499. 1926) and this practice has been followed by Solbrig in his paper on the South American species of *Erigeron* (Contr. Gray Herb. 91: 44. 1962). Typically, the entire-leaved plant is *E. mucronatus* whereas the trilobed leaf belongs to *E. karvinskianus* but the lobing of the leaves has been found to depend on the photoperiodic conditions to which the plant is subjected (see Gaillochet in Bull. Soc. Bot. France 111: 126–131. 1964 and Gaillochet, Mathon & Bourreau in Comptes Rendus 90 ᵉ Congr. Nat. Soc. Sav. 2: 481–490. 1965).

Border Erigerons developed from the North American *E. elatior* Greene (syn. *E. grandiflorus* var. *elatior*) and *E. speciosus* DC. var. *macranthus* (Nutt.) Cronq. may be grown in gardens at higher elevations. They are erect perennial plants with numerous elongated blue or mauve ligules.

12a. Aster laevis L. a low growing (30–45 cm tall) attractive North American species is commonly cultivated in gardens situated above 500 m. Several other species, however, are cultivated throughout the tropics and the taller Michaelmas Daisy kinds, e.g., *A. amellus* L. and *A. novi-belgii* L. may also be grown. Generally the true Asters have blue ray flowers and a yellow disc.

12b. Allied to *Aster* is **Callistephus chinensis** (L.) Nees, the China Aster, an annual with several series of leafy spathulate phyllaries and, by doubling, numerous ray flowers which vary in colour from white to crimson and blue. The achenes of this species bear a pappus of deciduous bristles.

12c. Brachycome iberidifolia Benth., the Swan River Daisy, a fine Australian annual with pinnatisect leaves and small blue, pink or white-flowered capitula. The receptacle of this species is conical and the achenes almost epappose.

12d. Felicia amelloides (L.) Voss, the South African Blue Daisy, has opposite entire leaves and bright blue ligules.

12e. Solidago is more distantly related to *Aster* and is characterised by having numerous small yellow-flowered capitula. **S. patula** Muhl. is grown in gardens even at sea level but other species, e.g., **S. nemoralis** Ait., **S. canadensis** L. and **S. gigantea** Ait. may also be cultivated.

13. CONYZA

Less., Syn. Comp. 203. 1832, nom. conserv. non L. 1753. Type species: *C. chiliensis* Spr. (typ. cons.).

Annual or perennial herbs. Stems erect, simple or ramose above. Leaves alternate, serrate or pinnatifid. Capitula urceolate-campanulate, heterogamous, numerous in terminal corymbs or panicles. Involucre 2–4 seriate, imbricate; phyllaries linear-lanceolate, acuminate. Female flowers numerous, in several series, tubular, filiform or shortly ligulate, ligules scarcely longer than involucre. Bisexual disc flowers few, tubular, 5-lobed. Anther bases obtuse, entire. Style of female flowers slender, much exserted, branches filiform, branches of bisexual flowers complanate, lanceolate. Receptacle naked, alveolate. Achenes oblong-elliptic, ± compressed, those of disc flowers usually sterile. Pappus 1–2 seriate, setose, scabrous.

KEY TO THE SPECIES

1 Plants finely pubescent and viscid glandular; leaf margins subentire; capitula in broad corymbiform panicles; corollas of female flowers minute..............1. **C. leucantha**
1 Plants hirsute pubescent, non-glandular; leaves, at least the lower ones, coarsely toothed or pinnately lobed; capitula in narrow racemiform panicles; corollas of female flowers ± as long as the pappus
  2 Main inflorescence axis regularly overtopped by lateral branches; phyllaries densely pubescent; pappus brownish....................................3. **C. bonariensis**
  2 Main inflorescence axis not overtopped by lateral branches (and often growing to 2 metres without branching); phyllaries sparsely pubescent; pappus creamy or dirty white..2. **C. floribunda**

1. Conyza leucantha (D. Don) Ludlow & Raven, Kew Bull. 17: 71. 1963; Backer & Bakh. f., Fl. Java 2: 386. 1965; Grierson, Ceyl. J. Sci., Biol. Sci. 10: 52. 1972.

Erigeron leucanthum D. Don, Prod. Fl. Nepäl 171. 1825. Type: Nepal, *Buchanan (Hamilton) s.n.* (BM).
Conyza viscidula DC., Prod. 5: 383, 1836; Thw., Enum. Pl. Zeyl. 163. 1860; C.B. Clarke, Comp. Ind. 63. 1876; Hook. f., Fl. Br. Ind. 3: 258. 1881; Trimen, Handb. Fl. Ceylon 3: 18. 1895. Type: *Wallich 3006*.

Perennial herbs, ± erect, 0.5–2 m tall, finely glandular pubescent. Leaves elliptic-lanceolate, 5–15 × 1–5 cm, attenuate and subpetiolate at the base, acuminate at the apex, margins fairly serrate. Capitula 3 mm diam. (5–6 mm broad when pressed) numerous in corymbose panicles. Involucre c. 4.5 mm high; phyllaries subequal, purplish tinged, densely glandular puberulous and with a few longer eglandular hairs, margins scarious. Female corollas tubular, c. 0.5 mm long, faintly rose-coloured. Bisexual flowers 3–5 per capitulum, corollas c. 3 mm long. Achenes obovate, glabrous, 0.5 mm long. Pappus reddish brown, 4 mm long, deciduous.

D i s t r. India, Java, Philippine islands, Australia.
E c o l. In open grassy places at mid elevations; uncommon. Flowering September–April.
S p e c i m e n s   E x a m i n e d. WITHOUT EXACT LOCALITY: *C.P. 1739* (PDA, K) annotated "Hantane, *Gardner*; Badulla, Apr. 1854"; unannotated (BM); Sept. 1885, *Trimen? s.n.* (PDA). BADULLA DISTRICT: near Passara, Jan. 1888, *Trimen? s.n.* (PDA). KANDY DISTRICT: Hantane, 3000 ft, *Gardner 396* (K, BM). WITHOUT LOCALITY: *Walker 140* (K).

2. Conyza floribunda HBK., Nov. Gen. et Sp. 4: 73. 1820. Type: Juxta urbem Quiti et pagum Gauncabambe Peruvianorum, *Humboldt & Bonpland* (P).

Erigeron floribundus (HBK): Sch. Bip., Bull. Soc. Bot. France 12: 81. 1865; B.L. Burtt. Kew Bull. 1948: 369–372. 1948.
Erigeron sumatrensis Retz. sec. Ridley, J. Roy. Asiat. Soc. Straits Br. 79: 90. 1918 et Fl. Malay Penins. 2: 196. 1923; Alston in Trimen, Handb. Fl. Ceylon 6: 161. 1931 et Kandy Fl. 52, fig. 277. 1938; Backer & Bakh. f., Fl. Java 2: 385. 1965; Koster, Nova Guinea 24: 560-dubie Retz., Obs. Bot. 5: 28. 1789; Peradeniya Manual No. 7 et fig. 1951.

Annual herbs commonly 0.5–2 m tall but sometimes as much as 2.5 m. Stems striate, usually unbranched below inflorescence, bearing a mixed indumentum of whitish appressed pubescent hairs and sparse ± spreading hirsute trichomes. Basal leaves oblanceolate, shallowly or coarsely serrate-dentate (but not pinnatifid), 5–10 × 1–1.5 cm, acute at the apex, attenuate, subpetiolate at the base, ± uniformly appressed whitish pubescent on both surfaces with a few coarser spreading hairs on the midrib beneath; upper leaves linear-lanceolate, commonly 4-5 cm long, 3-4 mm broad. Capitula 4–5 mm diam. (1 cm broad when pressed), numerous in elongate racemose panicles. Involucre c. 5 mm tall; outer phyllaries sparsely pubescent, inner ones glabrous. Female flowers yellowish, corollas 4 mm long ($\pm$ as long as involucre), minutely ligulate; bisexual flowers 3–6 per capitulum, corollas 4.5 mm long. Achenes sparsely pubescent, 1.5 mm long. Pappus dirty white, 20–25 setae, c. 4 mm long.

D i s t r. Native of South America (Brazil?) now in Malesia, Australia.

E c o l. Weed of roadsides, forest clearings, waste ground and abandoned cultivations; abundant. Flowering November, May and probably throughout the year.

V e r n. Sudana (S); Alavangu-pillu (T), Cochi-poompillu (T), Poom-pillu (T), Pinari poom pillu (T).

S p e c i m e n s E x a m i n e d. NUWARA ELIYA DISTRICT: Hakgala, Apr. 1919, *s. coll. s.n.* (PDA, K); below Ohiya Station, *Mueller-Dombois & Cooray 68051847* (US, PDA); 1 km NW of Ambawela Station, *Mueller-Dombois & Cooray 68011215* (US, PDA); Horton Plains on Ohiya road $\frac{1}{4}$ mile from Farr Inn, 2175 m, *Mueller-Dombois & Cooray 67070924* (US, PDA), *Gould & Cooray 13858* (E, US, PDA). KANDY DISTRICT: Peradeniya, 1916, whithout collecter (PDA); Peradeniya, 900 m, *Mueller-Dombois & Cooray 67111306* (US, PDA); Illegolla, near Rangala, 3200 ft, *Grierson 1016* (E, US, PDA, BR, CANB).

3. Conyza bonariensis (L.) Cronquist, Bull. Torrey Bot. Club. 70: 632. 1943; Grierson, Ceylon J. Sci., Biol. Sci. 10: 53. 1972.

Erigeron bonariensis L., Sp. Pl. 863. 1753; B. L. Burtt, Kew Bull. 1948: 371. 1948. Type: Herb. Dillen. (OXF).

Erigeron crispus Pourr., Mem. Acad. Sci. Toulouse 3: 318. 1788; Alston in Trimen, Handb. Fl. Ceylon. 6: 161. 1931. Type: *Pourret* (P.).

Erigeron linifolius Willd., Sp. Pl. 3: 1955. 1803; Hook., Fl. Br. Ind. 3: 254. 1881; Trimen, Handb. Fl. Ceylon 3: 17. 1895. Type: Herb. Willd. (B).

Conyza ambigua DC., Fl. Fr. 6: 468. 1815; Gamble, Fl. Pres. Madras 2: 683. 1921. Type: Herb. DC (G).

Annual herbs commonly 30–75 cm tall. Stems bearing a mixed indumentum of fine appressed hairs and coarser spreading trichomes. Lower leaves narrowly oblanceolate, 6–12 × 0.5–1.5 cm, attenuate at the base, acute at the apex, margins coarsely serrate-dentate or pinnatifid with up to 5 teeth or lobes on each side, pubescent on both surfaces with a few hirsute trichomes on the midrib beneath; upper leaves smaller, linear-lanceolate, entire-margined. Capitula c. 4.5 mm diam. (8 mm broad when pressed). Involucre c. 4 mm tall, phyllaries densely pubescent, purplish tipped. Female flowers yellowish, corolla 3–4 mm long (± as long as the pappus), minutely ligulate at the apex. Bisexual flowers 5–20 per capitulum, corollas 3 mm long. Achenes subglabrous, 1.25 mm long. Pappus brownish, 3–4 mm long.

Chromosome number. n = c. 27 (Powell & King, Amer. J. Bot. 56 (1): 116–121. 1969).

D i s t r. Indigenous to S. America (Argentina?) introduced into S. Europe, India and in other countries where climate is more or less of the Mediterranean type.

E c o l. Roadsides and waste ground, apparently uncommon. Flowering March–April, but probably throughout the year.

S p e c i m e n s   E x a m i n e d. NUWARA ELIYA DISTRICT: Hakgala, 5000 ft, Sept. 1866, *s. coll. C.P. 3928* (PDA, K, BM); ibid., *W. Nock s.n.* (PDA). BADULLA DISTRICT: Fort Macdonald valley, 11 Mar. 1906, *s. coll. s.n.* (PDA); between Welimada and Hakgala, *Grierson 1156* (E, US).

N o t e. According to Trimen (l.c.) this species was introduced at Hakgala Botanic Garden about 1864 among seeds from St. Petersburg. But, contrary to what he said, and unlike *C. floribunda*, it has not become widespread on the island. Alston (l.c.) recorded it as "local".

14. PSIADIA

Jacq., Hort. Schoenbr. 2: 13, t. 152. 1797. Type species: *P. glutinosa* Jacq.

Trees, shrubs or rarely lianes. Leaves alternate, simple, entire or dentate. Capitula small or medium sized in corymbs or panicles. Capitula heterogamous, usually radiate, homochromous. Involucre campanulate, several seriate, imbricate; phyllaries scarious at the margins. Female flowers ligulate, ligules small or, elsewhere, tubular filiform, eligulate. Disc flowers hermaphrodite, tubular-campanulate, 5-lobed. Anthers obtuse at the base. Style branches with short lanceolate appendages. Receptacle convex, naked. Achenes of female flowers fertile, oblong, not or only slightly compressed, angular, 3–5 (–10) ribbed, disc flower achenes sterile. Pappus uniseriate, scabrous, free or slightly coherent at the base.

Psiadia ceylanica (Arn.) Grierson, Ceylon J. Sci., Biol. Sci. 10: 52. 1972.

Solidago ceylanica Arn., Nova Acta Phys. Med. Acad. Caes. Leop. Carol. Nat. Cur. 18: 347. 1836. Type: In Ceylani montibus, alt. 1000 hexap., *Walker*.
Amphirhapis zeylanica (Arn.) DC., Prod. 7: 279. 1838; Thw., Enum. Pl. Zeyl. 162. 1860.
Microglossa zeylanica (Arn.) Benth. in Benth. & Hook. f., Gen. Pl. 2: 282. 1873; C.B. Clarke, Comp. Ind. 58. 1876; Hook. f., Fl. Br. Ind. 3: 257. 1881; Trimen, Handb. Fl. Ceylon 3: 17. 1895.

Shrubs 1–3 m tall. Stems ± densely whitish pubescent when young, dark brown glabrescent with age, c. 0.5 cm diam., with central pith. Leaves elliptic-lanceolate, petiolate, petioles 0.75–1.5 cm long; laminae 5–15 × 1–3 (−4) cm, acuminate at the apex, cuneate-attenuate at the base, margins distantly denticulate, glandular and pubescent on both surfaces but more densely so beneath. Capitula 1.5–2 mm diam. when fresh, 3–4 mm broad when pressed, numerous in dense terminal corymbs 3–4 cm across. Involucre 2–3 seriate, pubescent, phyllaries linear-oblong, c. 1.5 mm long, 0.5 mm broad, obtuse, margins somewhat scarious. Ray flowers 8–12 per capitulum, yellow, basal tube 1.5 mm long, ligule 2 mm long, 0.4 mm broad. Disc flowers 1–3, yellow, corollas 4 mm long. Achenes c. 1.25 mm long, obscurely 3-4 angular, finely sericeous. Pappus 2.25–2.5 mm long, whitish, becoming brown with storage.

Distr. Also in Madras.

Ecol. Common in moist upland areas in grassland and scrub. Flowering throughout the year.

Vern. Pupula (S).

Specimens Examined. WITHOUT PRECISE LOCALITY. *C.P. 152* annotated "Galagama and Adam's Peak, *Gardner*" (PDA); annotated "Adam's Peak, Mar. 1846" (K); unannotated (BM). KANDY DISTRICT: Hantane, 2300 ft. *Gardner 417* (K, BM); Peradeniya top of Ganoruwa Hill, 800 m, *Wirawan 624* (PDA, US); Hunasgiriya, *Amaratunga 71* (PDA); Teldeniya-Mahiyangana road near Madugoda, *Comanor 557* (E, US, PDA); Hakkinda, 29 Aug. 1925, *Alston s.n.* (PDA); Madugoda road, Urugala, *Simpson 8797* (BM); Kandy, *Meebold 4853* (K); Dolosbage, 3500 ft, *Grierson 1002* (E, US, PDA, BR, CANB); Eastern trail to Adam's Peak, 1900 m, *Gould 13603* (E, US, PDA). NUWARA ELIYA DISTRICT: Elk Plains, Awbawela road, 1850 m, *Comanor 933* (E, US, PDA); Hakgala, *J.M. Silva 160* (PDA); Nuwara Eliya, 6500 ft, *Gamble 27562* (K); Galagama, Feb. 1846, *s. coll. C.P. 213* (K). BADULLA DISTRICT: between Palugama and Boralanda, *Fosberg & Mueller-Dombois 50116* (E, US, PDA); 2 miles S of Welimada on Boralanda road, 1225 m, *Mueller-Dombois 67091515* (US, PDA). near Welimada, *Simpson 8329* (BM). RATNAPURA DISTRICT: above Pinnawala on Balangoda road, 1000 m, *Comanor 1099* (E, US, PDA). WITHOUT LOCALITY: 30 Jan. 1819, *Moon 69* (BM); *Gardner 412* (K); *Macrae 389* (BM), 743 (BM); *Walker s.n.* (K-type?) *Walker 51* (K) *Walker 1707* (E).

Note. There is an unpublished colour plate (No. 31) of this species by a native artist in Moon's "Drawings and descriptions of 37 Ceylon Plants" (1823) at the British Museum.

Tribe INULEAE

Herbs or shrubs with alternate leaves. Capitula heterogamous, radiate or disciform. Involucral bracts several-seriate, herbaceous or scarious. Anther bases sagittate, caudate. Style branches narrow, rounded at the apex, unappendaged. Receptacle naked or sometimes paleaceous. Achenes oblong or ellipsoid, compressed or angular. Pappus capillary or absent.

KEY TO THE GENERA

1 Capitula radiate. Annual herbs with bright yellow rays....................**22. Vicoa**
1 Capitula disciform. Annual or perennial herbs or shrubs
  2 Phyllaries scarious at the tips or papery, variously coloured but scarcely green. Plants ± covered with whitish araneose tomentum
    3 Female flowers numerous (50–100), hermaphrodite flowers few (10 or less). Involucres scarious, yellow, purplish or straw-coloured......................**20. Gnaphalium**
    3 Female flowers generally fewer than hermaphrodite (except *Anaphalis subdecurrens* with 25–30 female, 5–10 hermaphrodite). Involucres papery
      4 Involucres white or pinkish. Phyllaries ovate acute, spreading........**19. Anaphalis**
      4 Involucres yellow (red or white in cultivated plants) Phyllaries spathulate, obtuse, not spreading......................**21. Helichrysum**
  2 Phyllaries herbaceous or cartilaginous (not scarious or papery), green or purplish at the tips. Plants glabrous or varyingly pubescent sometimes lanate, but not araneose, tomentose
    5 Peduncles distinct. Capitula clearly separated from each other, not borne in glomerules
      6 Capitula cernuous. Outer involucral bracts leaf-like, spreading or reflexed.........
      ....**23. Carpesium**
      6 Capitula ± erect or, if cernuous, then outer involucral bracts not leaf-like
        7 Pappus absent. Glabrous, somewhat fleshy herbs...................**16. Epaltes**
        7 Pappus present, capillary. Pubescent, lanate or glandular herbs.................
        ....**15. Blumea (incl. Laggera)**
    5 Peduncles absent or concealed. Capitula crowded into globose or ovoid heads or glomerules
      8 Straggling shrubs 2–6 m tall. Leaves petiolate, not decurrent. Achenes compressed, with strongly ciliate margins.............................**18. Blepharispermum**
      8 Annual herbs up to 45 cm tall with decurrent leaves. Achenes oblong angular, glandular or puberulent but not strongly so.....................**17. Sphaeranthus**

15. BLUMEA

DC. in Guill., Arch. Bot. 2: 514. 1833 nom. cons., non Nees, 1825. Type species: *B. balsamifera* (L.) DC. (Syn. *Conyza balsamifera* L.) type cons.

Laggera Sch. Bip. ex Benth. & Hook. f., Gen. Pl. 2: 290. 1873. Type species: *L. crassifolia* Sch. Bip. ex Oliv. & Hiern.

Annual or perennial herbs or subshrubs. Stems simple or branched, usually erect, terete, unwinged, glabrous or pubescent. Leaves alternate (or the two uppermost subopposite as in *B. bifoliata*) simple, entire or lobed, sessile or shortly petiolate. Capitula heterogamous, disciform, either solitary axillary or in lax or compact panicles. Involucre campanulate or urceolate; phyllaries several-seriate, graduated in length, imbricate, linear or oblong.

Flowers numerous, outer ones female, central ones hermaphrodite. Female corollas filiform, 2–4 lobed, usually glabrous; hermaphrodite corollas narrowly tubular, 4–5 lobed, lobes papillate or pubescent. Stamens 4–5, apical appendages obtuse or acute, anther bases sagittate with long or short caudices. Style branches filiform, obtuse at the apex. Receptacle naked, flat or convex, glabrous or pubesent. Achenes oblong, 5–10 ribbed. Pappus uniseriate, hairs slender, reddish or white.

KEY TO THE SPECIES

1 Capitula solitary or 2–3 on axillary peduncles from among upper leaves
  2 Perennial herbs. Leaves narrowly linear-oblanceolate or oblong, all less than 1 cm broad
    3 Leaves mostly radical, narrowly oblanceolate, subentire..........**15. B. angustifolia**
    3 Leaves generally cauline only, linear-oblong, margins regularly denticulate.........
    ....**16. B. bovei**
  2 Annual herbs. Leaves ovate, oblong or oblanceolate but not narrowly so, some at least 1 cm or more broad
    4 Upper leaves rounded at the base, uppermost ones subopposite. Indumentum of villous hairs and stipitate glands. Involucre c. 7 mm long..............**14. B. bifoliata**
    4 Upper leaves auriculate at the base, uppermost ones alternate. Indumentum pubescent, eglandular. Involucre c. 5 mm long........................**13. B. obliqua**
1 Capitula numerous in dense or lax corymbose panicles
  5 Leaves tomentose or velutinous beneath
    6 Peduncles and involucres densely velutinous. Tall robust herbs....................
    ....**2. B. hieracifolia var. flexuosa**
    6 Peduncles and involucres pubescent. Slender herbs.................**10. B. barbata**
  5 Leaves pubescent or glabrate beneath (rarely subtomentose when juvenile)
    7 Outer phyllaries ovate or oblong-lanceolate. Tall periennial herbs with long (10–35 cm), oblanceolate, subglabrous leaves................................**1. B. lanceolaria**
    7 Outer phyllaries linear or linear-lanceolate
      8 Capitula shortly stalked in clusters at the ends of inflorescence branches. Phyllaries and peduncles densely velutinous or sericeous
        9 Leaves ovate, elliptic or obovate oblong, rounded at the base, sessile..**3. B. crinita**
        9 Leaves oblanceolate, attenuate, subpetiolate at the base............**4. B. zeylanica**
      8 Capitula in lax or dense panicles, branches of inflorescence ramose from base
      10 Stems winged
        11 Aromatic, viscid, glandular herbs. Stem wings lobed or toothed...............
        ....**5. B. pterodonta**
        11 Non-aromatic or scarcely aromatic herbs, ± eglandular. Stem wings entire....
        ....**6. B. alata**
      10 Stems unwinged but sometimes interruptedly decurrent
        12 Margins of leaves finely or coarsely dentate but always unlobed. Indumentum of soft villous pubescence and stipitate glands. Flowers purplish.......**8. B. mollis**
        12 Margins of lower leaves usually lobed. Indumentum of glandular or eglandular hairs or both, but never, at least in Ceylon, densely and softly pubescent. Flowers yellow or mauve
          13 Upper leaves with 1–2 stipuliform lobes at the base, shortly decurrent. Flowers mauve...**7. B. aurita**

13 Upper leaves attenuate at the base, unlobed, not decurrent. Flowers yellow
  14 Panicles lax, diffusely branched
    15 Indumentum completely eglandular. Plants of lower elevations.......**12. B. virens**
    15 Indumentum of eglandular hairs and stipitate glands. Plants of montane regions
    ....**11. B. membranacea**
  14 Panicles ± dense racemiform. Strongly glandular plants with few eglandular hairs
  (on leaf undersides and peduncles), at least in Ceylon...................**9. B. lacera**

1. Blumea lanceolaria (Roxb.) Druce, Bot. Soc. Exch. Club Br. Isles 4: 609.
1917; Randeria, Blumea 10: 218. 1960; Grierson, Ceylon J. Sci., Biol. Sci. 11:
13. 1974.

Conyza lanceolaria Roxb., Fl. Ind. 3: 432. 1832. Type: *Roxburgh s.n.* (K, type
  drawing).
Blumea spectabilis DC., Prod. 5: 445. 1836; Hook. f., Fl. Br. Ind. 3: 269. 1881;
  Trimen, Handb. Fl. Ceylon 3: 22. 1895. Based on *Wight 2/16* (K).
Blumea myriocephala DC., Prod. 5: 445. 1836; Thw., Enum. Pl. Zeyl. 163.
  1860. Based on *Wallich 3025/135.* (K, E).
Blumea wallichii C.B. Clarke, Comp. Ind. 87. 1876. Based on *Wallich 3026/
  136.*

Large perennial herbs 1–2 m tall. Stems erect, usually simple, woody at
the base, up to 1 cm broad, with solid pith, terete, glabrate or puberulous
especially above. Leaves elliptic-oblanceolate, 10–35 × 1.0–9.0 cm, attenuate
and subpetiolate at the base, gradually acuminate at the apex, margin serrate-
dentate or denticulate, somewhat revolute, glabrous and minutely bullate on
the upper surface, glabrous or sparsely pilose beneath. Capitula 5–6 mm
diam., numerous in dense terminal panicles, distinctly peduncled at flowering
time. Phyllaries 4–5 seriate, outer ones thick, ovate, sparsely appressed pilose,
c. 2 mm long; inner ones linear-lanceolate, subscarious at the margins, c. 8
mm long, ciliate at the apex. Flowers yellow, or creamy; corollas of female
flowers 5–6 mm long, glabrous; those of hermaphrodite flowers c. 5.5 mm
long, lobes minutely papillate. Receptacle bearing fine, white, brittle hairs.
Achenes linear-oblong, pale brown, c. 1.25 mm long, puberulous, 10-ribbed.
Pappus reddish (or yellow when fresh), 5.5–6 mm long.

D i s t r. Tropical Asia, China. Flowering October–April.
E c o l. In shady moist situations in forests, 1000–1500 ft, rare.
S p e c i m e n s E x a m i n e d. KANDY DISTRICT: Hantane, Feb. 1854,
Gardner (marked GC 399 at upper margin), *C.P. 1744* (PDA), unannotated (K,
BM); Dotalugala Kande, *J.M. Silva 126* (PDA). MATARA DISTRICT:
Deyandera, 5 miles NE of Hakmana, 24 Feb. 1881, *Trimen s.n.* (PDA).
KANDY DISTRICT: Wariagalla, *Simpson 8745* (BM). WITHOUT LOCA-
LITY, 1853, *s. coll. C.P. 2557* (K).
N o t e. Contrary to Renderia's findings (l.c.), I have seen no evidence

which would suggest that the Ceylon material of this species should be divided into two varieties.

2. Blumea hieracifolia (D. Don) DC. in Wight, Contrib. 15. 1834, var. **flexuosa** (C.B. Clarke) Randeria, Blumea 10: 249. 1960.

Blumea flexuosa C.B. Clarke, Comp. Ind. 86. 1876; Hook. f., Fl. Br. Ind. 3: 267, 1881; Trimen, Handb. Fl. Ceylon 3: 20. 1895, p.p. Type: *Thwaites C.P. 19* and *403* p.p. (K, PDA).
Blumea hieracifolia auct. non. DC.: Thw., Enum. Pl. Zeyl. 163. 1860, excl. var.

Perennial herbs 0.4–2 m tall. Stems usually unbranched or sometimes branched at the base, somewhat flexuose, erect or somewhat decumbent, terete, villous-hirsute, densely so towards the apex. Leaves elliptic-oblanceolate, 4–15 × 1–5 cm, attenuate and subpetiolate at the base, apex acute or acuminate, margin ± regularly serrate-dentate, teeth indurated, pubescent on the upper surface, ± densely greyish cottony tomentose beneath. Capitula urceolate-campanulate, 4–5 mm diam., somewhat cernuous, in axillary or terminal panicles, the capitula borne in clusters of 4–12 on densely hirsute peduncles. Involucre 4-seriate, phyllaries linear-lanceolate, 4–9 mm long, 0.5–1 mm broad, the outer ones at least densely hirsute, the inner ones often purplish. Flowers yellow or purple; female corollas 4.5–5.75 mm long, glabrous; those of hermaphrodite flowers 4.5–6.0 mm long, the lobes papillate usually with a few white multicellular hairs. Receptacle c. 2.5 mm broad, glabrous. Achenes oblong, c. 1.25–1.5 mm long, pale brown, 10-ribbed, glabrous or sparsely pubescent. Pappus 4.5–5 mm long, white.

D i s t r. Variety endemic to Ceylon.

E c o l. Growing in dry patana grasslands, roadsides and at the margins of forests above 1000 m, relatively common. Flowering October–May.

N o t e. This variety occurs in two forms as Trimen (l.c.) noticed: yellow-flowered and purple-flowered, but there is no very positive correlation between flower colour and any other character, although the phyllaries tend to be broader and less densely villose in the yellow form. The flower colour, where indicated on the field labels, is noted below.

S p e c i m e n s E x a m i n e d. WITHOUT PRECISE LOCALITY: "*C.P. 19* and *C.P. 403*" annotated "Nuwara Eliya and Adam's Peak, *Gardner*; Palegalla (?) Oct. 1853" (PDA) *C.P. 19*, without annotation, (PDA), annotated "Adam's Peak, Mar. 1846" (K), unannotated (BM). NUWARA ELIYA DISTRICT: Nuwara Eliya, 6000 ft, *Gardner 398* (BM, K); Nuwara Eliya, Feb. 1846, *s. coll. C.P. 532* (K); Nuwara Eliya, 1890, *Trimen s.n.* (PDA); Fort Macdonald valley, 11 Mar. 1906, *A.M. Silva s.n.* (PDA) (purple); Horton Plains, 26 Jan. 1906, *Willis s.n.* (PDA); between Nuwara Eliya and Hakgala,

6 Mar. 1906, *A.M. Silva s.n.* (PDA), (yellow); Sita Eliya, Apr. 1921, *A. de Alvis s.n.* (PDA); Nanu Oya, *Simpson 9121* (BM) (yellow); Hakgala, *Simpson 9586* (BM); Below Hakgala, *Alston 632* (PDA) (yellow); Ambawela, *Alston 1037* (PDA, K) (purple); between Ramboda and Nuwara Eliya at Milestone 36, 1400 m, *Mueller-Dombois & Comanor 67052827* (PDA) (purple); Piduruta-lagala, c. 6700 ft, *Grierson 1074* (E, US, PDA, BR, CANB) (yellow); Horton Plains—Pattipola road, 6500 ft, *Grierson 1092* (E, US, PDA, BR, CANB). KANDY DISTRICT: Peradeniya, Hantane near University Circuit Bunga-low, 1000 m, *Mueller-Dombois & Cooray 67103104* (PDA), 9 Nov. 1967, *Mueller-Dombois 67110905* (PDA); 3½ miles E of Rangala, 4000 ft, *Grierson 1019* (E, US, PDA, BR, CANB) (purple), *Grierson 1020* (E, US, PDA, BR, CANB) (yellow). BADULLA DISTRICT: between Bandarawela and Craig Estate, 25 Mar. 1906, *Willis s.n.* (PDA); near Haputale, 4600 ft, *Kostermans 23157* (PDA) (yellow); 2 miles from Ohiya on Boralanda road, 5000 ft, *Grierson 1114* (E, US, PDA, BR, CANB) (purple). RATNAPURA DISTRICT: Kuruwita Kande, 29 Mar. 1919, *s. coll.* (PDA). WITHOUT LOCALITY: *Macrae 58* (BM); *Walker s.n.* (K); *Harvey s.n.* (E).

3. **Blumea crinita** Arn., Nova Acta Phys. Med. Acad. Caes. Leop. Carol. Nat. Cur. 18: 348. 1836; DC., Prod. 7: 283. 1838; Thw., Enum. Pl. Zeyl. 163. 1860; C.B. Clarke, Comp. Ind. 84. 1876; Hook. f., Fl. Br. Ind. 3: 267. 1881; Trimen, Handb. Fl. Ceylon 3: 21. 1895; Randeria, Blumea 10: 250. 1960. Type: *Walker s.n.* (E-GL).

Perennial rhizomatous herbs, 30–100 cm tall. Stems erect, usually simple, hirsute with spreading yellowish hairs, especially on the younger parts. Leaves thick, ovate-elliptic to obovate-oblong, 1.5–6.5 × 0.5–3 cm, acute or obtuse and apiculate at the apex, rounded and sessile at the base, margins ± distantly callose-denticulate, sparsely hirsute with yellowish hairs on both sur-faces, glabrescent with age, upper surface becoming blackish on drying. Capitula 5–6 mm diam. in clusters of 3–5 on sericeous peduncles. Involucre 4–5 seriate; phyllaries purplish tinged; outer ones lanceolate, 4 mm long, inner ones linear-acuminate, 7–8 mm, ± as long as flowers. Flowers yellow; female corollas 6 mm long, glabrous; hermaphrodite corollas 6–6.5 mm long, lobes papillate. Achenes brown, 10-ribbed, glabrous, 1.75 mm long. Pappus white, 4.5 mm long.

D i s t r. Endemic.
E c o l. In marshy places and wet patanas, 4000–7000 ft, rare. Flowering Sept.–May.
S p e c i m e n s E x a m i n e d. WITHOUT PRECISE LOCALITY: *C.P. 147* (marked G.C. 397 at upper margin) annotated "Adam's Peak, Nuwara Eliya and Horton Plains, *Gardner*," and "Nuwara Eliya near the Black Port, Nov. 1859" (PDA), annotated "Adam's Peak, Mar. 1846" (K), unannotated

(BM). KANDY DISTRICT: Maskeliya, 2 March 1883, *Trimen s.n.* (PDA); ascent to Adam's Peak, Maskeliya Side, 16 May 1906, *Willis s.n.* (PDA). NUWARA ELIYA DISTRICT: Nuwara Eliya, 6000 ft, *Gardner 397* (BM, K); Horton Plains, Sept. 1890, *Trimen s.n.* (PDA); Hakgala, *W. Nock s.n.* (PDA); Sita Eliya, 3 Nov. 1906, without collector (Willis?) (PDA); Ambawela, *Alston 1276* (PDA). WITHOUT LOCALITY: "ad alt. 6000 ped". *Walker s.n.* (E-GL), *82* (K), *254* (K).

4. Blumea zeylanica (Hook. f.) Grierson, Ceylon J. Sci., Biol. Sci. 11: 14. 1974.

Blumea flexuosa C.B. Clarke var. *zeylanica* Hook. f., Fl. Br. Ind. 3: 267. 1881.
Type: Nuwara Eliya, *Gardner 395* (K).
Blumea hieracifolia auct. non DC.: Thw., Enum. Pl. Zeyl. 163. 1860, var. *β*.

Erect perennial (?) herbs. Stems terete, c. 1.5 m tall, sometimes purplish, covered with yellowish, spreading, hirsute hairs, becoming glabrescent with age. Lower leaves oblanceolate, up to 18 × 5 cm attenuate and subpetiolate at the base, acute or shortly acuminate at the apex, margins remotely dentate and bearing 2–3 denticules between the major teeth, sericeous on both surfaces but more densely so on the lower surface; upper leaves elliptic; 4–8 cm long, 0.75–2 cm broad, acuminate at the apex, attenuate and sessile at the base. Capitula campanulate, c. 5 mm diam., aggregated into clusters of 4–7 at the ends of densely hirsute peduncles. Involucre 4–5 seriate, phyllaries linear-lanceolate, acuminate, purplish at the apices, densely sericeous, outer ones somewhat squarrose. Flowers yellow; female corollas 7 mm long, glabrous; hermaphrodite flowers c.15, yellow, corollas c. 7 mm long, lobes bearing a few unicellular hairs. Receptacle glabrous. Achenes (submature) 1.5 mm long, 6–8-costate, sparsely pubescent. Pappus whitish, c. 7 mm long.

Distr. Endemic.
Ecol. In moist shady places at roadsides and margins of forests above 3000 ft, not common. Flowering throughout the year.
Specimens Examined. KANDY DISTRICT: Adam's Peak, *Gardner, C.P. "19 and 403"* p.p. (PDA), 1–7000 ft (K); Maskeliya, near Gartmore Estate, 29 Apr. 1926, *J.M. Silva s.n.* (PDA); Maskeliya, above Blair Atholl Estate, *Alston 1898* (PDA); Knuckles, 14 June 1926, *J.M. Silva s.n.* (PDA); Corbett's Gap, *Alston 1700* (PDA, K); Dolosbage, c. 3500 ft, *Grierson 1001* (E, US, PDA, BR, CANB); Adam's Peak Sanctuary, Bogawant-alawa-Boralanda road, 1400 m, *Comanor 1062* (E, US, PDA). NUWARA ELIYA DISTRICT: Nuwara Eliya, *Gardner 395* (K-holotype); between Horton Plains and Ohiya, c. 6000 ft, *Grierson 1111* (E, US). RATNAPURA DISTRICT: Belihul Oya above Non Pareil Estate, 25 Feb. 1881, *Trimen s.n.* (PDA). BADULLA DISTRICT: Namunakula, 4000 ft, 29 Apr. 1907, *Willis s.n.* (PDA).

N o t e. This species is related to *B. crinita* but differs in leaf shape and in the fact that leaves do not turn blackish on drying. From *B. hieracifolia* var. *flexuosa*, which it also resembles, it may be readily separated by its silky indumentum and the alternately dentate and denticulate leaf margins. *B. zeylanica* differs from both these species in having minute unicellular (not multicellular) hairs on the hermaphrodite corolla lobes.

5. Blumea pterodonta DC. in Wight, Contrib. 16. 1834; Prod. 5: 448. 1836; Grierson, Ceylon J. Sci., Biol. Sci. 11: 12. 1974. Type: *Wight 1437* (K, E-GL).

Laggera pterodonta (DC.) Sch. Bip. ex Oliv., Trans. Linn. Soc. London 29: 94. 1873; C.B. Clarke, Comp. Ind. 92. 1876; Hook. f., Fl. Br. Ind. 3: 271. 1881; Alston in Trimen, Handb. Fl. Ceylon 6: 162. 1931.

Large annual herbs, 2–3 m tall, glandular-viscid and strongly aromatic (citrous odour). Stem terete, 4-winged, wings deeply lobed or toothed, densely covered with subsessile glands. Leaves elliptic or oblanceolate-lanceolate, 3–15 × 1–3 cm, sessile and decurrent at the base, acute at the apex, margins coarsely serrate, densely covered on both surfaces with shortly stalked glands. Capitula pendulous, numerous in large lax terminal panicles. Involucre campanulate, c. 5 mm diam. when fresh, 1.25 cm broad when pressed. Phyllaries 6–7 seriate, linear-lanceolate, 2.5–9 mm long, outer ones squarrose herbaceous, densely stipitate glandular; inner ones somewhat scarious. Flowers mauve, female corollas 5–5.5 mm long, glabrous, hermaphrodite corollas 6–7 mm long, lobes glandular. Achenes dark brown, 0.8–1 mm long, faintly 5–6 ribbed, ribs white, pubescent. Pappus white, 4.5–5 mm long.

D i s t r. Trop. Asia and Africa.

E c o l. On patanas and roadside banks in montane zone, uncommon. Flowering February-March.

S p e c i m e n s   E x a m i n e d. NUWARA ELIYA DISTRICT: Condegalla, 17 Feb. 1927, *Alston 871* (PDA, K). BADULLA DISTRICT: between Ohiya and Boralanda, c. 5000 ft, 13 Mar. 1969, *Grierson 1115* (E, US, PDA, BR, CANB).

N o t e. This species is closely related to and is sometimes treated as a synonym of *B. alata* (e.g., Wild, Kirkia 7: 130. 1969) but in Ceylon, at least, the two remain distinct and the character of the stem-wings, which breaks down elsewhere, appears to remain constant here. *B. pterodonta* is additionally highly aromatic and extremely viscid whereas *B. alata* is not or only slightly aromatic. Elsewhere, e.g., Burma, the indumentum of the latter tends to be variable but in Ceylon it is quite densely pubescent with only a few glands in contrast to the indumentum of *B. pterodonta* which is strongly if not wholly glandular.

6. Blumea alata (D. Don) DC., Prod. 5: 488. 1836; Thw., Enum. Pl. Zeyl.

163. 1860; Grierson, Ceylon J. Sci., Biol. Sci. 11: 12. 1974. Type: Narainhetty, 18 Oct. 1802. *Buch.-Ham.* (PDA, K).

Erigeron alatum Don, Prod. Fl. Nepal. 171. 1825.
Laggera alata (D. Don) Sch. Bip. ex Oliver, Trans. Linn. Soc. London 29: 94. 1873; C.B. Clarke, Comp. Ind. 91. 1876; Hook. f., Fl. Br. Ind. 3: 271. 1881; Trimen, Handb. Fl. Ceylon 3: 23. 1895; Gamble, Fl. Pres. Madras 2: 689. 1921.

Annual (or perennial?) herbs 0.5–1.5 m tall, not or somewhat aromatic when bruised. Stems erect, branched above, 4-winged from decurrent leaf bases, wings entire, greyish-brown pubescent, eglandular. Leaves oblong, 2–10 × 0.5–2 cm, sessile and decurrent at the base, obtuse or acute at the apex, margins finely and regularly serrate, brownish pubescent on both surfaces, more densely so beneath. Capitula pendulous, numerous, borne in a large lax panicle, the branches racemose bearing 3–7 capitula. Involucres campanulate, c. 5 mm diam. when fresh, 1–1.5 cm broad when pressed. Phyllaries 6–7 seriate, purple-tipped, outer ones squarrose, linear-lanceolate, acuminate, 2–8 mm long, puberulous. Flowers mauve-purple; female corollas 6–7 mm long, glabrous; hermaphrodite corollas 8 mm long, lobes glandular. Achenes linear-oblong, dark brown, indistinctly 5–6 ribbed, 1–1.25 mm long, puberulous. Pappus white, 6–7 mm long.

Chromosome number. n = 10 (Shetty, Taxon 16: 570. 1967).

D i s t r. India, Burma, Malaya, China, Trop. Africa.

E c o l. In patanas or at margins of forests in montane zone, uncommon. Flowering February–March.

S p e c i m e n s E x a m i n e d. NUWARA ELIYA DISTRICT: Nuwara Eliya, 1856 and 1857, (*Gardner*) *C.P. 551* (PDA) annotated "Pusssellawa, Jan. 1846" (K) unannotated (BM); Nuwara Eliya, Jan. 1846, *s. coll. C.P. 683* (K); *Macrae 394* (K, BM); Beyond Hakgala, 25 Feb. 1906, *Willis s.n.* (PDA). KANDY DISTRICT: Maskeliya, 2 Mar. 1883, *Trimen s.n.* (PDA). BADULLA DISTRICT: Between Ohiya and Boralanda, c. 5000 ft, *Grierson 1113* (E, US, PDA, BR, CANB); Ugalduva valley, 25 Feb. 1882, *Trimen s.n.* (PDA).

7. Blumea aurita (L. f.) DC. in Wight, Contrib. 16. 1834; Prod. 5: 449. 1836.

Conyza aurita L. f., Suppl. 367. 1781; Roxb., Fl. Ind. 3: 428. 1832. Type: "in Indiae orientalis subhumidis" Herb. LINN (993. 33).
Blumea balsamifera auct. non DC.: Thw., Enum. Pl. Zeyl. 422. 1864.
Laggera aurita (L. f.) Benth. ex C.B. Clarke, Comp. Ind. 92. 1876; Hook. f., Fl. Br. Ind. 3: 271. 1881; Gamble, Fl. Pres. Madras 2: 689. 1921; Trimen, Handb. Fl. Ceylon 3: 24. 1895.

Annual (or perennial?) herbs, 30–75 cm tall, viscid, strongly aromatic.

Stems erect, terete, covered with long spreading, white, pilose hairs and short-er stipitate glands. Leaves 1–10 × 0.3–3 cm, the lower ones pinnatifid with broadly elliptic or oblanceolate terminal segments and 2–3 oblong lateral lobes on each side; upper leaves oblong or obovate, dentate, acute at the apex, auriculate and interruptedly decurrent at the base with 2–3 linear lobes on each side of the stem, sparsely covered on both surfaces with long white villous hairs and numerous stipitate glands. Capitula several (up to 15) in ter-minal corymbs. Involucres 1–1.25 cm broad; phyllaries 3–4 seriate, linear-lanceolate, 2.5–7 mm long, pubescent and glandular. Flowers pale mauve, female corollas 4.5–5 mm long, glabrous; corollas of hermaphrodite flowers 5–5.5 mm long, lobes usually glandular. Achenes 0.75–1 mm long, dark brown, subcompressed, sparsely sericeous. Pappus white, 4–4.5 mm long.

Chromosome number. n = 10 (Mehra *et al.*, Caryologia 18: 39. 1965).

D i s t r. India, Burma, Trop. Africa.

E c o l. In littoral scrub on clayey sand, rare and apparently only from one locality. Flowering March–June.

S p e c i m e n s   E x a m i n e d. TRINCOMALEE DISTRICT: Trinco-malee, Mar. 1862, *Glenie C.P. 3665* (PDA), unannotated (K); ibid. 4 May 1927, *Alston 534* (PDA, K).

N o t e. A single immature specimen was observed about 17 miles N of Trincomalee, beside the road to Palmoddai on 23 February 1969.

In his Catalogue (p. 58) Moon listed *Conyza balsamifera* and quoted Rumph. Herb. Amb. 6: t. 24 f. 1. The species that this figure portrays is un-doubtedly *Blumea balsamifera* (L.) DC. (syn. *Conyza balsamifera* L.) which has never been collected in Ceylon. Moon, however, may have mistaken the illustration for *B. aurita* and, possibly through him, Thwaites also misnamed *C.P. 3665*. See also Trimen's note (Handb. Fl. Ceylon 3: 23).

8. Blumea mollis (D. Don) Merr., Philipp. J. Sci. 5: 395. 1910; Alston in Tri-men, Handb. Fl. Ceylon 6: 162. 1931; Randeria, Blumea 10: 261. 1960.

Erigeron molle D. Don, Prod. Fl. Nepal. 172. 1825. Type: Hab. in Nepalia, *Wallich s.n.*

Blumea lacera auct. non DC.: Thw., Enum. Pl. Zeyl. 163. 1860. Trimen, Handb. Fl. Ceylon 19. 1895.

Blumea neilgherriensis Hook. f., Fl. Br. Ind. 3: 261. 1881. Based on *Wight s.n.* (K).

Annual herbs 30–40 cm tall, (rarely more). Stems erect, terete, softly white pilose with spreading hairs and shorter stipitate glands. Leaves elliptic-ovate or oblanceolate, 2–7 × 0.75–3 cm, apex acute or obtuse, apiculate, attenu-ate and subpetiolate at the base, margins sharply and regularly serrate, covered on both surfaces with fine, white, pilose hairs and shortly stipitate glands. Capitula 2–3 mm broad, numerous, in terminal panicles and usually with small axillary panicles or racemes in the axils of the upper leaves. Phyllaries linear-lanceolate, 3-seriate, 2–5 mm long, finely velutinous and glandular, the inner ones longer than the flowers, often purplish tinged, inner most ones ± scarious. Flowers lilac or mauve, female corollas of 2.5–3.5 mm long, glabrous; hermaphrodite corollas 3–4 mm long, minutely glandular-puberulous on the lobes. Achenes linear, angular, pale brown, c. 0.5 mm long. Pappus white, 2.5–3 mm long.

Chromosome number. n=11 (Turner & Lewis, J. S. Afr. Bot. 31: 215. 1965).

Distr. Tropical Africa and Asia.

Ecol. Along river banks, on bunds of rice fields, on rocks, waste and roadsides, quite common. Flowering September–July, but probably throughout the year.

Uses. Alston in a field note (1275) records its being used as a cattle medicine.

Vern. Kukula (S).

Specimens Examined. WITHOUT PRECISE LOCALITY: *C.P. 1735* (marked G.C. 401 at upper margin) annotated "Kurunegala, Batticaloa, *Gardner*; Kadugannawa, Hantane 1857" (PDA), *s. coll. s.n.* (K, BM). BADULLA DISTRICT: Ella Pass, Sept. 1890, *Trimen s.n.* (PDA); Bandarawela, Sept. 1890, *Trimen s.n.* (PDA); Badulla, *Simpson 8232* (BM). KANDY DISTRICT: Peradeniya, *Amaratunga 785* (PDA). Madewela, near Katugastota, *Alston 1858* (PDA); Haragama, near Talatuoya, *Alston 461* (PDA); Kandy, *Macrae 387* (K). MATALE DISTRICT: Nalanda, 12 May 1928, *Alston 2407* (PDA, K). KURUNEGALE DISTRICT: Wetakeyapotta, *Alston 1275* (PDA). WITHOUT LOCALITY: *Walker s.n.* (E-GL, K) *Brodie s.n.* (E).

9. Blumea lacera (Burm. f.) DC. in Wight, Contrib. 14. 1834; Hook. f., Fl. Br. Ind. 3: 263. 1881; C.B. Clarke, Comp. Ind. 76. 1876; Thw., Enum. Pl. Zeyl. 163. 1860; Randeria, Blumea, 10: 264. 1960; Grierson, Ceylon J. Sci., Biol. Sci. 11: 13. 1974, non Trimen, Handb. Fl. Ceylon 3: 19. 1895 (=*B. mollis*).

Conyza lacera Burm. f., Fl. Ind. 180, t. 59 f. 1. 1768. Type: *Burm. f.* (G).
Blumea membranacea auct. non DC.: Trimen, Handb. Fl. Ceylon 3: 22. 1895 in part.
Blumea glandulosa DC. in Wight, Contrib. 14. 1834 et Prod. 5: 438. 1836; Thw., Enum. Pl. Zeyl. 163. 1860. Based on *Wight 1429* (K, E).

Annual herbs 45–75 (–100) cm tall, glandular viscid and rank smelling. Stems simple or branched, ± erect, terete, glandular pubescent interspersed with a few eglandular hairs especially in the inflorescence. Leaves broadly elliptic or oblanceolate, the lower ones often pinnately or lyrately lobed, attenuate and subpetiolate at the base or petioled (petioles when present up to 3 cm long), acute or obtuse, apiculate at the apex, coarsely, and irregularly serrate-dentate, teeth subspinulose, glandular puberulent on both surfaces, sparsely pilose on the veins beneath. Capitula 3–4 mm diam., numerous, in terminal panicles and on short axillary shoots from among the upper leaves. Phyllaries c. 4-seriate; outer ones herbaceous, linear-lanceolate, c. 2 mm long, glandular; inner ones linear-acuminate, subscarious, 7 mm long, finely ciliate at the apex. Flowers yellow; female corollas glabrous, 3.5 mm long; hermaphrodite corollas 4 mm long, lobes glandular puberulous. Achenes brown, linear, 5-ribbed, sparsely puberulous, 0.5 mm long. Pappus white, c. 4 mm long.

Chromosome number. n = 11 (Mehra *et al.*, Caryologia 18: 39. 1965), n = 9 (Subramanyam & Kamble, Taxon 15: 163. 1966).

D i s t r. Africa, India, Malaysia, Australia.

E c o l. Roadsides and at edges of forests, fairly common. Flowering November–June.

S p e c i m e n s E x a m i n e d. WITHOUT PRECISE LOCALITY: *s. coll. C.P. 1734* (marked G.C. 1216 at upper margin) annotated "Kurunegale, Batticaloa, *Gardner*; 4-Korales and Colombo, Nov. 1858" (PDA), unannotated (K). POLONNARUWA DISTRICT: Minneriya, Sept. 1885, *Trimen s.n.* (PDA). TRINCOMALEE DISTRICT: 5 miles from Muthur, *Simpson 9712* (PDA). BADULLA DISTRICT: Ooma-oya, June 1881, *Trimen s.n.* (PDA). KANDY DISTRICT: Peradeniya, weed in Royal Botanic Garden, Dec. 1882, *Trimen s.n.* (PDA); Kandy, *Gardner 1216* (K, BM); Warriagala, 8 miles south of Kandy, *Alston 1277* (PDA). COLOMBO DISTRICT: Colombo, 31 Mar. 1796, *Rottler? s.n.* (E-GL).

N o t e. Randeria (l.c.) records this as the most variable species of the genus especially in respect of leaf lobing and indumentum. In Ceylonese specimens, the lower leaves vary from coarsely toothed to pinnately lobed or lyrate with 1–2 pairs of lateral segments (but the upper leaves are regularly unlobed or merely dentate unlike Burman's illustration). The indumentum of these specimens is almost uniformly glandular puberulent throughout with only a few eglandular hairs on the under sides of the leaves and on the peduncles but never tomentose or velutinous as originally described. Plants of this description match the type material of *B. glandulosa* which, however, Randeria places as a synonym of *B. lacera*.

10. Blumea barbata DC. in Wight, Contrib. 14. 1834; DC., Prod. 5: 434. 1836; Thw., Enum. Pl. Zeyl. 163. 1860; C.B. Clarke, Comp. Ind. 73. 1876; Hook. f., Fl. Br. Ind. 3: 262, 1881; Trimen, Handb. Fl. Ceylon 3: 20. 1895; Randeria, Blumea 10: 267. 1960. Type: *Wight 1426* (K, E).

Annual herbs, 50–75 cm tall. Stems often purplish, bearing a mixed indumentum of fine appressed pubescent hairs and spreading whitish, hirsute hair. Leaves obovate-oblong, 3–5 × 1.3–1.8 cm, attenuate at the base, acute at the apex, margins sharply and rather distantly serrate-dentate, teeth spinulose, sparsely appressed hirsute on the upper surface, densely white sericeous beneath, almost obscuring veins. Capitula c. 3–4 mm diam. when fresh, 3–20 borne on axillary or terminal racemes or panicles, rarely solitary. Phyllaries 3–4 seriate, 2.5–6 mm long, pubescent with fine stiff hairs and interspersed with stalked glandular hairs. Flowers yellow, female corollas 3.5 mm long, glabrous; hermaphrodite corollas 3.5 mm long, pubescent. Achenes c. 1 mm long, glabrous or sparsely puberulous near the apex, brown with 10 pale ribs. Pappus white, rather brittle, 3.5 mm long.

Distr. Confined to S. India and Ceylon.

Ecol. Montane zone, 1000–1500 m, rare. Fl. December–June.

Specimens Examined. WITHOUT PRECISE LOCALITY: *s. coll. C.P. 1731*, annotated "Pusselawa, Jan. 1847, *Gardner*; Rangala, Dec. 1854" (PDA), unannotated (K). KANDY DISTRICT: Aladeniya, *Amaratunga 635* (PDA).

11. Blumea membranacea Wall. ex DC. Prod. 5: 440. 1836; Randeria, Blumea 10: 269. 1960. Type: *Wallich 3019* (K).

Conyza membranacea Wall., Cat. 3019, nom. nud.
Blumea glandulosa auct. non DC.: Thw., Enum. Pl. Zeyl. 163. 1860.
Blumea membranacea var. *gardneri* Hook. f., Fl. Br. Ind. 3: 265. 1881; Trimen, Handb. Fl. Ceylon 3: 22. 1895 in part (see also *B. virens*). Based on Wight *1577* (K).

Erect annual herbs, 0.5–2 m tall. Stems generally simple, terete, striate, pilose and stipitate glandular. Leaves oblanceolate, 4–22 × 1–7 cm texture thin, the lower ones lyrately pinnatifid with 1–2 pairs of triangular segments and elliptic terminal lobe; upper leaves entire, apex acute, attenuate and gradually subpetiolate at the base, margins irregularly serrate-dentate or lobed, teeth callose tipped, sparsely pilose on both surfaces. Capitula c. 4–5 mm diam., numerous in lax terminal and axillary panicles. Phyllaries 5–6 seriate; outer ones lanceolate-acuminate, c. 2 mm long, purplish, puberulous; inner ones linear-acuminate, 6–7 mm long, subscarious at the margins, ciliate at the apex. Receptacle c. 2.5 mm broad, alveolate, glabrous. Flowers yellow; female corollas c. 4 mm long, glabrous; hermaphrodite corollas c. 5.5 mm long, lobes sparsely puberulous. Achenes brown, linear-oblong, 5-ribbed, sparsely and minutely pubescent, c. 1 mm long. Pappus white, c. 5 mm long.

Chromosome number. n = 11 (Mehra *et al.*, Carylologia 18: 39. 1965).

Distr. India, Burma, China, Indonesia.

E c o l. In forests and along streams in the montane zonè above 500 m, and reputedly becoming a weed. Flowering February–May (and probably longer: Randeria gives August–May).

S p e c i m e n s E x a m i n e d. WITHOUT PRECISE LOCALITY: *C.P. 2822* marked GC 394 at upper margin and annotated "Elk Plains, *Gardner*; Ambagamuwa, Feb. 1855; Galagama, May 1856", (PDA), unannotated (BM). KANDY DISTRICT: Hantane, Jan. 1846, *s. coll. C.P. 560* (K); Pusselawa, *Alston 993* (PDA). WITHOUT LOCALITY, *Walker s.n.* (E, K); *Harvey s.n.* (E).

N o t e. Randeria (l.c.) cites *Thwaites C.P. 2822* (at Paris) both under this species and under *B. laciniata* (Roxb.) DC. (syn. *B. sinuata* (Lour.) Merr.). I have not found any specimens of this number bearing the latter name at Peradeniya herbarium nor elsewhere. It is a species similar in appearance to *B. membranacea* but differing principally in having the receptacles pubescent. *Thwaites C.P. 560* (from Calcutta and Gray Herbaria) is also cited under *B. membranacea* but the specimens of this number at Peradeniya clearly belong to *B. virens*. The Ceylonese material of *B. membranacea* corresponds to the typical variety; the second variety, var. *jacquemontii*, is apparently confined to India. The species is similar in general appearance and is sometimes confused with *Vernonia cinerea* but the latter may be distinguished by its smaller homogamous capitula.

12. Blumea virens Wall. ex DC. in Wight, Contrib. 14. 1834; Prod. 5: 439. 1836; Hook. f., Fl. Br. Ind. 3: 264. 1881; Randeria, Blumea 10: 272. 1960; Grierson, Ceylon J. Sci., Biol. Sci. 11: 13. 1974. Type: *Wallich 3037* (K, E).

Conyza virens Wall., Cat. 3037. 1831, nom. nud.
Blumea glandulosa var. β Thw., Enum. Pl. Zeyl. 163. 1860.
Blumea membranacea var. *gardneri* Hook. f., Fl. Br. Ind. 3: 265. 1881; Trimen, Handb. Fl. Ceylon 3: 22. 1895 in part (see also *B. membranacea*).

Erect annual herbs, 50–100 cm (or sometimes 2 m) tall. Stems generally simple, terete, quite glabrous or very sparsely white-pilose. Leaves 3–15 × 1–4.5 cm, texture thin, lower ones usually lyrately lobed with 1–2 pairs of triangular-oblong lateral lobes and elliptic-ovate terminal segments, upper leaves oblanceolate, apex acute or shortly acuminate, base attenuate and gradually subpetiolate, margins irregularly serrate-dentate, teeth callose-tipped, very sparsely pilose on both surfaces but especially on the veins beneath. Capitula 3–4 mm diam., numerous in lax terminal panicles. Phyllaries 4–5 seriate, lanceolate, c. 2 mm long, inner ones linear, c. 6.5 mm long, glabrous or sparsely pubescent on the dorsal surface, ciliate at the apices, margins of inner ones subscarious. Receptacle alveolate, glabrous, 2.5–2.75 mm broad. Flowers yellow; female corollas c. 4.0 mm long, glabrous; hermaphrodite corollas 4–4.5 mm long, lobes minutely papillate. Achenes linear-elliptic, c. 8-ribbed, finally pubescent, 1–1.25 mm long. Pappus white, 3–4 mm long.

D i s t r. India, Burma, Malaysia, China.

E c o l. Growing in dry situations in scrub or forest at low to medium elevations, apparently not common. Flowering March–April, but probably longer; Randeria records October–June.

S p e c i m e n s E x a m i n e d. WITHOUT PRECISE LOCALITY: *C.P. 560* annotated "Hantane—(indecipherable) *Gardner*; Ooma Oya, Apr. 1854; Polonnaruwa, March 1858" (PDA). ANURADHAPURA DISTRICT: Steps to Mihintale Temple, Aug. 1885, *Trimen s.n.* (PDA). MONERAGALA DISTRICT: Bibile-Lunugala Road, *Simpson 9638* (PDA).

N o t e s. As already remarked, *B. virens* has been confused with *B. membranacea* (see notes under that species). Both are similar in appearance but *B. virens* has an eglandular indumentum and is a plant of lower elevations than *B. membranacea*. The involucre of the latter is generally darker in colour in the dried state than that of *B. virens*.

13. Blumea obliqua (L.) Druce, Bot. Soc. Exch. Club Br. Isles 4: 609. 1917; Alston in Trimen, Handb. Fl. Ceylon 6: 161. 1931; Randeria, Blumea 10: 286. 1960.

Erigeron obliquum L., Mant. 2: 573. 1771. Type: Herb. LINN 994/1.
Blumea amplectens DC. in Wight, Contrib. 13. 1834; Thw., Enum. Pl. Zeyl. 163. 1860; Hook. f., Fl. Br. Ind. 3: 260. 1881; Trimen, Handb. Fl. Ceylon 3: 19. 1895.
Blumea arenaria DC. in Wight, Contrib. 13. 1834. Based on *Wight 1422*.
Blumea amplectens var. *arenaria* Hook. f., Fl. Br. Ind. 3: 260. 1881; Trimen, Handb. Fl. Ceylon 3: 19. 1895 p.p.

Annual herbs 3–45 cm tall. Stems erect, much branched, terete, covered with spreading pilose hairs. Leaves 0.5–6 × 0.3–2.5 cm; the lower ones oblong-lanceolate or oblanceolate-spathulate, attenuate at the base, obtuse or subacute at the apex; upper leaves ovate-oblong, sessile, cordate, rounded or auriculate, semiamplexicaul at the base, acute or obtuse at the apex, margins entire or coarsely dentate, sparsely or densely pubescent on both surfaces. Capitula campanulate or urceolate-campanulate, 4 mm diam., few or numerous, each solitary on peduncles 1–5 cm long from the axils of the upper leaves. Phyllaries 4-seriate, linear-lanceolate, 3–5 mm long, purplish tinged, squarrose, inner ones subscarious. Flowers mauve or purple; female corollas 3–3.75 mm long, glabrous; hermaphrodite corollas 3.5–4.5 mm long, strongly whitish pubescent on lobes. Receptacle glabrous. Achenes dark brown oblong-elliptic, somewhat compressed, unribbed, c. 0.5 mm long, puberulous. Pappus yellowish-white, 3–4 mm long.

D i s t r. India, Pakistan.

E c o l. In sandy or clayey areas especially near the sea in dry regions, common. Flowering December-June, but probably throughout the year; Randeria records July-March.

V e r n. Nara Karamba (T, fide Nevill); Mudamahana (S).

S p e c i m e n s   E x a m i n e d. WITHOUT PRECISE LOCALITY: *C.P. 1730* annotated "Jaffna, Ranisseram (?) *Gardner*; Batticaloa, Mar. 1858" (PDA), unannotated (K, BM); a second sheet of this number at PDA bears the pencilled note "and *C.P. 3523*" (but a sheet bearing this number at BM is *B. bifoliata*). JAFFNA DISTRICT: Jaffna, Feb. 1890, *Trimen s.n.* (PDA), *Simpson 7987* (BM); Delft Island, *Grierson 1119* (E, US, PDA). VAVUNIYA DISTRICT: Matalan (possibly Putummattalan ?) Feb. 1889, *H. Nevill s.n.* (PDA); Mullaitivu, *Alston 644* (PDA). MANNAR DISTRICT: Talaimannar, 16 July 1916, *J.M. Silva s.n.* (PDA). TRINCOMALEE DISTRICT: 17 miles N of Trincomalee on road to Palmoddai, *Grierson 1035* (E, US, PDA, BR, CANB). AMPARAI DISTRICT: Ulapasse Wewa 1.5 miles N of Panama, *Fosberg & Sachet 52943* (US, E, PDA). HAMBANTOTA DISTRICT: Palatupana Mahalewaya near Kirinde, 21 Dec. 1882, *Trimen s.n.* (PDA); Ruhuna Nat. Park, Patanagala, *Fosberg 50342* (US, PDA); Ruhuna Nat. Park, Komawa Wewa, *Mueller-Dombois 68052901* (US, PDA), *Cooray 68060103R* (US, PDA). WITHOUT LOCALITY: *s. coll. C.P. 1732* p.p. (BM, K—see also under *B. bifoliata*); *Moon 658* (BM).

N o t e. Randeria is probably correct in remarking that this is an extremely plastic species which varies according to the habitat conditions. The variety (*B. amplectens*) var. *arenaria* which Trimen recorded was distinguished by the presence of oblanceolate leaves with entire or merely denticulate margins and more abundant pubescence on the leaf undersides and on the involucres. Such plants are found in almost pure sand or in impoverished coastal soils but appear not to be truly distinct as they may show several stages of intermediacy with more typical specimens growing in locally more favourable situations. It should be noted that *C.P. 1732*, which Trimen cited under this variety, is a mixture at Peradeniya and possibly in other herbaria as well; most of the specimens on the sheets are *B. bifoliata* and only two could be attributed to this variety.

B. obliqua, especially the plants attributable to the above mentioned variety, is in fact similar in appearance to *B. bifoliata* and sometimes grows in association with it which may possibly account for the confusion that has often arisen both as to the separation of these species and as to the flower colour particularly of *B. obliqua*. Alston (l.c. p. 162) discussed these problems and came to the tentative but erroneous conclusion that there might be three species involved. Trimen and Randeria both incorrectly recorded the flower colour of *B. obliqua* as yellow. From my own observations in Ceylon and from the relatively few field notes which record flower colour, it is unquestionably always purplish-mauve. *B. bifoliata* on the other hand, has yellow

flowers and may be further separated by its spreading indumentum of long
villous hairs and stipitate glands; its leaves which are less coarsely toothed or
almost entire; the uppermost leaves are larger (than those of *B. obliqua*) and
suboppositely arranged; the involucre is longer.

14. Blumea bifoliata (L.) DC. in Wight, Contrib. 14. 1834; C.B. Clarke,
Comp. Ind. 72. 1876; Hook. f., Fl. Br. Ind. 3: 261. 1881; Trimen, Handb. Fl.
Ceylon 3: 19. 1895; Gamble, Fl. Pres. Madras 2: 686. 1921; Randeria, Blumea
10: 288. 1960.

Conyza bifoliata L., Sp. Pl. ed. 2. 1207. 1763. No specimen in Herb. LINN.
but Pluk. Alm. 140 t. 177, f. 1. cited.
Blumea oligocephala DC. in Wight, Contrib. 13. 1834. Based on *Wight 3104*.
Blumea amplectens var. *arenaria* auct. non Hook. f.: Trimen, Handb. Fl. Cey-
lon 3: 19. 1895 p.p.
Blumea arenaria auct. non DC.: Thw., Enum. Pl. Zeyl. 163. 1860. p.p.

Annual herbs 5–60 cm tall, ± erect. Stems simple or more often branched
from the base, terete, covered with spreading villous hairs and stipitate glands.
Leaves 1–6 × 0.4–2 cm, the lower ones alternate, oblanceolate, attenuate, subpetiolate at the base, margins dentate, the upper ones ovate-elliptic, acute
and apiculate at the apex, rounded, sessile and semiamplexicaul at the base,
margins entire or denticulate, villous and stipitate, glandular on both surfaces; the uppermost leaves subopposite. Capitula urceolate-campanulate,
c. 4 mm diam., several, each solitary on axillary peduncles 1–5 cm long. Phyllaries 4–5 seriate, linear-lanceolate, 2.5–7 mm long, the outer ones villous
and glandular, the inner ones longer than the flowers, subscarious, ciliate at
the apex. Flowers yellow, female corollas 3.5–4 mm long, glabrous; hermaphrodite corollas c. 4.5 mm long, lobes sparsely pubescent. Receptacle
glabrous. Achenes linear-oblong, c. 1 mm long, brown, sparsely puberulous,
terete, ± unribbed. Pappus white, 3–4 mm long.

Distr. India, Pakistan, Burma.
Ecol. In damp forest, fields and amongst scrub on clay; sometimes at
the sea shore, quite common. Flowering August–May.
Specimens Examined. WITHOUT PRECISE LOCALITY: *C.P.
1732* (PDA) p.p. (see note under *B. obliqua*). There are two sheets: one bearing specimens of this species only is annotated "Batticaloa, Dec. 1857; Trincomalee, *Glenie*" the other which bears some specimens of *B. obliqua* as well
is annotated "Jaffna, Ranisseram, *Gardner*". ANURADHAPURA DIST-
RICT: near Medawachchiya, *Alston 1274* (PDA); between Medawachchiya
and Horowupotana, *Simpson 9398* (PDA, BM); between Mihintale and Sip-
pukulama, 21 Aug. 1885, *Trimen s.n.* (PDA). POLONNARUWA DISTRICT:
Between Polonnaruwa and the river, 29 Mar. 1905, *J.M. Silva s.n.* (PDA).
VAVUNIYA DISTRICT: Panikkankulam (Appa Fen, Panichchankani)

Simpson 9701 (PDA, BM). JAFFNA DISTRICT: Delft Island, *Grierson 1120* (E, US). KURUNEGALA DISTRICT: Batalagoda, *Alston 1627* (PDA). KANDY DISTRICT: Galagedera, *Amaratunga 1090* (PDA). HAMBANTO-TA DISTRICT: Ruhuna Nat. Park, *Cooray 68060103R* (US, PDA). WITH-OUT LOCALITY: *s. coll. C.P. 3523* (K, BM).

15. Blumea angustifolia Thw., Enum. Pl. Zeyl. 164. 1860; C.B. Clarke, Comp. Ind. 81. 1876; Hook. f., Fl. Br. Ind. 3: 264. 1881; Trimen, Handb. Fl. Ceylon 3: 23, t. 56. 1895; Randeria, Blumea 10: 291. 1960. Type: *Thwaites C.P. 691*.

Perennial herbs. Stems 15–25 cm tall, slender, glabrous or nearly so. Basal leaves narrowly oblanceolate, 5–7 cm × 3–8 mm, acute or acuminate at the apex, gradually attenuate to petioles 1.5–2 cm long, margins entire or obscurely denticulate near the apex, narrowly revolute, glabrous; upper leaves similar, gradually diminishing in size. Capitula c. 2–3 mm diam., solitary or in groups of 2–3 on pubescent axillary peduncles. Phyllaries 3-seriate, 2–5 mm long, the outer ones puberulous, the inner ones glabrous. Flowers yellow, female corollas c. 2.5–3 mm long, glabrous; hermaphrodite corollas c. 3.5 mm, lobes papillate. Receptacle c. 1.5 mm diam., glabrous. Achenes pale brown, oblong, 0.75 mm long (immature ?), glabrous. Pappus white, c. 3 mm long.

D i s t r. Endemic.

E c o l. On damp places among rocks, c. 1000 m, very rare. Flowering January–March.

S p e c i m e n s E x a m i n e d. WITHOUT PRECISE LOCALITY: *C.P. 691* annotated "Ambagamuwa, *Gardner*; Hantane 1851; Peradeniya, Jan. 1854" (PDA), annotated Ambagamuwa, 1000–5000 ft, Feb. 1846 (K), unannotated (BM). KANDY DISTRICT: Rocks by Mahaweli River, Hakinda, near Peradeniya, 3 Mar. 1886, *Trimen s.n.* (PDA). WITHOUT LOCALITY: "Ceylon, *Moon s.n.*" (Herb. R. Wight Propr.) (K).

16. Blumea bovei (DC.) Vatke in Linnaea 39: 485. 1875.

Conyza bovei DC. in Ann. Sci. Nat. Bot. 2, 2: 261. 1834. Type: Sinai, *Bove* (G-DC).

Perennial herbs. Stems 20–30 (−40) cm tall, glabrous or sparsely pubescent. Basal leaves absent at flowering time; cauline leaves linear-oblong, 1.5–4 cm × 3–6 mm, acute at apex, sessile and roundly auriculate at base, margins sharply and sometimes distantly denticulate, glabrous. Capitula 5–7.5 mm broad, solitary or 2–3 on peduncles 4–7 cm long. Phyllaries 3–4 seriate, linear-lanceolate, 4–6 mm long, acuminate, the outer ones pubescent, inner ones hair-like at the apex. Flowers mauve according to some collectors, yellow according to Randeria; female corollas c. 3 mm long, glabrous: hermaphrodite corollas c. 4 mm long, lobes pubescent. Achenes oblong, 0.5–0.75 mm long, brown, pubescent. Pappus white, c. 3.5 mm long.

D i s t r. Arabia, Sinai, Egypt, Palestine, Somaliland, Baluchistan.

E c o l. Flowering February.

S p e c i m e n s E x a m i n e d. ANURADHAPURA DISTRICT: Wilpattu National Park, between the Office and the gate, *Cooray 70020229* R (E, US). Known only from this collection.

16. EPALTES

Cass., Bull. Soc. Philom. 139. 1818. Type species: *E. divaricata* Cass.

Divaricately branched annual herbs. Leaves alternate, entire, decurrent. Capitula small, several or numerous at branch ends, subcorymbose, heterogamous, disciform. Involucres imbricate, 5–6-seriate, phyllaries cartilaginous. Female flowers numerous, tubular, 3–4 lobed at the apex. Hermaphrodite flowers fewer (c. 20–30), infundibuliform, 5-lobed at the apex. Anthers rounded at the apex, auriculate and shortly caudate at the base. Styles of hermaphrodite flowers filiform, undivided or shortly bifid at the apex. Receptacle naked. Achenes of female flowers obovoid or ellipsoid, angular or 10-ribbed; achenes of hermaphrodite flowers empty, sterile. Pappus absent.

KEY TO THE SPECIES

1 Involucres c. 4 mm diam., phyllaries acute, ± appressed, shorter than the flowers. Achenes 0.5 mm long, ellipsoid, smooth, glossy-black, angular, unribbed............
....**2. E. pygmaea**
1 Involucres 5–6 mm diam., phyllaries acuminate, ± squarrose, slightly longer than the flowers. Achenes 1 mm long, obovoid, brown with paler ribs.........**1. E. divaricata**

1. Epaltes divaricata (L.) Cass., Bull. Soc. Philom. 139. 1818; DC. in Wight, Contrib. 16, et Prod. 5: 461. 1836; Thw., Enum. Pl. Zeyl. 164. 1860; Hook. f., Fl. Br. Ind. 3: 274. 1881; Trimen, Handb. Fl. Ceylon 3: 24. 1895; Grierson, Ceylon J. Sci., Biol. Sci. 11: 15. 1974.

Ethulia divaricata L., Mant. 1: 110. 1767; Burm. f., Fl. Ind. 170 t. 58, f. 1. 1768; Moon, Cat. 57. 1824. Type: Herb. Burman (G?).

Stems 3–30 cm tall, spreading, much branched, glabrous, 3–4 winged from decurrent leaf bases, wings entire or dentate. Leaves narrowly oblanceolate, or spathulate, 0.75–6.5 × 0.15–1.25 cm, somewhat attenuate at the base, acute or obtuse, mucronate at the apex, margin rather distantly denticulate or entire, glabrous on both surfaces, somewhat fleshy. Involucre urceolate, c. 5 mm diam.; phyllaries ovate-lanceolate, 3–5 mm long, 1–1.5 mm broad, acuminate, recurved and squarrose at the apex, glabrous, longer than the flowers. Flowers mauve, female corollas 1.25–1.5 mm long; hermaphrodite flower corollas 2–3 mm long. Achenes of female flowers brown, obovoid, 1 mm long, with 10 paler ribs.

D i s t r. Also in India, Burma, Java, China.

E c o l. Among short grass on sand, often over-laying clay, generally near the coast in the dry region, sometimes in rice-fields and on railway tracks, very common, flowering October–May.

U s e s. The roots are said to be bitter and astringent and used as a tonic.

V e r n. Hin or Heen Muda mahana (S).

S p e c i m e n s   E x a m i n e d. WITHOUT PRECISE LOCALITY: *C.P. 234* marked G.C. 392 at upper margin and annotated "Jaffna and Batticaloa, *Gardner*" (PDA) annotated "Ratnapura, Mar. 1846" (K) unannotated (BM). WITHOUT LOCALITY: *Fraser 70* (BM), *Champion s.n.* (K), *Ferguson s.n.* (K), *J.S. Mackenzie s.n.* (K), Herb. *Hermann s.n.* (BM). JAFFNA DISTRICT: Jaffna, Feb. 1890, *Trimen s.n.* (PDA); About 7 miles W of Jaffna, *Grierson 1123* (E, US, PDA, BR, CANB). MANNAR DISTRICT: Madhu Road, 80° 09' E, 8° 46' N, *Jayasuriya et al. 592* (US, E, PDA). POLONNARUWA DISTRICT: between Mannampitiya and Polonnaruwa, 12 Feb. 1926, *Alston s.n.* (PDA). ANURADHAPURA DISTRICT: Wilpattu, Maradanwilu, *Grierson 1131* (E, US, PDA, BR, CANB). BATTICALOA DISTRICT: Vakaneri, 21 Apr. 1907, *Trimen s.n.* (PDA). TRINCOMALEE DISTRICT: 17 miles N of Trincomalee on road to Palmoddai, *Grierson 1033* (E, US, PDA, BR, CANB). AMPARAI DISTRICT: Arugam Bay, *Alston 2457* (PDA, K). COLOMBO DISTRICT: Heneratgoda near Gampaha, 10 Nov. 1926, *A. de Silva s.n.* (PDA); Danowita near Mirigama, *Amaratunga 434* (PDA). KALUTARA DISTRICT: Kalutara (Caltura), *Macrae 171* (BM, K), *265* (BM). KEGALLE DISTRICT: Four Korales (Hathera Korale) near Kegalle, Oct. 1882, *Trimen s.n.* (PDA). HAMBANTOTA DISTRICT: Ruhuna Nat. Park, Uraniya, *Mueller-Dombois 68050309* (PDA).

2. Epaltes pygmea DC., Prod. 5: 461. 1836; Hook. f., Fl. Br. Ind. 3: 274. 1881; Alston in Trimen, Handb. Fl. Ceylon 6: 163. 1931; Grierson, Ceylon J. Sci., Biol. Sci. 11: 15. 1974. Type: in agro Carnatico, *Belanger* (G).

Stems 5–25 cm tall, spreading, glabrous, narrowly 4-winged from decurrent leaf bases, wings entire. Leaves linear, elliptic or oblanceolate, 1–4 cm × 0.2–5 mm, attenuate and decurrent at the base, acute or obtuse at the apex, margins entire or distantly denticulate, glabrous on both surfaces. Involucres urceolate, 4–6 mm diam.; phyllaries 4–5 seriate, ovate-lanceolate, 2.5–3 mm long, acute, erect and ± appressed at the apex, glabrous, shorter than the flowers. Flowers mauve; female corollas 2.5 mm long; hermaphrodite corollas 3.5–4 mm long. Achenes of female flowers oblong-ellipsoid, black, smooth, terete, glossy, 0.5 mm long.

D i s t r. Also in S. India.

Ecol. In sandy coastal areas in arid regions, quite rare. Flowering February–April.

Specimens Examined. MANNAR DISTRICT: Illupaikkadivai, Feb. 1890, *Trimen s.n.* (PDA); VAVUNIYA DISTRICT: 20 Mar. 1927, *Alston 1278* (PDA).

17. SPHAERANTHUS

L., Sp. Pl. 927. 1753; Gen. Pl. ed. 5, 399. 1754. Type species: *S. indicus* L.

Erect branching annual herbs. Leaves alternate, often decurrent. Capitula in terminal glomerules, small, heterogamous, disciform, each subtended by a single stiff bract. Phyllaries few to numerous (3–15), subequal, membranous. Marginal flowers female, narrowly tubular, 2–4-lobed. Inner flowers 1–7, hermaphrodite, tubular, 5-dentate. Receptacle naked. Anther bases sagittate. Achenes oblong, angular and often glandular; Pappus absent.

KEY TO THE SPECIES

1 Stems unwinged or very narrowly winged. Glomeruli cone-shaped, all subtending bracts visible and obscuring flowers.............................1. **S. amaranthoides**
1 Stems obviously winged. Glomeruli ovoid or spherical, subtending bracts ± completely obscured by the flowers
  2 Margins of leaves and wings entire or denticulate. Peduncles smooth, unwinged or with very narrow entire wings......................................3. **S. africanus**
  2 Margins of leaves and wings irregularly and sharply toothed. Peduncles bearing narrow, toothed wings...2. **S. indicus**

1. **Sphaeranthus amaranthoides** Burm. f., Fl. Ind. 186. 1768; DC. in Wight, Contrib. 11. 1834 et Prod. 5: 370, 1836; Thw., Enum. Pl. Zeyl. 162. 1860; C.B. Clarke, Comp. Ind. 96. 1876; Hook. f., Fl. Br. Ind. 3: 274. 1881; Trimen, Handb. Fl. Ceylon 3: 25. 1895; Gamble, Fl. Pres. Madras 2: 691. 1921; Robyns, Kew Bull. 187. 1924; Alston in Trimen, Handb. Fl. Ceylon 6: 163. 1931; Ross-Craig, Hook. Ic. Pl. 36: 85 t. 3524. 1955; Grierson, Ceylon J. Sci., Biol. Sci. 11: 16. 1974. Type: Herb. Burman (G).

Sphaeranthus zeylanicus Wall. ex Robyns, Kew Bull. 187. 1924. Type: *Wight 1416.*

Annual herbs, 5–30 cm tall. Stems terete or, especially the branches, very narrowly winged, glabrous. Leaves linear-spathulate or oblong, 3–7 cm × 3–12 mm, attenuate, semi-amplexicaul and shortly decurrent at the base, obtuse and mucronate at the apex, margins distantly serrate-denticulate, glabrous and glandular punctate beneath, smelling strongly of mint when crushed. Glomerule ovoid-conical, 1.5–2 cm long, 1–1.5 cm diam., subtending bracts imbricate, ovate-acuminate, 5–6 mm long, 1.5–3 mm broad, sub-pungent, reddish brown, glabrous. Phyllaries 3, scarious, subequal; two lateral ones c. 3 mm long, folded lengthwise, each enclosing two female flowers; third bract posterior, oblong-elliptic, flat. Female flowers 4, corollas filiform, c. 1.75 mm long, glandular; hermaphrodite flowers 1, corolla c. 1.75 mm long, glandular. Achenes of female flowers stipitate, 1.5 mm long (including stipe 0.4 mm long), puberulent. Achenes of hermaphrodite flowers exstipitate, c. 1.25 mm long, glabrous, apparently empty and sterile.

D i s t r. Also from Southern Madras.

E c o l. In short grass in moist probably brackish situations near the coast in the arid region, rare. Flowering February–August.

V e r n. Chiva-charantai (T).

S p e c i m e n s   E x a m i n e d. WITHOUT PRECISE LOCALITY: *C.P. 1768* annotated "Mannar and Jaffna, *Gardner*; Kurenagala, Aug. 1868 (PDA; BM unannotated). MANNAR DISTRICT: Illupaikkadavai, Feb. 1890, *Trimen s.n.* (PDA); ibid., *Grierson 1129* (E, US, PDA, BR); ANURADHA-PURA DISTRICT: Wilpattu National Park, near Eerige Ara confluence with Moderagama Aru, 30 m, *Fosberg et al. 50761* (E, US, PDA).

N o t e s. *S. zeylanicus* Robyns, a taller leafier plant with smaller stramineous capitula, was reduced to synonymy under the above species by Ross-Craig. Robyns, under the heading of "without locality but probably from Ceylon", cited two specimens: *Wallich 3180 B* which bears the name "*S. zeylanicus* Herb. Heyne" in the Wallich Catalogue, and *Wight 1416* which he designated as type. It is doubtful if either of these were in fact collected in Ceylon; there appears to be no published record of Heyne having visited the island and Wight's specimen is almost certainly from Southern India. Ross-Craig gave the locality "Negapatam" against the latter specimen at the British Museum and a duplicate of it at Edinburgh bears the place name "Madura". Presumably this refers to Madura (Madurai) in Madras State and not to the Madura Oya River in Ceylon.

2. Sphaeranthus indicus L., Sp. Pl. 927. 1753; Moon, Cat. 59. 1824; Hook. f., Fl. Br. Ind. 3: 275 p.p. 1881; Trimen, Handb. Fl. Ceylon 3: 25. 1895; Gamble, Fl. Pres. Madras 2: 692. 1921; Robyns in Kew Bull. 197. 1924; Ross-Craig in Hook. Ic. Pl. 36: 21, t. 3501 B. 1955. Type: Herb. Hermann (BM).

Sphaeranthus hirtus Willd., Sp. Pl. 3: 2395. 1804; Thw., Enum. Pl. Zeyl. 162. 1860.

Erect aromatic annual herbs 10–30 cm tall. Stems divaricately branched, 4-winged, wings irregularly and sharply toothed, glandular and spreading whitish pilose. Leaves oblanceolate or spathulate, 1.5–6 × 0.5–3 cm, obtuse or acute and spinulous-mucronate at the apex, attenuate, semiamplexicaul and strongly decurrent at the base, margins ± coarsely serrate-dentate, minutely glandular on both surfaces and spreading whitish pilose especially on the veins. Glomeruli ovoid-globose, 1–1.5 cm long, 0.8–1.5 cm diam., terminal on the branches. Subtending bracts linear, apiculate, c. 3 mm long, ciliate and glandular. Phyllaries 12–15, 2-seriate, c. 3 mm long, outer ones similar to the subtending bracts, inner ones linear-oblanceolate acuminate. Flowers purplish; female flowers 10–12, corollas tubular, 1.5 mm long narrowing at the apex, the lower half becoming swollen and thickened at maturity; hermaphrodite flowers 1–3, corollas 1.75–2 mm long, lower part becoming swollen (c. 1 mm diam.) and ovoid at maturity, upper part tubular, 5-lobed. Achenes of female flowers c. 1 mm long, brown, 4–5 angled, minutely puberulous on the ribs; achenes of hermaphrodite flowers narrowly obconical, ± confluent with the base of the corolla, c. 1.5 mm long, probably sterile.

D i s t r. India, Assam, Burma, Malay Archipelago, Australia.

E c o l. In moist soil and at the margins of paddy-fields, quite common. Flowering September–March.

U s e s. A range of medicinal uses has been ascribed to this plant of which its anthelmentic properties appear to be most widely recognised. It is also reported to be used as a tonic, an aphrodisiac, a cure for toothache and as a fish poison.

V e r n. Muda-mahana (S), Aet-muda-mahana (S—according to Moon).

S p e c i m e n s E x a m i n e d. WITHOUT PRECISE LOCALITY: *C.P. 1769* (marked GC 496 at upper margin) annotated "Haragama, Aug. 1853, —(illegible), Sept. 1857, Trincomalee, Glenie" and on second sheet "Kurunegala and Jaffna, Gardner" (PDA). ANURADHAPURA DISTRICT: between Wilpattu Nat. Park and Anuradhapura, *van Beusekom 1642* (US, E). KURUNEGALA DISTRICT: Rambawewa, *Simpson 9399* (PDA, BM, K); Melsiri-pura, *Amaratunga 1094* (PDA). POLONNARUWA DISTRICT: Meegaswewa, *Simpson 8709* (PDA, BM). MONERAGALA DISTRICT: Butalla Road outside Wellawaya, *Townsend 73/150* (US, E, K, PDA). WITHOUT LOCALITY: in 1860, *Dubuc s.n.* (E); *Macrae 264* (BM); 1839; *Mackenzie s.n.* (K); *Walker s.n.* (K).

3. Sphaeranthus africanus L., Sp. Pl. ed. 2, 1314. 1762; Hook. f., Fl. Br. Ind. 3: 275. 1881; Trimen, Handb. Fl. Ceylon 3: 26. 1895; Gamble, Fl. Pres. Madras 2: 692. 1921; Robyns, Kew Bull. 196. 1924; Ross-Craig, Hook. Ic. Pl. 36: 18, t. 3501 A. 1955; Grierson, Ceylon J. Sci., Biol. Sci. 11: 16. 1974. Type: Herb. Hermann (BM).

Sphaeranthus microcephalus Willd., Sp. Pl. 3: 2395. 1884; Thw., Enum. Pl. Zeyl. 162, 1860.

Erect annual herbs 15–45 cm tall, with an oily smell. Stems much branched, 3-4-winged, wings entire or distantly denticulate, glabrous. Leaves oblanceolate or obovate, 2–8 × 0.5–3 cm, attenuate, semiamplexicaul and decurrent at the base, acute and apiculate at the apex, margin serrulate, sparsely brownish pubescent on both surfaces. Glomerules ± spherical, 0.6–1 cm broad, solitary, terminal or on short axillary peduncles up to 2 cm long. Lowermost bracts 3–4 mm long, linear-lanceolate, ± obscured. Subtending bracts c. 2 mm long, narrowly oblanceolate, concave. Phyllaries c. 8 per capitulum, spathulate, 2–2.5 mm long, 0.5–1 mm broad, obtuse or apiculate at the apex, margins scarious. Flowers white; female flowers c. 20, corollas c. 1 mm long, lower half pale, swollen and hardened, abruptly narrowed into the thin slender terminal portion, glabrous; hermaphrodite flowers 3, corollas 1.5–2 mm long, lower half thickened and hardened, upper part thinner, spreading, lobed. Achenes 1.25 mm long, glandular, with a short stipe at the base, those of hermaphrodite flowers apparently sometimes fertile.

D i s t r. Africa, India, Burma, China, Indochina, Malaysia, Philippines, Australia.

E c o l. In marshy or brackish situations at low elevations sometimes on the sea shore, quite common. Flowering November–May.

V e r n. Velmudda (S).

S p e c i m e n s E x a m i n e d. WITHOUT PRECISE LOCALITY: *C.P. 1770* (marked GC 391 at upper margin and annotated "Kurunegala, Batticaloa, Jaffna, *Gardner*; Ratnapura, Dec. 1853, Batticaloa, Nov. 1858" (PDA; unannotated: BM, K). AMPARAI DISTRICT: Arugam Bay, *Alston 2459* (PDA, K). TRINCOMALEE DISTRICT: 17 miles N of Trincomalee towards Palmoddai, *Grierson 1034* (E, US, PDA, BR, CANB); near Muthur, *Simpson 9719* (PDA, BM). COLOMBO DISTRICT: Colombo, 26 Mar. 1796, *Rottler? s.n.* (E-GL); Talahena near Negombo, *Amaratunga 497* (PDA); Pamunugama, *Simpson 7951* (PDA, BM, K); between Madampe and Mahawewa, *Grierson 1135* (E, US, PDA, BR, CANB). KALUTARA DISTRICT: Kalutara, *Macrae 170* (PDA, BM, K). HAMBANTOTA DISTRICT: Ruhuna Nat. Park, Kumana, *Cooray 69073121 R* (US, E, PDA).

18. BLEPHARISPERMUM

Wight ex DC. in Wight, Contrib. 11. 1834. Type species: *B. petiolare* Wight.

Tall glabrous shrubs. Leaves ovate, alternate, entire. Capitula small, laterally compressed, heterogamous, discoid, aggregated into spherical glomerules. Phyllaries few, stiff with scarious margins. Female flowers usually 2, corollas filiform, 2–3 dentate at the apex. Hermaphrodite flowers 2 (or up to 8 in Indian species), corollas tubular, 5-lobed. Receptacle paleaceous. Anther bases caudate. Style branches of female flowers linear, spreading, those of hermaphrodite flowers papillose, scarcely spreading at the apex. Achenes of female flowers fertile, compressed, margins strongly ciliate. Pappus of 2–3 long hairs.

Blepharispermum petiolare DC. in Wight, Contrib. 12. 1834 et Prod. 5: 368. 1836; Hook. f., Fl. Br. Ind. 3: 276. 1881; Trimen, Handb. Fl. Ceylon 3: 27. 1895; Grierson, Ceylon J. Sci., Biol. Sci. 10: 53. 1972. Type: *Wight 1417* (Holo. K; iso, E).

Scrambling shrub 2–6 m tall. Mature stems (c. 3 cm diam.) dark brown with small scattered grey lenticels, branches divaricate at angles of c. 45°. Leaves ovate, 5–10.5 × 2–5 cm, acuminate at the apex, shortly attenuate into a petiole 0.5–1.5 cm long at the base, glabrous on both surfaces, glandular beneath, margins narrowly revolute. Glomerules 1–1.5 cm diam., 2–5 in a leafy terminal racemose cluster. Capitula numerous, laterally compressed, each subtended by an ovate, acute bract 2.5–3.5 mm long, 1.5 mm broad. Phyllaries stiffly membranous, the 2 lateral ones flat or slightly concave, keeled on the back, 4.5–5 mm long, 1.5–1.75 mm broad, each bearing one female flower in the axil; inner phyllaries 2, 5–6 mm long, strongly plicate, each enfolding a single hermaphrodite flower. Flowers white; female corollas 1.5–2 mm long, 2-lobed at the apex, hermaphrodite corollas 4.5–5 mm long. Paleae 2, scarious, linear-oblong, 5.5–6 mm long, 0.5–1 mm broad. Achenes of female flowers fertile, oblanceolate, c. 3.5 mm long, 1 mm broad, dark brown or blackish, margins brownish ciliate, ± truncate at the apex and bearing two longer (c. 1.5 mm) stiffer hairs; those of hermaphrodite flowers linear, glabrous, 2 mm long, sterile, epappose.

D i s t r. Also in Travancore, S. India.

E c o l. Scrambling through small trees in sparse lowland forest, local and rare.

S p e c i m e n s E x a m i n e d. HAMBANTOTA DISTRICT: Tissamaharama, 19 Dec. 1882. *Trimen s.n.* (PDA, K, BM); Ruhuna National Park, Sithulpahuwa—Politupawa road, 4–8 m, *Comanor 651* (E, US, PDA), *Comanor 902* (E, US, PDA). AMPARAI DISTRICT: prope Ugandamalej (Okanda), *Rottler* or *Klein s.n.* (see Trimen l.c.).

19. ANAPHALIS

DC., Prod. 6: 271. 1837. Type species: none indicated. Possibly *A. royleana* might be considered as lectotype.

Erect or decumbent, annual or perennial herbs or shrubs. Leaves alternate, often greyish tomentose. Capitula small or medium-sized, numerous in terminal corymbs, heterogamous (elsewhere subdioecious), disciform. Involucre campanulate, 4–5 seriate; phyllaries imbricate, basal parts thickened, brownish, upper part scarious, generally white, showy. Receptacle naked. Female flowers several or numerous up to 30, corollas filiform, minutely but distinctly 2–4 lobed. Hermaphrodite flowers few or numerous (up to 60), tubular, 5-lobed. Anther bases sagittate, auricles connate, caudate. Achenes small, oblong, subterete. Pappus 1-seriate, finely barbellate, decidous or persistent.

KEY TO THE SPECIES

1 Stems bearing numerous small leaves, 0.5–1.2 cm long................**5. A. brevifolia**
1 Stems not as above; leaves generally more than 1.5 cm long
  2 Leaf bases auriculate or shortly decurrent on the stem
    3 Auricles short, acute, 2–3 mm long (best observed by pulling leaf from stem); suffrutescent. Female flowers about half as numerous as hermaphrodite flowers........
    ....**9. A. zeylanica**
    3 Auricles absent, leaf base shortly decurrent; small annual herbs. Female flowers twice or five times more numerous than hermaphrodite flowers...................
    ....**10. A. subdecurrens**
  2 Leaf bases semiamplexicaul but not as above
    4 Leaves, at least on the upper surface, covered by a pellicle or skin of interwoven hairs
      5 Leaf oblanceolate, attenuate to a narrow base, 1-nerved, pelliculate only on upper surface...**6. A. marcescens**
      5 Leaves oblong-elliptic, scarcely narrow at base, semiamplexicaul, 3-nerved, pelliculate on both surfaces...**1. A. pelliculata**
    4 Leaves glabrous or covered by a tomentum of free unwoven hair on the upper surface
      6 Low growing slender plants, stems decumbent. Leaves 1-nerved....**7. A. sulphurea**
      6 Medium sized shrubs, stems erect or spreading. Leaves 3-nerved
        7 Leaves crowded at branch ends. Corymbs borne on obvious peduncles bearing similar though smaller or more acute leaves
          8 Indumentum loose, soft, whitish. Leaves oblong-spathulate. Capitule 6–7 mm diam., relatively few (20–30) per corymb.....................**4. A. thwaitesii**
          8 Indumentum closely appressed, pale brown
            9 Leaves narrowly oblanceolate, 2–3 mm broad. Capitula small, c. 3 mm diam., 5–25 per corymb...**8. "Species x"**
            9 Leaves oblanceolate 6–9 mm broad. Capitula numerous 4–5 mm diam., 50–80 per corymb...**3. A. fruticosa**
        7 Leaves ± distant. Little or no distinction between stem and peduncle...........
        ....**2. A. pseudocinnamomea**

1. Anaphalis pelliculata Trimen, Handb. Fl. Ceylon 3: 28, t. 57. 1895.

Anaphalis zeylanica "form 3" Hook. f., Fl. Br. Ind. 3: 286. 1881—fide Trimen. Type: none designated but presumably *W. Nock s.n.* marked "Specimen figured" (PDA).

Small branching shrubs 39–50 cm tall; foliage peppery scented. Stems covered by interwoven hairs forming a white pellicle when young and, in older parts, generally retaining leaves of previous years. Leaves oblong-elliptic, 4–6 cm × 4–10 mm, somewhat attenuate at the base, semiamplexicaul, narrowed and sub-acute or ± attenuate at the apex or apiculate or recurved apiculate, margin revolute, covered above by a silvery white pellicle which, when removed, leaves the surface puberulous with trichome bases, white or pale brown beneath, young foliage often yellowish-green in colour, 3- or 5-nerved. Capitula c. 4 mm broad, numerous (10–60) in dense corymbs. Phyllaries 4-seriate, oblanceolate, 3.75–4 mm long, 1.25 mm broad, brown, stiff and tomentose in the lower half, white scarious, spreading above, acute or sub-acute at the apex. Female flowers c. 10, corollas 2–2.5 mm long; herma-phrodite flowers c. 20, corollas 2.25–2.75 mm long. Achenes 0.5 mm long, minutely puberulous. Pappus 2.5 mm long, deciduous.

D i s t r. Endemic.

E c o l. Among rocks, 7000–8000 ft, rare. Flowering September–November.

S p e c i m e n s E x a m i n e d. The following were regarded by Trimen as *A. pelliculata* and appear to constitute a broader leaved form (8–10 mm broad): NUWARA ELIYA DISTRICT: Horton Plains, Nov. 1893, *W. Nock s.n.* (marked "Specimen figured"—presumably holotype, PDA); Horton Plains, Slope of Totapella, 17 Sept. 1890, *W. Nock s.n.* (PDA); Horton Plains, Side of Totapella, 11 Nov. 1892, *W. Nock s.n.* (PDA); Foot of Totapella, Nov. 1893, *W. Nock s.n.* (PDA); Totapella Mountain, c. 7400 ft, Sept. 1892, *Trimen s.n.* (K). In addition, one of the sheets of *s. coll. C.P. 568* (PDA—see below) annotated "Hakgala, Sept. 1866" has leaves of similar dimensions. It is further annotated, possibly in Trimen's hand, "Conf. Totapella plant, *A. pelliculata*". The following have narrower (4–6 mm broad) leaves. WITH-OUT EXACT LOCALITY: *C.P. 568* (PDA) annotated "Bopatalawa, Oct. 1867; Nuwara Eliya, *Gardner*, Nov. 1859; Nuwara Eliya, 1863" (PDA; this is a mixed collection some specimens being similar to *A. pseudocinnamomea*. The specimen at Kew was determined as *A. cinnamomea* by Hooker). NUWARA ELIYA DISTRICT: Ohiya below Horton Plains, Sept. 1890 *s. coll.* (*Nock?*) (PDA); Between Hakgala and Nuwara Eliya, Oct. 1893, *W. Nock s.n.* (PDA); Jungle path beyond lab, Hakgala Sept. 1906, *s. coll.* (*Silva?*) *s.n.* (PDA); Kirigalpota, 7850 ft, 12 Mar. 1969, *Grierson 1102* (E, US, PDA, BR, CANB) (withered capitula, without flowers). KANDY DISTRICT: summit of Adam's Peak, 7300 ft, 17 Oct. 1927, *Alston 965* (PDA, K).

2. Anaphalis pseudocinnamomea Grierson, Ceylon J. Sci., Biol. Sci. 11: 19. 1974. Type: Ceylon, *Thwaites C.P. 568* (K).

Anaphalis cinnamomea auct. non C.B. Clarke: Hook. f., Fl. Br. Ind. 3: 281. 1881 pp., quoad plantae Zeylanicae; Trimen, Handb. Fl. Ceylon 3: 28. 1895.

Gnaphalium adnatum Thw., Enum. Pl. Zeyl. 422. 1864 p.p., non *Anaphalis adnata* DC.

Erect perennial herbs. Stems 30–60 cm tall, covered by tawny coloured appressed tomentum. Leaves elliptic-lanceolate, 4–6 cm × 3–12 mm, acute or

gradually acuminate to a fine point at the apex, attenuate and semiamplexicaul at the base, margin narrowly revolute, completely glabrous or, more
usually, sparsely floccose-araneose and glabrescent (dark brown when dried)
on the upper surface, closely whitish or pale brown tomentose beneath, obscurely 3-nerved. Capitula 5–6 mm diam., numerous (20–70) in branched or
tight corymbs. Phyllaries 4–5 seriate, oblanceolate, 4 mm long, 1–1.5 mm
broad, brown and tomentose at base, white scarious above, apex obtuse or
subacute. Female flowers c. 15, corollas 2 mm long; hermaphrodite flowers
c. 32, corollas 2.25 mm long. Achenes 0.75–1 mm long. Pappus 2.25 mm
long.

Distr. Probably endemic.

Ecol. Upper montane region, 6000–7000 ft, not common. Flowering
September–March.

Specimens Examined. *s. coll. C.P. 568* annotated "Nuwara Eliya,
Jan. 1846 and Cent. Prov. 5,000 ft" (K). BADULLA DISTRICT: Top of
Namunakula, 6670 ft, 12 Mar. 1907. *Silva s.n.* (PDA). RATNAPURA DIS-
TRICT: Kunadiya-parawita, Dec. 1917, *F. Lewis s.n.* (PDA). NUWARA
ELIYA DISTRICT: Condegala near Hakgala, *Alston 1730* (PDA); Watte-
kelle, Sept. 1866, *s. coll. C.P. 528* (PDA); Hakgala 6200 ft, *Grierson 1080*
(withered capitula without flowers) (E, US, PDA); Horton Plains, 25 Jan.
1906, *Silva s.n.* (PDA). KANDY DISTRICT: Summit of Rangala Ridge,
Sept. 1888, *Trimen s.n.* (PDA).

Note. The above specimens bear a strong resemblance to the Himalayan
A. cinnamomea which, from the specimens examined, is regularly subdioecious. As already mentioned in the generic description, there is no evidence of
a subdioecious distribution of sexes in the Ceylonese *Anaphalis* and the above
specimens represent a distinct species.

In his concept of *A. cinnamomea*, Trimen, I believe, included some specimens which should properly belong to *A. pelliculata* and treated the latter to
too strict an interpretation. *A: pseudocinnamomea* is distinguished by the
colour of its underleaf and by the completely glabrous or sparsely tomentose
upper leaf surface which dries to a dark brown colour. *A. pelliculata* usually
has a whitish under leaf only rarely becoming pale brown but the young
foliage often has a yellowish tinge to it. Both leaf surfaces are covered by a
skin-like pellicle of interwoven hairs which if removed from the upper surface
leaves a brown stubble of trichome bases. If, on the other hand, the tomentum is stripped from the upper surface of the leaf of *A. pseudocinnamomea* it
is rendered completely glabrous, without persistent trichome bases. *A. pelliculata* is, of course, an endemic species and no species with a similar skin-
like hair covering occurs in the Himalayas. Thus it seems correct to remove
such specimens from our interpretation of *A. pseudocinnamomea* and to regard the pellicle as a character of considerable diagnostic value.

There is variation in the colour of the underleaf tomentum both in Ceylon and in the Himalayas from pale to mid-brown. To some extent this may be conditioned by length of storage in the herbarium but it is not impossible that there is an innate colour difference. For the present, specimens with pale or whitish tomenta should be included.

3. Anaphalis fruticosa Hook. f., Fl. Br. Ind. 3: 282. 1881; Trimen, Handb. Fl. Ceylon 3: 29. 1895. Type: *Thwaites C.P. 132.*

Gnaphalium adnatum var. *spathulifolium* Thw., Enum. Pl. Zeyl. 422. 1860 p.p. (other part: *A. thwaitesii*).

Shrub over 0.5 m tall, Stems 4 mm thick, covered with numerous leaf bases. Leaves oblanceolate or spathulate, 4–4.5 cm × 6–9 mm, conferted, attenuate to a narrow (3–4 mm) base, semiamplexicaul, acute at the apex, margin narrowly revolute, upper surface 3-nerved, almost completely glabrous or with a few araneose hairs on the midrib, under surface covered with pale brown (possibly white when fresh), closely appressed tomentum; upper leaves on the peduncles similar, decreasing in size. Capitula 4–5 mm broad, numerous (50–80) in large branched corymbs borne on peduncles 30–45 cm long. Phyllaries 4-seriate, outer ones brown, sparsely araneose, inner ones lanceolate, 5.5 mm long, 2 mm broad, stiff and brown at base, spreading and white scarious above. Female flowers 2.5–2.75 mm long; hermaphrodite flowers 2.75–3 mm, lobes glabrous. Achenes 0.75 mm. Pappus 3.25 mm long.

D i s t r. Endemic.
E c o l. Flowering March.
S p e c i m e n s   E x a m i n e d. KANDY DISTRICT: Adam's Peak, Mar. 1846 (*Gardner*) *C.P. 132* (PDA, BM, K).
N o t e. This species, which was marked as being rare by Trimen, has not been recollected since Gardner's time and nothing is known of its habitat and flowering time. It is probably most closely related to *A. thwaitesii* with which it was once confused but can be readily distinguished from the latter by its longer leaves with compact indumentum and by its larger corymbs of smaller capitula.

4. Anaphalis thwaitesii C.B. Clarke, Comp. Ind. 110. 1876; Hook. f., Fl. Br. Ind. 3: 284. 1881; Trimen, Handb. Fl. Ceylon 3: 29. 1895; Grierson, Ceylon J. Sci., Biol. Sci. 11: 18. 1974. Type: *Thwaites C.P. 528.*

Gnaphalium adnatum var. *spathulifolium* Thw., Enum. Pl. Zeyl. 422. 1860 p.p.

Small shrubs 25–50 cm tall. Stems cottony tomentose, ± obscured by the numerous close set leaves which persist for several years after withering. Leaves spathulate, 2–2.5 cm × 5–10 mm, conferted, apex subacute or obtuse,

attenuate to a broad semiamplexicaul base, margin flat, upper surface covered with a dense pale grey tomentum, or subglabrous and bearing only a few
white araneose hairs, 3-nerved, lower surface covered with loose, white, pannose tomentum, upper leaves on the peduncles similar, decreasing in size.
Capitula 6–7 mm broad in dense corymbs of 20–30, borne on peduncles 10–15
cm long. Phyllaries 4-seriate, outer ones brownish, araneose, inner ones lanceolate, 6–7 mm long, the lower third brown, stiff, upper part white, scarious,
spreading. Female flowers c. 17, 2.5–3 mm long; hermaphrodite flowers c.
25, 3–3.5 mm long, lobes glandular. Achenes 0.75–1.0 mm long, glabrous or
with a few minute eglandular hairs. Pappus 3.5 mm long.

D i s t r. Endemic.

E c o l. In damp ground beside streams at 7000 ft, rare. Flowering March–
April.

There are two distinct varieties.

KEY TO THE VARIETIES

1 Leaves 6–8 mm broad, obtuse or subacute, persistently grey tomentose on the upper
surface...**1. var. thwaitesii**
1 Leaves 3–5 mm broad, ± acute, sparsely tomentose on the upper surface and rapidly
becoming glabrous...**2. var. glabrescens**

1. var. thwaitesii

S p e c i m e n s E x a m i n e d. NUWARA ELIYA DISTRICT: Pidurutalagala, (*Gardner*) *C.P. 528* (PDA, BM, K) (the sheet at PDA bears the number G.C. 405 at the upper margin); same locality, Apr. 1893, *Nock s.n.* (PDA);
at 7000 ft, *Sinclair 10113* (K, E); at 7500 ft, *Grierson 1064* (E, US, PDA,
BR, CANB); Horton Plains. *Nock s.n.* (PDA). WITHOUT LOCALITY:
Walker 84 (K); in 1847, *Gardner 405* (K); in 1845, *G. Thomson 10/45* (K).

2. var. glabrescens Grierson, Ceylon Sci., Biol. Sci. 11: 18. 1974.

S p e c i m e n s E x a m i n e d. NUWARA ELIYA DISTRICT: Horton
Plains, Feb. 1857, *s. coll. C.P. 528* (PDA, K, BM); same locality, on banks of
Belihul Oya at Ford Pool, 7000 ft, *Grierson 1098* (E—holotype, US, PDA,
BR, CANB isotypes). WITHOUT LOCALITY: *s. coll. C.P. 2408* (K)—
(Note: Hooker cites this incorrectly as *C.P. 2048*).

5. Anaphalis brevifolia DC., Prod. 6: 273. 1837; C.B. Clarke, Comp. Ind. 110.
1876; Hook. f., Fl. Br. Ind. 3: 286. 1881; Trimen, Handb. Fl. Ceylon 3: 31.
1895; Bond, Wild Fls. of Ceylon Hills 104, fig. 53. 1953. Type: "In insulae
Zeylonae montibus ad alt. 1000 hexapod," *Walker* (E-GL).

Gnaphalium brevifolium Thw., Enum. Pl. Zeyl. 166. 1860.

Anaphalis bournei Fyson, Fl. Nilgiri & Pulney 1: 232. 1915.

Much branched annual or biennial herbs. Stems 10–30 cm tall, bearing numerous small leaves and covered with closely applied whitish tomentum. Leaves linear-lanceolate, 5–12 × 1.5–3 mm at the base, semiamplexicaul, acute at the apex, margins entire, revolute, covered above and beneath with loose araneose tomentum; 1-nerved. Capitula 7–8 mm diam. in dense corymbs of 7–15. Phyllaries 4–5 seriate, ovate-lanceolate, c. 5 mm long, 1.5 mm broad, lower half stiff, straw-coloured, upper half white, scarious, spreading. Flowers yellow, female corollas c. 12, 2–2.5 mm long, hermaphrodite corollas c. 60, 2.25–2.5 mm long, lobes bearing glandular hairs. Achenes 0.5 mm long, minutely puberulent. Pappus hairs 2.25 mm long, deciduous.

D i s t r. Also recorded from Anamalai Hills, S. India (but Alston in Trimen, l.c. p. 164 notes "Endemic").

E c o l. In grassy banks and patanas, 5000–7000 ft, common. Flowering September–April.

S p e c i m e n s E x a m i n e d. NUWARA ELIYA DISTRICT: Nuwara Eliya, (*Gardner*) *C.P. 1761* (PDA, BM, K); Horton Plains, Sept. 1890, *W. Nock s.n.* (PDA); Ambawela, Sept. 1890, *W. Nock s.n.* (PDA); Hakgala, Nov. 1893, *W. Nock s.n.* (PDA); Horton Plains, 26 Jan. 1906, *Willis s.n.* (PDA); Hakgala, 26 Feb. 1906, *Silva s.n.* (PDA); Sita Eliya, Apr. 1921, *De Alvis s.n.* (PDA); Ambawela, *Alston 1025* (PDA); Horton Plains, 7000 ft, ("nowhere in flower") 27 Apr. 1932, *Simpson 9566* (BM); near Nuwara Eliya lake, 8 Aug. 1932, *Simpson 9911* (BM); near Ambawela Railroad Station on road to Horton Plains, 1830 m, 8 July 1967, *Mueller-Dombois & Comanor 67070814* (US, PDA); between Nuwara Eliya and Hakgala, 6000 ft, *Grierson 1077* (E, US, PDA, BR, CANB); Horton Plains, 2400 m, *Grierson 1093* (E, US, PDA, BR, CANB), *Gould & Cooray 13833* (E, US, PDA). WITHOUT LOCALITY at alt. 6000 ped, *Walker s.n.* (E-GL, Arnott Herb.), *121* (K); *Macrae 305* (BM, K), *Gardner 406* (K).

N o t e. *A. neelgherriana* DC. which, according to Hooker (l.c.), is unsatisfactorily differentiated from this species, has more densely leaved shoots and the leaves themselves are generally shorter and narrower. Within the capitula, however, the ratio of female to hermaphrodite flowers may be significant for in *A. neelgherriana* their numbers are almost equal (25: 24).

6. **Anaphalis marcescens** (Wight) C.B. Clarke, Comp. Ind. 110. 1876; Hook. f., Fl. Br. Ind. 3: 286. 1881; Trimen, Handb. Fl. Ceylon 3: 31. 1895.

Gnaphalium marcescens Wight, Ic. Pl. Ind. Or. t. 1115. 1846; Thw., Enum. Pl. Zeyl. 166.1860. Type: Nilgiri Hills, 5500–7000 ft, *Wight s.n.*

Sprawling shrub 1.5–2 m tall. Young stems thinly white tomentose becoming glabrescent, older stems retaining some shrivelled leaves from previous years. Leaves narrowly oblanceolate, 3–4 cm × 3–6 mm, gradually attenuate to a slender base, acute at the apex, margins revolute, upper surface (dark blackish-green when dried) covered by a thin skin-like pellicle of interwoven hairs, closely white tomentose beneath; (very pale brown when dried), upper leaves on the peduncles similar, decreasing in size gradually. Capitula 3–5 mm diam., numerous (30–40), borne in corymbs at the ends of peduncles 20–25 cm long. Phyllaries 4-seriate, outer ones brown, arachnoid, inner ones oblong-lanceolate, 4 mm long, 0.75–1 mm broad, stiff and straw-coloured at the base, white scarious, spreading above, obtuse or subacute at the apex. Female flowers c. 10, corollas 2–2.5 mm long; hermaphrodite flowers c. 15, corollas 2.25–2.75 mm long, lobes bearing dark coloured glandular hairs. Achenes 0.5 mm long, glabrous. Pappus 2.5–2.75 mm long.

D i s t r. Also in Nilgiri Mts. S. India.

E c o l. Among shrubs and small trees at the margins of forests, about 7000 ft, local. Flowering October-November.

S p e c i m e n s E x a m i n e d. WITHOUT PRECISE LOCALITY: *C.P. 1765* annotated "High ground between Maturata and Pidurutalagala, Oct. 1853; Pidurutalagala, *Gardner*, Nov. 1859" and bearing the number G.C. 407 at the upper margin (PDA), unannotated (BM, K). NUWARA ELIYA DISTRICT: Nuwara Eliya, *Gardner 407* (PDA, BM, K); Pidurutalagala, Apr. 1893, *Nock s.n.* (PDA); Hakgala, (without date), *Nock s.n.* (PDA); Pidurutalagala, *Grierson 1072* (without flowers—E, US, PDA, BR, CANB). WITHOUT LOCALITY: *Walker 85* (E-GL) *s.n.* (K); Sept.–Dec. 1853, *Harvey s.n.* (E) 6000 ft, *G. Thomson s.n.* (K).

N o t e. This medium sized shrub is characterised by its slender leaves which are covered on the upper surface by a thin pellicle and is quite distinct from *A. sulphurea* with which Trimen associated it at varietal level.

7. Anaphalis sulphurea (Trimen) Grierson, Ceylon J. Sci. Biol. Sci. 11: 18. 1974.

Anaphalis marcescens var. *sulphurea* Trimen, Handb. Fl. Ceylon 3: 31. 1895.
  Type: *Thwaites C.P. 3522.*

Low-growing sprawling shrub. Stems decumbent, 20–45 cm long, white tomentose. Leaves oblanceolate or spathulate, 1.3–2.5 cm × 3–6 mm, attenuate at the base, obtuse or subacute at the apex, margin narrowly revolute upper surface covered by thin greyish tomentum, 1-nerved, under-surface more densely and yellowish tomentose (becoming pale brown with age). Capitula 2–3 mm broad, borne in dense corymbs of 7–15 (–25) at the ends of ± distinct peduncles, 15–30 cm long. Phyllaries 4-seriate, outer ones lanceolate, yellowish, araneose-tomentose, inner ones lanceolate or oblanceolate, 3.5 mm long, 0.75–1 mm broad, stiff, straw-coloured in the lower half, white, scarious, spreading above. Female flowers c. 6, 1.5–2.0 mm long; hermaphrodite flowers c. 13, 2–2.25 mm long, lobes glandular. Achenes 1.0 mm long, glabrous. Pappus 2–2.5 mm.

D i s t r. Endemic.

E c o l. Common in grassy banks and patanas, 6000–7000 ft, common. Flowering September–May.

S p e c i m e n s E x a m i n e d. WITHOUT PRECISE LOCALITY: *C.P. 3522* annotated "N. Ellia, *Gardner:* Horton Plains, Feb. 1857" (PDA), unannotated (BM, K). NUWARA ELIYA DISTRICT: Horton Plains, 16 Sept. 1890, *s. coll.* (*Nock?*) (PDA); near Horton Plains, 2 May 1906, *Willis s.n.* (PDA); near Nuwara Eliya lake, 9 Apr. 1906, *Silva s.n.* (PDA); Horton Plains, 3 May 1906, *Silva s.n.* (PDA), *Gould 13863* (E, US, PDA); Pidurutalagala, 21 Apr. 1906, *Silva s.n.* (PDA); Ambawela, 21 Feb. 1927, *Alston 1279* (PDA); between Hakgala and Nuwara Eliya, 6000 ft, *Grierson 1077* (E, PDA, US, BR, CANB); Horton Plains, 7000 ft, *Grierson 1093* (E, US, PDA, BR, CANB). WITHOUT LOCALITY: In 1829, *McRae s.n.* (K).

N o t e. Although similar to *A. marcescens*, this species can readily be distinguished because of its short, thin decumbent stems, its shorter leaves which are tomentose on both surfaces but yellowish beneath, and by the corymbs of less numerous and smaller capitula. Ecologically, they are found in quite different habitats, and whereas *A. marcescens* appears to flower only in October and November, *A. sulphurea* continues to bloom until May.

8. Anaphalis "species X" Grierson, Ceylon J. Sci., Biol. Sci. 11: 19. 1974.

Slender shrub at least up to 30 cm tall (possibly more). Stems covered with remains of leaf bases and, in younger parts, with cottony tomentum. Leaves conferted at the apices of branches, narrowly oblanceolate, 2–4.5 cm × 2.5–3.5 mm, obtuse at the apex, attenuate at the base, distinctly trinerved, glabrous or, in the young state, sparsely cottony on the upper surface, with densely appressed pale brown cottony tomentum on the lower surface but less dense or ± glabrous on the midrib, margin entire, revolute. Flowering stems 4–15 cm long, densely whitish tomentose, bearing several leaves of similar shape and size but tending to become more acute. Capitula c. 3 mm diam. in compact corymbs of 6–25 capitula. Phyllaries 4–5 seriate, outer ones lanceolate, acuminate, pale brown (in the dried condition), c. 4.5 mm long, 1 mm broad, inner ones lanceolate, brown at the base, white above, 6.5 mm long, 1.5 mm broad. Female flowers c. 12, corollas 2.5–2.75 mm long, hermaphrodite flowers c. 22, corollas 2.75–3 mm long. Receptacle alveolate. Achenes of female flowers, only, apparently fertile, dark brown, c. 1 mm long, angular or subcompressed, minutely puberulent. Pappus 2.75–3 mm long, whitish, hairs somewhat coherent at the base, readily detached.

This species is only known from three herbarium specimens all of them unlocalised. They are *Col. Walker 1702* (E); *s.n.* (K—there are two sheets and a specimen on one of them is of *A. marcescens*).

This species has been confused with *A. marcescens* but, although the capitula are of similar size, the two are readily separable. Here the old leaves are
not retained on the stems below the new leaves to the extent that they are in
A. marcescens. The leaves in this new species appear to be more congested
at the branch ends and thus, on the older leafless parts, the shoots are closely
and regularly scarred with leaf bases. The leaves themselves are narrower
than those of *A. marcescens* and more obtuse. They are glabrous on the upper
surface and not covered by a pellicle. The phyllaries of this new species are
acute whereas those of *A. marcescens* are obtuse. The corolla lobes of *A.
marcescens* (both of female and hermaphrodite flowers) bear numerous dark
coloured stipitate glands; those of this novelty are glabrous or bear only a
few pale glands.

9. Anaphalis zeylanica C.B. Clarke in Hook. f., Fl. Br. Ind. 3: 286. 1881;
Trimen, Handb. Fl. Ceylon 3: 30. 1895. Type: *Thwaites C.P. 1763 and 568.*

Gnaphalium wightianum Thw., Enum. Pl. Zeyl. 166. 1860. p.p. and 422. 1864.
Anaphalis wightiana acut. non DC.: C.B. Clarke, Comp. Ind. 111. 1876.

Small and sometimes slender suffrutex. Stems 30–60 cm tall, thinly or
densely araneose when young. Leaves oblong-lanceolate, 1.5–2.5 cm ×
3–5 mm, acute, apiculate at the apex, (apiculus sometimes recurved and then
appearing subacute), shortly (c. 2 mm) and acutely auriculate at the base,
margin recurved, glandular puberulent and araneose on both surfaces, sometimes almost glabrous, trinerved. Capitula 6–8 mm broad in dense terminal
corymbs of (1–) 6–20. Phyllaries 4–5-seriate, 4–5 mm long, 1.5 mm broad,
oblanceolate, acute; lower half brown, stiff, araneose; upper half white scarious spreading. Female flowers c. 13, corollas 2.5 mm long, lobes brownish-
glandular; hermaphrodite flowers c. 24, corollas 2.5–3 mm long, lobes
brownish-glandular. Achenes 0.5 mm long, puberulent. Pappus 2.5–3 mm
long, deciduous.

D i s t r. Endemic.
E c o l. On marshy patanas, 6000–7000 ft, common. Flowering June–
October.
S p e c i m e n s E x a m i n e d. WITHOUT PRECISE LOCALITY: *C.P.
1763* annotated "between Maturata and Pidurutalagala, Oct. 1853; Nuwara
Eliya, *Gardner*; Hakgala", and bearing the number G.C. 408 at upper margin
(PDA), annotated "Nuwara Eliya, 5000–6000 ft" and "Pidurutalagala,
7000 ft" (K), unannotated (BM). NUWARA ELIYA DISTRICT: Nuwara
Eliya, 6000 ft, *s. coll. C.P. 568* (K); same locality, 6000 ft, *Gardner 408* (K,
BM); Hakgala, *W. Nock s.n.* (PDA); Horton Plains, Sept. 1890, *Trimen s.n.*
(PDA); Elk plains between Nuwara Eliya and Kande Ela Reservoir, 6300 ft,

Mueller-Dombois 68051805 (US, PDA); Horton Plains on the way to Kirigalpota, 7000 ft, *Grierson 1105* (E, US, PDA, BR). WITHOUT LOCALITY: *Walker 44* (K), *124* (K).

N o t e. There is uncertain evidence of variability in the density and persistence of the indumentum on the stems and leaves, the undersides of the latter sometimes becoming quite glabrous. From the few available specimens, this variability would indicate no more than formal recognition but future collections of this species may prove otherwise.

10. Anaphalis subdecurrens (DC.) Gamble, Fl. Pres. Madras 695. 1921; Alston in Trimen, Handb. Fl. Ceylon 6: 164. 1931; excl. var. *lutea*; Bond, Wild Fl. Ceylon Hills 104, fig. 2. 1953, excl. var. *lutea*.

Gnaphalium subdecurrens DC. in Wight, Contrib. 21. 1834. Type: *Wight 1469* (K).
Anaphalis oblonga DC., Prod. 6: 274. 1837; Trimen, Handb. Fl. Ceylon 3: 30. 1895; C.B. Clarke, Comp. Ind. 112. 1876; Hook. f., Fl. Br. Ind. 3: 283. 1881.
Gnaphalium indicum auct. non L.: Thw., Enum. Pl. Zeyl. 166. 1860.
Gnaphalium oblongum Thw., Enum. Pl. Zeyl. 422. 1864.

Annual herbs 15–40 (–70) cm tall, erect. Stems simple or branched, densely white tomentose. Leaves oblong, oblanceolate or spathulate, basal ones sometimes almost rosulate, 3–5 cm × 6–12 mm, attenuate at the base, acute or apiculate at the apex, margin entire, flat, thinly white tomentose on the upper surface, more densely so on the lower surface, 3- or sometimes 5-nerved; upper leaves on the peduncles ± erect, similar to basal leaves but decreasing in size, semiamplexicaul and very shortly decurrent on the stem. Capitula 2.5–3 mm broad, numerous (20–60 or several hundreds in luxuriant specimens), in dense or branching terminal corymbs. Phyllaries 4–5-seriate, oblanceolate, 3 mm long, 1 mm broad, green, stiff tomentose in the lower half, scarious, spreading above, pink at first when fresh, becoming white when dried. Flowers yellow, female corollas 25–30, 1.5–2 mm long; hermaphrodite corollas 5–10, 1.75–2.25 mm long. Achenes of both kinds of flower apparently fertile, 0.5–0.75 mm long, brown, minutely puberulent. Pappus 2.25 mm long, hairs white, ± coherent at the base into a ring, deciduous.

Chromosome number: n = 14 (shetty in Taxon 16: 568. 1967).

D i s t r. Also in S. India.

E c o l. On grassy banks and in patanas, 4000–7000 ft; very common. Flowering throughout the year.

S p e c i m e n s E x a m i n e d. WITHOUT PRECISE LOCALITY: *C.P. 1762*, annotated "Hantane to Rambodde, *Gardner*; Rambodde, Oct. 1853; Nuwara Eliya, *Gardner*" (PDA), annotated "5000 ft" (K). BADULLA

DISTRICT: Between Palugama and Boralanda, *Mueller-Dombois 68051838* (US, PDA); Below Horton Plains towards Halmadulla, 16 Sept. 1890, *s. coll.* (*W. Nock?*) (PDA); Haputale, Sept. 1890 m, *s. coll.* (*Nock?*) *s.n.* (PDA); Namunakula, 6670 ft, 12 Mar. 1907, *J.M. Silva s.n.* (PDA). KANDY DISTRICT: Hantane, 24 May 1924, *J.M. Silva s.n.* (PDA); near Knuckles, *J.M. Silva 99* (PDA); Path to Adam's Peak from Dalhousie, *Grierson 1041* (E, US, PDA). NUWARA ELIYA DISTRICT: Towards Nuwara Eliya, 2 Mar. 1906, *Willis s.n.* (PDA); Hakgala, 20 Feb. 1906, *Silva s.n.* (PDA); Maturata, 6 Apr. 1906, *Silva s.n.* (PDA); Hakgala, 24 Aug. 1926, *Silva 164* (PDA); above Condegala, near Hakgala, *Alston 1915* (PDA); Sita Eliya, *Simpson 9591* (BM); near Purpuressa, *Simpson 8388* (BM); near Nuwara Eliya Lake, 6150 ft, 20 Jan. 1930, *Mrs. Carson Roberts s.n.* (K); Pidurutalagala, 8200 ft, *Sinclair 10101* (E, K), *Grierson 1067* (E, PDA, US); Horton Plains, 2167 m, *Grierson 1094* (E, US, PDA, BR, CANB), *Comanor 439* (E, US, PDA), *Gould & Cooray 13863* (E, US, PDA); between Pussellawa and Ramboda, 1000 m, *Mueller-Dombois 67091303* (US, PDA); between Ramboda and Nuwara Eliya, 1200 m, *Comanor 331* (E, US, PDA). WITHOUT LOCALITY: *Walker 89* (E-GL, K, Herb. Arnott), *40* (K); in 1829, *McRae s.n.* (K); *J.S. Mackenzie s.n.* (K), 1847, *Gardner 410* (K).

N o t e. This species appears to be quite uniform throughout Ceylon and Trimen's remark about the Horton Plains plant being different (var. *elliptica* Hook. f.) seems to be without foundation.

This species bears a superficial resemblance to white European forms of *Gnaphalium luteo-album* but the female corollas of the latter are much narrower and the hermaphrodite flowers have obviously sterile achenes.

20. GNAPHALIUM

L., Sp. Pl. 850. 1753. Gen. Pl. ed. 5. 368. 1754. Type Species: *G. uliginosum* L.

Annual herbs, densely white tomentose. Leaves alternate, entire; capitula small in dense terminal corymbs, heterogamous, disciform. Involucre campanulate, phyllaries imbricate, scarious yellow or brown, (elsewhere white). Female flowers numerous, corollas filiform, 3–4 lobed; hermaphrodite flowers few (about a tenth as many as females) tubular, 5-lobed. Anther bases sagittate, caudate appendiculate. Achenes oblong, subcompressed, minutely glandular; those of hermaphrodite flowers sterile. Pappus 1-seriate, setae not thickened apically.

KEY TO THE SPECIES

1 Phyllaries greenish-yellow. Capitula in dense ± flat-topped corymbs.................
....**1. G. luteo-album** subsp. **affine**
1 Phyllaries stramineous, brownish or tinged purple

2 Leaves noticeably discolorous, thinly pubescent or subglabrous above, densely white tomentose beneath, margins somewhat crisped. Capitula in dense ± unbranched terminal panicles, clusters subtended by short leaves. Phyllaries often purplish or brown, glabrous except at the base. Perennial plants..................**3. G. spicatum**

2 Leaves less obviously discolorous, pubescent on both surfaces but more densely so beneath, margins flat. Terminal panicles usually branched at least at the base, clusters of capitula subtended by longer leaves. Phyllaries stramineous, outer ones sparsely lanate. Annual plants...**2. G. pensylvanicum**

1. Gnaphalium luteo-album L. subsp. **affine** (Don) Koster, Blumea 4: 484. 1941.

Gnaphalium affine D. Don, Prod. Fl. Nepal 173. 1825. Type: "Hab. in Nepalia" *Hamilton.*
Gnaphalium luteo-album var. *multiceps* Hook. f., Fl. Br. Ind. 3: 283. 1881.
Anaphalis subdecurrens var. *lutea* Alston in Trimen, Handb. Fl. Ceylon 6: 164. 1931.

Herbs 10–60 cm tall. Stems white tomentose, erect, simple. Leaves linear-oblanceolate or spathulate, 1.5–6 cm long, 1–10 mm broad, acute at the apex, semiamplexicaul and shortly decurrent at the base, margin entire, flat, densely white tomentose on both surfaces. Capitula 3 mm long, 2 mm diam., 10-numerous in dense or branched terminal corymbs. Phyllaries 3-seriate, yellow, ovate or oblong, 2–3 mm long, 0.75–1.25 mm long. Flowers yellow; females 50–100, corollas c. 2 mm long; hermaphrodites 5–10, corollas c. 2 mm long. Achenes 0.5 mm, oblong, pale brown. Pappus 2 mm long, white, hairs separately deciduous.

Chromosome number. n = 7 (Shetty, Taxon 16: 569. 1967).

D i s t r. Java, Philippines, China, Japan, Australia, Indo-China, India.

E c o l. Common weed of tea plantations and by roadsides above 3000 ft. Flowering throughout the year.

S p e c i m e n s E x a m i n e d. BADULLA DISTRICT: Bandarawela, 29 June 1931, *Simpson 8335* (PDA, BM). KANDY DISTRICT: Ferndale Estate, Rangala, *Alston 1509* (PDA); Between Gampola and Dolosbage, 3000 ft, *Grierson 1005* (E, US, PDA, BR, CANB); near Adam's Peak Waterfall, 2 miles SW of Maskeliya, 4000 ft, *Grierson 1055* (E, US, PDA, BR, CANB). NUWARA ELIYA DISTRICT: Ambawela, Mar. 1906, *Silva s.n.* (PDA); Horton Plains, 7000 ft, *Grierson 1106* (PDA); Horton Plains at Ohiya road, ¼ mile from Farr Inn, *Mueller-Dombois & Cooray 68011316* (US, PDA); *Gould & Cooray 13864* (E, US, PDA); 1 km. NW of Ambawela Rail road station, 1940 m, *Mueller-Dombois 68051518* (US, PDA); Nuwara Eliya, *Harris s.n.* (E).

N o t e. It seems extraordinary that this weed was not present in Ceylon in Trimen's time but there are no herbarium collections earlier than 1906.

2. Gnaphalium pensylvanicum Willd., Enum. Hort. Berol. 867. 1809; Grierson, Ceylon J. Sci., Biol. Sci. 10: 55. 1972. Type: "Habitat in Pensylvania" (P).

Gamochaeta pensylvanicum (Willd.) Cabrera, Bol. Soc. Argent. Bot. 9: 375. 1961; Fl. Prov. Buenos Aires 175, fig. 48. 1963.
Gnaphalium peregrinum Fern., Rhodora 45: 479 t. 795. 1943. Type: Louisiana, *D.S. & H.B. Correll 9937* (GH).
Gnaphalium polycaulon auct. non Pers.: Alston in Trimen, Handb. Fl. Ceylon 6: 164. 1931.
Gnaphalium purpureum auct. non L.: Hook. f., Fl. Br. Ind. 3: 289. 1881.

Annual herbs 10–30 cm tall. Stems erect, simple or branching from the base, greyish tomentose. Leaves obovate-spathulate, 2–6 × 0.5–2 cm, rounded or subobtuse and apiculate at the apex, attenuate at the base, margins entire, flat, sparsely lanate on the upper surface, greyish tomentose beneath. Capitula urceolate-campanulate, 2.5–3 mm diam., numerous in axillary clusters forming a more or less interrupted and leafy (leaves 1.5–5.5 cm long) spicate panicles, lower branches usually stalked. Phyllaries greenish, 2–3-seriate, outer ones ovate-lanceolate, scarious, 2–2.5 mm long, lanate, inner ones oblong-lanceolate, c. 3 mm long. Flowers greenish-white; females c. 100, corollas 2.25 mm long; hermaphrodites c. 2, corollas 2.25 mm long. Achenes brown, elliptic, 0.5 mm long, minutely glandular. Pappus hairs 15–20, white, 2.25–2.5 mm long, coherent at the base, deciduous.

Distr. Native of N. America.
Ecol. Weed of tea estates and generally of cultivated or disturbed ground, usually above 2000 ft. Flowering throughout the year.
Vern. The following Sinhalese names have been recorded but may apply to *G. spicatum* as well: Sudana Kola, Maha-Sudana, Musal Kathu Pillu (Lit. rabbits' ear wool). According to one herbarium sheet at Peradeniya it was called "Wild Mignonette" by the planters.
Specimens Examined. KANDY DISTRICT: Maskeliya, 2 Mar. 1883, *Trimen s.n.* (PDA); Hatale Estate, Madulkelle, *Grierson 1051* (E, US, PDA, BR, CANB). NUWARA ELIYA DISTRICT: Near Ragalla, *Simpson 8700* (BM); Hewahetta, *Simpson 9013* (BM). BADULLA DISTRICT: Namunakula, 13 Mar. 1907, *s. coll. s.n. (J.M.S. ?)* (PDA).

3. Gnaphalium spicatum Lam., Enc. 2: 757. 1786; Grierson, Ceylon J. Sci., Biol. Sci. 10: 55. 1972. Type: Paraguay, Monte Video, *Commerson*.

Gamochaeta spicata (Lam.) Cabrera, Bol. Soc. Argent. Bot. 9: 380. 1961; Fl. Prov. Buenos Aires 174. 1963.

Perennial herbs 20–30 cm tall. Stems erect, usually simple, appressed whitish—tomentose. Leaves oblanceolate or spathulate, 2–10 × 0.4–2 cm, obtuse or subacute, apiculate at the apex, attenuate at the base, margins entire, somewhat crisped, green, glabrous or very sparsely araneose on the upper surface, appressed whitish tomentose beneath, discolorous. Capitula urceolate-campanulate, c. 2.5 mm diam., numerous on short axillary clusters forming a more or less interrupted spicate inflorescense, leaves short (0.5–3 cm). Phyllaries 3-seriate, outer ones ovate-elliptic, 2.5 mm long, araneose only at the base, otherwise glabrous, inner ones oblong-lanceolate, c. 3.25 mm long, purplish. Flowers pinkish purple; females 50–60, corollas c. 2 mm long; hermaphrodites 3, corollas c. 2.5 mm long. Achenes oblong-elliptic, c. 0.5 mm long, minutely glandular. Pappus hairs whitish, 2.5 mm long, coherent at the base, deciduous.

D i s t r. Native of S. America.

E c o l. Roadside clearings at forest margins; probably quite common. Flowering probably throughout the year.

S p e c i m e n s E x a m i n e d. NUWARA ELIYA DISTRICT: North of Pattipola, 6000 ft, *Grierson 1084* (E, US, PDA, BR, CANB); Abbotsford Estate, Lindula, Oct. 1882, *Trimen s.n.* (PDA).

21. HELICHRYSUM

P. Mill., Gard. Dict. abr. ed. 4. 1754 ('*Elichrysum*'); corr. Pers., Syn. Pl. 2: 414. 1807 nom. cons. Type species: *H. orientale* (L.) Gaertn. (syn. *Gnaphalium orientale* L.).

Herbs or subshrubs, usually densely white tomentose, sometimes merely pubescent. Leaves alternate, entire-margined, capitula small, numerous, in dense corymbs (or capitula few and large in cultivated plants), heterogamous, disciform. Involucre campanulate (or hemispherical). Phyllaries imbricate, scarious, yellow (or variously coloured). Female flowers marginal, filiform, few, 3-lobed at the apex; hermaphrodite flowers tubular, 5-lobed, twice or more times as numerous as the female flowers. Anther bases caudate. Achenes oblong, obscurely 4–5 angled. Pappus 1-seriate, setae barbellate, often thickened at the apex and subplumose near the base.

Helichrysum buddleioides DC. var. **hookerianum** (Wight & Arn.) Hook. f., Fl. Br. Ind. 3: 291. 1881; Grierson, Ceylon J. Sci., Biol. Sci. 11: 17. 1974.

Helichrycum hookerianum Wight & Arn. in DC., Prod. 6: 201. 1837; C.B. Clarke, Comp. Ind. 116. 1876. Type: none specified, possibly *Walker s.n.* (E-GL).
Helichrysum buddleioides DC. in Wight, Contrib. 20. 1834; Trimen, Handb. Fl. Ceylon 3: 32. 1895.
Gnaphalium hookerianum (Wight & Arn.) Thw., Enum. Pl. Zeyl. 166. 1860.

Suffrutex, 1.5–2 m tall, sometimes scrambling through small trees up to 4

m. Stems cylindrical, densely covered in white or pale brown cottony tomentum. Leaves oblong-lanceolate, 4–6.5 × 1–1.5 cm, numerous, marcescent and becoming reflexed with age, obscuring the stem; acute at the apex, sessile and semiamplexicaul at the base, margins recurved, 3–5 nerved at the base, upper surface glabrous or sparsely araneose along the midrib, lower surface densely tomentose, white or tawny. Capitula c. 3 mm diam., very numerous in dense terminal corymbs 8–12 cm broad. Phyllaries 4-seriate, oblanceolate or spathulate, obtuse, 3–3.5 mm long, 1.25–1.75 mm broad, cartilaginous, stiff and straw-coloured at the base, scarious and yellow above. Flowers yellow; females 7–9 per capitulum, filiform, 2–2.25 mm long; hermaphrodite flowers tubular, 16–22 per capitulum, 2.25–2.5 mm long. Achenes oblong, 0.5 mm long, minutely puberulous. Pappus hairs white, 2.25 mm long, fragile, separately deciduous.

D i s t r. Endemic variety: species also in S. India.

E c o l. Roadsides, and rocky slopes and in forest clearings, common above 5000 ft. Flowering January–April.

S p e c i m e n s   E x a m i n e d. WITHOUT PRECISE LOCALITY: *C.P. 681* annotated "Nuwara Eliya, Jan. 1854; Nuwara Eliya & Horton Plains, *Gardner*, Feb. 1857" (PDA), annotated "Nuwara Eliya 6000–7000 ft, Jan. 1846" (K), unannotated (BM). NUWARA ELIYA DISTRICT: Between Hakgala and Nuwara Eliya, 8 Apr. 1906, *Silva s.n.* (PDA); Nuwara Eliya, 6500 ft, Apr. 1899, *Gamble s.n.* (K); Hakgala Peak, *Simpson* 9098 (BM); Summit of Pidurutalagala, *Sinclair 10096* (E), *Grierson 1067* (E, US, PDA, BR, CANB). KANDY DISTRICT: Ascent to Adam's Peak, 16 May 1906, *Silva s.n.* (PDA) (flowers withered). WITHOUT LOCALITY: *Walker 78* (K), *s.n.* (E-GL, K).

N o t e. Though not of specific status, a distinction does appear to exist between the Ceylonese and the Southern Indian populations of this species. As Trimen remarked, the plants from the latter region are larger, the leaves (6–10 cm long, 1.5–4 cm broad) are less densely tomentose and more obviously 5–7 veined. Their capitula may contain more flowers (up to 10 more have been found) but the ratio between the sexes is essentially unchanged. The achenes of the typical variety are more strongly pubescent than those of var. *hookerianum*. On the other hand, the receptacles of the Nilgiri plants, contrary to the original description, are not constantly fibrilliferous.

In general, the shoots of the two plants have a different appearance: the leaves of var. *hookerianum*, formed during the previous season while the shoot was making vegetative growth, are more densely crowded and the older dead or moribund leaves are retained, becoming reflexed against the stems. The leaves on the typical variety are larger, more widely spaced and merely shrivel rather than becoming truly reflexed.

Both Trimen (l.c.) and Alston (l.c. 6: 164) record the occurrence of *Heli-*

chrysum bracteatum (Vent.) Andr. in a "semi-wild state" in the Nuwara Eliya area. It is a medium-sized herb 0.5–1 m tall with pubescent (not tomentose) lanceolate leaves and few large capitula surrounded by yellow, red or white phyllaries. There are, however, no specimens at the Peradeniya Herbarium from this locality nor did I observe it there. Thus, though it may escape from cultivation, it does not appear to have become an established alien.

22. VICOA

Cass., Ann. Sci. Nat. 17: 418. 1829. Type species: *V. indica* (L.) DC. (= *V. auriculata* Cass.).

Annual or sometimes perennial ramose herbs. Leaves alternate, simple, the upper ones often cordate at the base. Capitula medium-sized, solitary, terminal on the branches, heterogamous, radiate. Involucre campanulate, phyllaries pluriseriate, imbricate, narrow. Ray flowers female, 1–2 seriate, fertile. Ligule narrow, 2–3-dentate at the apex. Disc flowers hermaphrodite. fertile, 5-lobed. Anther bases sagittate, caudate. Style branches complanate, broad, obtuse. Receptacle flat or convex, naked. Achenes small, obscurely ribbed. Pappus 1-seriate, scabrous, sometimes with a few shorter outer hairs.

Vicoa indica (L.) DC. in Wight, Contrib. 10. 1834 et Prod. 5: 474. 1836; Thw., Enum. Pl. Zeyl. 164. 1860; Alston in Trimen, Handb. Fl. Ceylon 6: 165. 1831.

Inula indica L., Sp. Pl. ed. 2. 1237; Moon, Cat. 58. 1824.
Vicoa auriculata Cass., Ann. Sci. Nat. Bot. 17: 418. 1829; DC., Prod. 5: 474.
1836; Hook. f., Fl. Br. Ind. 3: 297. 1881; Trimen, Handb. Fl. Ceylon 3: 33.
1895. Type: Herb. Burman (G?).

Erect annual herbs up to 1 m tall. Stems terete, reddish, sparsely pubescent. Leaves oblong-lanceolate, 3–7 × 0.4–2 cm, sessile, cordate, auriculate at the base, auricles rounded, attenuate and subacuminate at the apex, margins serrate, pubescent on both surfaces, glandular punctate beneath. Capitula 5–6 mm diam. on slender peduncles. Phyllaries linear-lanceolate, 1.5–4 mm long, 0.3–0.4 mm broad, margins scarious, pubescent on the midribs. Flowers yellow; ray flowers 25–30, ligules c. 5 mm long, 1 mm broad; disc flowers narrowly tubular, corollas 2–3 mm long. Achenes oblong, terete, faintly 5-ribbed, c. 0.75 mm long, brown, appressed white pubescent. Pappus hairs 10, c. 2 mm long, white.

Chromosome number. n = 9 (Mehra *et al.*, Caryologia 18: 39. 1965).

D i s t r. India, China, Thailand, W. Tropical Africa.
E c o l. Roadsides and abandoned chenas, common especially in the dry northern regions. Flowering throughout the year.
V e r n. Ran-hiriya (S).

Specimens Examined. WITHOUT PRECISE LOCALITY: *C.P. 1757* (marked GC 419 at upper margin) annotated "Sigiriya, Kurunegala, *Gardner*; Ramboda, 1851; Haputale, May 1856" (PDA, K, BM unannotated). VAVUNIYA DISTRICT: 121 miles on road from Kandy to Jaffna, *Townsend 73/69* (US, E, K, PDA). RATNAPURA DISTRICT: Belihul Oya, 27 Dec. 1904, *J.K. Nock s.n.* (PDA). TRINCOMALEE DISTRICT: Kantalai Tank, *Comanor 752* (E, US, PDA). POLONNARUWA DISTRICT: Roadside between Polonnaruwa and Batticaloa, Milestone 57, *Grierson 1028* (E, US, PDA, BR, CANB); Habarana—Polonnaruwa road, 160 m, *Comanor 1212* (E, US, PDA). JAFFNA DISTRICT: Between Pallavarayan Kaddu and Vellankulam, *Grierson 1125* (E, US, PDA, BR, CANB). BADULLA DISTRICT: Welimada-Boralanda, 2 miles S of Welimada, *Mueller-Dombois 68051833* (US, E, PDA). HAMBANTOTA DISTRICT: Ruhuna Nat. Park, Plot R18, *Cooray 70032706R* (US, E, PDA). ANURADHAPURA DISTRICT: Wilpattu Nat. Park, *Cooray 70020236 R* (US, E, PDA).

23. CARPESIUM

L., Sp. Pl. 859. 1753; Gen. Pl. ed. 5. 369. 1754. Type species: *C. cernuum* L.

Erect branched herbs. Leaves alternate, entire or dentate. Capitula small or medium sized, terminal or axillary, usually cernuous, heterogamous, disciform. Involucre hemispherical, phyllaries several-seriate, outer ones long, foliaceous, inner ones shorter, subscarious. Outer female flowers numerous, tubular, 3–5 lobed; disc flowers hermaphrodite, 5-lobed. Anther bases sagittate, caudate; filaments sometimes bearing two glands. Style branches linear, rounded at the apex. Receptacle flat, naked. Achenes linear, elongate, striate-costate, narrowed and rostrate above, rostrum often glandular, surmounted by a thickened corona. Pappus absent.

Carpesium cernuum L., Sp. Pl. 859. 1753; DC., Prod. 6: 281. 1837; C.B. Clarke, Comp. Ind. 130. 1876; Hook. f., Fl. Br. Ind. 3: 300. 1881; Trimen, Handb. Fl. Ceylon 3: 34. 1895 in nota; Gamble, Fl. Pres. Madras 2: 700. 1921; Alston in Trimen, Handb. Fl. Ceylon 6: 165. 1931. Type: Herb. LINN. 991/1.

Perennial herbs. Stems 30–60 cm tall, hirsute-pubescent. Leaves ovate-lanceolate, petiolate, petioles winged, 1–4 cm long, upper leaves sessile; laminae up to 12 cm long, 5 cm broad, acute at the apex, attenuate at the base, margins sinuate-denticulate, hirsute-pubescent on both surfaces but especially on the veins beneath. Capitula solitary, terminal at the end of each branch, 0.5–1 cm diam. Outer phyllaries leaflike, spreading or reflexed, inner ones cartilaginous with membranous tips, oblong or oblanceolate, 5–7.5 mm long, 1–1.5 mm broad. Flowers yellow; female corollas tubular or ovoid, c. 2 mm long, 3-lobed, glandular at the base of the lobes; hermaphrodite corollas infundibuliform, 3 mm long, sparsely villous pubescent. Achenes linear-oblong, subcompressed, 5–5.5 mm long (including rostrum, 1–1.5 mm long) with about 10 fine ribs, glabrous; rostrum glandular; corona entire, margined.

Chromosome number. $2n = 40$ (Mehra *et al.*, Caryologia 18: 40. 1965).

D i s t r. Europe, Asia Minor, India, Malaya, China, Japan, Australia.

E c o l. Generally occurring in moist areas at roadsides and forest clearings. Flowering August–September.

S p e c i m e n s E x a m i n e d. BADULLA DISTRICT: Ohiya below Horton Plains, 15 September 1890, *Trimen s.n.* (PDA). NUWARA ELIYA DISTRICT: Patipola below Horton Plains, 17 September 1890, *Trimen s.n.* (PDA); Horton Plains, c. 7000 ft, September 1890, *Trimen s.n.* (K).

N o t e. According to Trimen (l.c.) this is probably an introduced plant but it does not appear to have become widespread and has not in fact been collected since his time.

Tribe HELIANTHEAE (including Helenieae)

Herbs or rarely trees usually with all leaves opposite or sometimes with the upper ones alternate, but sometimes all alternate. Capitula heterogamous, radiate, sometimes homogamous and sometimes (*Xanthium*) monoecious. Involucres one or several-seriate, herbaceous, phyllaries free or united. Anther bases obtuse or sagittate. Style branches truncate or undivided. Receptacle usually paleaceous, paleae flat, concave or enfolding the flower, occasionally tightly enveloping the achene or sometimes epaleaceous. Achenes angular or compressed. Pappus paleaceous, aristate or coronate, sometimes absent.

KEY TO THE GENERA

1 Capitula in terminal glomerules, 1-flowered. Involucres gamophyllous, calyx-like......
....**24. Lagascea**
1 Capitula more than 1-flowered, not glomerulate
  2 Capitula unisexual. Male capitula hemispherical, many-flowered, borne on upper parts of branches. Female capitula ovoid, burr-like, 2-flowered covered in hooked spines and borne on lower parts of branches...................................**28. Xanthium**
  2 Capitula bisexual
   3 Receptacle paleaceous (paleae in *Eclipta* very narrow, bristle-like)
    4 Ray achenes only fertile, epappose (though in *Acanthospermum* apparently with a pappus of 1–3 stout hooked bristles). Styles of disc flowers undivided
     5 Achenes (tightly and persistently enclosed in inner phyllaries) trigonous or laterally compressed
      6 Covering of achene wrinkled, not prickly....................**25. Melampodium**
      6 Covering of achene prickly with hooked bristle.............**26. Acanthospermum**
     5 Achenes flat, dorsally compressed, abruptly contracted to a short neck at the apex
....**27. Moonia**

4 Ray achenes sterile or fertile but disc achenes, at least in part, always fertile
  7 Ligule ± sessile and persistent on ray achenes..........................**28a. Zinnia**
  7 Ligule usually with a distinct basal tube, not persistent on ray achenes
    8 Disc achenes rounded or laterally compressed. Pappus absent or consisting of two short or weak scales
      9 Outer bracts of involucre clavate, spreading and conspicuously glandular........
      ....**29. Sigesbeckia**
      9 Outer bracts of involucre erect or, if spreading, not conspicuously glandular
        10 Receptacle flat or convex not becoming conical at maturity
          11 Paleae bristle-like. Surface of achenes warted in the middle, smooth at the margins..**30. Eclipta**
          11 Paleae linear or oblanceolate, concave or folded
            12 Small trees (2–3 metres tall). Paleae accrescent. Achenes epappose. Cultivated
            ....**30a. Montanoa**
            12 Herbs or suffrutescent perennials. Paleae not accrescent
              13 Apex of paleae obtuse, lacerate. Flowers white. Pappus of 2 weak awns....
              ....**31. Blainvillea**
              13 Apex of paleae acute, ± entire. Flowers yellow
                14 Pappus absent or consisting of 2 minute scales
                  15 Capitula always erect, solitary or several in loose corymbs......**32. Wedelia**
                  15 Capitula erect at first cernuous after anthesis, borne singly or in pairs on short axillary peduncles.............................**33. Eleutheranthera**
                14 Pappus of 2 small scales with a number of minute scales between them
                  16 Peduncles hollow. Pappus persistent........................**34. Tithonia**
                  16 Peduncles solid. Pappus deciduous.....................**34a. Helianthus**
        10 Receptacle becoming distinctly conical. Pappus of 2 weak bristles or absent....
        ....**35. Spilanthes**
    8 Disc achenes dorsally compressed or angular and scarcely compressed
      17 Pappus absent or consisting of 2–3 bristles or awns
        18 Achenes compressed
          19 Margins of achenes winged
            20 Wings lacerate. Pappus of 2 stiff unbarbed awns...............**36. Synedrella**
            20 Wings entire. Pappus of 2 weak bristles.......................**37. Coreopsis**
          19 Margins of achenes unwinged...............................**38a. Dahlia**
        18 Achenes fusiform or angular
          21 Pappus absent. Achenes narrowed at apex but scarcely rostrate.....**38. Cosmos**
          21 Pappus consisting of 2–3 retrorsely barbed awns
            22 Apex of achene truncate not narrowed into a rostrum
              23 Small herbs. Leaves basal, rosulate. Style branches with long villous appendages...**40. Glossogyne**
              23 Medium-sized or tall herbs. Leaves mostly cauline. Style branches subulate
              ....**39. Bidens**
            22 Apex of achene narrowed into a thin rostrum...................**38. Cosmos**
      17 Pappus consisting of about 10 bristles or scales
        24 Annual herbs, ± erect. Pappus of short fimbriate scales, c. 1.5 mm long........
        ....**41. Galinsoga**
        24 Perennial herbs, prostrate or decumbent. Pappus of fine plumose bristles about 5 mm long..**42. Tridax**
3 Receptacle epaleaceous (Helenieae)
  25 Phyllaries in 2 or more series, free. Leaves alternate
    26 Stems winged. Style branches truncate.............................**43a. Helenium**

26 Stems unwinged. Style branches subulate.......................**43b. Gaillardia**
25 Phyllaries uniseriate, connate. Leaves opposite......................**43. Tagetes**

24. LAGASCEA

Cav., Anales Ci. Nat. 6: 331. 1803. Type species: *L. mollis* Cav.

Annual herbs with erect branching stems. Leaves opposite, simple. Capitula one-flowered, aggregated into terminal glomerules. Involucres tubular, calyx-like of 5 phyllaries, connate at the base. Flowers all hermaphrodite, tubular, infundibuliform above, limb 5-lobed. Anthers with oblong, obtuse appendages at the apex, sagittate, ecaudate at the base. Style branches elongate, subulate. Achenes narrowly obovoid or fusiform, somewhat compressed. Pappus minutely coroniform or absent.

Lagascea mollis Cav., Anales Ci. Nat. 6: 333, t. 44. 1803; Hook. f., Fl. Br. Ind. 3: 302. 1881; Trimen, Handb. Fl. Ceylon 3: 34. 1895; Alston in Trimen, Handb. Fl. Ceylon 6: 165. 1931. Type: Cultivated from seeds received from Havana.

Erect, branching, annual herbs. Stems up to 60 cm tall, terete, finely whitish pubescent. Leaves pale green or greyish, ovate or elliptic-lanceolate, petiolate, petioles 5–15 mm long, lamina 1.5–4.5 × 0.5–2.5 cm, attenuate at the base, gradually acuminate at the apex, margin shallowly and distantly serrate, densely whitish pubescent on both surfaces. Glomerules broadly campanulate, 1–1.5 cm diam. containing 30–50 capitula, surrounded by 5–6 spreading trinerved, obovate bracts 0.5–1 cm long, 2–5 mm broad. Involucre 4 mm long, lobes purplish c. 1 mm long, densely puberulous. Flowers white tinged with mauve, c. 4.5 mm long. Achenes remaining within the involucre, black, 3 mm long, weakly ribbed, glabrous below, finely white puberulous at the apex. Pappus apparently absent.

Chromosome number. $2n = 36$ (Chopde, Sci. & Cult. 31: 30. 1965).

D i s t r. Native of Tropical America, now adventive in India and Malaya.
E c o l. Weed of cultivated ground. Flowering September–May.
S p e c i m e n s E x a m i n e d. KANDY DISTRICT: Peradeniya Royal Botanic Garden, May 1887, *Trimen s.n.* (PDA); same locality, Sept. 1896, *Trimen s.n.* (PDA); Teldeniya, *Alston 1081* (PDA); Haragama—Mailapitiya Road, *Simpson 9726* (BM); Mailapitiya, 14 Feb. 1953, Comm. *Jayawardhana s.n.* (PDA); Banks of Mahaweli below Peradeniya Garden, 1700 ft, *Grierson 1160* (E, US, PDA). WITHOUT LOCALITY, *Harvey s.n.* (E).

25. MELAMPODIUM

L., Sp. Pl. 921. 1753; Gen. Pl. ed. 5. 392. 1754. Type species: *Melampodium americanum* L.

Annual or perennial herbs. Leaves opposite, entire or dentate. Capitula terminal on dichotomous upper branches, solitary, heterogamous, radiate. Involucre 2-seriate, outer phyllaries 4–5, foliaceous, often connate at the base and sometimes accrescent, inner phyllaries completely enclosing outer achenes. Ray flowers 1–2 seriate, disc flowers 5-lobed. Anther bases entire. Style branches of hermaphrodite flowers undivided. Receptacle convex or conical, bearing membranous concave paleae enfolding the disc flowers. Achenes of the ray flowers fertile, obovoid, somewhat laterally compressed, covered with a smooth or reticulate skin (i.e. phyllary), achenes of disc flowers sterile. Pappus absent.

Melampodium divaricatum (Rich. ex Pers.) DC., Prod. 5: 520. 1836.

Dysodium divaricatum Rich. ex Pers., Syn. Pl. 2: 489. 1807.

Melampodium paludosum HBK., Nov. Gen. et Sp. 4: 273. 1820. Type: ad Gairam prope St. Marham, *Richard* (P).

Annual herbs. Stems up to 0.5 m tall with two lines of pubescence on opposite sides, otherwise glabrous. Leaves broadly elliptic or ovate, petiolate, petioles winged, 0.5–3 cm long, pubescent on the wing margins; laminae 3–10 cm long, 1–5 cm broad, attenuate at the base, acute at the apex, margins ± coarsely and irregularly sinuate serrate, teeth rounded, sparsely and shortly hispid on both surfaces, 3-nerved at the base. Capitula campanulate, c. 0.75 c. diam. Outer phyllaries broadly ovate, c. 5 mm long, 4.5 mm broad, slightly accrescent in fruit, lower third connate, margins ciliate. Ray flowers c. 12, yellow, basal tube minute, ligules elliptic, 6–8 mm long, 3–4 mm broad. Disc flowers yellow, 3–3.5 mm long, turning brown on fading. Receptacular scales oblong, c. 3 mm long, apex rounded, flattened and finely lacerate at the margin. Achenes of ray flowers (enclosed in inner phyllaries) trigonous, with a short point on the posterior angle, top flattened, 3–3.5 mm long, 2–2.5 mm broad, wrinkled on the sides (phyllaries removed: achenes crescentic, black, smooth).

D i s t r. Native of Central America introduced in Malaya.

E c o l. Cultivated but escaping and growing wild especially near Buddhist shrines wherein this species is commonly used as a floral offering. Flowering probably throughout the year.

S p e c i m e n s E x a m i n e d. KANDY DISTRICT: Ganoruwa, *Austin 847* (PDA). RATNAPURA DISTRICT: Near Gilimale, c. 130 ft, *Grierson 1023* (E, US, PDA, BR, CANB). Other cultivated specimens at PDA date back to March 1887.

26. ACANTHOSPERMUM

Shrank, Pl. Rar. Hort. Monac. Pl. 53. 1819. Type species: *A. australe* (Loefl.) Kuntze (syn. *A. brasilum* Shrank).

Dichotomously branched annual herbs. Leaves opposite, simple or pinnatifid. Capitula small, ± sessile in the forks of branches, heterogamous, radiate. Involucre 2-seriate, outer phyllaries foliaceous, inner ones completely enveloping ray achenes. Ray flowers ligulate, small, yellow. Disc flowers yellowish with cylindrical basal tube, campanulate above, 5 lobed. Anther bases rounded; apical appendage ovate, somewhat inflexed. Style of hermaphrodite flowers undivided, puberulous. Receptacle convex, paleae membranous, concave. Achenes of ray flowers fertile, enveloped in toughened inner phyllaries, trigonous, slightly compressed, echinate with straight or usually uncinate prickles, those at apex of fruit usually longer and stouter; achenes of disc flowers sterile. Pappus none.

Acanthospermum hispidum DC., Prod. 5: 522. 1836; Blake, Contr. U.S. Natl. Herb. 20: 386. 1921; Alston in Trimen, Handb. Fl. Ceylon 6: 165. 1931.

Acanthospermum humile auct. non DC.: Petch, Ann. R. Bot. Gard. Peradeniya 7: 330. 1922. Type: In Brasiliae sabulosis maritimis circa Bahiam, *Salzmann*.

Stems much branched, 20–50 cm tall, terete, covered with spreading hirsute hairs and smaller glandular hairs. Leaves elliptic, oblanceolate or obovate, 1.5–7 × 0.75–2 cm, acute or obtuse at the apex, attenuate and subpetiolate at the base, margins shallowly serrate, whitish pilose on both surfaces. Capitula 4–5 mm diam. in flower, c. 15 mm in fruit on peduncles 2–5 (–10) mm long. Outer phyllaries 5, elliptic or ovate, 3–3.5 mm long, pubescent mainly at the margins. Ray flowers 5–8, ligules elliptic, pale yellow, 1.5 mm long. Disc flowers 5–7, corollas yellow, 1.75–2 mm long. Paleae narrowly spathulate, 1.5–2 mm long, lacerate-ciliate at the obtuse apex. Achenes of radiate flowers enveloped in inner phyllaries, obovate-cuneate, compressed, 5–6 mm long, covered with stiff, hooked bristles and with two longer ± straight divergent spines at the apex 3–4 mm long (achene with phyllary removed: strongly compressed, smooth, black); achenes of disc flowers sterile, glandular.

D i s t r. Native of South America, introduced into Tropical and South Africa, India, Nepal, Hawaiian islands.

E c o l. Common at roadsides, margins of tanks and moist places in the dry zone at lower elevations. Flowering throughout the year.

V e r n. Katu-nerenchi (S).

S p e c i m e n s E x a m i n e d. KURUNEGALA DISTRICT: Kurunegala, 10 July 1952, *Seneratna s.n.* (PDA). PUTTALAM DISTRICT: Andigama, 17 Aug. 1921, *F. Lewis s.n.* (PDA); Tabbowa wewa, *N.D. Simpson 9172* (PDA). POLONNARUWA DISTRICT: Polonnaruwa, c. 200 ft, *Grierson 1027* (E, US, PDA, BR, CANB). ANURADHAPURA DISTRICT: Wilpattu National Park, Kali Villu near Bungalow, *Fosberg et al. 50677* (E, US, PDA).

MATALE DISTRICT: Dambulla-Trincomalee road at mile marker 99/3, 210 m, *Comanor 738* (E, US, PDA). HAMBANTOTA DISTRICT: Ruhuna Nat. Park, Komawa wewa, *Cooray 69111614R* (US, E, PDA).

27. MOONIA

Arn., Nova Acta Phys. Med. Acad. Caes. Leop. Carol. Nat. Cur. 18: 348. 1836. Type species: *M. heterophylla* Arn.

Perennial herbs with somewhat woody rhizomatous rootstocks. Stems ± erect, branched, leafy. Leaves opposite, petiolate, simple or ternately divided. Capitula solitary, terminal on slender peduncles, homogamous, radiate. Involucre 2–3 seriate, phyllaries herbaceous. Ray flowers ligulate, fertile. Disc flowers tubular, limb narrowly campanulate, 4-lobed. Anthers blackish, apices with small obtuse appendages, bases sagittate. Style branches of ray flowers linear, styles of disc flowers almost undivided. Receptacle paleaceous, scales membranous, somewhat concave. Achenes of the ray elliptic, ± compressed, smooth, marginally 2-ribbed, contracted above to a short neck and sometimes produced into two short horns; achenes of the disc sterile. Pappus absent.

Moonia heterophylla Arn., Nova Acta Phys. Med. Acad. Caes. Leop. Carol. Nat. Cur. 18: 349. 1836; DC., Prod. 7: 289. 1836, Thw., Enum. Pl. Zeyl. 164. 1860; Alston in Trimen, Handb. Fl. Ceylon. 6: 166. 1931; Gamble, Fl. Pres. Madras 704. 1921; Bond, Wild Fls. Ceylon Hills 106, t. 54. 1953. Type: In Ceylano, *Walker s.n.* (E-GL).

Chrysogonum heterophyllum (Arn.) C.B. Clarke, Comp. Ind. 132. 1876; Trimen, Handb. Fl. Ceylon 3: 34. 1895.

Stems purplish, 25–50 cm tall, ± glabrous except at the villous-pubescent nodes. Leaves ovate, simple, trilobed or ternate with two oblong-elliptic lobes or leaflets and an elliptic or trilobed terminal segment; petioles 2–6 cm long, villous generally only near the base, amplexicaul; simple leaves 5–9 × 1.5–4 cm, ± coarsely serrate-dentate, acute at the apex, attenuate at the base, sparsely villous pilose on both surfaces, ciliate at the margins; lateral leaflets of compound leaves 1.5–4 cm long, 0.75–2 cm broad, oblique, with lower margin decurrent on the petiole, terminal leaflets 1.5–8 cm long, 0.75–4 cm broad, attenuate at the base, gradually acuminate at the apex, margins coarsely and irregularly serrate-dentate or trilobed. Involucres campanulate, when fresh 5–6 mm diam., 0.75–1 cm broad when pressed. Phyllaries 10–15, outer ones foliaceous, spreading, ciliate, villous at the base, inner ones thinner, ± erect. Ray flowers yellow, 6–8 per capitulum; basal tube 0.5–0.75 mm long, ligules deeply trilobed, 3–5 mm long and broad. Disc flowers 3.5–4.5 mm long, anthers blackish. Paleae linear-oblong, 5–6 mm long, 0.5–0.75 mm broad. Achenes (of ray) 4–4.5 mm long, 2–3 mm broad, glabrous, blackish; disc achenes sterile.

D i s t r. Also in S. India.

E c o l. Forest margins often in shady situations, common, 6000–8000 ft. Flowering October–June and probably throughout the year.

S p e c i m e n s E x a m i n e d. WITHOUT PRECISE LOCALITY: *C.P. 1758*, (marked GC 421 at upper margin), annotated "Ramboda and Nuwara Eliya, *Gardner*, Feb. 1857" (PDA) annotated "Horton Plains", Feb. 1846 and bearing *C.P.* 318 on separate label (K); unannotated (BM). *C.P. 34* (marked GC 420 at upper margin) annotated "Adam's Peak, Nuwara Eliya, Horton Plains, and Ramboda, Feb. 1857" (PDA), unannotated (K, BM). KANDY DISTRICT: Ascent to Adam's Peak, Maskeliya side, 12 May 1906, *Willis s.n.* (PDA); NUWARA ELIYA DISTRICT: Nuwara Eliya, *Gardner 421* (Herb. R. Wight Prop.) (PDA, K); Hakgala, 26 Feb. 1906 and 3 Oct. 1906, *Willis s.n.* (PDA), *Simpson 9106* (BM); Horton Plains, 25 Jan. 1906, *Willis s.n.* (PDA); Horton Plains near World's End, c. 7000 ft, *Grierson 1087* (E, US, PDA, BR, CANB); Same locality, 2130 m, *Mueller-Dombois & Comanor 67070850* (US, PDA), *Gould & Cooray 13799* (E, US, PDA); Pidurutalagala, 7000 ft, *Sinclair 10091* (E, K). BADULLA DISTRICT: Namunakula, 3 June 1924, *J.M. Silva s.n.* (PDA). WITHOUT LOCALITY: "Ceylon", *Walker s.n.* (Herb. Walker-Arnott) (E-GL, holotype) *Walker 150* (E), *324* (K), *1699* (E); 1847, *Gardner 420* (K); 1853, *Harvey s.n.* (K) 12 Mar. 1819, *Moon 459* (BM).

N o t e. Thwaites (l.c.) divided the species into two varieties: One with entire leaves the other with compound leaves. There is no justification for this division; plants bearing both simple and compound leaves have been found. In colonies of this species, both leaf forms usually occur though the entire-leaved form is generally less frequent.

28. XANTHIUM

L., Sp. Pl. 987. 1753; Gen. Pl. ed. 5. 424. 1754. Type species: *X. strumarium* L.

Hispid or pubescent annual herbs. Stems generally erect, branched, elsewhere sometimes spiny. Leaves petiolate, alternate, entire or variously lobed. Capitula unisexual, monoecious. Male involucres multiflorous, subsessile, borne at the apices of branches, phyllaries numerous, free, receptacle conical or cylindrical, paleaceous. Female involucres usually two-flowered, sessile, axillary in the lower parts of branches, outer phyllaries free, inner phyllaries connate, covered with uncinate spines and bearing two larger spines (rostra) at the apex. Male flowers 5-lobed; anthers strongly exserted, rounded at the base. Styles none or rudimentary. Pappus absent. Female flower corollas absent or rudimentary. Style branches reaching almost to apex of terminal spines. Achenes two in each capitulum, included in the hardened spiny involucre at maturity. Pappus absent.

Xanthium indicum Koenig in Roxb., Fl. Ind. 3: 601. 1832; DC. in Wight, Contrib. 17. 1834 ex Prod. 5: 523. 1836, excl. syn. *X. orientale* L., *X. chinense* Mill. et *X. strumarium* Delil.; Widder, Feddes Repert. Beih. 20: 25. 1923. Type: Roxburgh drawing (K).

Xanthium indicum Koenig in Roxb., Hort. Beng. 67. 1814, nom. nud.
Xanthium strumarium L., Sp. Pl. 987. 1753 p.p. quoad syn. Fl. Zeyl. 564. 1747;
Thw., Enum. Pl. Zeyl. 164. 1860 excl. syn. *X. inaequilaterum* DC.; Hook. f.,
Fl. Br. Ind. 3: 303. 1881, excl. syn. *X. strumarium* Boiss. et *X. orientale*
Blume; Trimen, Handb. Fl. Ceylon 3: 35. 1895, p.p. excl. syn. *X. orientale*.
Xanthium orientale auct. non L.: Moon, Cat. 63. 1824.

Stems erect, 1–1.5 m tall, hispidulous or glabrescent. Leaves broadly ovate, 3–5 lobed, petiolate, petioles 2–12 cm long; laminae 3–15 × 2.5–15 cm, acute or acuminate at the apex, rounded or cordate at the base, margins ± irregularly serrate, hispidulous on both surfaces, glandular beneath. Male capitula globose, c. 5 mm diam.; phyllaries 1–2 seriate, lanceolate, 2–2.5 mm long, pubescent; corollas c. 2.5 mm long; stamens exserted 1 mm beyond corolla mouth; paleae oblong, obtuse, 2.5 mm long, pubescent near the apex. Female capitula ovoid. 5–6 mm long at flowering time, covered with spines and glands; flowers 2, each consisting of a narrowly ovoid ovary, 2–2.5 mm long, and style 2.5–4 mm long, divided almost to the base. Fruiting capitulum 15–18 mm long including rostra, 5–6 (–9) mm broad excluding spines, spines c. 3 mm long, glandular and hispidulous. Rostra thick, divergent, hooked at the apex, ± as long as the spines. Achenes (excised) narrowly ovoid or elliptic, 1.3–1.5 mm long, 3–4 mm broad, greyish black, smooth, tapering to a fine point (persistent style base) at the apex.

Chromosome number. n = 18 (count given for *X. strumarium* but as Indian material was used this result probably refers to *X. indicum*—Mehra *et al.*, Caryologia 18: 40. 1965).

D i s t r. India, Assam, Malaya, Sumatra, Java.

E c o l. In moist places at roadsides and cultivated ground in drier regions, rare. Flowering August–March.

V e r n. Wal Rambutang (S), Urukossa (S).

N o t e. This species is reputed to have sudorific and sedative medicinal properties and its leaves to yield a yellow dye. In susceptible persons contact is said to produce dermatitis. Reports that it may be harmful to domesticated animals may be attributable to effects caused by mechanical injury to internal organs through eating the hook-covered involucres rather than to any poisonous principle.

Specimens Examined. WITHOUT PRECISE LOCALITY: *C.P. 1771* annotated "Mihintale, *Gardner*; Batticaloa, Mar. 1858 (PDA), unannotated (BM). BADULLA DISTRICT: Passara, Jan. 1888, *Trimen s.n.* (PDA). TRINCOMALEE DISTRICT: Kantalai, Aug. 1888, *Trimen s.n.* (PDA). ANURADHAPURA DISTRICT: Nachchaduwa wewa, *Simpson 8538* (BM); Mahakanadara wewa near Mihintale, c. 300 ft, *Grierson 1130* (E, US, PDA, BR, CANB). WITHOUT LOCALITY: *Koenig s.n.* (BM).

28a. ZINNIA

A genus of Central American herbs which like other members of the Heliantheae is characterised by opposite leaves and paleaceous receptacles but is differentiated by the cylindrical 3- or more seriate involucre and by the fact that the ligules are almost without basal tubes and persistent on the achenes at maturity. Three species are represented in cultivation: the larger *Z. elegans* Jacq., "Youth and Age", an allusion to the fact that the heads remain a long time in flower without fading, and *Z. angustifolia* HBK (syn. *Z. linearis* Benth.) a bushy herb 15–30 cm tall with linear leaves. The rays of the latter are orange-yellow but those of *Z. elegans* vary from white to dark red or purple. A third species, probably *Z. greggii* Robins & Greenm., a small plant with creamy ligules, is also grown.

29. SIGESBECKIA

L., Sp. Pl. 900. 1753; Gen. Pl. ed. 5. 383. 1754. Type species: *S. orientalis* L.

Erect, branching, annual herbs. Leaves opposite, simple. Capitula small, in lax leafy corymbose panicles, heterogamous. Involucre campanulate, 2-seriate, phyllaries few, foliaceous, glandular, outer ones clavate, patent, inner ones concave, enfolding achenes. Ray flowers few with short basal tubes, ligules usually short. Disc flowers tubular-campanulate, 5-lobed. Anther bases sagittate, apical appendages ovate. Style branches short, flattened, obtuse. Receptacle small, convex; paleae concave, membranous, enfolding the achenes. Achenes obovoid, tetragonous, curved, rounded at the apex. Pappus none.

Sigesbeckia orientalis L., Sp. Pl. 900. 1753; Moon, Cat. 58. 1824; DC., Prod. 5: 495. 1836; Wight, Ic. Pl. Ind. Or. 3: 8 t. 1103. 1846; Thw., Enum. Pl. Zeyl. 164. 1860; C.B. Clarke, Comp. Ind. 133. 1876; Hook. f., Fl. Br. Ind. 3: 304. 1881; Trimen, Handb. Fl. Ceylon 3: 36. 1895. Lectotype: Herb. Hort. Cliff. p. 412 (BM).

Stems up to 1.5 m tall, tinged purple, whitish pubescent. Leaves ovate, petiolate, petioles 1–5 cm long, laminae 5–15 × 3–10 cm acute and apiculate at the apex, cuneate at the base, margins coarsely and irregularly serrate-dentate, pubescent on both surfaces, glandular beneath, strongly trinerved. Capitula 4–5 mm diam. Outer phyllaries 5, 0.5–1.5 cm long, 1–1.5 mm broad, pubescent on the lower surface, densely studded with glandular hairs above, inner phyllaries 5, navicular, 5 mm long, similarly glandular on the outer surface. Ray flowers 5, basal tube c. 1 mm long, glandular, ligule 1.5 mm long, 3-lobed, yellow, reddish beneath. Disc flowers c. 12 per capitulum, 1.75 mm long, glandular at the base, yellow. Paleae navicular, 4–4.5 mm long, pubescent and sometimes glandular, generally persistent around the achenes. Achenes of ray and disc both fertile, 3–4 mm long, dark brown or blackish, glabrous.

Chromosome numbers. n = 15 or 30. (Mehra *et al.*, Caryologia 18: 40 & 51. 1965). Diploid and tetraploid races are known from the Mussourie Hills, India, of which the diploids are smaller in size, usually unbranched and occupying shady positions on northern slopes. The tetraploids on the other hand, are met with at higher elevations in exposed places or on southern slopes. The latter are more densely pubescent plants and may be branched or unbranched.

D i s t r. In all warmer countries in both Old and New Worlds.

E c o l. Roadsides, waste spaces and cultivated ground at mid elevations, common. Flowering September–March and probably throughout the year.

S p e c i m e n s   E x a m i n e d. KANDY DISTRICT: Peradeniya (marked GC 416 at upper margin) *s. coll. C.P. 1752* (PDA, BM). BADULLA DISTRICT: Bandarawela, *Simpson 8653* (PDA, BM); between Ohiya and Boralanda, 5250 ft, *Grierson 1116* (E, US, PDA, BR, CANB). MATALE DISTRICT: Govindahela, 27 Feb. 1906, *Willis s.n.* WITHOUT LOCALITY: *Macrae 166* (BM), *378* (BM); *Gardner 416* (K); *Walker s.n.* (K).

30. ECLIPTA

L., Mant. 157. 1767, nom. cons. Type species: *Eclipta erecta* L., nom. illeg.

Erect or prostrate annual herbs. Stems branched, leafy. Leaves opposite, simple, subentire. Capitula small, 1–2 on short peduncles in axils of upper leaves, heterogamous, radiate. Involucres campanulate, phyllaries 2-seriate, herbaceous. Ray flowers numerous, 2-seriate. Disc flowers fewer, tubular, limb campanulate, 4-lobed at the apex. Anthers obtuse, unappendaged at the apex, sagittate at the base. Style branches linear, ± obtuse. Receptacle flatish, paleae subulate, sometimes absent near the centre. Achenes oblong or obovate, triquetrous or compressed with one central rib on each side, tuberculate, margins thinner, smooth, truncate at the apex. Pappus 2 minute weak scales.

Eclipta prostrata (L.) L., Mant. 2: 286. 1771; Moon, Cat. 58. 1824; Roxb., Fl, Ind. 3: 438. 1832; Santapau, J. Bombay Nat. Hist. Soc. 54: 475–476. 1957.

Verbesina prostrata L., Sp. Pl. 902. 1753. Type: Herb. Plukenet (BM).
Verbesina alba L., Sp. Pl. 902. 1753. Type: Herb. Hort Cliff (BM).
Verbesina pseudo-acmella L., Sp. Pl. 901, 1753; Koster & Philipson, Blumea 6: 349. 1950. Type: Herb. Hermann (BM).
Cotula alba L., Syst. 2: 564. 1767.
Eclipta erecta L., Mant. 2: 286. 1771; Thw., Enum. Pl. Zeyl. 164. 1860; Dalzell & Gibson, Bombay Fl. 171. 1861, nom. illeg.
Eclipta alba (L.) Hassk., Pl. Jav. Rar. 528. 1848; C.B. Clarke, Comp. Ind. 134. 1876; Hook. f., Fl. Br. Ind. 3: 304. 1881; Trimen, Handb. Fl. Ceylon 3: 37. 1895; Alston, Kandy Fl. 53, fig. 281. 1938.

Stems reddish, 5–45 cm long, often rooting at the nodes, stiffly appressed pilose. Leaves elliptic-lanceolate, 0.75-5.5 cm × 1.5-15 mm, attenuate and subpetiolate at the base, narrowly acute at the apex, margin entire or faintly serrate, stiffly appressed pilose on both surfaces, quite strongly trinerved at the base. Peduncles 0.5–4 cm long, involucres 3–5 mm diam. when fresh, c. 1 cm broad when pressed; phyllaries oblong-ovate, acute, 4–6 mm long, 1.5–3 mm broad, covered with stiff appressed pilose hairs. Ray flowers numerous, white, basal tubes 0.5 mm long; minutely hairy at the apex; ligules 1.5–2.5 mm long, c. 0.25 mm broad. Disc flowers 10–15, white, corollas 1.5–1.75 mm long. Paleae bristle-like, 3–3.5 mm long. Achenes 3–3.5 mm long, 1.5 mm broad, sparsely and minutely pubescent at the top. Pappus scales c. 0.25 mm long.

Chromosome number. n = 11 (Mehra *et al.*, Caryologia 18: 40. 1965).

D i s t r. Common. Cosmopolitan in warm countries.

E c o l. In moist ground, paddy fields and margins of tanks and pools. Flowering November–July.

V e r n. Sindu Kirindi (according to Moon), Kikirindi (S); Karippan, Karichalankanni, Kaikechi, Kaivichillai (T).

S p e c i m e n s   E x a m i n e d. WITHOUT PRECISE LOCALITY: *C.P. 1754* annotated "Jaffna, Kegalle, Ramboda, *Gardner*; Elk Plains, Apr. 1854" (PDA), unannotated (BM). PUTTALAM DISTRICT: Kalpitiya, *N.D. Simpson 9158* (PDA, BM). KURUNEGALA DISTRICT: Wariapola Tank, *Amaratunga 443* (PDA). AMPARAI DISTRICT: Lahugala Tank, 36 m, *Mueller-Dombois & Comanor 67072516* (US, PDA). ANURADHAPURA DISTRICT: Wilpattu Nat. Park, Kaliwilu, *Grierson 1133* (E, US, PDA); Between Magul Illaim and Malimaduwa, *Wirawan et al. 1129* (US, E, PDA). MONERAGALA DISTRICT: Gal Oya reservoir near Spillway, 270 m, *Comanor 572* (E, US, PDA). HAMBANTOTA DISTRICT: Ruhuna Nat. Park, 200 m, S of bridge, *Mueller-Dombois 68050323* (US, PDA); Ruhuna Nat. Park at Bambawa, *Mueller-Dombois & Cooray 68060702* (US, PDA); Ruhuna Nat. Park, Thirawewala, *Mueller-Dombois & Comanor 67062311* (US, PDA); Ruhuna Nat. Park, Norris' Camp. *Wirawan & Mueller-Dombois 69030710* (US, PDA); Borrowpit, Tissamaharama, *Simpson 9930* (BM). WITHOUT LOCALITY: *Macrae 57* (BM), *Herb. Hermann* (BM).

30a. Montanoa grandiflora (DC.) Hemsl. an arborescent member of the family from Mexico is cultivated and makes a small tree, 2–3 metres tall, with woody stems 4–5 cm thick. Leaves are opposite, pinnately divided into 7 acuminate segments and have winged petioles. The numerous medium-sized capitula are borne in corymbose panicles and have white ray flowers. The genus is characterised by epappose achenes and accrescent receptacular scales.

31. BLAINVILLEA

Cass., Dict. Sci. Nat. 29: 493. 1823. Type species: *B. rhomboidea* Cass.

Erect, branching, annual herbs. Leaves simple, opposite or the upper ones alternate, petiolate, dentate. Capitula small, at the apex of dichotomous branches, heterogamous, radiate or, elsewhere, subdisciform. Involucre campanulate; phyllaries 1–2 seriate; outer ones herbaceous, subequal, inner ones merging with paleae. Ray flowers few, small, ligule 2–3 lobed. Disc flowers tubular-campanulate, 5-lobed. Anther bases obtuse, apical appendages ovate. Style branches flattened, ± acute. Receptacle convex, paleae concave or folded, membranous. Achenes of the ray triquetrous or dorsally compressed, disc achenes laterally compressed, truncate at the apex. Pappus of 2–5 weak, unequal bristles, sometimes with small intermediate scales.

Blainvillea acmella (L.) Philipson, Blumea 6: 350. 1950.

Verbesina acmella L., Sp. Pl. 901. 1953. Type: Herb. Herman (BM).
Blainvillea latifolia (L. f.) DC. in Wight, Contrib. 17. 1834 et Prod. 5: 492. 1836; Thw., Enum. Pl. Zeyl. 164. 1860; C.B. Clarke, Comp. Ind. 135. 1876; Hook. f., Fl. Br. Ind. 3: 305. 1881; Trimen, Handb. Fl. Ceylon 3: 37. 1895.
Eclipta latifolia L. f., Suppl. 378. 1781. Type: Herb. LINN. (1020/4).
Verbesina dichotoma Moon, Cat. 58. 1824, nom. nud. non Murr.?

Stems 60–100 cm tall, pilose. Leaves ovate, petiolate, petioles up to 2 cm long; laminae 3–12 × 1–8 cm, acuminate at the apex, trinerved, rounded or cuneate at the base, moderately or shallowly serrate-dentate, appressed pubescent on both surfaces. Capitula solitary on short (up to 2 cm long) peduncles from the axils of the upper branches, 4–5 mm diam. Phyllaries oblong-ovate, 5–6 mm long, 1.75–2 mm broad, pubescent, acute at the apex.

Ray flowers 3–5, white, basal tube 1.5 mm long, ligule 1–1.5 mm long, 2- or 3-lobed. Disc flowers white, corolla 3 mm long. Paleae folded, c. 6 mm long, Achenes dark brown or blackish, 4.5 mm long, appressed puberulous, ray achenes triquetrous; disc achenes laterally compressed, truncate at the apex, angles projecting upwards into minute points. Pappus of 1–3 weak bristles up to 1 mm long on the margin of a shallow cup (becoming less readily apparent at maturity).

Chromosome number. n = 39 (Mehra *et al.*, Caryologia 18: 40. 1965).

D i s t r. India, China.

E c o l. In moist areas at roadsides, waste places and cultivated ground at lower elevations, common, Flowering October–June.

V e r n. Agada, Tumba (S).

S p e c i m e n s E x a m i n e d. WITHOUT PRECISE LOCALITY: *C.P. 1753* annotated "Peradeniya, *Gardner*; Batticoloa, Mar. 1855" (PDA) unannotated (K, BM). KANDY DISTRICT: Peradeniya, *Gardner 402* (BM); Teldeniya, *Alston 1077* (PDA). NUWARA ELIYA DISTRICT: Between Ramboda and Nuwara Eliya, 1210 m, *Comanor 907 A* (E, US, PDA). MATALE DISTRICT: E of Dambulla, *Simpson 9794* (PDA, BM). KEGALLE DISTRICT: Galpitamada, *Amaratunga 1135* (PDA); HAMBANTOTA DISTRICT: Ruhuna National Park, Uraniya near Buttawa, *Mueller-Dombois & Cooray 68012822* (US, PDA); near Karaugaswala Junction, *Mueller-Dombois & Cooray 67121071* (US, PDA). MATALE DISTRICT: Nalanda, *Alston 2404* (PDA). WITHOUT LOCALITY: *Moon 159* (BM); *Gardner 402* (K); *Walker s.n.* (K); *Fraser 128* (BM).

32. WEDELIA

Jacq., Stirp. Amer. 217, t. 130, 1763, non. Leofl. nom cons. Type species: *W. frutescens* Jacq.

Scabrid, procumbent perennial herbs or scandent sub-shrubs. Leaves simple, opposite, dentate or entire. Capitula usually medium-sized, solitary, terminal or on peduncles among the upper branches, heterogamous, radiate. Involucre campanulate, 1–2 seriate, outer phyllaries herbaceous, inner ones stiffly membranous. Ligules entire or 2–3 dentate, yellow. Disc flowers tubular-campanulate, 5-lobed, yellow. Anther bases sagittate, apical appendage ovate. Style branches short, flattened, deltoid-acute at the apex. Receptacle convex, paleaceous, paleae concave or folded, Achenes of ray and disc flowers both fertile, cuneate-obovate, triquetrous or laterally compressed, truncate or rounded at the apex. Pappus none or cup-like or consisting of 1–2 weak awns.

KEY TO THE SPECIES

1 Procumbent or ascending perennial herbs. Leaves oblanceolate, subpetiolate. Capitula
  solitary, 0.5–0.75 cm diam. Pappus minute, cup-like, shrivelled at maturity...........
  ....**1. W. chinensis**
1 Scandent, straggling subshrubs. Leaves ovate, obviously petiolate. Capitula several,
  cymose 0.75–1.25 cm diam. Pappus a minute shrivelled cup with 1–2 weak awns.......
  ....**2. W. biflora**

1. Wedelia chinensis (Osbeck) Merr., Philipp. J. Sci. 12: 111. 1917 et Trans.
Amer. Philos. Soc. N.S. 24: 390. 1935. Type: Osbeck Herb. (LINN.).

Solidago chinensis Osbeck, Dagbok Ostind. Resa. 241. 1757.
Wedelia calendulacea (L.) Less., Syn. 222. 1832; DC. in Wight, Contrib. 17.
  1834 et Prod. 5: 539. 1836; Thw., Enum. Pl. Zeyl. 165. 1860; C.B. Clarke,
  Comp. Ind. 136. 1876; Hook. f., Fl. Br. Ind. 3: 306. 1881; Trimen, Handb.
  Fl. Ceylon 3: 38. 1895, non Pers. 1807.
Verbesina calendulacea L., Sp. Pl. ed. 2. 1272. 1763; Moon, Cat. 58. 1824.
  Type: Herb. Herman (BM).

Stems procumbent or ascending, frequently rooting at the nodes, glabrous
often reddish. Leaves oblanceolate, 2.5–5.5 cm long, 0.5–1.3 cm broad, acute
or apiculate at the apex, trinerved, attenuate and subpetiolate at the base,
margin flat or narrowly inrolled, entire or with 1–2 shallow serrations on each
side, shortly appressed hispid on both surfaces. Capitula c. 5 mm diam. when
fresh, 0.75 cm when pressed, solitary on terminal peduncles 3.5–7 cm long.
Outer phyllaries 5, oblong, 7–8 mm long, 2.5–3 mm broad, acute or obtuse at
the apex, appressed pubescent, inner phyllaries lanceolate, 5–7 mm long,
1.5–2.5 mm broad. Ray flowers 8–12, basal tube c. 1 mm long, ligules 6–8
mm long, 3.5–4 mm broad, 2–3 lobed at the apex. Disc flower corollas 3.5
mm long. Paleae lanceolate, 5–5.5 mm long, concave. Achenes 4–4.5 mm
long, 2.5–2.75 mm broad, dark brown, rugulose, glabrous, those of ray
flowers triquetrous, those of disc flowers compressed. Pappus a minute
irregularly margined withered cup at maturity (membranous and finely
dentate at flowering time).

D i s t r. India, Assam, Malaya, China.
E c o l. In marshy situations usually near the coast, common. Flowering
August–March.
V e r n. Ranwan-Kikirindi (S).
S p e c i m e n s E x a m i n e d. WITHOUT PRECISE LOCALITY: *C.P.
1756 p.p.* annotated Batticaloa, Kurunegala, *Gardner*; Belligama, Dec. 1853
and Marked G.C. 403 at upper margin (PDA—some material of *W. biflora* is
included in this number.), unannotated (K, BM). GALLE DISTRICT:
Hiyare, *Alston 1280* (PDA). COLOMBO DISTRICT: Negombo, *Simpson*

7912 (PDA, BM); Hamilton Canal Road, S. of Negombo, *Comanor 1141* (E, US, PDA). PUTTALAM DISTRICT: Between Madampe and Maha-wewa, *Grierson 1134* (E, US, PDA, BR, CANB). WITHOUT LOCALITY: *Walker 1153* (E), *s. n.* (K, PDA); *Wight 142* (E); *Macrae 296* (BM); *Fraser 10* (BM); *Moon s.n.* (BM). Also recorded from Muturajawela (Colombo Dist.) by Amaratunga (Phytologia 20: 459. 1970).

2. Wedelia biflora (L.) DC. in Wight, Contrib. 18. 1834; C.B. Clarke, Comp. Ind. 137. 1876; Hook. f., Fl. Br. Ind. 3: 306. 1881; Trimen, Handb. Fl. Ceylon 3: 39. 1895. Type: Herb. LINN (1021/4).

Verbesina biflora L., Sp. Pl. ed 2. 1272. 1763; Moon, Cat. 58. 1824.
Wollastonia biflora (L.) DC., Prod. 5: 546. 1836; Wight, lc. Pl. Ind. Or. t. 1108, 1846; Thw., Enum. Pl. Zeyl. 165. 1860.

Scandent straggling subshrubs attaining 3–5 m in height. Stems sparsely pilose, glabrescent. Leaves ovate, petiolate, petioles 0.75–2 cm long; laminae 2.5–6 cm long, 0.75–3.5 cm broad, trinerved, cuneate or rounded at the base, acute or acuminate at the apex, margins finely serrate, shortly appressed hispid on both surfaces. Capitula c. 0.75 cm diam., several in loose cymes. Phyllaries 8–10, ovate-elliptic, 5–6 mm long, 2–2.5 mm broad, pubescent. Ray flowers 8–12, basal tubes almost none, ligules 1–1.3 cm long, 4–5 mm broad, shallowly 2–3 lobed at the apex. Disc flower corollas c. 4.5 mm long, lobes puberulous. Paleae oblanceolate, concave, finely ribbed, c. 6 mm long, acute, pubescent. Achenes dark brown, truncate at the apex, 3.5 mm long, those of the ray triquetrous, those of disc ± compressed. Pappus a minute dentate cup with 1–2 weak bristles c. 1.5 mm long.

Chromosome number. $n = 15$ (Turner in King, Phytologia 11: 217. 1965).

D i s t r. India, Malaya, China, Polynesia, Australia, East Tropical Africa.

E c o l. Along the sea coast on sandy beaches or at margins of mangrove swamps, fairly common. Flowering August–May and probably throughout the year.

V e r n. Moodu-gam-palu (S—according to Moon).

S p e c i m e n s E x a m i n e d. WITHOUT PRECISE LOCALITY: *C.P. 1760* annotated "Trincomalee, Ranisseram, *Gardner*; Belligama, Dec. 1853" (PDA), unannotated (K, BM). PUTTALAM DISTRICT: Karativu Isl., Kalpitiya, Aug. 1883, *Trimen s.n.* (PDA). ANURADHAPURA DISTRICT: Wilpattu National Park, Pallugaturai, *Fosberg et al. 50920* (E, US, PDA). JAFFNA DISTRICT: "Small Fox Island", Feb. 1890, *Trimen s.n.* (PDA). TRINCOMALEE DISTRICT: Muthur, *Simpson 9645* (PDA); Trincomalee, *Alston 532* (PDA); Koddiyar, Aug. 1885, *Trimen s.n.* (PDA); Irrakkakandi, N of Trincomalee, *Comanor 774* (E, US, PDA); 12 miles N of Trincomalee, *Grierson 1032* (E, US, PDA, BR, CANB). BATTICALOA DISTRICT:

Batticaloa, Mar. 1885, *N. Nevill s.n.* (PDA). AMPARAI DISTRICT: S. point of Arugam Bay, *Fosberg & Sachet 52925* (US, E, PDA). WITHOUT LOCALITY: "Zeylonia in nemoribus, scandens", *Koenig s.n.* (BM); *Gardner 404* (K); *Dubuc s.n.* (E); *Klein s.n.* (E).

33. ELEUTHERANTHERA

Poit. ex Bosc, Nouv. Dict. Hist. Nat. Ed. 1. 7: 498. 1803. Type species: *E. ruderalis* (Sw.) Sch. Bip. (syn. *E. ovata* Poit. ex Steud.).

Erect, branching annual herbs. Leaves opposite, simple. Capitula small, borne in axils of upper leaves, homogamous, discoid or heterogamous and radiate. Involucre ± campanulate; phyllaries few, herbaceous. Ray flowers when present few, ligulate, disc flowers tubular, narrowly campanulate, 5-lobed at the apex. Anther ± truncate at the apex, bases sagittate. Styles branches linear, acuminate, covered with minute hairs at the apex. Receptacle convex; scales membranous, concave. Achenes narrowly obovoid, somewhat compressed, 3–4 angular, abruptly narrowed to a small cylindrical boss at the apex. Pappus absent.

Eleutheranthera ruderalis (Swartz) Sch. Bip., Bot. Zeit. 24: 165, 239. 1866: Petch, Ann. R. Bot. Gard. Peradeniya 9: 349. 1925; Alston in Trimen, Handb. Fl. Ceylon. 6: 166. 1931. Type: Herb. Swartz (S).

Melampodium ruderale Swartz, Fl. Ind. Occ. 3: 1372. 1806.

Erect branching annual herbs. Stems up to about 75 cm tall, sparsely pubescent. Leaves ovate, petiolate, petioles 0.5–1.5 cm long, lamina 3–6 × 1.2–3 cm, trinerved, rounded and shortly attenuate at the base, obtuse or acute at the apex, margins shallowly crenate or serrate, sparsely pubescent on both surfaces. Capitula solitary or 2–4 in each axil, on short peduncles 0.5–1 cm long, erect at first, cernuous in fruit. Involucres accrescent, c. 3 mm diam. when fresh, 5–7 mm broad when pressed; phyllaries 5–8 in 1–2 series, elliptic-lanceolate, obtuse or acute, spreading and foliaceous, 5–8 mm long, 2–3 mm broad. Flowers yellow, ray flowers often absent, sometimes 2–3, neuter, ligules 2.5 mm long, 1 mm broad; disc flowers 9–15, corollas 2.25–2.5 mm long, lobes papillose. Receptacular scales oblong-elliptic, acuminate, scarious, 3–4 mm long, ciliate at the margins. Achenes 3–3.5 mm long, verrucose on the angles, minutely white puberulous near the apex.

D i s t r . Native of Tropical America.

E c o l . A weed of abandoned chenas and in cultivated ground, fairly common. Flowering November–May and possibly throughout the year.

S p e c i m e n s E x a m i n e d . COLOMBO DISTRICT: Heneratgoda Gardens near Gampaha, 26 Nov. 1920, *"G.B." 10284* (PDA); ibid., 26 Nov. 1920, *Stockdale s.n.* (K) (Probably the same collection). KANDY DIS-

TRICT: University Botany building, Peradeniya, 508 m, *Comanor 339* (E, US, PDA) weed at Peradeniya Gardens, *Grierson 1159* (E, US, PDA).

N o t e. This grows in much the same situations as, and closely resembles, *Synedrella nodiflora* but can be distinguished from the latter by its cernuous fruiting capitula and by its unwinged achenes.

A note on one of the specimens at PDA collected in 1920, quoted by Alston, is to the effect that the specimens came from a bed in which *Chenopodium* seed from a museum had been sown but that, as other plants were also found growing wild in the bed at the time of collection, this probably was not the first introduction.

34. TITHONIA

Desf. ex Juss., Gen. 189.1789. Type species: *T. rotundifolia* (Mill.) Blake (syn. *T. tagetiflora* Desf.).

Herbaceous or suffruticose perennials. Leaves alternate or sometimes opposite at base of the stem, trilobed or sometimes entire. Capitula large, solitary or several on thick peduncles, heterogamous, radiate. Involucres broadly campanulate, 2–5 seriate, phyllaries oblong-lanceolate, indurate and ribbed at the base, herbaceous at the apices. Ray flowers 1-seriate, yellow. Disc flowers tubular-infundibuliform, 5-lobed, yellow. Anther bases sagittate, apical appendages ovate. Style branches with linear-lanceolate appendages. Receptacle convex, paleae concave, rigid, acuminate, embracing achenes, persistent. Achenes oblong, compressed, subtetragonous. Pappus 1–2 awns with smaller intermediate scales or, elsewhere, absent.

Tithonia diversifolia (Hemsl.) A. Gray, Proc. Amer. Acad. Arts 19: 5. 1883; Trimen, J. Bot. 23: 171. 1885 et Handb. Fl. Ceylon 3: 39. 1895 in nota; Blake, Contr. U. S. Natl. Herb. 20: 434. 1921; Alston in Trimen, Handb. Fl. Ceylon 6: 166. 1931 et Kandy Fl. 54. 1938.

Mirasolia diversifolia Hemsl., Bot. Centr. Amer. 2: 168, t. 47. 1881. Type: Vera Cruz, Valley of Orizaba, *Bourgeau 2319*.

Perennial herbs 2–3 m tall or taller. Stems striate, sparsely pubescent, glabrescent. Leaves alternate, 3 (–5) lobed or the upper ones oblanceolate or ovate-deltoid, unlobed, petiolate, petioles 2–10 cm long, broadly winged almost to the base, biauriculate (substipulate), auricles caducous; laminae 5–15 × 2.5–10 cm, ±trinerved and cuneate at the base into the petiole, lobes acuminate, margins crenate-serrate, hispidulous above, pubescent and glandular beneath. Capitula 1–1.75 cm diam. on peduncles 10–25 cm long, glabrous or sparsely pubescent. Phyllaries 3-4 seriate, graduated, imbricate, 1–2 cm long, 2.5–5.5 mm broad, finely pubescent, acute or obtuse at the apex. Ray flowers c. 12, basal tubes 1–2 mm long, ligule elliptic, 4.5–6 cm long,

0.7–1.5 cm broad, 2–3 lobed at the apex. Disc corollas puberulous, 9–11 mm long including basal tubes (c. 1 mm long). Paleae oblong-spathulate, 10–12 mm long, abruptly narrowed and acuminate at the apex. Achenes dark brown, sericeous, 5–6 mm long. Pappus of 2 awns 4–5 mm long with about 6 short broad scales (2–2.5 mm long, 1 mm broad), connate at the base.

Chromosome number. n = 17 (Powell & King, Sida 3 (5) 319–320. 1969).

D i s t r. Native of Tropical South America, introduced in India, Burma, Malaya, China, S. Africa.

E c o l. Abundant at roadsides and waste ground particularly at mid elevations (between 1000–5000 ft). Flowering July–April.

V e r n. Val-suriya-Kanti, Wata-suriya (S).

S p e c i m e n s   E x a m i n e d. KANDY DISTRICT: Peradeniya, July 1883, *Trimen s. n.* (PDA, K, BM); Peradeniya, near University, 507 m, *Comanor 466* (E, US, PDA); Highway A5, 10 miles S of Peradeniya, 548 m, *Mueller-Dombois & Comanor 67060901* (US, PDA); University Campus, Peradeniya, 507 m, *Comanor 318* (E, US, PDA); Kandy-Nuwara Eliya road near Pussellawa, 750 m, *Comanor 915* (E, US, PDA); Kandy-Colombo road below Kadugannawa, 1500 ft, *Grierson 1157* (E, US, PDA, BR, CANB).

N o t e s. According to Trimen (in J. Bot. 23: 171. 1885), seeds of this species were first sent to Thwaites by Lindley in 1851; yet even at the time he wrote, and earlier, on the specimens cited above, it had "become one of the commonest weeds" which "rivals *Lantana* in abundance".

T. rotundifolia (Mill.) Blake is also met with in cultivation. It is generally a smaller plant with ovate or trilobed leaves, the petioles of which are exauriculate, densely pubescent peduncles and 2-seriate involucres composed of subequal phyllaries.

34a. Helianthus is morphologically very similar to *Tithonia* but differs in having solid (not hollow) peduncles and a deciduous pappus. Two species are probably cultivated in Ceylon: *H. annuus* L., the Sunflower, which is cited by Abeywickrama in his check list (in Ceylon J. Sci., Biol. Sci. 2(2): 239. 1959). I have not seen outside cultivation (it is grown for its seeds which yield a valuable edible oil) nor are there specimens at Peradeniya to substantiate the claim that it ever grows wild. Moon (Cat. p. 58) gives the Sinhalese vernacular 'Suriyakanti' for it. *H. tuberosus* L. the Jerusalem Artichoke was reported to be cultivated by Moon (Cat. p. 58) and, no doubt, still is though I did not encounter it nor have I seen specimens collected in Ceylon.

35. SPILANTHES

Jacq., Enum. Pl. Carib. 8: 28. 1760. Type species: *S. urens* Jacq.

Annual herbs with weak erect or decumbent, branching, foliate stems

usually rooting from the lower nodes. Leaves simple, opposite, ovate or elliptic. Capitula solitary on terminal or axillary peduncles, heterogamous, radiate or homogamous, discoid. Involucre short, 1–2 seriate. Ray flowers (when
present) shortly and broadly ligulate. Disc flowers tubular, limb infundibuliform, 3–5 lobed. Anthers rounded at the apex, minutely sagittate at the base.
Style branches subulate, obtuse at the apex. Receptacle convex at first becoming ovoid-conical, paleaceous, paleae concave or conduplicate ± enfolding
the disc flowers. Achenes of ray flowers triquetrous, fertile, margins often
ciliate. Pappus of 2 weak bristles, sometimes absent.

KEY TO THE SPECIES

1 Achenes completely epappose and eciliate..............................3. S. calva
1 Achenes with weak fragile pappus bristles, ciliate on one or both margins
  2 Capitula small, 3–5 mm diam. Achenes 1.25–1.5 mm long with weak pappus bristles,
    c. 0.25 mm long...2. S. iabadicensis
  2 Capitula larger, 0.7–1 cm diam. Achenes c. 2–2.5 mm long with stronger pappus brist-
    les, c. 1 mm long...1. S. paniculata

1. Spilanthes paniculata Wall. ex DC., Prod. 5: 625. 1836; Koster & Philipson,
Blumea 6: 354. 1950; Grierson, Ceylon J. Sci., Biol. Sci. 10: 56. 1972.

S. paniculata Wall., Cat. 3186. 1831, nom. nud. Type: ad Martabania, *Wallich*
3186/296 (K).

Stems subglabrous or very sparsely pubescent, eventually attaining about
40 cm tall. Leaves ovate, lamina 2–9 × 1–7 cm, acute or obtuse at the tip, abruptly or gradually attenuate into a petiole 0.6–4.5 cm long, margin undulate
serrate, sparsely pubescent on the lower surface. Capitula at first 7–9 mm
diam., becoming conical—ovoid, up to 1.5 cm long, 1 cm diam., rather few,
on peduncles 5–11 cm long. Phyllaries 2-seriate, elliptic-lanceolate, 4–6 mm
long, 1.5–2 mm broad, acute or obtuse at the apex, sparsely pubescent. Ray
flowers absent in Ceylonese specimens examined (elsewhere sometimes present, generally 5, yellow, ligule 1.5 or rarely 4 mm long). Disc flowers 2 mm
long, yellow, 4–5 lobed. Paleae 3.5–5 mm long. Achenes narrowly obovate,
c. 2 mm long, 1 mm broad, black, very sparsely puberulous near the apex,
margins pale brown, strongly ciliate. Pappus bristles 1–1.25 mm long.

  D i s t r. S. India (Martaban), Malaysia.
  E c o l. Moist grassy areas, rice fields, etc., possibly not common. Flowering July–October.
  S p e c i m e n s E x a m i n e d. COLOMBO DISTRICT: Colombo, Tem-
ple-Trees, PM's residence, Oct. 1882, *Trimen s.n.* (PDA). KANDY DIS-
TRICT: Peradeniya, *Amaratunga 649* (PDA). WITHOUT LOCALITY: In
1847, *Gardner 418* (K, BM); *Macrae 600* (BM); *s. coll. C.P. 684* (BM); *Koenig
s.n.* (BM).

N o t e s. Possibly, since his specimen came from a garden, this may be the species that Trimen referred to in his note (Handb. 3: 40) as *S. oleracea* L. although his sheet does not bear that name. Alternatively, *S. oleracea* itself may also be in Ceylon for this Brazilian species is cultivated in India and Malaya as a medicinal plant. The leaves and flower heads have a hot pungent taste and, from their use, it gains the name "Toothache Plant". It is also used to treat sore throats and is given to women in child-birth. *S. oleracea* is a larger plant with capitula at first 8–12 mm and later up to 18 mm in diameter; its flowers are reddish brown in the bud.

2. **Spilanthes iabadicensis** A. H. Moore, Proc. Amer. Acad. Arts. 42: 542. 1907; Koster & Philipson, Blumea 6: 354. 1950; Grierson, Ceylon J. Sci., Biol. Sci. 10: 56, 1972. Type: ex horto bogoriensi Javae misit, 1868, *Teijsmann* (GH).

Stems generally rising to 30–40 cm tall, dichotomously branched above, glabrous or sparsely pubescent when young. Leaves narrowly ovate or elliptic, 1.5–5 cm long, 0.5–2 cm broad, gradually attenuate into a petiole at the base up to about 1 cm long or, the upper leaves subsessile, obtuse or subacute at the apex, margin subentire or undulate, subglabrous or sparsely pubescent on both surfaces. Capitula conical-ovoid, c. 3 mm diam. at first, later 5 mm diam. c. 8 mm long, fairly numerous, on peduncles 2–5 cm long. Phyllaries 1-seriate, ovate-lanceolate, 2.5–3 mm long, 1mm broad., glabrous. Ray flowers yellow, ligule 1.5–2 mm long, 1–1.25 mm broad. Disc flowers 1–1.25 mm long, 3–5 lobed. Paleae linear, obtuse or retuse at the apex, 2.5 mm long, concave but not closely enfolding achene. Achene oblong, 1.25–1.5 mm long, 0.5–0.6 mm broad, black with pale margins, sparsely and weakly ciliate along both margins (or sometimes only one). Pappus bristles weak, fragile, c. 0.25 mm long.

D i s t r. Also in Sumatra, Java, New Guinea.

E c o l. Moist ground, ricefields and ditches, common. Flowering December–March.

S p e c i m e n s E x a m i n e d. KANDY DISTRICT: Peradeniya, University Campus, *Amaratunga 762* (PDA); Katugastota, *Amaratunga 985* (PDA); Gampola, 2000 ft, *Gardner 418* (BM). MATALE DISTRICT: Margin of tank, Sigiriya, *Grierson 1038* (E, US, PDA, BR, CANB). RATNAPURA DISTRICT: Ruwanwella, *Amaratunga 1091* (PDA).

3. **Spilanthes calva** DC. in Wight, Contrib. 19. 1834; Prod. 5: 625. 1836; Koster & Philipson, Blumea 6: 354. 1950; Grierson, Ceylon J. Sci., Biol. Sci. 10: 56. 1972. Type: Wight 1456 (E).

Spilanthes acmella auct. non. L.: Thw., Enum. Pl. Zeyl. 165. 1860; Trimen, Handb. Fl. Ceylon 3: 40. 1895; Moon, Cat. 57. 1824.

Stems sparsely pubescent, only rising to about 15–30 cm tall. Leaves ovate, 2.5–5.5 cm long, 1–2.5 cm broad, on petioles up to 1.5 cm long, obtuse or acute at the apex, abruptly attenunate or, especially in the upper leaves, gradually attenuate into the petioles, margins entire or undulate-serrate, sparsely pubescent on both surfaces. Capitula at first c. 5 mm, later, 7–8 mm diam., 8–9 mm long on peduncles 4–10 cm long. Phyllaries 1-seriate, ovate, 3.5–4.5 mm long, 1.5–2.5 mm broad, sparsely pubescent. Ray flowers absent. Disc flowers 1.75–2 mm long, 4–5 lobed at the apex, yellow. Paleae c. 3.25 mm long, enfolding achene. Achene narrowly obovate, c. 2 mm long, 1 mm broad, dark brown, minutely granular, glabrous and eciliate. Pappus absent.

D i s t r. Also in Java and Lesser Sunda Islands, S. India, Mysore & Travancore.

E c o l. Moist boggy ground at the margins of pools in the montane zone, fairly common. Flowering February–March.

V e r n. Maha-akmaella (S) according to Moon who referred either to this species or to *S. iabadicensis*; the plate which he doubtfully cited ("Rumph., Amb. 6, t. 65?") could portray either.

S p e c i m e n s E x a m i n e d. WITHOUT PRECISE LOCALITY: *C.P. 684 p.p.* (see also under *S. iabadicensis*) annotated "Rambodde, Hantane, *Gardner*, Feb. 1857" (PDA), annotated "Ramboda, Jan. 1846" (K). NUWARA ELIYA DISTRICT: On Hakgala Hill, c. 6000 ft, *Grierson 1061* (E, US, PDA); Nuwara Eliya, *Harris s.n.* (E) KANDY DISTRICT: Rangala, *Simpson 8363* (BM). WITHOUT LOCALITY: *Walker 87* (E-GL), *108* (K); in 1829, *McRae s.n.* (K).

36. SYNEDRELLA

Gaertn., Fruct. 2: 456, t. 171. 1791. Type species: *S. nodiflora* (L.) Gaertn.

Branched annual herbs. Leaves opposite, simple, petiolate. Capitula small, ± sessile in upper leaf axils, heterogamous, radiate. Involucre ovoid, phyllaries few, subequal, outer ones foliaceous, inner ones membranous. Ligules short, 2–3 dentate. Disc flowers tubular, 4-lobed at the apex. Anther bases sagittate; apical appendages minute, rounded. Style branches complanate with long filiform appendages. Receptacle small, convex; paleae concave or flat. Ray achenes dorsally compressed, 2-alate, wings lacerate; disc achenes compressed or triquetrous, unwinged. Pappus of 2–3 rigid awns.

Synedrella nodiflora (L.) Gaertn., Fruct. 2: 456, t. 171. 1791; DC., Prod. 5: 629. 1836; C.B. Clarke, Comp. Ind. 139. 1876; Hook. f., Fl. Br. Ind. 3: 308. 1881; Trimen, Handb. Fl. Ceylon 3: 40. 1895, in nota; Alston, ibid. suppl.6: 167. 1931 et Kandy Fl. 54. 1938.

Verbesina nodiflora L., Amoen. Acad. 4: 290. 1787. Type: Herb Sloane? (BM).

Ximenesia encelioides auct. non Cav: Thw., Enum. Pl. Zeyl. 422. 1860.

Stems up to 1.5 m tall, usually 30–45 cm tall, appressed pilose. Leaves ovate, petioles up to 3 cm long, narrowly winged; laminae 3.5–8.5 × 1–5 cm, ± distinctly trinerved, rounded or cuneate at the base, acute at the apex, margins shallowly serrate-dentate, appressed pilose on both surfaces but more densely so beneath. Capitula c. 4 mm diam. Involucre 2–3 seriate, phyllaries elliptic-ovate, outer two foliaceous, pilose, 1–1.25 cm long, 3–3.5 mm broad, inner ones membranous, smaller, 6–7 mm long, 1.5–2 mm broad. Ray flowers 5–8, yellow, basal tubes 2.5–3 mm long, ligule oblong, c. 2.5 mm long, 1–1.25 mm broad. Disc flowers yellow, c. 4 mm long. Paleae flat, lanceolate, c. 6.5 mm long. Ray achenes oblanceolate, 4–4.5 mm long, 1.75–2 mm broad, blackish with pale narrow wings each bearing 2–6 lacerate appendages; disc achenes compressed, narrowly oblanceolate, 4–4.25 mm long, 1 mm broad, puberulous. Pappus awns of ray achenes 1.5–2 mm long; awns of disc achenes 3.5–4.5 mm long, puberulous.

Chromosome number. n=c. 20 (Turner in King, Phytologia 11: 218. 1965); 2n=40 (Harvey, Taxon 15: 163. 1966); 2n=36 (Mangenot & Mangenot, Rev. Cytol. Biol. Veg. 25: 431. 1962); n=19 or 20 (Powell & King, Sida 3 (5): 319–320. 1969).

D i s t r. Native of West Indies introduced in India, China, Malaya, Polynesia.

E c o l. Common weed at roadsides and on cultivated land. Flowering August–May and probably throughout the year.

S p e c i m e n s   E x a m i n e d. TRINCOMALEE DISTRICT: Trincomalee, (Rev. S.O. *Glenie*) *C.P. 3839* (PDA, K, BM). HAMBANTOTA DISTRICT: Ruhuna National Park, *Mueller-Dombois 67083007* (PDA, US); ibid., near Yala Camp Site, *Mueller-Dombois & Cooray 68013017* (US, PDA); Tissamaharama, *Simpson 9918* (PDA, BM). GALLE DISTRICT: near Bentota, 22 Mar. 1887, *Trimen s.n.* (PDA). COLOMBO DISTRICT: Ja-Ela—Gampaha road, 10–20 m, *Comanor 1018* (E, US, PDA). KANDY DISTRICT: Peradeniya University Campus, 504 m, *Comanor 472* (E, US, PDA); above Teldeniya, 1700 ft, *Grierson 1012* (E, US, PDA, BR, CANB). NUWARA ELIYA DISTRICT: Between Pussellawa and Rambodda, 950 m, *Comanor 327* (E, US, PDA).

37. COREOPSIS

L., Sp. Pl. 907. 1753; Gen. Pl. ed. 5, 388. 1754. Type species: *C. lanceolata* L.

Annual or perennial herbs or shrubs. Leaves opposite, undivided or pinnatisect. Capitula medium or large, pedunculate, solitary or in corymbose panicles, heterogamous, radiate. Involucres 2–3 seriate, phyllaries ± connate at the base, outer ones herbaceous, inner ones brownish or yellow, membranous. Ray flowers 1-seriate, ligules entire or 2–3 dentate, yellow or reddish. Disc flowers yellow, tubular, 4–5 lobed. Anther bases minutely sagittate, apical appendages ovate. Style branches truncate often with conical appendages. Receptacle flat or convex; paleae flat or concave. Achenes compressed, orbicular or oblong, often 2-winged. Pappus of 2 scales or absent.

Coreopsis lanceolata L., Sp. Pl. 908. 1753; Sims, Bot. Mag. t. 2451. 1824; Sherff, Field Mus. Nat. Hist. Bot. 11: 341. 1936. Type: Herb. Dillen? (OXF).

Perennial herbs. Stems 20–30 (– 60) cm tall, glabrous, foliose at the base ± naked above. Leaves opposite, sessile or petiolate at the base (petioles 3–10 cm long), simple, elliptic or oblanceolate, 5–10 cm long, 4–10 mm broad, or pinnatisect bearing 1–2 elliptic lobes on each side, 1.5–3 cm long, 3–7.5 mm broad, terminal segments 4–6 cm long, 0.6–1.4 cm broad, obtuse or acute at the apex, margins entire, sparsely pilose on both surfaces. Capitula solitary on peduncles 15–25 cm long. Involucre urceolate, c. 1 cm diam., outer phyllaries 8–10, lanceolate, spreading, c. 1 cm long, 2.5–3.5 mm broad, ciliate near the apex, inner phyllaries ovate, c. 1 cm long, 6–7 mm broad, glabrous, appressed. Ray flowers 8, yellow, ligules obovate, 1.5–3 cm long, 0.75–1.5 cm broad, irregularly 3-lobed at the apex. Disc corollas 5–5.5 mm long. Paleae linear-lanceolate, 7.5–8 mm long, becoming subulate above. Achenes oblong-orbicular, c. 3 mm long, black, pappillose on the inner surface, surrounded by a brown membranous wing. Pappus scales 2, minute, weak, vestigial.

Distr. Eastern North America, Wisconsin southwards to Florida; introduced and becoming established in Eastern China.

Ecol. Cultivated as an ornamental but sometimes escaping and growing wild. Flowering March–July.

Specimens Examined. KANDY DISTRICT: Peradeniya, *Senaratna 54* (PDA). NUWARA ELIYA DISTRICT: Pattipola, c. 6000 ft, *Grierson 1085* (E, US, PDA).

Notes. Other commonly cultivated species of *Coreopsis* include *C. tinctoria* Nutt. (Syn. *C. bicolor* Rchb.) a slender annual with narrow pinnatisect leaves and deeply lobed yellow ligules each with a dark purple blotch at the base.

38. COSMOS

Cav., Ic. et Descr. 1: 9. 1791. Type species: *C. bipinnatus* Cav.

Annual or perennial herbs. Leaves opposite, bipinnatisect or tripinnatisect. Capitula medium-sized, pedunculate, heterogamous, radiate. Involucre campanulate, 2-seriate, phyllaries connate at the base, membranous. Ray flowers neuter, rose, purple or rarely yellow. Disc flowers yellow, tubular, 5-lobed. Anther bases entire or minutely 2-dentate, apical appendages ovate-cordate. Style branches short, thickened above, acutely appendaged. Recept-acle flat or convex, paleae flat or somewhat concave. Achenes fusiform, tetragonous, often narrowed into a rostrum above and generally bearing a pappus of 2–3 (–8) retrorsely barbed awns, sometimes exaristate.

KEY TO THE SPECIES

1 Achenes rostrate, bearing retrorsely barbed awns. Ligules rose or purple..............
....**1. C. caudatus**
1 Achenes erostrate, exaristate. Ligules yellow...........................**2. C. calvus**

1. Cosmos caudatus HBK., Nov. Gen. et Sp. 4: 188. 1820; Sherff, Field Mus. Nat. Hist. Bot. ser. 8: 411. 1932. Type: Cuba, Havana, Mar. 1801, *Humboldt & Bonpland s.n.* (P).

Cosmos bipinnatus auct. non Cav.: Trimen, Handb. Fl. Ceylon 3: 40. 1895 in nota; Alston, ibid., 6: 167. 1931.

Erect annual herbs. Stems 0.5–2 m tall, sparsely pilose. Leaves bipinnati-sect or somewhat tripinnatisect, deltoid in outline, petiolate, 5–15 cm long, including petiole up to 7 cm long, ultimate segments oblong-lanceolate or elliptic, 1.5–3.5 cm long, 3–6 mm broad, acute, apiculate at the apex, margins entire, appressed spinulose-ciliate. Capitula solitary on peduncles 10–15 cm long, sparsely pilose. Involucre campanulate, c. 5 mm diam., outer phylla-ries 8, linear-lanceolate, patent, 0.75–1 cm long, herbaceous, finely ciliate; inner phyllaries oblong-lanceolate, membranous, erect, glabrous, 1–1.3 cm long, 1.5–2.5 mm broad. Ray flowers 8, basal tubes c. 1 mm long, ligules obovate, 1–1.3 cm long, 4–7 mm broad, 3-lobed at the apex. Disc flower corollas 5–7 mm long, yellow. Paleae linear, membranous, 1–1.3 cm long. Achenes dark brown or black, 2–2.6 cm long including rostrum 0.75–1.5 cm long. Pappus awns 2, divergent, 4–5 mm long.

D i s t r. Native of West Indies and Central America, now introduced in Mauritius, India, Philippine Islands.

E c o l. Roadsides, waste ground and margins of cultivation, common. Flowering January–August and probably throughout the year.

S p e c i m e n s   E x a m i n e d. GALLE DISTRICT: Pointe de Galle, 1 June 1860, *Dubuc s.n.* (E). ANURADHAPURA DISTRICT: 4 miles S of Anuradhapura, *Simpson 8071* (PDA, BM). KANDY DISTRICT: Hakkinda,

Alston 2214 (PDA); Peradeniya, *Alston 1989* (PDA); Peradeniya river bank, *Senaratna 55* (PDA). MATALE DISTRICT: Balacadua, 3 miles S of Matale, c. 1500 ft, *Grierson 1025* (E, US, PDA, BR, CANB).

2. Cosmos calvus (Sch. Bip. ex Miq.) Sherff, Field Mus. Nat. Hist. Bot. 8: 405. 1932; Backer & Bakh. f., Fl. Java 2: 413. 1965.

Adenolepis calva Sch. Bip., Flora 30: 375. 1847 nom. nud., Miq., Fl. Ind. 2: 79. 1856 cum descr. Type: Java, *Zollinger 2945* (P).

Erect annual herbs. Stems 0.5–1 m tall, glabrous. Leaves bipinnatisect or almost tripinnatisect, petiolate, 5–15 cm long including petiole 1–5 cm long, ultimate segments linear-lanceolate or elliptic, 0.75–3 cm long, 1–4.5 mm broad, apex acute or acuminate, margin entire, minutely appressed ciliolate. Capitula solitary on peduncles 10–15 cm long. Involucre campanulate, c. 5 mm diam., glabrous, outer phyllaries 8, linear-lanceolate, 5–9 mm long, 1–1.5 mm broad, patent, herbaceous; inner phyllaries oblong-lanceolate, 7.5–10 mm long, 2–3 mm broad, erect, membranous, yellowish-green. Ray flowers c. 8, yellow, basal tube c. 1.5 mm long, ligule oblanceolate, 1–1.5 cm long, 4–5 mm broad, 2–3-denticulate at the apex. Disc flower corollas 5–6.5 mm long. Achenes greyish-black, 10–14 mm long, narrowed above, truncate at the apex, exaristate.

D i s t r. Native of Venezuela and Trinidad now established in India, Siam, Java, Philippine Islands.

E c o l. Roadsides, fields and waste places, not common. Flowering throughout the year.

S p e c i m e n s   E x a m i n e d. RATNAPURA DISTRICT: Malawa between Kuruwita and Avissawella, c. 200 ft, *Grierson 1024* (E, US, PDA, BR, CANB).

N o t e s. In a note (Handb. Fl. Ceylon 3: 40) Trimen mentioned the occurrence of *C. sulphureus* Cav. possibly in error for this species. To support this belief, it may be pointed out that *C. calvus* was once regarded as a variety of *C. sulphureus*. Trimen, however, apparently made no herbarium specimen of either species. *C. sulphureus* on the other hand, is a known dye plant and the species may be cultivated for this purpose. It is differentiated by its orange-yellow rays and rostrate achenes.

38a. Garden Dahlias developed from *Dahlia pinnata* Cav. were introduced into Ceylon before 1880 and several cultivars and hybrids may be present in gardens. Seneratna (in Ceylon J. Sci. Sect. A. Bot. 12: 217–219, Pl. 24 et 25. 1947) gave an account of two hybrids that he had raised: *Dahlia* 'Fr. Le Goc' and 'Ceylon Sunrise'.

39. BIDENS

L. Sp., Pl. 831. 1753; Gen. Pl. ed. 5. 362. 1754. Type: species: *B. tripartita* L.

Diffuse or erect annual herbs. Stems tetragonous, branched, foliate. Leaves opposite, ternately or biternately divided. Capitula medium-sized, pedunculate, solitary and axillary or, more commonly, numerous and corymbose, heterogamous, radiate or homogamous, discoid. Involucre campanulate, 2-seriate, phyllaries shortly connate at the base, outer ones foliaceous. Rays white or yellow, neuter and sometimes absent. Disc flowers yellow, 5-lobed. Anthers with acute ovate appendages at the apex, minutely sagittate at the base. Style branches linear with subulate villous appendages. Receptacle flat, paleaceous; paleae narrowly linear-lanceolate. Achenes oblong or linear, tetragonous, somewhat attenuate, truncate and erostrate at the apex. Pappus of 2–4 stiff, retrorsely barbed bristles.

KEY TO THE SPECIES

1 Leaves ternate; leaflets simple with serrate margins. Ray flowers 4–7 or absent........
....**1. B. pilosa**
1 Leaves with 3–5 deeply dentate or pinnatifid leaflets. Ray flowers generally 3.........
....**2. B. biternata**

1. Bidens pilosa L., Sp. Pl. 832. 1753; Sherff, Publ. Field Mus. Nat. Hist., Bot. 16: 412. 1937.

Stems 45–50 (–200) cm tall, glabrous. Leaves 5–15 cm long on petioles 1.5–4 cm long, lateral leaflets ovate, 4–9 × 1.5–3.5 cm, ± abruptly attenuate into a short petiolule, 0.5–1 cm long, acute or shortly acuminate at the apex; terminal leaflets ovate-lanceolate, 6.5–12 cm long, attenuate at the base to a longer petiolule, 1.5–2.5 cm long, gradually acuminate at the apex, leaflets glabrous on both surfaces. Capitula usually numerous in loose dichotomously branched panicles. Involucre 4–5 mm diam. when fresh, c. 1 cm broad when pressed; outer phyllaries 8, spathulate, c. 3 mm long, 0.75–1 mm broad, slightly accrescent, sparsely ciliate at the margins, puberulous at the base, inner phyllaries oblong-lanceolate, c. 5 mm long, 1.5 mm broad, ciliate at the apex, margins membranous, yellowish. Rays 5–6, white, c. 6 mm long, 4 mm broad, sometimes absent. Disc flowers yellow, 3.5–5 mm long. Receptacular scales c. 4 mm long, accrescent and almost as long as the achenes at maturity. Achenes 7–8 mm long, 0.75–1 mm broad, black, bearing a few pale stiff hairs on the angles in the upper part. Pappus bristles 2–4, straw coloured, 2–3 mm long.

There are two varieties.

KEY TO THE VARIETIES

1 Capitula discoid..**1.** var. **pilosa**
1 Capitula radiate with (4–) 5–6 (–7) rays................................**2.** var. **minor**

1. var. **pilosa** Sherff, Field Mus. Nat. Hist., Bot. 16: 412. 1937.

Bidens chinensis auct. non Willd: Bond, Wild Fls. Ceylon Hills 108, t. 55.
1953 p.p. Type: Herb. LINN. (975/8).

Although eradiate, the capitula usually contain whitish marginal flowers
2.5–3 mm long with deeply 3–4 lobed tubular corollas which contain stamens
and styles.

D i s t r. Central and S. America, Africa, S.E. Asia, Australia, New Zealand.

E c o l. Only known as a weed from the Peradeniya-Kandy area. Flowering November–March.

S p e c i m e n s E x a m i n e d. KANDY DISTRICT: Peradeniya-Kandy
road near Dagaba, 515 m, *Comanor 518* (E, US, PDA); Aladeniya, 8 miles
NW of Kandy, *Grierson 1137* (US, PDA, E, BR, CANB).

2. var. **minor** (Blume) Sherff, Bot. Gaz. 70: 387. 1925 et Publ. Field Mus.
Nat. Hist., Bot. 16: 421. Pl. 102 fig. c, d and k–r. 1937.

Bidens sundaica var. *minor* Blume, Bijdr. 914. 1826. Type: Java, prope Bui-
tenzorg, Blume 900, 146.
Bidens chinensis auct. non Willd: Moon, Cat. 57. 1824; Alston in Trimen,
Handb. Fl. Ceylon 6: 168. 1931 et Kandy Fl. 53, fig. 280. 1938; Bond, Wild
Fls. Ceylon Hills 108. t. 55. 1953 p.p.
Bidens pilosa L. sensu Thw., Enum. Pl. Zeyl. 165. 1860; Trimen, Handb. Fl.
Ceylon 3: 40. 1895.

Chromosome number. n = 38 + 2 (Turner & Lewis, J. Bot. Soc. South
Africa 31: 215. 1965).

E c o l. Weed of roadsides and cultivated ground, very common. Common
everywhere in the montane zone. Flowering throughout year.

V e r n. "Ceylon Tea" (according to Moon), Spanish Needle, Val-te-Kola,
or Wal-teekola (S); Ottu-pillu (T).

S p e c i m e n s E x a m i n e d. NUWARA ELIYA DISTRICT: Maturate,
Feb. 1802, *C.P. 1802* (PDA) unannotated *C.P. 3630* (BM); Horton Plains 1½
miles S of Farr Inn on Ohiya road, 2400 m, *Gould & Cooray 13859* (E, US,
PDA). KANDY DISTRICT: Peradeniya, University Circuit Bungalow, 900
m, *Muller-Dombois & Cooray 67103124* (US, PDA); Peradeniya, University
Campus, 505 m, *Comanor 716* (E, US, PDA); Peradeniya-Kandy Road near

Dagaba, 515 m, *Comanor 518* (US, PDA); Above Rangala, 4600 ft, *Grierson 1021* (E, US, PDA, BR, CANB). BADULLA DISTRICT: Haputale Estate, *T.N. Hyde 836* (PDA). Govindihela, 22 Feb. 1906, *Willis s.n.* (PDA); Galaha, *Simpson 8218* (BM). Ferndale nr. Rangala, *Simpson 8729* (BM). WITHOUT LOCALITY: *s. coll. C.P. 3630* (BM); *Walker s.n.* (E).

2. Bidens biternata (Lour.) Merr. & Sherff, Sherff in Bot. Gaz. 88: 293. 1929 et Publ. Field. Mus. Nat. Hist., Bot. Ser. 16: 388. 1937, Pl. 99 fig. a and c–m.

Coreopsis biternata Lour., Fl. Cochinch. ed. 1. 508. 1790. Type: Canton, Loureiro.
Bidens chinensis Willd., Sp. Pl. 3: 1719. 1803. Type: Ceylon, Okanda ("Oganda Malej") Rottler? *Willd. Herb. 15023* (B).
Bidens decomposita Wall. ex DC., Prod. 5: 602. 1836; Thw., Enum. Pl. Zeyl. 1860. Type: *Wallich 298* (K).
Bidens pilosa var. *bipinnata* (L.) Hook. f., Fl. Br. Ind. 3: 309. 1881; Trimen, Handb. Fl. Ceylon 3: 41. 1895, excl. type.
Bidens "pinnatus" Alston in Trimen, Handb. Fl. Ceylon 6: 168. 1931.

Stems 10–45 or more cm tall, angular, sparsely pubescent when young. Leaves 5–10 cm long on petioles 1–2 cm long; lateral leaflets ovate, 1.5–3 cm long, 0.5–2 cm broad, deeply dentate or pinnatifid, acute at the apex, subsessile or attenuate at the base to a short petiolule up to 0.5 cm long, terminal segment elliptic, 2–6 cm long, 1–2.5 cm broad, with 3–5 pinnatifid lobes on each side, attenuate at the base to a short petiolule up to 0.5 cm long, terminal segment elliptic, 2–6 cm long, 1–2.5 cm broad, with 3–5 pinnatifid lobes on each side, attenuate to a winged petiolule, 0.5–1.5 cm long, apex gradually acuminate. Capitula several, borne on dichotomously branched peduncles up to 15 cm long. Involucres 4–7 mm broad; outer phyllaries narrowly linear-oblanceolate, 5 mm long, 0.5 mm broad, ciliate at the margins slightly accrescent, inner phyllaries ovate-lanceolate, 6 mm long, 2 mm broad, glabrous, narrowly membranous at the margins, accrescent. Rays usually 3, scarcely longer than involucre, ligules whitish or yellow (fide Alston), 3–4 mm long, 1.75 mm broad. Disc flowers c. 3.5 mm long. Receptacular scales linear-lanceolate, 3-nerved, accrescent, 10–12 mm long in fruit. Achenes linear, c. 0.7–1.5 cm long, ± tetragonous, blackish, glabrous or pubescent above. Pappus bristles 3.5–4 mm long, paler.

Chromosome number. n = 36 has been recorded for Indian material of "*B. pilosa* var. *bipinnata*" (Mehra *et al.*, Carylologia 18: 40. 1965).

Distr. Apparently not common. Also Trop. Africa, India, Malaysia, E. Asia, Australia.

Specimens Examined. BATTICALOA DISTRICT: Batticaloa, Mar. 1858, *s. coll. C.P. 3583* (PDA, K), *s.n.* (BM).

N o t e. In the vicinity of Nuwara Eliya, another species, *B. triplinervia* HBK. var. *macrantha* (Wedd.) Sherff, is encountered in cultivation. This is a weak, low growing (15–20 cm tall) perennial herb with finely dissected and relatively large yellow ray flowers (capitula measuring about 2.5 cm across the extended ligules). Sherff recorded (Publ. Field. Mus. Nat. Hist., Bot. Sér. 16: 511. 1937) that this native of Tropical South America has become a weed in the Nilgiri Hills in S. India.

40. GLOSSOGYNE

Cass., Dict. Sci. Nat. 51: 475. 1827. Type species: *G. tenuifolia* Cass.

Glabrous perennial herbs with thick woody rootstocks. Stems erect, ramose, almost leafless. Leaves mostly basal, pinnatisect with narrow segments. Capitula solitary, terminal on branch apices, heterogamous, radiate. Involucre 2–3 seriate, phyllaries shortly connate at the base. Ray flowers few, ligules yellow, oblong, 3-lobed. Disc flowers tubular, 4–5 lobed, yellow. Anther bases obtuse, apices acute, unappendaged. Style branches with long linear appendages. Receptacle flat, paleae concave, scarious. Achenes dorsally compressed, linear or ovate-oblong, bearing two retrorsely barbed awns at the apex.

Glossogyne bidens (Retz.) Alston in Trimen, Handb. Fl. Ceylon 6: 168. 1931.

Zinnia bidens Retz., Obs. 5: 28. 1789. Type: In Bengala, *Koenig s.n.* (LD).
Glossogyne pinnatifida DC. in Wight, Contrib. 19. 1834 et Prod. 5: 632. 1836;
  C.B. Clarke, Comp. Ind. 141. 1876; Hook. f., Fl. Br. Ind. 3: 310. 1881;
  Trimen, Handb. Fl. Ceylon 3: 41. 1895. Type: *Wight 1454* (K).

Flowering stems 15–40 cm tall. Basal leaves pinnatisect, petiolate, 5–15 cm long, including petioles 3–7 cm long, segments 3–7, linear-lanceolate, 0.5–3 cm long, 1–3.5 mm broad, acute at the apex; cauline leaves similar, smaller, uppermost simple, scale-like. Involucres campanulate, 3–4 mm diam.; phyllaries c. 12, linear-oblong, 3–4 mm long, 0.5–0.75 mm broad, obtuse or acute at the apex. Ray flowers c. 12, basal tubes c. 0.75 mm long, ligules broadly ovate, c. 2 mm long, 1.5 mm broad. Disc flower corollas 4-lobed, 2.5–2.75 mm long. Paleae 4 mm long. Achenes dark brown or blackish, linear-oblong, 6–7 mm long, 5-ribbed on both surfaces. Awns divergent, brown, 2–3 mm long.

Chromosome number. n = 12 (Shetty, Taxon 16: 569. 1967).

D i s t r. Also in S. India.
E c o l. A rare plant of the dry zone. Flowering January–April.
U s e s. In India, a preparation made from the root is applied to snake bites and scorpion stings.

Specimens Examined. MONERAGALA DISTRICT: Nilgala
Hill, Jan. 1888, *Trimen s.n.* (PDA); between Bibile and Ekiriankumbura, Jan.
1888, *Trimen s.n.* (PDA). WITHOUT LOCALITY: 7 Apr. 1819, *Moon 649*
(BM).

41. GALINSOGA

Ruiz & Pavon, Prod. Fl. Peruv. 110, t. 24. 1794. Type species: *G. parviflora*
Cav.

Erect branching annual herbs. Leaves simple, opposite, entire or dentate.
Capitula small, borne on axillary peduncles, heterogamous, radiate. Involucre
campanulate, 1–2 seriate. Ray flowers few, ligules white. Disc flowers tubular-
campanulate, 5-lobed, yellow. Anther bases minutely sagittate. Style branches
shortly and acutely appendaged. Receptacle conical; paleae scarious. Achenes
angular or dorsally compressed. Pappus paleaceous, scales oblong, fimbriate;
ray achenes usually epappose.

Galinsoga parviflora Cav., Ic. et Descr. 3: 41, t. 281. 1796; DC., Prod. 5: 677.
1836; C.B. Clarke, Comp. Ind. 142. 1876; Hook. f., Fl. Br. Ind. 3: 311. 1881;
Trimen, Handb. Fl. Ceylon 3: 42. 1895 in nota; Alston in Trimen, Handb. Fl.
Ceylon 6: 168. 1931. Type: Cult. Reg. Hort. Matritense (MA).

Stems 15–75 cm tall, glabrous. Leaves ovate, petiolate, petioles up to 1.5
cm long, laminae 1–5.5 × 0.5–3 cm, acute or acuminate at the apex, rounded
or cuneate at the base, margins shallowly undulate-serrate, sparsely pilose on
both surfaces, later glabrescent. Capitula on axillary, glandular peduncles up
to 3 cm long. Involucre c. 4 mm diam., outer phyllaries c. 5, 2.5–3 mm long,
1–1.5 mm broad; inner phyllaries 5–6, concave, ovate, 3–3.5 mm long, 2–2.5
mm broad. Ray flowers 4–5, basal tubes c. 1 mm long, pubescent, ligule
obovate, 1–1.5 mm long. Disc flower corollas c. 1.5 mm long. Paleae elliptic,
2.5–3 mm long, 1–1.5 mm broad. Achenes fusiform, black, 1.5–2 mm long,
puberulous. Pappus scales c. 10, elliptic-oblong, 1.5 mm long.

Chromosome number. n=8 (Mehra *et al.*, Caryologia 18: 40. 1965); n=16
(Turner & Flyr., Amer. J. Bot. 53: 28, 1966); n=c. 8 (Powell & King, Amer.
J. Bot. 56 (1) 116–121. 1969).

Distr. Native of tropical south America now a widespread weed
throughout tropical and temperate Asia.

Ecol. Common weed of cultivated and waste land. Flowering throughout the year.

Specimens Examined. KANDY DISTRICT: Peradeniya, Jan.
1882, *Trimen s.n.* (PDA); University Campus, *Amaratunga 781* (PDA); Paragalla between Gampola and Dolosbage, 3000 ft, *Grierson 1008* (E, US,
PDA, BR, CANB). NUWARA ELIYA DISTRICT: Ambawela, 26 Mar.

1906, *A.W. Silva s.n.* (PDA); Ohiya, *Mueller-Dombois 68051845* (US, PDA); between Pussellawa and Ramboda, 950 m, *Comanor 329* (E, US, PDA); Govindihela, 27 Feb. 1906, *Willis s.n.* (PDA); Atabage Oya, Delta Estate, *Simpson 8763* (PDA, BM). BADULLA DISTRICT: Haputale, Rochampton Estate, Sept. 1890, *Trimen s.n.* (PDA); Namunakula, 29 Apr. 1924, *J.M. de Silva s.n.* (PDA).

N o t e. Trimen (l.c.) recorded that this species was occasionally found as a garden weed in the hill country. It is now quite widespread.

42. TRIDAX

L., Sp. Pl. 900. 1753; Gen. Pl. 382. 1754. Type species: *T. procumbens* L.

Annual or perennial, erect or procumbent herbs. Stems pilose or glandular, often rooting at the nodes. Leaves opposite, simple or pinnately lobed. Capitula usually solitary (elsewhere, several or many) on elongate peduncles, heterogamous, radiate. Involucre campanulate, 2–3 seriate, phyllaries subequal. Ray flowers white (elsewhere yellow or purplish), sometimes bilabiate. Disc flowers tubular-campanulate, yellow, 5-lobed. Anther bases sagittate; apical appendages ovate. Style branches with subulate appendages. Receptacle convex or conical; paleae persistent, scarious, concave, subtending the achenes. Achenes turbinate, terete or ribbed. Pappus of slender awns, pulmose.

Tridax procumbens L., Sp. Pl. 900. 1753; DC., Prod. 5: 679. 1836; Hook. f., Fl. Br. Ind. 3: 311. 1881; Trimen, Handb. Fl. Ceylon 3: 42. 1895 in nota; Alston, ibid. 6: 168. 1931 et Kandy Fl. 54. 1938; Powell, Brittonia 17: 80. 1965. Type: Veracruz, *Houstoun s.n.* (BM).

Hirsute perennials with procumbent stems 15–45 cm long. Leaves ovate or lanceolate, petiolate, petioles up to 3 cm long; laminae 1.5–7 × 0.75–4 cm, acute or acuminate at the apex, cuneate at the base, margins serrate to coarsely incised-dentate or trilobed, ± scabrid hirsute on both surfaces. Capitula solitary on erect, retrorsely hirsute and sparsely glandular peduncles 10–20 cm long. Involucre 7–10 mm diam.; outer phyllaries ovate, 3.5–6 mm long, 2–3.5 mm broad, herbaceous, acuminate, densely hirsute, inner phyllaries membranous, oblong, 5–8 mm long, 1.5–2 mm broad. Ray flowers 5–6, basal tubes 3–3.5 mm long, pubescent, ligules obovate-oblong, creamy white, 4–5 mm long, deeply 2–3 lobed at the apex. Disc corollas 5.5–6.5 mm long, pubescent. Paleae linear-lanceolate, 8–9 mm long. Achenes narrowly obconical, blackish, sparsely sericeous, 2–2.5 mm long, truncate at the apex. Pappus bristles c. 20, 4.5–6.5 mm long, unequal in length, alternately longer and shorter.

Chromosome number. n = 18 (Powell l.c.).

D i s t r. Native of Central America, now widespread throughout tropical and subtropical regions of the world.

E c o l. Roadsides, wasteground, common weed of lawns and cultivated ground. Flowering throughout the year.

V e r n. 'Kurunegala Daisy'.

S p e c i m e n s E x a m i n e d. KANDY DISTRICT: Weed in South Garden, Royal Botanic Garden, Peradeniya, Sept. 1896, Apr. 1897, *Trimen s.n.* (PDA); Hantane, 900 m, *Mueller-Dombois & Cooray 67111301* (US, PDA); university campus, 508 m, *Comanor 340* (E, US, PDA), *696* (E, US, PDA). MATALE DISTRICT: Dambulla near Sigiriya, 210 m, *Comanor 741* (E, US, PDA). MONERAGALA DISTRICT: Gal Oya Reservoir, *Comanor 566* (E, US, PDA), between Passara and Moneragala near milestone 5, c. 1500 ft, *Grierson 1140* (E, US, PDA, BR, CANB). HAMBANTOTA DISTRICT: Ruhuna Nat. Park, Yala at mouth of Mennik Ganga, *Fosberg et al. 51070* (US, E, PDA).

43. TAGETES

L., Sp. Pl. 887. 1753; Gen. Pl. ed. 5. 378. 1754. Type species: *T. erecta* L.

Annual (or perennial) herbs with branched stems. Leaves opposite or the lower opposite and the upper alternate, usually pinnate, leaflets conspicuously gland-dotted. Capitula medium-sized, solitary, pedunculate or sometimes in leafy cymes, heterogamous, radiate. Involucre cylindrical-campanulate, uniseriate, phyllaries connate to near the apex and bearing oil glands. Ray flowers few, pistillate, fertile, ligules often broad yellow or orange, 3-lobed. Disc flowers infundibuliform, 5-lobed, yellow. Anther bases rounded, apical appendages narrowly ovate. Style branches thin, thickening slightly and acute at the apices. Receptacle flat, naked. Achenes linear, subcompressed, angular, lower parts empty, pale in colour. Pappus scales 3–10, very unequal, ± united, with 1–2 longer than the rest and aristate.

Both *T. erecta* and *T. patula* L. have been reported from Ceylon (see Alston in Trimen, Handb. Fl. Ceylon 6: 169. 1931) but I have not seen herbarium material of the latter species to support this statement nor did I myself observe it to be present on the island. The two species are very similar but *T. patula* according to Towner (Amer. J. Bot. 48: 743–751. 1961) is a tetraploid (2n=48) probably resulted from a hybridisation between *T. erecta* and *T. tenuifolia*. Additionally, according to American authors, it is confined to Mexico and Guatemala and is not reputed to have become naturalised in the Old World as has *T. erecta*. This does not finally preclude the occurrence of *T. patula* in Ceylon and, accordingly, I have set out the differentiating characters in the key below, but can give no account of this species.

KEY TO THE SPECIES

1 Involucre c. 2 cm long; glands of the lower half in 3–4 series, linear-oblong. Capitula solitary on swollen peduncles. Glands of leaflets few, marginal near the base of teeth
....**T. erecta**
1 Involucre c. 1–1.2 cm long; glands of the lower half in two series, elongate, narrowly linear. Capitula cymose, peduncles scarcely enlarged above. Glands of leaflets more numerous, scattered...**T. patula**

Tagetes erecta L., Sp. Pl. 887. 1753; Moon, Cat. 58. 1824; DC., Prod. 5: 643. 1836; C.B. Clarke, Comp. Ind. 143. 1876; Trimen, Handb. Fl. Ceylon 3: 42. 1895 in nota; Alston in Trimen, Handb. Fl. Ceylon 6: 169. 1931. Type: Herb. Cliff (BM).

Erect annual herbs, 15–60 cm tall. Stems glabrous, angular. Leaves pinnate, 2.5–15 cm long, leaflets 11–17, lanceolate, 1–5 cm long, 2–10 mm broad, attenuate at the base, acute or acuminate at the apices, margins serrate, teeth of upper leaves generally finely setose pointed, glands few, usually at the base of teeth. Capitula solitary on swollen peduncles, 5–15 cm long. Involucre 1.75–2 cm long, 7–12 mm broad, glabrous, phyllaries 5–8 with acute deltoid apices, generally bearing 6–7 glands along the margin of each phyllary with 3 glands on the apical free portion. Ray flowers 5–8, basal tubes c. 7 mm long, ligule obovate, c. 1 mm long, 1.3 cm broad, with 2 broad lobes at the apex and a narrower central one, or sometimes, in cultivated forms, marginal flowers tubular, radiant, subligulate, 4-lobed, lobes c. 5 mm long, 1.5–2 mm broad. Disc flower corollas 1.3–1.5 mm long, lobes 4 mm long, pubescent within. Achenes blackish, 8–9 mm long, scabrous on the angles. Pappus scales united, 4–4.5 mm long with 1–2 longer aristate scales, 6–10 mm long.
Chromosome number. 2n = 24 (Towner, Amer. J. Bot. 48: 745. 1961).

D i s t r. Native of Mexico now naturalised in tropical and subtropical regions in both New and Old World.

E c o l. At roadside and as a weed on cultivated ground, common. Flowering throughout the year.

S p e c i m e n s E x a m i n e d. KANDY DISTRICT: Peradeniya, 10 Aug. 1928, *Alston s.n.* (PDA); Peradeniya, above University Circuit Bungalow, 1000 m, *Mueller-Dombois 67110920* (US, PDA). RATNAPURA DISTRICT: Brampton Estate near Belihul Oya, 3500 ft, *Grierson 1149* (E, US, PDA, BR, CANB).

Apart from *Tagetes*, two other genera previously counted among the epaleaceous *Helenieae*, both from North America, may be grown in gardens in Ceylon:

43a. Helenium autumnale L. a perennial herb with winged stems up to 2 metres tall. Its rays vary in colour from yellow to dark crimson.

43b. Gaillardia pulchella Foug. (syn. *G. picta*) an annual plant usually less than 50 cm tall in which the rays have crimson bases and lobed yellow tips.

Tribe ANTHEMIDEAE

Leaves alternate, pinnately lobed or dissected. Capitula heterogamous, radiate or disciform (sometimes homogamous, discoid). Phyllaries several-seriate, scarious at the apex and margins. Anthers sagittate or obtuse at the base. Style branches truncate. Receptacle paleaceous or naked. Achenes oblong or obconical, angular or winged. Pappus absent or consisting of a hyaline corona.

KEY TO THE GENERA

1 Capitula eradiate
  2 Low growing prostrate herbs
    3 Female flowers without corollas. Leaves pinnatisect.....................**47. Cotula**
    3 Female flowers with short 2-3 lobed corollas. Leaves toothed or lobed at the apex..
    ....**44. Centipeda**
  2 Erect herbs or shrubs
    4 Capitula numerous, small, disciform, few-flowered, drooping. Tall herbs...........
    ....**48. Artemisia**
    4 Capitula medium-sized, discoid, erect. Shrubs......................**45b. Santolina**
1 Capitula with white or coloured ray flowers
  5 Receptacle paleaceous...**45c. Achillea**
  5 Receptacle naked
    6 Marginal achenes winged or strongly angular.................**45. Chrysanthemum**
    6 Marginal achenes ± similar to the inner ones, not winged..........**46. Tanacetum**

44. CENTIPEDA

Lour., Fl. Cochinch. 492. 1790. Type species: *C. minima* (L.) A. Br. & Aschers. (syn. *C. orbicularis* Lour.).

Low growing annual herbs. Leaves alternate, oblanceolate or spathulate, entire or toothed. Capitula small, heterogamous, disciform, solitary, ± sessile in leaf axils. Involucre 1-2 seriate, phyllaries membranous, subequal. Female flowers numerous, shortly tubular, 2-3 lobed at the apex. Hermaphrodite flowers fewer, limb campanulate, 4-lobed. Anther bases minutely sagittate. Style branches of hermaphrodite flowers very short, ± acute. Receptacle convex, naked. Achenes 4-5 angled, sparsely puberulent on the ribs, flower parts generally persistent; achenes of hermaphrodite flowers sometimes empty, sterile. Pappus a minute, spongy, pale-coloured corona, obscurely toothed at the margin.

Centipeda minima (L.) A. Br. & Aschers., Ind. Sem. Hort. Berol. App. 6.

1867; Alston in Trimen, Handb. Fl. Ceylon 6: 170. 1931; Peradeniya Manual
No. 7, fig. 1951.

Artemisia minima L., Sp. Pl. 849. 1753. Type: Herb. LINN. (988/48).
Cotula minima (L.) Willd., Sp. Pl. 3: 2170. 1803; Moon, Cat. 58. 1824.
Centipeda orbicularis Lour., Fl. Cochinch. 493. 1790; Hook. f., Fl. Br. Ind.
    3: 317. 1881; C.B. Clarke, Comp. Ind. 151. 1876; Trimen, Handb. Fl. Cey-
    lon 3: 42. 1895. Type: Cochinchina, *Loureiro* (BM).
Myriogyne minuta (Forst.) Less., Linnaea 6: 219. 1831; DC., Prod. 6: 139.
    1837; Thw., Enum. Pl. Zeyl. 165, 1860.
Cotula minuta Forst., Prod. 57 (no. 301). 1786. Type: New Caledonia, *Forster*
    (BM?).

Stems prostrate, up to 15 cm long, minutely glandular papillate, otherwise glabrous. Leaves oblanceolate or spathulate, 5–10 × 2–4 mm, somewhat
fleshy, 3–5 toothed or lobed, acute at the apex, attenuate, subpetiolate at the
base, minutely puberulous and glandular on the lower surface. Capitula subglobose, 2.5–4 mm diam., ± sessile in leaf axils; phyllaries spathulate, c. 1.5
mm long, glabrous. Flowers yellowish-green, females numerous with minute
tubular corollas, c. 0.3 mm long; hermaphrodite flowers about 20, corollas
0.5–0.7 mm long. Achenes narrowly oblanceolate, including spongy apical
corona 0.75–1 mm long.

Chromosome number. n = 10 (Mangenot & Mangenot, Rev. Cytol. Biol.
Veg. 25: 432. 1962).

D i s t r. Afghanistan, Australia, Pacific islands and throughout tropical
western Asia.

E c o l. Damp places at margins of irrigation channels and river banks in
montane zone, rather uncommon but locally abundant. Flowers August–May
and probably throughout the year.

U s e s. Promotes sneezing and thus relieves nasal congestion in colds.
According to Trimen, it is used to treat swellings and inflammation.

V e r n. Visaduli, Heen-Kimbu (According to Moon), Visa chunniya (S);
Marukolunthu (T).

S p e c i m e n s E x a m i n e d. WITHOUT PRECISE LOCALITY: *C.P.
2715* annotated "Doonootiboo Oya, Feb. 1853; Maturata, Aug. 1853" (PDA),
unannotated (K). KANDY DISTRICT: Maskeliya, 2 Mar. 1882, *Trimen
s.n.* (PDA); Dolosbage, Sept. 1885, Trimen s.n. (PDA); Rosella, May 1886,
Trimen s.n. (PDA); Koshinna, Kandy—Gampola Road, c. 1700 ft., 27 Apr.
1969, *Grierson 1158* (E, US, PDA). WITHOUT LOCALITY: *Wight 551* (E);
1821, *Macrae s.n.* (K), *266* (BM).

45. CHRYSANTHEMUM

L., Sp. Pl. 887. 1753; Gen. Pl. ed. 5. 379. 1754; emend. Briquet in Burnat, Fl.
Alpes Marit. 6: 71. 1916. Type species: *C. coronarium* L.

Annual herbs. Leaves alternate, simple and coarsely dentate or pinnately divided. Capitula solitary, terminal at branch ends, heterogamous, radiate. Involucre broadly campanulate or hemispherical, 3–4 seriate, imbricate; phyllaries ovate with scarious margins. Ray flowers uniseriate, yellow, pistillate, fertile. Disc flowers tubular-campanulate, 5-lobed. Anther bases rounded, apices with ovate appendages. Receptacle convex, naked. Achenes dimorphic, without vallecular canals and myxogenic cells, those of the ray triquetrous, often winged at the angles, those of the disc cylindrical, 10-ribbed or laterally compressed and winged on posterior angle. Pappus absent.

Chrysanthemum segetum L., Sp. Pl. 889. 1753; DC., Prod. 6: 64. 1837; Alston in Trimen, Handb. Fl. Ceylon 6: 169. 1931. Type: Herb. Cliff (BM).

Stems glabrous, branched, 15–50 cm tall. Leaves oblong or spathulate, 1.5–7 × 0.5–1.5 (–3) cm, deeply incised and pinnately dentate or lobed at the apex, lobes obtuse, mucronate, attenuate or subpetiolate and semiamplexicaul at the base, glabrous on both surfaces. Involucre 1–1.5 cm diam., phyllaries 4.5–7 mm long, 3–4.5 mm broad, with scarious pale brown margins up to 3 mm broad at the apex. Ray flowers c. 12, basal tubes 3 mm long, enlarged and infolded at the base and covering the tops of the achenes, ligules oblong or obovate, 8–10 mm long, 4–8 mm broad, 2–3 lobed at the apex. Disc flowers 4–5 mm long, bases similar to those of ray flowers, lobes papillose within and with narrow brown median secretory canals. Achenes of the ray triquetrous, truncate at the apex, 2–2.5 mm long, 1.5–2 mm broad, the lateral ribs larger and almost winged; disc achenes 1–1.25 mm diam., cylindrical, ± equally 10-ribbed.

D i s t r. Native of Europe, now naturalised in North America and Java.
E c o l. Roadsides and at margins of cultivation, locally common. Flowering December–February, and probably longer.
S p e c i m e n s E x a m i n e d. NUWARA ELIYA DISTRICT: Nuwara Eliya, *Alston 875* (PDA); ibid., Dec. 1927, *Alston s.n.* (PDA).
N o t e s. According to Alston (l.c.) this species was introduced in 1925. Today it is seen in cultivation but is not by any means a widespread alien.

The garden *Chrysanthemum* which resulted from the hybridisation of *C. indicum* and *C. morifolium* has long been cultivated in Ceylon. Moon listed three varieties in his catalogue (p. 58. 1824) under the name *C. indicum* with yellow, white and purple flowers, and gives the Sinhalese vernacular name "Kolondu" for the species. Macmillan (Trop. Pl. and Gard. ed. 5.128) records that Seranthi-poo (T) and Kapurumal (S) are other native names used for the border chrysanthemum.

Linnaeus took up the name *Matricaria sinensis flore monstroso* Vaill. in his Flora Zeylanica (p. 198) for the specimens that Hermann collected in Ceylon in 1670 and this he later made a synonym of his *C. indicum* var. *β* in his Species Plantarum (p. 889, 1753).

Taxonomically, this species cannot remain in the same genus as the true Chrysanthemums because of its different achenial structure and it is now placed as *Dendranthema indicum* (L.) Des Moul.

Similarly *Chrysanthemum leucanthemum* L. must be called **45a. Leucanthemum vulgare** (L.) Lam. because of its 10-ribbed achenes which are all alike.

Other species of *Chrysanthemum* s. str. are cultivated: the yellow flowered, European *C. coronarium* L. and the Moroccan *C. carinatum* Schousb. which has radiating bands of colour (yellow, red, purple) on its ray flowers.

The Paris Daisy, *C. frutescens* L. a species from the Canary Islands with white ligules is more correctly placed as *Argyranthemum frutescens* (L.) Sch. Bip. and the Feverfew, once reckoned among the Chrysanthemums, but now known as *Tanacetum parthenium* (L.) Sch. Bip., is cultivated, especially the flore pleno form.

45b. Santolina chamaecyparissus L. of S. Europe is cultivated and makes a small bushy shrub 45–60 cm tall with greyish aromatic leaves and button-like discoid yellow heads of flowers borne on peduncles 15 cm long. Unlike *Chrysanthemum* and *Tanacetum*, the receptacle is paleaceous as it is in *Anthemis* itself.

45c. Achillea also has a paleacous receptacle but has radiate capitula. Two species are represented: **A. millefolium** L., Yarrow, with finely cut leaf segments and dense corymbs of small capitula the flowers of which vary from white to pinkish-red and **A. ptarmica** L., Sneezewort, with lanceolate, toothed leaves and corymbs of white-flowered capitula that are often doubled.

46. TANACETUM

L., Sp. Pl. 844. 1753; Gen. Pl. ed. 5. 366. 1754; emend. Briquet in Burnat, Fl. Alpes Marit. 6: 118. 1916. Type species: *T. vulgare* L.

Annual or perennial herbs. Leaves alternate, pinnately lobed or divided. Capitula solitary, terminal, pedunculate or few-numerous in corymbs, heterogamous, and radiate or disciform, or homogamous. Involucre ovoid or campanulate; phyllaries 3–4 seriate, imbricate with scarious margins. Ray flowers when present 1-seriate, tubular or ligulate, white or yellow, 3-lobed. Disc flowers tubular, 5-lobed, yellow. Anther bases minutely sagittate, apices ovately appendaged. Style branches truncate. Receptacle convex, naked. Achenes homomorphic, narrowly obconical, 5–10 ribbed, without myxogenic cells or secretory canals. Pappus coroniform, variable in shape.

Tanacetum cinerariifolium (Trev.) Sch. Bip., Tanacet. 58. 1844.

Pyrethrum cinerariifolium Trev., Ind. Sem. Hort. Vratis. App. 2. 2. 1829; DC., Prod. 6: 55. 1837.

Chrysanthemum cinerariifolium (Trev.) Vis., Fl. Dalmat. 2: 88. 1847; Backer & Bakh. f., Fl. Java 2: 421. 1965. Type: ? possibly based on *Chrysanthemum exoticum incano cinerariaefolia* Boccone, Mus. Pl. Rar. 23, t. 4 and t. 130, 1697.

Perennial herbs. Stems 15–45 cm tall, ± unbranched, appressed whitish pubescent. Basal leaves tripinnatisect, 6–25 cm long (including petiole, 3–15 cm), primary segments c. 7, 1–2.5 cm long, ultimate segments narrow, 0.75–2 mm broad, acute, appressed greyish pubescent on both surfaces or glabrescent above; upper leaves smaller, becoming sessile. Capitula solitary, terminal, radiate. Involucre campanulate, 5–7.5 mm diam., phyllaries greyish pubescent, outer ones lanceolate, 3.5–4.5 mm long, 1.5 mm broad, inner ones oblong or spathulate, 5–6 mm long, 2.5–3 mm broad with distinct whitish scarious tips and margins. Ray flowers 12–15, white, basal tubes c. 1 mm long, ligule oblong, 7–15 mm long, 3–5 mm broad, ± truncate and crenately lobed at the apex. Disc flower corollas 3–4 mm long. Achenes 3–3.5 mm long, 5-ribbed, finely glandular between the ribs. Pappus corona irregular, 0.5–1 mm long.

D i s t r. Native of Yugoslavia and NE Italy, cultivated in India and Malaya as an insecticide.

E c o l. Cultivated and sometimes escaping. Flowering February–May.

S p e c i m e n s   E x a m i n e d. NUWARA ELIYA DISTRICT: Maha Coodoogala, *Holmes 544* (Forestry Dept. Herb. Colombo); Hakgala, 18 Sept. 1937, *Nock s.n.* (PDA).

47. COTULA

L., Sp. Pl. 891. 1753; Gen. Pl. ed. 5. 380. 1754. Type species: *C. coronopifolia* L.

Low growing annual or perennial herbs. Leaves alternate, pinnatifid, or pinnatisect, rarely undivided. Capitula small, pedunculate, heterogamous, disciform. Involucre broadly campanulate or hemispherical, phyllaries 2-seriate, subequal, herbaceous, membranous margined. Female flowers several-seriate, corollas shortly conical or absent. Hermaphrodite flowers tubular, sometimes 2-winged, shortly 4-lobed at the apex. Anther bases obtuse, entire; apices ovately appendaged. Style branches truncate or obtuse. Receptacle convex, naked. Achenes, especially the marginal ones, stipitate, dorsally compressed, usually 2-ribbed or winged. Pappus absent or sometimes auriculiform.

Cotula australis (Sieb. ex. Spreng.) Hook. f., Handb. New Zealand Fl. 1: 128. 1853; Gamble, Fl. Pres. Madras 2: 712. 1921; Alston in Trimen, Handb. Fl. Ceylon 6: 170. 1931.

Anacyclus australis Sieb. ex Spreng., Syst. Veg. 3: 497. 1826. Type: Pl. Exs. Nov. Holl., *Sieber 331*.

Strongylosperma australis (Sieb. ex Spreng.) DC., Prod. 6: 82. 1837.

Slender spreading annual herbs commonly 10–15 cm tall. Stems decumbent or erect, sparsely covered with long weak silky hairs. Leaves pinnatisect or bipinnatisect, 1–4 cm long, including petiole up to 1 cm long, auriculate at the base, primary segments usually 7, 3–5 (–10) mm long, ultimate segments lanceolate or oblanceolate, 1–1.5 mm broad, acute, apiculate at the apex, sparsely silky pilose on the lower surface, glabrous above. Capitula borne on peduncles 3–5 cm long. Involucre 2–5 mm diam; phyllaries oblong, 2 mm long, 0.75 mm broad, with whitish scarious margins, sometimes brown-tipped. Female flowers without corollas, styles 3–4 mm long. Disc flower corollas c. 0.75 mm long. Marginal achenes obovate, 1–1.25 mm long, 0.7–0.8 mm broad, with a broad (c. 0.2 mm) rib or wing along each margin, glandular. Stipes c. 0.5 mm long; hermaphrodite flower achenes narrowly obovoid, subcompressed or terete, 0.8–0.9 mm long, sessile, apparently fertile.

D i s t r. Native of Australia but now a widespread weed reported in Western USA, Canary Island, S. Africa and Norway where it is associated with Australian grain imports (see Jorgensen & Ouren in Nytt Mag. Bot. 16: 132. 1969).

E c o l. By roadsides and cultivated land, not common. Flowering October–December but probably longer.

S p e c i m e n s E x a m i n e d. NUWARA ELIYA DISTRICT: Nuwara Eliya, Sept.–Nov. 1889, *W. Nock s.n.* (PDA); Abbotsford Estate, Dimbula, Oct., 1890, *W. Nock s.n.* (PDA); Single Tree Hill, 30 Dec. 1925, *Alston s.n.* (PDA).

48. ARTEMISIA

L., Gen. Pl. ed. 5. 367. 1754. Type species: *A. vulgaris* L.

Erect perennial herbs. Leaves alternate, deeply pinnatisect, aromatic. Capitula numerous, small, pendulous, heterogamous, disciform in paniculate racemes. Involucres campanulate or ovoid, phyllaries scarious margined. Receptacle convex, naked. Marginal flowers female, tubular, 2–3 lobed at the apex. Disc flowers tubular-campanulate, 5-lobed. Anthers with acuminate apical appendages and obtuse bases. Style branches truncate. Achenes small, linear-oblong, 2-costate, epappose.

Artemisia dubia Wall. ex Bess. var. **grata** (Wall. ex DC.) Pampan., Nuovo Giorn. Bot. Ital. N.S. 36: 437. 1929.

Artemisia grata Wall., Cat. 3294. 1828, nom. nud; DC., Prod. 6: 114. 1837. Type: *Wallich 3294* (K).

Artemisia indica auct. non Willd: Moon, Cat. 58. 1824.
Artemisia vulgaris auct. non L.: Thw., Enum. Pl. Zeyl. 165. 1860; C.B. Clarke, Comp. Ind. 161. 1875; Hook. f., Fl. Br. Ind. 3: 325. 1881; Trimen, Handb. Fl. Ceylon 3: 43. 1895.

Stems up to 3 m tall, thinly lanate. Leaves c. 10–12 cm long, deeply pinnatisect, puberulous or glabrescent above, greyish lanate tomentose beneath, bearing 3 pairs of lateral segments 3–5 cm long, segments elliptic, simple or irregularly pinnatifid and bearing 1 or 2 secondary lobes, otherwise entire; terminal segments 5.5–9 cm long, 0.9–1.5 cm broad, acuminate at the apex; uppermost leaves trifid or simple lanceolate. Capitula ± pendulous, 1.5 mm diam. Involucres sparsely lanate, 3 mm long, outer phyllaries lanceolate, inner ones ovate, scarious-margined. Flowers reddish; female flowers c. 10, corollas 1.3–1.5 mm long; disc flowers c. 12, corollas 2 mm long. Achenes brown, c. 0.75 mm long.

D i s t r. Kashmir, Himalaya.

E c o l. On grassy banks and forest clearings above 1000 ft elevation, sometimes becoming a troublesome weed. Flowering October–June.

U s e s. This species is reputedly used in discouraging insects from infesting clothes and furniture. Medicinally it is claimed to be an anthelmintic, expectorant and antiseptic, but large doses are said to cause convulsions.

V e r n. Mugwort (E); Wal-Kolondu (S according to Moon).

S p e c i m e n s E x a m i n e d. KANDY DISTRICT: Galagadera (*Gardner*) *C.P. 1755* (PDA, BM-unannotated); Royal Botanic Garden, Peradeniya, Students' Garden, *Alston 1602* (PDA); 20 Apr. 1921 *J.M. Silva s.n.* (PDA), Hatton, *Alston 927* (PDA). NUWARA ELIYA DISTRICT: Nuwara Eliya, *Amaratunga 207* (PDA); Piduratalagala, c. 6200 ft, *Grierson 1076* (E, US, PDA, BR, CANB); Tea Research Institute, Talawakelle, Nov. 1945, *s. coll.* (K); ibid., Aug. 1935, *F. R. Tubbs s.n.* (K). WITHOUT LOCALITY: *De Silva 646* (K) *Champion s.n.* (K).

N o t e. *Artemisia* is probably one of the most difficult genera, taxonomically, of the Compositae and one that suffers badly from the lack of a comprehensive monograph. Differences between species and, more especially, between varieties are often difficult to follow unless one is an expert in the genus.

Ceylon material of this plant was previously included in the concept of *A. vulgaris* by Clarke, Trimen and Hooker but it appears to be fairly distinct from the European material of that species by its smaller and pendulous capitula as well as by its more simply divided leaves. But all these are matters of proportion, there is nothing more definite. In Flora URSS, *A. vulgaris* is treated as a European species whose distribution spreads as for as Eastern Siberia and North America but only as far south as the Pamir Alai.

Further complications arise from the literature wherein among the syno-

nyms that Pampanini cited under *A. dubia* is "*A. vulgaris* C. B. Clarke....
excl. var. α and δ" that is, respectively, var. *vulgaris* and var. *nilagirica*. Under the former, Clarke cited *Thwaites C.P. 1755*. Pampanini, however, lists
this variety under his *A. indica* Willd. (p. 457) but makes no mention there of
any Ceylonese material although some S. Indian collections are listed. He
later appears to have disavowed his *A. indica*, though he does not say as
much in black and white, for it is not included in his key nor in his list of
species (in Vol. 36, pp. 492 and 497).

The only Ceylonese material that Pampanini cited is an unnumbered specimen of Champion's under *A. dubia* var. *grata*. This variety he diagnosed as
"capitula campanulata et subglobosa; foliorum segmentis lobisque apice
ovate et mucronato, panicula et in forma praecedenti" which is also relatively
nebulous though, granted, he illustrated the leaf form (p. 461 fig. 6) which
agrees with the specimens listed here.

One thing seems fairly clear: the Ceylonese and Indian materials of this
species have a different facies from the European *A. vulgaris* and, therefore,
one doubts Trimen's estimation of the plant when he stated it to be "rather
common, but only as an escape from gardens and scarcely to be included in
our flora". On the contrary, there is a distinct possibility that it may be indigenous.

According to Macmillan (Tropical Planting and Gardening ed. 5, 449)
A. roxburghiana Bess. is planted as a "hedge around coolies gardens up
country". This species produces stems 5–7 feet tall and has tripinnatisect
leaves. I have not encountered it, nor seen specimens from Ceylon.

Tribe SENECIONEAE

Herbs or shrubs, sometimes scandent, with alternate leaves. Capitula
heterogamous, radiate or homogamous, discoid. Involucre uniseriate, often
with a calyculus of small bracts at the base. Anther bases sagittate or caudate.
Style branches truncate or penicillate. Receptacle naked. Achenes terete or
angular. Pappus hairs numerous, capillary, sometimes absent from ray
achenes.

KEY TO THE GENERA

1 Capitula eradiate, discoid or disciform
  2 Female flowers present, filiform. Pappus bright pink.................**49. Erechtites**
  2 Female flowers absent
    3 Woody shrubs or vines
      4 Glabrous, somewhat fleshy, shrubs................................**54. Notonia**
      4 Araneose-tomentose climbers.....................................**53. Senecio**
    3 Herbaceous plants
      5 Involucre with several smaller bracts at the base. Foliage not glaucous

49. ERECHTITES

Raf., Fl. Ludovic. 65. 1817. Type species: *E. prealta* Raf.

Annual herbs with erect, foliate stems, generally branched above. Leaves alternate, lyrately divided or subentire. Capitula usually numerous in terminal or axillary corymbose panicles, heterogamous, disciform. Involucre urceolate-campanulate, 1-seriate with a few outer calyculate bracts. Marginal flowers female, numerous, filiform, 4–5 lobed at the apex. Disc flowers hermaphrodite, narrowly infundibuliform, 5-lobed at the apex. Anther bases obtuse, apices with short linear appendages. Style branches elongate with short appendages of fused papillose hairs. Receptacle flat, naked. Achenes subcylindric, 10-ribbed. Pappus hairs numerosu, capillaceous, ± as long as flowers and exceeding involucre.

Erechtites valerianifolia (Wolf) DC., Prod. 6. 294. 1838; Alston in Trimen, Handb. Fl. Ceylon. 6: 170. 1931 et Kandy Fl. 52. 1938; Belcher, Ann. Mo. Bot. Gard. 43: 25. 1956; Backer & Bakh. f., Fl. Java 2: 424. 1965.

Senecio valerianifolia Wolf, Ind. Sem. Hort. Berol. 1825, teste Reichenb., Ic. Bot. Exot. 59, t. 85. 1827. Neotype: "Senecio valerianifolius ex h. Raffeliano, 1825" (W, Reichenbach Coll.).

Stems 0.5–1.5 (–2) m tall, ± glabrous. Lower leaves petiolate, ovate-lanceolate, 10–12 cm long (including petiole 4–5 cm long), 4–5 cm broad, usually irregularly incised-dentate; middle and upper leaves pinnatisect, up to 18 cm long (including petioles up to 7 cm long), segments 7–13, oblong-lanceolate, 1.5–3.5 cm long, 0.5–1 cm broad, acuminate at the apex, margins sharply serrate, terminal segments larger, up to 5 cm long, 2.5 cm broad. Involucre 3–5 mm broad, phyllaries 12–14, linear, 8–9 mm long, 0.5–1 mm broad, glabrous, margins connivent, scarious; calyculate bracts 2–4 mm long. Flowers reddish or mauve; female flower corollas 7–8.5 mm long, lobes 5, linear acute, 0.5 mm long, 0.2 mm broad, thickened; hermaphrodite flower corollas 8–9 mm long, lobes 0.5 mm long, 0.3 mm broad, thickened. Achenes 3–3.5 mm long, brown, finely and sparsely puberulous. Pappus hairs white at base, pink above, 7–8 mm long, deciduous.

Chromosome number. $n = c$. 20 (Powell & King, Sida 3 (5) 319–320. 1969).

D i s t r. Native to Central and South America, now adventive in Malaya, Australia, Polynesia, China, Japan.

Ecol. Roadsides and cultivated ground, not common. Flowering December–June.

Specimens Examined. KANDY DISTRICT: Peradeniya, 14 Dec. 1914, *Petch s.n.* (PDA), ibid., Jan. and May 1915, *s. coll.* (*Petch?*) *s.n.* (PDA, K); Pupuressa, *Simpson 8222* (BM). RATNAPURA DISTRICT: Delgoda, 24 Mar. 1919, *F. Lewis & J.M. Silva s.n.* (PDA).

Notes. According to Belcher (l.c.) this species has become "an aggressive weed" in some countries into which it has been introduced. In Ceylon, however, it does not appear to have become very widespread or troublesome.

50. GYNURA

Cass., Dict. Sci. Nat. 34: 391. 1825. Type species: *Gynura auriculata* Cass.

Decumbent or erect perennial herbs. Stem angular, striate, foliate at least at the base. Leaves alternate, entire, serrate or lyrate-pinnatisect. Capitula medium-sized, borne in corymbs on the upper ± leafless subscapiform parts of the stems, homogamous, discoid. Involucre 1-seriate, cylindrical, with a ring of shorter outer calyculate bracts; phyllaries coherent into a tube, somewhat fleshy with membranous margins. Corollas tubular at the base, widening rather abruptly into the narrowly campanulate 5-lobed limb. Anthers acute at the apex, ± bluntly sagittate at the base. Style branches filiform, tapering gradually into the longer penicillate appendages. Receptacle slightly convex, naked, alveolate. Achenes narrowly fusiform, somewhat compressed, 10-ribbed. Pappus capillary, copious, white, separately caducous.

KEY TO THE SPECIES

1 Leaves undivided, margins undulate-dentate, auricles small, oblanceolate, entire......
....**3. G. hispida**
1 Leaves, at least the lower ones, pinnately divided, auricles larger, rounded and coarsely toothed
  2 Involucre 0.8–1 cm long, pubescent, 4–5 mm shorter than the flowers..**2. G. zeylanica**
  2 Involucre 1.2–1.7 cm long, subglabrous, ± as long as flowers......**1. G. lycopersicifolia**

1. Gynura lycopersicifolia DC., Prod. 6: 300. 1837.

Stems sometimes rather fleshy, angular, often purplish, 0.3–2 m tall, glabrous or coarsely villous. Leaves lyrate-pinnatisect, 10–20 cm long with two rounded, dentate auricles at the base; lateral segments 1–3 pairs (or sometimes 0 and often with minor intermediate lobes), elliptic, 1–4 cm long, 0.4–2 cm broad, irregularly and coarsely dentate; terminal segments of lower leaves ovate, 2–10 cm long, 1–8 cm broad, of upper leaves elliptic-lanceolate, coarsely lobed or dentate, pubescent or ± harshly brownish hispid on both surfaces. Capitula 10–20 in loose terminal corymbs. Involucres campanulate, 5–8 mm when fresh, c. 1.75 cm broad when pressed; phyllaries c. 12, 10–14 mm long, 1.5–2.5 mm broad, ± glabrous. Flowers orange, 10–14 mm long, ± as long as the phyllaries. Achenes brown, 4.5 mm long, sparsely pubescent between the ribs. Pappus white, 10–13 mm long.

KEY TO THE SUBSPECIES

1 Leaves softly pubescent. Peduncles bearing several bracts at base of capitulum. Involucres 1.2–1.3 cm long; phyllaries 1.5–2 mm broad, 3 ribbed. Corollas 10–11 mm long. .
. . . . **1. subsp. lycopersicifolia**
1 Leaves ± hispid. Peduncles with regularly spaced bracts along their length. Involucres 1.5–1.7 cm long; phyllaries 1.5–2.5 mm broad, 4–5 ribbed. Corollas 13–14 mm long. . .
. . . . **2. subsp. taprobanensis**

1. subsp. lycopersicifolia. Type: ad Courtallum et in montibus Dindigul, 2000 ft, *Wight 2/17* (G).

Di s t r. S. India.

Ec o l. Flowering February.

Specimens Examined. ANURADHAPURA DISTRICT: Wilpattu National Park, Manikapola Uttua, *Cooray 70020246R* (PDA).

2. subsp. taprobanensis. Grierson in Ceylon J. Sci., Biol. Sci. 11: 20. 1974.

Gynura lycopersicifolia DC., Thw., Enum. Pl. Zeyl. 166. 1860; Hook. f., Fl. Br. Ind. 3: 334. 1881; Trimen, Handb. Fl. Ceylon 3: 43. 1895; Alston in id. 6: 170. 1931; Bond, Wild Fls. Ceylon Hills 110, t. 56. 1953, quoad pl. zeyl. Type: *Thwaites C.P. 420* (holo PDA, Syn. K, BM).

Di s t r. Also in S. India.

Ec o l. At margins of forests in moist places generally above 5000 ft, common. Flowering throughout the year.

Ve r n. Hulanthala, Wal Tampala (Simpson) (S); Pangi pillu, Singula tunda, Mookuthi, Thandu cheddi pattu-nal (T).

Specimens Examined. WITHOUT PRECISE LOCALITY: *C.P. 420* annotated "Dimbula and Nuwara Eliya, *Gardner*; Palagalla, Oct. 1853" and "Kurunegala, *Gardner*" (PDA), annotated "Dimbula, Mar. 1846" (K), unannotated (BM). NUWARA ELIYA DISTRICT: Hakgala, c. 5800 ft, May 1890, *Trimen s.n.* (PDA); Jungle above Hakgala, 22 Feb. 1906, *Willis s.n.* (PDA); ibid., *Alston 628* (PDA, K); Between Horton Plains and Ohiya, c. 6000 ft, *Grierson 1108* (E, US, PDA, BR, CANB). KANDY DISTRICT: Hantane, 3000 ft, *Gardner 424* (K, BM); Rangala, *Alston 497* (PDA); Slopes of Adam's Peak, c. 4500 ft, *Grierson 1046* (E, US, PDA, BR, CANB); near Madugoda on Urugala road, *Simpson 8787* (BM); Laksapana, *Simpson 8995* (BM). MATALE DISTRICT: Dambulla Hill, *Alston 600* (K), *Simpson 9778*

(BM); Elkaduwa, *Simpson 8965* (BM). RATNAPURA DISTRICT: Maha-walatenne, *Amaratunga 460* (PDA). KEGALLE DISTRICT: Atagalla, *Amaratunga 679* (PDA). KURUNEGALA DISTRICT: Giriulla, *Amaratunga 1043* (PDA). WITHOUT LOCALITY: *s. coll. C.P. 1750* (K), *C.P. 2826* (BM); *Walker 1448* (E, K); 11 Feb. 1819, *Moon 139* (BM); 27 Feb. 1819, *Moon 306* (BM).

2. Gynura zeylanica Trimen, Handb. Fl. Ceylon 3: 44. 1895 and Atlas, Pl. 58; Alston in id. 6: 170. 1931. Type: *Thwaites C.P. 3539* (PDA).

Gynura nepalensis auct. non DC.: Thw., Enum. Pl. Zeyl. 166. 1860.

Stems up to 60 cm long, angular, leafy, sparsely to densely pubescent. Leaves oblanceolate, simple or lyrate-pinnatisect, 7–12 cm long, with 1–3 pairs of lateral segments 7–12 cm long, 2–5 cm broad, acute at the apex, attenuate at the base, with rounded, coarsely toothed auricles; lateral segments oblong or oblanceolate, 1–3 cm long, 5–15 mm broad, terminal segments elliptic, 5–10 cm long, 3–6 cm broad, with coarsely and unevenly toothed margins, densely and softly whitish pilose on both surfaces. Capitula 5–15 in terminal corymbs. Involucres campanulate, c. 7 mm diam. when fresh, 1.5 cm broad when pressed, sparsely pubescent, phyllaries lanceolate, purple at tips, 8–10 mm long, 1.5–2.5 mm broad. Flowers yellow, corollas 9–10 mm long, exserted 4–5 mm above the involucre. Achenes brown, 4 mm long, sparsely puberulous between the ribs. Pappus c. 8 mm long, deciduous.

D i s t r. Endemic.

E c o l. Rock crevices and between stones of walls, 3000–4000 ft, local and quite rare. Flowering January–May.

S p e c i m e n s E x a m i n e d. NUWARA ELIYA DISTRICT: Galagama, *s. coll. C.P. 3539* (PDA); Upper Hiralouvah Estate near Belihul Oya, 4000 ft, *Grierson 1152* (E, US, PDA, BR, CANB). BADULLA DISTRICT: Badulla Road, Feb. 1886, *Trimen s.n.* (PDA); between Passara and Lunugala, Jan. 1888, *Trimen s.n.* (PDA); Bandarawela, *Simpson 8658* (BM).

N o t e s. The leaves of the specimens from Badulla District are pinnatisect with 2–3 pairs of lateral leaflets and Trimen's illustration was taken from such a plant; the specimens from around Nuwara Eliya have simple leaves or bear only one pair of segments at the base.

3. Gynura hispida Thw., Enum. Pl. Zeyl. 166. 1860; C.B. Clarke, Comp. Ind. 172. 1876; Trimen, Handb. Fl. Ceylon 3: 45. 1895; Alston in id. 6: 170. 1931; Bond, Wild Fls. Ceylon Hills 112, t. 57. 1953. Type: *Thwaites C.P. 3507.*

Gynura pseudo-china var. *hispida* (Thw.) Hook. f., Fl. Br. Ind. 3: 335. 1881.

Stems 75–100 cm tall, unbranched except at the inflorescence, fleshy, purplish, sparsely or densely villous, hirsute at the base, ± leafless above. Leaves oblanceolate, crowded into the lower region of the stem (up to about 20 cm from the root), 5–10 × 1.5–3 cm, acute at the apex, attenuate, subpetiolate at the base, margin distantly and shallowly dentate, densely hispid on both surfaces; auricles oblanceolate 6–7 mm long, 1–2 mm broad, acute, entire. Capitula 1–7 on terminal branches, ± corymbose. Involucre glabrous or pubescent, urceolate, 1–1.3 cm diam. when fresh, 1.75 cm broad when pressed; phyllaries 8–10 mm long, 2–2.5 mm broad, lanceolate, with purplish tips, margins thinner, almost membranous, with a few shorter calyculate bracts at the base. Flowers orange-yellow, corollas 8–10 mm long, exserted and 4–5 mm longer than the involucre. Achenes linear-oblong, 3–4 mm long, glabrous or puberulent between the ribs. Pappus 8–9.5 mm long, deciduous.

Distr. Endemic.

Ecol. In moist rocky crevices above 6000 ft, rare. Flowering March–May.

Specimens Examined. NUWARA ELIYA DISTRICT: Horton Plains, May 1856, *s. coll. C.P. 3507* (PDA), unannotated, 7000 ft, (K, BM); Nuwara Eliya, *Champion 3* (K). Hakgala, in 1886, *W. Nock s.n.* (PDA); Same locality, 6200 ft, 9 Mar. 1969, *Grierson 1079* (E, US, PDA, BR, CANB).

G. pseudo-china DC. is cultivated as a pot plant in Ceylon and throughout Tropical Asia. Its leaves are almost radical and the short flower scapes 15–30 cm tall are leafless except at the base. The tuberous roots are used as a cooling medicine and in the treatment of leprosy. The Sinhalese vernacular names Ala-beth, Cheena-ala and Mul-beth have been recorded for this species. The taller *G. bicolor* DC. from the Moluccas is also cultivated in Ceylon. Its large ovate leaves, which are borne on the stems, are remarkable for their purple pubescence.

51. CRASSOCEPHALUM

Moench, Meth. 516. 1794. Type species: *C. rubens* (Juss. ex Jacq.) S. Moore (syn. *C. cernum* (L.f.) Moench).

Annual herbs with erect, branching, foliate stems. Leaves alternate, simple or lyrate pinnatifid. Capitula in loose leafy terminal racemes, homogamous, discoid. Involucre with a calyculus of smaller free bracts at the base, uniseriate, phyllaries connivent. Flowers numerous, corollas tubular, narrowly infundibuliform, 5-lobed. Anthers lanceolate at the apex, minutely sagittate at the base. Style branches filiform with long subulate appendages of fused papillose hairs and usually with a distinct whorl of longer hairs at the junction between the stigmatic part of the branch and the appendage. Receptacle convex, naked, shallowly alveolate. Achenes cylindrical, weakly 8–10 ribbed. Pappus fine, capillaceous, brittle, longer than the flowers at maturity.

Crassocephalum crepidioides (Benth.) S. Moore, J. Bot. 50: 211. 1912; Belcher, Kew Bull. 462. 1955.

Gynura crepidioides Benth. in Hook., Niger Fl. 438. 1849; Alston in Trimen, Handb. Fl. Ceylon. 6: 171. 1931, et Kandy Fl. 53, fig. 382. 1938. Type: Sierra Leone, *G. Don* (BM).

Stems usually simple or branched above, 30–50 cm tall, but sometimes as much as 1.5 m, ± densely brown puberulous, especially when young. Leaves elliptic-oblanceolate, 5–18 × 1–6 cm, gradually attenuate at the base into a petiole up to 3 cm long, or lyrately lobed with 1–2 pairs of oblong acute lateral segments, up to 4 cm long, 1 cm broad, apex acute or shortly acuminate, margins coarsely and irregularly dentate, teeth indurated, puberulous on both surfaces, more densely so beneath. Capitula up to 10 in pedunculate racemes, pendulous at first in the bud, later becoming ± erect. Involucre cylindrical or urceolate, c. 5 mm diam. when fresh, 0.75 cm when pressed and broadening to 1 cm diam. at base; phyllaries linear-lanceolate, 0.8–1 cm long, puberulous, calyculate bracts pale green with purplish tips c. 5 mm long. Flowers brickred or dark orange, 0.8–1 cm long. Achenes oblong, 2 mm long, dark brown, sparsely white puberulous on the ribs. Pappus white, up to 12 mm long.

Chromosome number. n = 20 (Belcher l.c.); n = c. 20 (Turner & Lewis J.S. African Bot. 31: 216. 1965).

D i s t r. Native of Trop. Africa, now a weed throughout palaeotropical regions.

E c o l. Widespread weed of cultivated land. Flowering October–August and probably throughout the year.

V e r n. Keera thandu pillu or Tanduk-kiriap-pillu (T).

S p e c i m e n s E x a m i n e d. KANDY DISTRICT: Royal Botanic Gardens, Peradeniya, *Alston s.n.* (PDA), *Alston 580* (PDA, K), *Alston 1735* (PDA, K), Rangala, 29 Aug. 1926, *Alston 497* (K); Knuckles, 14 June 1926, *J.M. Silva s.n.* (PDA); Above Teldeniya, c. 1700 ft, *Grierson 1011* (US, PDA, E, BR, CANB); Galaha, *Simpson 8221* (BM); Peradeniya University Botany Garden, 507 m, *Comanor 337* (E, US, PDA). MATALE DISTRICT: Hunugala near Elkaduwa, 15 Nov. 1926, *Silva s.n.* (PDA); Elkaduwa, *Simpson 8966* (BM); Adam's Peak Sanctuary, Bogawantalawa-Boralanda Road, 1400 m, *Comanor 1464* (E, PDA, US). NUWARA ELIYA DISTRICT: Horton Plains, 7000 ft, Grierson 1096 (US). TRINCOMALEE DISTRICT: Kantalai Tank, 55 m, *Comanor 749* (E, US, PDA). WITHOUT LOCALITY: *Walker 1708* (E), *s.n.* (K).

N o t e. See also van Steenis, Notes on Introduction of *Crassocephalum crepidioides* in Indo-Australia, J. Indian Bot. Soc. 46 (4): 463–469. 1967.

52. EMILIA

Cass., Bull. Soc. Philom. 68. 1817. Type Species: *E. sonchifolia* (L.) DC. (Based on treatment by F.R. Fosberg, Ceylon J. Sci., Biol. Sci. 10: 61–69. 1972).

Weak to robust annual to perennial herbs, rarely slightly suffrutescent at base, herbage usually somewhat glaucous; leaves alternate varying greatly from basal to upper cauline, frequently clasping at base; inflorescence 1-few headed, usually loosely and corymbosely branched or subumbelloid; capitula homogamous, discoid, involucre of few (usually 8–10) linear-oblong phyllaries in one series, coherent but tending to pull apart on drying and with age, edges imbricate; receptacle convex, naked, gently rugose; flowers 10 to 100 or more, corolla very slender, with a firm, cup-shaped, somewhat dilated base, upper portion gradually expanding upward, lobes 5, triangular to oblong-lanceolate, spreading; stamens 5, filaments very slender except the top 0.3–1.0 mm which is firm and cylindric; style-branches exserted, slightly recurved; achenes prismatic, truncate distally, with 5 angles, these with open to almost closed grooves with minute puberulence in them, sometimes with intermediate ribs, outer achenes fertile, inner sterile; pappus abundant, capillary, minutely scabridulous, caducous.

The genus *Emilia*, though small, is intrinsically difficult, taxonomically. The species, though distinct in appearance when living, seem to lose some of their distinguishing features when dried. Some species are so weak and delicate, deficient in supporting tissue in the stems that, though firm and turgid when living, they wilt and collapse on being uprooted, often before they are pressed, making tangled nondescript specimens.

The native range of the genus is Africa south of the Sahara, the moister parts of Asia south of the Himalaya, South China eastward to Japan and the Philippines; one species extends into the Pacific Islands. In Ceylon there are a number of species, one or more of them occurring in most habitats. They have been treated differently by Trimen, Garabedian and Alston. Alston paid considerable attention to the genus, but because he accepted Garabedian's interpretation of *E. javanica* (in Kew Bull. 1924: 144), his conclusions were in some respects less than satisfactory. Garabedian's rather ill-defined concepts of *E. sonchifolia* and *E. scabra* further contribute to confusion in the classification of the Ceylon species of the genus. Alston admitted 4 species for Ceylon and, hesitantly, a fifth, *E. prenanthoidea* DC.

KEY TO THE SPECIES

1 Plants with a firm, usually upright stem; heads almost as broad as high
  2 Cauline leaves oblong with dentate margins and a conspicuously expanded terminal segment, lower part well over 1 cm wide................**1a. E. zeylanica** var. **walkeri**

2 Cauline leaves narrower, linear or narrowly oblong to oblanceolate, firm, margins subentire, terminal segment narrowly triangular to ovate, lower part less than 1 cm wide
....1b. E. zeylanica var. zeylanica
1 Weak low plants with subscapose sparingly branched inflorescences of few cylindric
heads; involucres clearly narrower than height of heads
3 Fleshy glaucous plants, much branched when well developed, forming dense mat-like
clumps from a heavy cord-like root-crown; leaves, except uppermost, petiolate, sub-
lobate, broader than long, uppermost (except inflorescence bracts) cuneate at base;
flowers exserted, 1–2 mm..6. E. baldwinii
3 Not fleshy, sparsely branched, uppermost leaves not cuneate
4 Well developed lower leaves deeply and irregularly pinnately lobed, when poorly
developed reduced to a strap-shaped petiole with a triangular ovate blade
5 Flowers scarcely exserted from involucre......................2. E. sonchifolia
5 Flowers strongly exserted, 5–6 mm................................3. E. exserta
4 Leaves not usually deeply lobed, terminal segment ovate to reniform, not notably
triangular; flowers exserted 3 mm or less
6 Terminal segment of leaves orbicular to reniform, uppermost leaves more or less
oblong or somewhat enlarged distally; flowers exserted 2–3 mm from the 6 mm
long involucre...4. E. alstonii
6 Terminal segment ovate to orbicular, uppermost leaves sagittate-cordate; flowers
scarcely exserted from the 8–9 mm long involucre.................5. E. speeseae

1. **Emilia zeylanica** C.B. Clarke, Comp. Ind. 175. 1876; Trimen, Handb. fl.
Ceylon 3: 46. 1895; Garabedian, Kew Bull. 144. 1924; Alston in Trimen,
Handb. fl. Ceylon 6: 171. 1931; Fosberg in Ceylon J. Sci., Biol. Sci. 10: 63.
1972. Type: In Zeylania, *T. Anderson* (not seen).

Erect firm herbs; stems leafy, simple or sparsely branched at or near base;
leaves sessile, bases auriculate to sagittate, clasping, blades becoming smaller
upward; inflorescence exserted 1–2 cm, irregularly branched, of few heads;
involucres cylindric, as broad or almost as broad as high, bracts loosely coherent, edges imbricate longitudinally, tending to separate when drying;
flowers strongly exserted from involucre, corolla lobes 2–2.3 mm long, minutely papillate-puberulent at tips, pale purple; achenes prismatic, heavily
5-ribbed, a very narrow groove on summit of each rib, minutely hispidulous
in a fine line in each groove, truncate at summit; pappus caducous.

The two varieties, maintained as species by Garabedian, intergrade in a
confusing manner, but since the extremes are conspicuously different, are here
given varietal rank, following, in part, Trimen.

1. var. zeylanica

Cauline leaves narrowly oblong-lanceolate or even linear, entire or subentire, 1 cm or less wide, apical portion usually not conspicuously wider than
middle to basal part, or somewhat but not abruptly dilated, blades firm.

Distr. Found in patanas, 2000–2300 m.
Specimens Examined. WITHOUT PRECISE LOCALITY: "A

(dams) Peak & N (uwara) Elia, *Gardner"* C.P. *430* (PDA, BM). KANDY DISTRICT: Ascent to Adam's Peak, 4500 ft, *Grierson 1045* (US, E); Laxapana, Maskeliya, *Simpson 8986* (BM); "Kandy", *Moon* in 1819 (BM); near Gartmore Estate, Maskeliya, in 1926, *Silva s.n.* (PDA). RATNAPURA DISTRICT: Kunadiyaparawita, in 1917, *Lewis s.n.* (PDA). BADULLA DISTRICT: Thotulagalla Ridge, Haputale, *Fosberg 51835* (US, PDA, FO). NUWARA ELIYA DISTRICT: Horton Plains, about 1½ miles from Farr's Inn at Ohiya Road, *Mueller-Dombois & Cooray 68011310* (PDA, US); north edge of Horton Plains, 2200 m, *Gould 13564* (US, TAES); Pedrotalagalla, 7000 ft, *s. coll. s.n.* in 1881 (PDA); 7500 ft, *Grierson 1066* (US, E); Nuwara Eliya, in 1880, *s. coll. s.n.* (PDA); Moon Plains, *Alston 624* (PDA); Nuwara Eliya 6000 ft, *Gardner 422* (BM).

2. var. **walkeri** (Hook. f.) Trimen, Handb. Fl. Ceylon 3: 46. 1895.

Emilia walkeri Hook. f., Fl. Br. Ind. 3: 33. 1882; Garabedian, Kew Bull. 142. 1924. Type: *Thwaites C.P. 430* (BM).

Cauline leaves with apical half expanded, ovate or triangular, basal part 1.5 or more cm wide, usually somewhat toothed, membranous.

On peaks, ridges, patanas and in edges of forest, at high elevations.

Specimens Examined. WITHOUT PRECISE LOCALITY: "A (dams) Peak & N (uwara) Eliya", *s. coll.* C.P. *430* (PDA, 3 sheets); "media provincia ins: 6000-8000 ped." *s. coll. 430* (BM). NUWARA ELIYA DISTRICT: Pedrotalagalla, 7500 ft, *s. coll. s.n.* (PDA); 6700 ft, *Grierson 1075* (US, E); Horton Plains, at "World's End", 2130 m, *Mueller-Dombois & Comanor 67070853* (PDA, US); Horton Plains-Pattipola Road, 6500 ft, *Grierson 1091* (US, E); Ambawela-Pattipola road, 1860 m, *Comanor 937* (US, FO, E, BM, NY, POM); Ambawela, *Alston 1021* (PDA); N. edge of Horton Plains, 2200 m, *Gould 13564* (EE, US, PDA). KANDY DISTRICT: near Gartmore Estate, Maskeliya, *Silva* in 1926 (PDA); Adam's Peak Waterfall, 7 mi. S.W. Maskeliya, 4000 ft, *Grierson 1054* (US, E); Adam's Peak Sanctuary, Bogawantalawa-Boralanda Road, 1400 m, *Comanor 1088* (US, FO, E, BM, TI, NY); Adam's Peak, at base of cone, *Alston 959* (PDA). BADULLA DISTRICT: Top of Naminakuli, in 1907, *Silva s.n.* (PDA, 2 sheets); Haputale near Adishan Monastery, *Mueller-Dombois 68051902* (PDA, US).

Some sheets, e.g. *Mueller-Dombois 68051902, Gould 13564* and *Grierson 1091*, are so intermediate as to be very difficult to assign to a variety. Actually, there are no satisfactory lines between these two varieties, and if the extremes were not so conspicuously distinct it would be easy to regard them as one variable variety.

2. Emilia sonchifolia (L.) DC., in Wight, Contrib. 24. 1834; Prod. 6: 302. 1837; Trimen, Handb. Fl. Ceylon 3: 45. 1895 p.p.; Garabedian, Kew Bull.

141. 1924; Alston, in Trimen, Handb. Fl. Ceylon 6: 171. 1931 (but see *E. baldwinii* below); Fosberg in Ceylon J. Sci., Biol. Sci. 10: 65. 1972.

Cacalia sonchifolia L., Sp. Pl. 835. 1753. Type: Habitat in Zeylona, *Herb. Hermann* (BM).

Weak, subglabrous to sparsely unevenly pilose, rather glaucous herbs; leaves deeply and irregularly pinnately lobed, terminal segments triangular, rarely broadly cordate in shaded plants, and shallowly and bluntly dentate, petioles of lower leaves narrowly winged, those of cauline broad, auriculate-clasping; inflorescence subscapose, about twice length of leaves, or longer, with 1–2 ovate-lanceolate bracts, cordate-clasping at base, sparsely corymbosely branched near top, with 3–6 heads; involucres narrowly cylindric, 7–9 × 2.5–3 mm; flowers 30–60, exserted no more than about 1–1.5 mm or scarcely at all, "pale mauve", corolla lobes scarcely 1 mm long; achenes prismatic, about 2.5 mm long, 5-ribbed, the ribs grooved, the grooves puberulent.

D i s t r. Most tropical countries.
E c o l. On open grassy or weedy places from sea level to 500 m.
S p e c i m e n s E x a m i n e d. KANDY DISTRICT: Peradeniya, 3/4 mile upslope from University Circuit Bungalow, 1000 m, *Mueller-Dombois & Cooray 67103113* (US); Kandy in 1819, *Moon s.n.* (BM), *Fosberg 50669* (US, PDA); Peradeniya, *Alston 1407* (PDA), *Fosberg 50658* (US, PDA); Hindagalla, 1900 ft, *de Silva 10* (US). HAMBANTOTA DISTRICT: Ruhuna National Park, Patanagalla 2–3 m, *Fosberg 50366* (US), *51161* (US, PDA), *51165* (US), *50366* (US, PDA, FO, NY, BM, TI, POM, UC, AAH); Ruhuna National Park, Block 1, Rakina Wewa, near Gonalabbe Lewaya, 2 m, *Fosberg 50263* (US); Main Yala Road, Mile marker 7, 6–10 m, *Comanor 826* (US, FO, E, BM). COLOMBO DISTRICT: Mt. Lavinia, Colombo, 1 m, *Fosberg & Read 51796* (US, PDA, FO). PUTTALAM DISTRICT: Wilpattu National Park, Marai Villu, *Fosberg et al. 5087* (US, PDA). MANNAR DISTRICT: Velankulam, *Fosberg & Balakrishnan 53587* (US, E, PDA). MATALE DISTRICT: Apuwatta, 2 miles S of Dambulla, *Fosberg & Balakrishnan 53379* (US, E, PDA). BATTICALOA DISTRICT: Kalmune Road, 4 miles S of Batticaloa, *Townsend 73/264* (US, K, E, PDA).

N o t e s. This is the most widespread species of *Emilia*, found in most tropical countries, and has been variously interpreted, in Ceylon as well as elsewhere. Whether it is really as variable as commonly supposed is doubtful. In Ceylon a critical examination shows that at least 5 reasonably well-marked species have been included in *E. sonchifolia*. In Hawaii even *E. javanica* has been lumped with it. Here it is restricted to the very delicate form shown by Baldwin (Bull. Torrey Bot. Club 73: 18–23. 1946) to be a diploid. Baldwin's fig. 1 is an excellent illustration of *E. sonchifolia* as described here.

3. Emilia exserta Fosberg in Ceylon J. Sci., Biol. Sci. 10: 65. 1972.

Emilia sonchifolia auct. non (L.) DC.: Trimen, Handb. Fl. Ceylon 3: 45. 1895.
Emilia javanica sensu Alston, in Trimen, Handb. Fl. Ceylon 6: 171. 1931, non
(Burm. f.) Rob. Type: Peradeniya, *Fosberg 50659* (US).

Weak herb, stem creeping with erect branches, these leafy in lower parts, leaves variable, lower ones tending to be pinnately lobed with large triangular or ovate terminal segments, more usually the lobes suppressed and petiole winged or scarcely so, somewhat clasping, upper cauline leaves oblong to lanceolate or strap-shaped, entire to very shallowly and remotely dentate, strongly clasping, leaves tending to be pilose, hairs on wilting tending to crumple and become woolly; inflorescence 1–3 cm long, very loosely several times branched, with reduced leaves or bracts becoming smaller upward, each branch ending in 1–3 pedunculate heads; involucre short cylindric, about 6 × 3 mm; flowers 26–54, exserted about 5–6 mm, pinkish lavender, spreading to about 13 mm, corolla lobes 1.5–2 mm long; anther tube about 1.5 mm long, appendages 0.3 mm long, thickened parts of filaments 0.4 mm long; achenes prismatic, minutely setulose or scabridulous on the 5 angles, pubescence originating in a narrow groove, this more evident in sterile than fertile achenes.

D i s t r. Endemic low to middle elevations.

E c o l. On disturbed places, patanas, road embankments, on western lower slopes of the mountains, 50–600 m elevation, tending to be weedy.

V e r n. "Hulantala" and "Kadupara" (S) and "Musalkal-pillu", "Mammoty-pullu", "Elunthani", "Ilaip-patti", and "Inumpatti-pillu" (T), according to Haigh et al., Manual of the Weeds of the Major Crops of Ceylon (Colombo, 1951) as *E. iavanica*.

S p e c i m e n s E x a m i n e d. WITHOUT LOCALITY: *C.P. 3343* (PDA, 2 sheets); no data (PDA). KANDY DISTRICT: Watawalla, *Burtt & Townsend 61* (US, E, K, PDA); Gammaduwa, *Alston 663, 664* (PDA); Peradeniya, *Mueller-Dombois & Cooray 67103113* (PDA), *Alston 2041* (PDA), *Fosberg 50651* (US, PDA, FO, E, BM, TI, NY), *50659* (US, type, PDA, FO, E, BM), *51805* (US, PDA, FO, E), *51858* (US, PDA); Lower Hantane, Peradeniya, *Fosberg 51862* (US, PDA, FO, E, BM, TI, NY, POM); Madugoda, 535 m, *Comanor 689* (US, FO, E, BM, TI, NY, POM); *Simpson 8791* (BM); Kandy, Anniwatte, 500 m, *Comanor 345* (US, FO); Parragalla, bet. Gampola and Dolosbage, 3000 ft, *Grierson 1006* (US, E). COLOMBO DISTRICT: 3 mi. E of Ingiriya on Panadura-Ratnapura Road, *Fosberg & Read 51801* (US, PDA, FO, E, BM, TI, NY, POM, UC). RATNAPURA DISTRICT: Road from Ginigathena to Avissawella, marker 67.7, 500 m, *Comanor 554* (US, FO, E, BM, TI, NY, POM, US); Ratnapura, 130 ft, *Grierson 1022* (US, E). MATARA DISTRICT: Matara, 2 miles N of Kottegoda, *Fosberg & Sachet 52847* (US, E, PDA).

4. Emilia alstonii Fosberg in Ceylon J. Sci., Biol. Sci. 10: 62. 1972.

Emilia scabra auct non DC.: Alston in Trimen, Handb. Fl. Ceylon 6: 172. 1931. Type: Yahalle Badde below Haputale, *Fosberg 51822* (US).

Differs from *E. exserta* in lower leaves with only a slight tendency toward pinnate lobing, but with terminal segment orbicular to reniform with rounded apex, margin of this undulate rather than dentate, petiole scarcely winged to narrowly so, middle leaves with broad wing in lower part, slightly lobed above or not, cordate, clasping at base, terminal segment orbicular to reniform, upper leaves more or less oblong or somewhat enlarged distally, usually notably undulate-dentate or crenate; inflorescence almost bractless, heads slightly wider than in *E. exserta*; florets 56–100 in a head, not so much exserted, about 2–3 mm exceeding involucre, bright to dark purple, corolla lobes about 1.2 mm long.

D i s t r. Endemic.

E c o l. An upland species, known from the eastern and southern parts of the mountain mass, along weedy roads, in eroded patanas, and tea-plantations.

S p e c i m e n s E x a m i n e d. KANDY DISTRICT: Castlereagh Estate, *Alston 1905* (PDA); Hunasiriya Group, Wakeyama, *Alston? s.n.* (PDA). BADULLA DISTRICT: Thotulagalla Ridge, Haputale, *Fosberg 52841* (US, PDA, FO), *51844* (US), *51839* (US), *51829* (US, PDA, FO, E); Yahalle Badde, below Haputale, *Fosberg 51819* (US, PDA), *51820* (US, PDA, FO, E) *51821* (US), *51822* (US, type, PDA, FO, E), *51823* (US, PDA, FO, E), *51824*, (US, PDA, FO), *51817* (US, PDA, FO); Glenanore, below Addisham, Haputale, *Fosberg 51857* (US, PDA, FO), *51852* (US, PDA, FO). RATNAPURA DISTRICT: Brampton Group Estate near Belihul Oya, 4500 ft, *Grierson 1150* (US, E).

One specimen, a single individual, from Thotulagalla Ridge, Haputale, *Fosberg 51836* (US), seems intermediate between this species and *E. zeylanica*, both of which grow nearby.

5. Emilia speeseae Fosberg, in Ceylon J. Sci., Biol. Sci. 10: 67. 1972. Type: Thotulagalla Ridge, Haputale, *Fosberg 51837* (US).

A somewhat robust plant for this group, somewhat pilose, rather leafy in basal half, the middle cauline leaves on well developed plants with terminal segment orbicular to ovate, petiole broadly winged, uppermost leaves sagittate-cordate, all leaves at least obscurely and bluntly dentate; inflorescences with bracts much reduced, linear, peduncles 3–5, 2–12 cm long, irregular and subumbellate in arrangement, each with a single head; involucre cylindric to slightly urceolate, 4–5 × 7–9 mm, flowers about 60, only slightly (1–2 mm) exserted, bright purple or dark mauve, corolla lobes 1.1–1.5 mm long.

D i s t r. Endemic.

E c o l. Found at fairly high elevations in the mountain mass, rather weedy.

S p e c i m e n s   E x a m i n e d. KANDY DISTRICT: Dalhousie Estate, *Alston 969* (PDA); along eastern trail to Adam's Peak, 1900 m, *Gould 13600* (US, E, TAES). BADULLA DISTRICT: Yahalle Badde, below Haputale, *Fosberg 51818* (US); Haputale, *Alston 2469* (PDA), *2470* (PDA); Thotula-galla Ridge, Haputale, *Fosberg 51837* (US, type, PDA). NUWARA ELIYA DISTRICT: Above Ramboda at highway A5 on way to Nuwara Eliya, near mile marker 36, *Mueller-Dombois & Cooray 68051509* (PDA, US); Horton Plains, *Fosberg & Sachet 53349* (US, E, PDA).

N o t e s. This would probably have come within Alston's concept of *E. scabra* though it might run to *E. sonchifolia* in his key. These localities are not cited by him. Although it is doubtless closest to *E. alstonii*, it is more robust with differently shaped leaves and the florets are less exserted.

6. Emilia baldwinii Fosberg, in Ceylon J. Sci., Bot. Sci. 10: 68. 1972.

Emilia sonchifolia auct. non (L.) DC.: Alston in Trimen, Handb. Fl. Ceylon 6: 171. 1931. Type: Patanagala, *Fosberg 50344* (US).

Much branched from a deep strong cord-like root crown, forming a loose mat when well developed (but flowering already when scarcely branched); leaves glaucous, rather fleshy, almost glabrous, petiolate except, uppermost, blades at most 1.5 cm wide, decurrent onto slender petioles 1–2 cm long, uppermost leaves sessile, ovate with cuneate base, very coarsely dentate; in-florescence about 1 cm high, with one oblong reduced bract about half-way up, 1 or 2 heads; involucre cylindric, about 10 mm long, 4 mm wide, bracts 8; flowers 40–50, scarcely exserted, 1.5–2 mm, pale mauve, rarely white, corolla lobes about 1 mm long; achenes to 4 mm long, prismatic, scabrous in 5 grooves situated on angles, 3 ribs between each 2 grooves.

D i s t r. Endemic.

E c o l. A halophyte, found around the south and west coasts, on sand flats and, rarely, on rocks just behind the seashore within the influence of the sea.

S p e c i m e n s   E x a m i n e d. LOCALITY UNKNOWN: *C.P. 3343* (PDA); North *s.n.* (BM). PUTTALAM DISTRICT: Chilaw, *Simpson 8169* (BM). HAMBANTOTA DISTRICT: Kirinda, *Alston 1643* (PDA, BM); Ruhuna National Park, Patanagala, *Mueller-Dombois 67082509* (US, PDA), *Fosberg 50344* (US, type, PDA, FO, E, BM, TI, NY, POM, UC, A), *Comanor 889* (US, FO, E, BM, TI, NY, POM); Buttawa, 10 ft, *Grierson 1143* (US), *Fosberg 51164* (US), *51162* (US, PDA, FO, E); 1 mile west of Hambantota, *Fosberg 51217* (US, PDA, FO). COLOMBO DISTRICT: Mt. Lavinia,

Colombo, *Fosberg & Read 51797* (US, PDA, FO, E). GALLE DISTRICT: Hikaduwa, 11 miles north of Galle, *Fosberg 36768* (US).

N o t e s. At Patanagala plants of this (*Fosberg 51164*) and of *E. sonchifolia* (*Fosberg 51165*) grew within 10–20 cm of each other in the edges of strand forest and maintained their distinctive characters. Hence it does not seem likely that they are ecological forms of one species as earlier supposed.

53. SENECIO

L., Sp. Pl. 866. 1753; Gen. Pl. ed. 5. 373. 1754. Type species: *Senecio vulgaris* L.

Erect or scandent, annual or perennial herbs or shrubs. Leaves alternate, simple, entire or toothed, or pinnately divided. Capitula several or numerous in corymbs or corymbose panicles, sometimes few-flowered, heterogamous, radiate or homogamous, discoid. Involucres cylindrical or campanulate, phyllaries uniseriate, subequal, coherent, usually with a few smaller calyculate bracts at the base. Ray flowers several (or absent), yellow. Disc flowers tubular, limb narrowly campanulate, 5-lobed. Anthers oblong, obtuse at the apex, minutely sagittate or distinctly caudate at the base. Style branches truncate or penicillate. Achenes cylindrical or fusiform, 5–10-ribbed. Pappus hairs white or brownish, ± as long as the disc flowers, persistent or deciduous, ray achenes sometimes epappose.

KEY TO THE SPECIES

1 Erect or decumbent herbs. Stems seldom attaining 1–2 m tall
  2 Leaf margins, except sometimes of the lower leaves, revolute, entire (or nearly so), leaves linear-lanceolate. Achenes of ray flowers pappose (Subgenus Senecio)........ ....**1. S. zeylanicus**
  2 Leaf margins not or only slightly revolute, distinctly toothed or lobed. Achenes of ray flowers epappose (subgenus Madaractis)
    3 Leaves all alike, linear-lanceolate, regularly and distantly dentate, never auriculate at the base...**2. S. gardneri**
    3 Leaf shape variable, lower ones ovate, exauriculate, upper ones lanceolate, pinnately toothed or lobed and lyrate, often auriculate..........................**3. S. ludens**
1 Climbing herbs or shrubs sometimes reaching 3–4 m (Subgenus Synotis)
  4 Herbs with thin stems. Leaves lyrate-pinnatisect, auriculate, terminal segment deltoid. Capitula radiate. Anthers sagittate at the base.....................**4. S. scandens**
  4 Shrubs with stout stems. Leaves ovate-cordate, exauriculate. Capitula discoid. Anthers distinctly caudate at the base..........................**5. S. corymbosus**

1. **Senecio zeylanicus** DC., Prod. 6: 365. 1837; Thw., Enum. Pl. Zeyl. 167. 1860; Hook. f., Fl. Br. Ind. 3: 340. 1881; Bond, Wild Fls. Ceylon Hills 114, t. 58. 1953. Neotype: Ceylon, *Wight 541* (E, K).

Senecio gracilis Arn., Nova Acta Phys. Med. Acad. Caes. Leop. Carol. Nat.

Cur. 18: 249. 1836; Trimen, Handb. Fl. Ceylon 3: 48. 1895, non Pursh. 1814. Type: Ceylon, *Thwaites C.P. 1749* (PDA, BM, K).

Erect or decumbent perennial herbs. Stems 30–70 cm tall, glabrous generally unbranched except in the inflorescence. Leaves linear or narrowly oblanceolate, 2–11 cm long, 1–5 mm broad, acute at the apex, attenuate, subpetiolate at the base, margin entire, revolute; uppermost leaves erect, bract-like; lowest leaves oblanceolate, 1.3 cm, broad, denticulate, margins flat. Capitula several (2–12) in lax corymbs, 5–7 mm broad. Involucres campanulate but becoming urceolate in fruit, 5–7 mm diam. when fresh, c. 1 cm broad when pressed. Phyllaries c. 20, lanceolate, 5–6 mm long, glabrous, purple-tipped. Ray flowers 12–20, yellow, ligules 4–5 mm long, 1.5–2 mm broad. Disc flowers 5–6 mm long, yellow. Achenes oblong, 10-ribbed, glabrous. Pappus white, fragile, readily detached from achene.

D i s t r. Also in S. India.

E c o l. In dry patanas above 6000 ft; common. Flowering throughout the year.

S p e c i m e n s E x a m i n e d. NUWARA ELIYA DISTRICT: Nuwara Eliya, Apr. 1856 (*Gardner*), *C.P. 1749* (PDA, K, BM); Hakgala, 17 Mar. 1906, *Willis s.n.* (PDA); Ambawela, *Alston 1015* (PDA); Horton Plains, 2100–2175 m, *Mueller-Dombois & Comanor 67070922* (US, PDA), *67091319* (US, PDA), *Comanor 433* (E, US, PDA); Pidurutalagala, 7500 ft, *Grierson 1063* (E, US, PDA, BR, CANB). WITHOUT LOCALITY: *Wight 541* (E), *Walker 81* (E-GL, K), *s.n.* (E, K) *Gardner 414* (K).

2. Senecio gardneri (Thw.) C.B. Clarke, Comp. Ind. 202. 1876; Trimen, Handb. Fl. Ceylon 3: 48. 1895.

Doronicum gardneri Thw., Enum. Pl. Zeyl. 167. 1860. Type: "*Thwaites C.P. 435 (459)*" given thus by Thwaites.

Perennial herbs. Stems erect or decumbent, 15–40 cm long, glabrous. Leaves linear-lanceolate, 4–8 cm long, 3–8 mm broad, acute at the apex, gradually attenuate and indistinctly petiolate at the base, margins regularly and distantly serrate, glabrous on both surfaces. Capitula several in loose corymbs. Involucre campanulate, c. 3 mm diam.; phyllaries about 15, glabrous, c. 3.5 mm long, 0.75–1 mm broad. Ray flowers usually 8 per capitulum, c. 6 mm long, 2–2.5 mm broad, deep yellow (according to collector). Disc flowers c. 3 mm long, yellow. Achenes c. 2–2.5 mm long, brown with 5 pale sparsely puberulous ribs. Pappus 3 mm long, dirty white or buff; ray achenes epappose.

D i s t r. Endemic.

E c o l. Apparently very rare. Flowering December–March.

S p e c i m e n s E x a m i n e d. WITHOUT PRECISE LOCALITY: *C.P.*

435 annotated "Adam's Peak, *Gardner*; Ambagamuwa, Mar. 1854 (?)" (PDA) annotated "Adam's Peak, Mar. 1846" (K); unannotated (BM); Adam's Peak Mar. 1846 *s. coll. C.P. 459* (K) KANDY DISTRICT: Upcot, 14 Dec. 1940, Meeriacotta Est., West, *s.n.* (PDA); WITHOUT LOCALITY: *Walker 44* (K); *Mackenzie s.n.* (K).

3. Senecio ludens C.B. Clarke, Comp. Ind. 199. 1876; Hook. f., Fl. Br. Ind. 3: 345. 1881; Trimen, Handb. Fl. Ceylon 3: 49. 1895; Bond, Wild Fls. Ceylon Hills 114, t. 59. 1953. Type: *Thwaites C.P. 151* (PDA, CA?).

Doronicum walkeri Arn., Nova Acta Phys. Med. Acad. Caes. Leop. Carol. Nat. Cur. 18: 349. 1836; Thw., Enum. Pl. Zeyl. 167. 1860. Type: ad alt. 6000 ped., *Walker s.n.* (E-GL) non *S. walkeri* Arn.

Generally perennial herbs but sometimes with apparently annual rootstocks, usually rhizomatous. Stems decumbent or weakly erect, (10–) 15–30 (– 200) cm tall, slender or robust, glabrous or coarsely villous. Lower leaves ovate-subrotund, dentate, petiolate or pinnatisect with 1–3 pairs of lateral segments, upper leaves sessile, oblanceolate, pinnately lobed or toothed, auriculate or exauriculate at the base, subglabrous or villous on both surfaces, sometimes asperate above. Capitula few in lax or dense corymbs. Involucres campanulate, 3 mm diam. when fresh, 4–5 mm broad when pressed. Ray flowers 6–8, ligules yellow, 4–9 mm long, 2.5–3 mm broad. Disc flowers about 40, 3–3.5 mm long, yellow. Achenes fusiform, 5-ribbed, 2 mm long, greyish pubescent. Pappus brownish, c. 2.5 mm long, ray achenes epappose.

D i s t r. Also in southern India.

E c o l. Common in moist situations at roadsides, on patanas and in forest scrub above 4000 ft. Flowering October–April and possibly throughout the year.

N o t e s. Variation in this "most sportive plant", as Hooker termed it, is almost continous and a biosystematic study is probably the only basis upon which to divide it into sensible infraspecific categories. It may, however, prove useful to describe the two extremes of the species and emphasise that numerous specimens intermediate in habit, leaf shape, indumentum etc. occur. The type material that Clarke examined (probably at Calcutta) obviously includes such a range.

1) Patana-roadside form

Stems slender, 15–30 (–50) cm tall, sparsely pubescent, lower leaves broadly ovate, petiolate (petioles 1–2 cm long), the lowermost exauriculate but the medium ones with rounded auricles, laminae 2–4 cm long, 1.5–3 cm broad, margins ± coarsely serrate-dentate, subglabrous or villous, pubescent on both surfaces; upper leaves lanceolate, up to 3.5 cm long, 1 cm broad, sessile and auriculate at the base. Capitula few (3–7 or sometimes 12) in lax corymbs. Ligules 5–9 mm long.

Occurring more particularly at lower elevations in roadside drainage ditches and in grassy situations.

S p e c i m e n s   E x a m i n e d. KANDY DISTRICT: Rangala (Dec. 1854) *s. coll. C.P. 151* p.p. (PDA); Hantane, 27 Jan. 1957, *Appuhamy s.n.* (PDA); 3.5 miles E of Rangala, c. 4000 ft, *Grierson 1018* (E, US, PDA, BR, CANB). NUWARA ELIYA DISTRICT: Between Elk Plains and Horton Plains, 20 Feb. 1882, *Trimen s.n.* (PDA); Nuwara Eliya, *Macrae 395* (K); Pattipola, 2 May 1906, *Willis s.n.* (PDA); Bogawantalawa—Horton Plains road, 26 Jan. 1906, *Willis s.n.* (PDA); Nuwara Eliya Lake, 9 Apr. 1906, *Silva s.n.* (PDA); Moon Plains near Nuwara Eliya Government Farm, *Mueller-Dombois & Cooray 68011401* (US, PDA), *68011403* (US, PDA); between Nuwara Eliya and Kande Ela reservoir, *Mueller-Dombois 68051801* (US, PDA); Horton Plains on Ohiya road, *Simpson 9551* (BM). WITHOUT LOCALITY: *Gardner 415* p.p. (BM); *Gardner s.n.* (K—the possibly aquatic form mentioned by Hooker with stems bearing numerous roots).

There is an unpublished coloured plate (No. 27) of this form painted by a native artist among Moon's "Drawings and Descriptions of 37 Ceylon plants" (1823) at BM.

2) Forest-scrub form

Stems robust, generally 1–2 m tall, sometimes as little as 30 cm, densely villous especially near the base. Lower leaves broadly ovate or subrotund, petiolate (petioles 6–8 cm long with rounded auricles at the base), laminae 6–8 cm long, 5.5–7 cm broad, cordate at the base, obtuse or subacute at the apex, margin coarsely and irregularly dentate or lobed, villous on both surfaces, bases of hairs becoming asperate on the upper surface; median leaves usually pinnatisect with terminal segment as above and 1–2 pairs of lateral segments c. 2 cm long, 1 cm broad, upper leaves oblong or oblanceolate, 4–12 cm long, 0.7–3 cm broad, coarsely pinnately toothed and lobed, obtuse or subacute at the apex, sessile and auriculate at the base. Capitula numerous in dense corymbs. Ligules 4–5 mm long.

Generally at higher elevations amongst shrubs on open hillsides and at forest tracksides.

S p e c i m e n s   E x a m i n e d. WITHOUT PRECISE LOCALITY, *C.P. 151* p.p. annotated "Ramboda and Nuwara Eliya, *Gardner*" (PDA), annotated "Adam's Peak, Mar. 1946" (K), unannotated (BM). NUWARA ELIYA DISTRICT: Ramboda and Nuwara Eliya, *Gardner 415* p.p. (PDA); Horton Plains—Pattipola road, 6500 ft, *Grierson 1089* (E, US); Kirigalpota, 7850 ft, *Grierson 1100* (E, US, PDA, BR, CANB); Hakgala Peak, *Simpson 9091* (BM). KANDY DISTRICT: Adam's Peak, 1 Mar. 1883, *Trimen s.n.* (PDA);

Knuckles, Mar. 1887, *Ferguson s.n.* (PDA); near Rangala, 4000 ft, *Simpson 8742* (BM). WITHOUT LOCALITY: *Macrae 56* (BM), *Walker 1705* (K).

In addition to some of the specimens of *Thwaites C.P. 151* at K and PDA the following may also be regarded as intermediate: KANDY DISTRICT: Hunasgiriya, *J.M. Silva 68* (PDA): NUWARA ELIYA DISTRICT: Piduratalagala, c. 7500 ft, *Grierson 1065* (E, US, PDA, BR, CANB); Horton Plains to World's End, 7000 ft, *Grierson 1088* (E, US, PDA). RATNAPURA DISTRICT: Between Nagrak and World's End, c. 7000 ft, *Grierson 1153* (E, US, PDA, BR, CANB). WITHOUT LOCALITY: *Gardner 415* p.p. (K), *Walker 75* (K).

4. Senecio scandens Buch.-Ham. ex D. Don, Prod. Fl. Nepal. 178. 1825; Hook. f., Fl., Br. Ind. 3: 352. 1881; Trimen, Handb. Fl. Ceylon 3: 50. 1895. Type: In Nepalia, *Hamilton.*

Senecio wightianus DC. in Wight, Contrib. 22. 1834; Thw., Enum. Pl. Zeyl. 167. 1860. Type: *Wight 1480.*

Scandent perennial herbs. Stems striate, glabrous, divaricately branched attaining 2–4 m in height. Leaves 5–10 cm long, lyrately pinnatisect with rounded auricles at the base; lateral segments 1–2 pairs, oblong-spathulate, up to 1.5 cm long, 7 mm broad, shallowly dentate near the apex, terminal segments deltoid, 2.5–5 cm long, 1–3 cm broad at the base, acuminate at the apex, margins sharply dentate, glabrous or pubescent on the veins beneath, pellucid-reticulate. Capitula several or numerous in divaricately branched corymbs. Involucres narrowly campanulate, 3 mm diam. when fresh, 6–7 mm broad when pressed, phyllaries c. 12, oblong, c. 5 mm long, glabrous. Ray flowers usually 8, yellow, ligules 5.5–6.5 mm long, 1–1.5 mm broad. Disc flowers yellow, 4.5–5 mm long. Achenes 2.5–3 mm long, brown, 5-ribbed, minutely whitish puberulent on the ribs. Pappus white, 3.5–4 mm long, persistent.

Chromosome number. n = 10 (Shetty, Taxon 16: 571. 1967).

D i s t r. S. India, Himalayas, SE. Tibet, SW. China, Thailand.

E c o l. In light montane forests, locally quite common. Flowering January–April.

S p e c i m e n s E x a m i n e d. KANDY DISTRICT: Hantane, Jan. 1854 (*Gardner*), *C.P. 1751* (PDA, BM). NUWARA ELIYA DISTRICT: Nuwara Eliya, 1847, *Gardner 413* (K, BM); *Macrae 435* (K, BM): On the way to Fort Macdonald, 11 Mar. 1906, *Willis s.n.* (PDA); same locality, Apr. 1921, *A. De Alvis s.n.* (PDA); Hakgala, *N.D. Simpson 9067* (PDA, BM). BADULLA DISTRICT: Above Welimada on Bandarawela road, *N.D. Simpson 9630* (K); between Welimada and Hakgala, c. 4000 ft, *Grierson 1155* (E, US, PDA, BR, CANB); between Boralanda and Palugama, *Amaratunga 465* (PDA).

WITHOUT LOCALITY: *Wight 542* (E), *Walker 66* (K), *s.n.* (E, K); 1 Mar. 1819, *Moon 320* (BM).

N o t e s. *Senecio scandens* is variable throughout its geographical range and several varieties have been recognised. Generally the leaves are simple but in Ceylon they are pinnately divided and in this respect the plants most closely resemble var. *incisus* Franchet (in J. Bot. 10: 418. 1896) which was described from Szechuan, W China and is also found in SE Tibet. There are indeed few differences between the specimens from the two regions: the leaf venation of the Ceylon specimens is more finely reticulate but the Chinese plants usually, though not always, have longer capitula containing about 40 disc flowers (as against 30 in Ceylon) and the disc corollas are longer, 5.5–6 mm as against 4–4.5 mm.

5. Senecio corymbosus Wall. ex DC. in Wight, Contrib. 22. 1834 et Prod. 6: 364. 1837; Hook. f., Fl. Br. Ind. 3: 351. 1881. Type: Nilgiri, *Wallich 3121* (K).

Senecio corymbosus Wall., Cat. 3121. 1831, nom. nud.

Scandent shrubs attaining about 8 m in height. Stems araneose, glabrescent or glandular. Leaves broadly ovate, petiolate, petioles 2–4 cm long, uncinate and becoming woody at the base, lamina 3–9 × 2.5–6 cm, cordate at the base, acute or acuminate at the apex, margins ± callous, denticulate, araneose on both surfaces when young, sometimes glabrescent. Capitula numerous in axillary corymbs, discoid, 7–12 flowered. Involucres cylindrical-campanulate, 3–4 mm diam. when fresh, c. 5 mm when pressed. Phyllaries 6–8, ± araneose at the base, 4.5–7 mm long. Flowers yellow, corollas 6–8 mm long. Achenes 3–4 mm long, glabrous, 5-ribbed. Pappus white, 6–7 mm long, persistent.

D i s t r. Also in S. India.

E c o l. Margins of forests in montane zone, not uncommon. Flowering January–March.

There are two varieties and intermediates between them.

KEY TO THE VARIETIES

1 Leaves relatively thick and opaque, densely tomentose beneath; margins shallowly denticulate. Involucres 6–7 mm long...........................**1.** var. **corymbosus**
1 Leaves thin with transparent veins, sparsely araneose or subglabrous; margins quite prominently denticulate. Involucres (6–) 8–9 mm long...............**2.** var. **walkeri**

1. var. corymbosus

S p e c i m e n s E x a m i n e d. KANDY DISTRICT: Ambagamuwa, 3000 ft, *s. coll. C.P. 3894* (K). WITHOUT LOCALITY: *Walker s.n.* (K).

2. var. walkeri (Arn.) Grierson in Ceylon J. Sci., Biol. Sci. 11: 22. 1974.

Senecio walkeri Arn., Nova Acta Phys. Med. Acad. Caes. Leop. Carol. Nat. Cur. 18: 349. 1836; Trimen, Handb. Fl. Ceylon 3: 49. 1895, non *S. walkeri* Thw. 1860. Type: "Ceylon ad 1000 hexapod", *Walker* (E).

Senecio corymbosus var. *β* Thw., Enum. Pl. Zeyl. 167. 1860.

Senecio araneosus DC. var. *walkeri* (Arn.) C.B. Clarke, Comp. Ind. 182. 1876.

Specimens Examined. WITHOUT PRECISE LOCALITY: *s. coll. C.P. 565* annotated "Hantane, Jan. 1854; Bopatalawa, Feb. 1857" (PDA), annotated "Nuwara Eliya, Jan. 1846" (K), unannotated (BM). NUWARA ELIYA DISTRICT: Piduratalagala, Feb. 1846, *s. coll. C.P. 272* (K, BM); above Hakgala, 22 Feb. 1906, *Willis s.n.* (PDA); ibid., 1 Mar. 1906, *Willis s.n.* (PDA); ibid., 6200 ft, *Grierson 1081* (E, US, PDA, BR, CANB), Sita Eliya, Mar. 1922, *A. de Alwis s.n.* (PDA); between Horton Plains and Ohiya, c. 6000 ft, *Grierson 1110* (E, US, PDA, BR, CANB). KANDY DISTRICT: Hantane, 3000 ft, *Gardner 412* (K, BM). BADULLA DISTRICT: Top of Namunakula, 12 Mar. 1907, *J.M. Silva s.n.* (PDA). WITHOUT LOCALITY: *Moon s.n.* (BM); *Walker 38* (E), *55* (K), *252* (E-GL), *253* (E-GL, K), *s.n.* (PDA).

Intermediates between these two varieties occur which have the thicker leaves and shorter involucres of var. *corymbosus* but the more strongly denticulate margins of var. *walkeri*. The undersides of the leaves lack the felted tomentum of var. *corymbosus* and vary between white floccose and brownish araneose.

Specimens Examined. WITHOUT PRECISE LOCALITY: *C.P. 272* annotated "Pidurutalagala (*Gardner*)" (PDA), annotated "Ambagamuwa, 3000 ft" (K), annotated "Dick Oya, Feb. 1846" (BM). NUWARA ELIYA DISTRICT: Horton Plains, North Entrance, 2100 m, *Fosberg & Mueller-Dombois 50009* (E, US, PDA); Pidurutalagala, 7500 ft, *Grierson 1071* (E, US, PDA, BR, CANB); Kirigalpota, 7875 ft, *Grierson 1103* (E, US, PDA).

Several species of *Senecio* are reportedly cultivated in Ceylon: *S. cineraria* L. from Southern Europe with pinnatifid leaves which are silvery tomentose, is grown as a foliage plant; *S. elegans* L. from South Africa, an erect herb with pinnately lobed leaves and pink flowers; *S. mikanioides* Oth. (Syn. *S. scandens* DC.) a climber from South Africa with rounded 5–7 lobed leaves and clusters of small white flower-heads and another climbing species: *S. macroglossus* DC. "German Ivy", also from South Africa, with glossy often variegated leaves and longer capitula of yellow flowers.

Florists' Cinerarias are also cultivated in a wide range of flower colour from white to crimson and blue. They arose from hybridisations between various Canary Island species of *Senecio* e.g. *S. cruentus* DC., *S. heritieri* DC. and *S. populifolius* DC. All of them have broadly ovate or reniform leaves that are greyish tomentose beneath.

54. NOTONIA

DC. in Guillemin, Arch. Bot. (Paris) 2: 518. 1833. Type species: *Notonia grandiflora DC.*

Glabrous, somewhat fleshy shrubs. Leaves obovate or lanceolate, simple, entire or finely serrate, succulent or herbaceous. Capitula large or medium-sized, pedunculate, subcorymbose or paniculate, homogamous, discoid. Involucres cylindrical, phyllaries 1-seriate, equal with a few shorter calyculate bracts at the base. Flowers all hermaphrodite. Corollas narrowly tubular at the base widening gradually into the cylindrical-campanulate limb, 5-lobed at the apex. Anthers acutely appendaged at the apex, bluntly sagittate at the base. Style branches linear, elongate; appendages short, ovate. Receptacle flat, naked, alveolate. Achenes cylindrical, 10-ribbed. Pappus copious, capillaceous, persistent or deciduous.

KEY TO THE SPECIES

1 Leaves elliptic-lanceolate, acuminate at the apex. Involucres c. 1 cm long............
....2. N. walkeri
1 Leaves elliptic-oblong or spathulate, obtuse, apiculate at the apex, margins entire, narrowly revolute. Involucres 1.5–2 cm long...........................1. N. grandiflora

1. Notonia grandiflora Wall. ex DC. in Guillemin, Arch. Bot. (Paris) 2: 518. 1833; DC. in Wight, Contrib. 24. 1834; Hook. f., Fl. Br. Ind. 3: 336. 1881; Wight, Ic. t. 484 1841; Thw., Enum. Pl. Zeyl. 168. 1860; Deless., Ic. Sel. Pl. 4, t. 61. 1840; Trimen, Handb. Fl. Ceylon 3: 47. 1895.

Cacalia grandiflora Wall., Cat. 3147. 1828, nom. nud. Type: *Wallich 3147* (K).

Stems 0.6–2 m tall, cylindrical, fleshy, little branched, covered with prominent leaf scars, glabrous, pale green, glaucous. Leaves elliptic-oblong or spathulate, 6–15 × 2.5–4 cm obtuse and mucronate or acute at the apex, attenuate and subpetiolate at the base, margin entire, narrowly revolute, glabrous, glaucous especially beneath. Capitula cylindrical, 5–6 mm diam., either 3–6 in short terminal corymbs or 15–20 in longer lax-branching panicles. Involucres cylindrical, 2–3 cm broad when pressed, phyllaries 8–12, lanceolate, 1.3–1.8 cm long, 2.5–3.5 mm broad, striate, pale green and purplish, margins thinner, submembranous. Flowers greenish-white, exserted about 5 mm above phyllaries, corollas 1.7–2 cm long. Achenes somewhat compressed, glabrous, 5–7 mm long. Pappus white, 1.5–1.75 cm long, persistent.

Distr. Also in S. India.
Ecol. Dry regions near the coast in scrub, rare. Flowering August–May.
Specimens Examined. WITHOUT PRECISE LOCALITY: *C.P.*

1743 annotated *"Gardner*, Batticaloa, Mar. 1856, Trincomalee, *Glenie"* (PDA), unannotated (K, BM). JAFFNA DISTRICT: Karativoe Island, Aug. 1883, *Trimen s.n.* (PDA). ANURADHAPURA DISTRICT: Wilpattu Nat. Park, 1½ miles N of Maradanmaduwa, *Mueller-Dombois & Wirawan 68091305* (US, PDA). WITHOUT LOCALITY: 30 Jan. 1819, *Moon 67* (BM).

N o t e s. No explanation appears to have been advanced to account for the two forms of inflorescence in this variable species. De Candolle (Prod. 6: 442) noted this as well as the variability of the leaves and declared it possible that the species should be divided. Clarke (Comp. Ind. p. 176) attempted this on the basis of a supposed correlation between leaf characteristics and capitulum size. Possibly, however, the elongated paniculate inflorescence is the product of a vigorous terminal bud whereas the corymbs are produced by weaker lateral buds.

2. Notonia walkeri (Wight) C.B. Clarke, Comp. Ind. 176. 1876; Hook. f., Fl. Br. Ind. 3: 337. 1881; Trimen, Handb. Fl. Ceylon 3: 47. 1885.

Senecio walkeri Thw., Enum. Pl. Zeyl. 167. 1860, non Arn. 1836, nom. illeg. *Gynura walkeri* Wight, Ic. Pl. Ind. Or. 3: 11, t. 1122. 1846. Type: *Walker 350* (K).

Stems erect, c. 2 m tall "over 1 inch in diameter at base" (fide Wight), softly woody, covered with leaf scars, glabrous. Leaves elliptic-lanceolate, petiolate, petioles 2–4 cm long, lamina 7–13 × 2–4 cm gradually acuminate at the apex, gradually attenuate at the base, margins entire or regularly and sharply serrate, glabrous on both surfaces, venation pinnate, prominent beneath, not fleshy. Capitula cylindrical-campanulate, 3–4 mm diam., numerous in large loose, terminal, corymbs; pedicels bearing linear bracts, 2–3 mm long. Involucres cylindrical-campanulate, c. 1.5 cm broad when pressed; phyllaries linear-lanceolate, glabrous, 0.8–1 cm long, 1–1.25 mm broad, 1–2-striate in the middle, margins thinner, sub-membranous. Flowers white or creamy, exserted about 2 mm above phyllaries, corollas 0.8–1 cm long. Achenes somewhat compressed, puberulous between the ribs. Pappus white, hairs 6–8 mm long, separately deciduous.

Chromosome number. n = 10 (Shetty, Taxon 16: 570. 1967).

D i s t r. Also in Nilgiri Hills.

E c o l. In forest shade of upper montane zone, rare. Flowering September–April.

Specimens Examined. WITHOUT PRECISE LOCALITY: *s. coll. C.P. 533* annotated "Nuwara Eliya and Horton Plains, 1851" (PDA, K), unannotated (BM). BADULLA DISTRICT: Wattakelle Hill, 10 Apr. 1887, *W. Ferguson s.n.* (PDA). WITHOUT LOCALITY: *Walker 350* (K), *s.n.* (PDA, E).

Tribe CALENDULEAE

Herbs with alternate leaves. Capitula heterogamous, radiate. Phyllaries 1–2-seriate. Anthers acute, non-caudate. Styles of hermaphrodite flowers entire or slightly bilobed at the apex, those of fertile flowers with two truncate branches. Achenes usually strongly incurved, tuberculate on the back. Pappus absent.

Sole (cultivated) genus in Ceylon: *Calendula*.

54a. Calendula officinalis L. the common or Pot Marigold from the Mediterranean area was recorded to be in cultivation by Moon (Cat. p. 59). It is a variable species in size, colour (from yellow to orange) and doubling of the flower heads. The heteromorphic epappose achenes, the outer ones of which are incurved and warted, are typical of the tribe Calenduleae.

Tribe ARCTOTEAE

Herbs. Leaves radical or cauline, entire or pinnatisect. Capitula heterogamous, radiate. Involucral bracts in several series, scarious or herbaceous. Anther bases entire or sagittate, not caudate. Style branches usually connate to near apex, style thickening or changing in texture slightly below them. Receptacle naked or paleaceous. Pappus of hyaline scales or absent.

KEY TO THE GENERA

```
1 Receptacle paleaceous. Leaves gland-dotted.......................54d. Sphenogyne
1 Receptacle naked or alveolate. Leaves greyish green, not gland-dotted
  2 Leaves radical. Involucral bracts connate at the base, herbaceous.......54c. Gazania
  2 Leaves cauline. Involucral bracts free, scarious at the apex..............54b. Arctotis
```

This largely South Africa tribe has yielded several popular and widely cultivated plants some of which are suitable for gardens at higher elevations. In many respects the tribe is similar to the Anthemideae particularly in having conspicuous hyaline margins on the phyllaries and scaly pappuses, but differs principally in the shape of the style branches.

54b. Arctotis stoechadifolia Berg. (syn. *A. grandis* Thumb.) has pale violet ray flowers and grooved achenes that bear a pappus of scales arranged in two series. *Arctotis (Venidium) fastuosa* Jacq.: Ray flowers golden yellow with purplish bases; disc flowers brownish purple; achenes epappose.

54c. Gazania rigens R. Br. (and hybrids of it). Treasure Flower. Grown as edging plants and in tubs; leaves pinnatisect, prostrate against soil; capitula solitary on short peduncles; ligules yellow or orange with a dark blotch at the base.

54d. Sphenogyne (Ursinia) anethoides DC. Leaves finely pinnatisect, glanddotted; ray flowers orange with purple bases; achenes hairy at the base; pappus of 5 scales.

Tribe CARDUEAE

Leaves alternate, often spinous. Capitula homogamous, discoid. Receptacle hairy (sometimes paleaceous or naked). Anther bases caudate. Style slightly swollen below the two short branches. Pappus capillary (sometimes plumose or paleaceous).

Only genus in Ceylon: *Carduus*.

55. CARDUUS

L., Sp. Pl. 820. 1753; Gen. Pl. ed. 5. 358. 1754. Type species: *C. nutans* L.

Erect, simple or branched, annual or perennial herbs. Leaves alternate, often decurrent, simple or pinnately divided, margins spinous. Capitula medium-sized, homogamous, discoid. Involucre ovoid or campanulate, phyllaries in several series, imbricate, spinous-tipped. Corollas filiform at the base, suddenly widening and narrowly campanulate above, 5-lobed. Filaments pilose; anther bases caudate, apices acuminate. Style branches obtuse, slightly swollen below their junction. Receptacle convex, densely setose. Achenes obovate, somewhat compressed, glabrous, areole basal. Pappus hairs simple, barbellate, coherent in a ring at the base.

Carduus pycnocephalus L., Sp. Pl. 1151. 1763; Alston in Trimen, Handb. Fl. Ceylon 6: 172. 1931; Kazmi, Mitt. Bot. Staatssaml. Munchen 5: 444. 1964. Type: Herb. LINN. (966/9).

Annual (or biennial) herbs up to 1 m tall. Stems simple or branched, white tomentose, alate, wings dentate, lobed, spiny. Basal leaves obovate with rounded lobes, median cauline leaves lanceolate or oblanceolate in outline, lyrate-pinnatifid, up to 15 × 7 cm decurrent at the base, bearing up to 9 sharply lobed segments, lobes spinous, upper leaves smaller, entire or dentate, glabrous or slightly arachnoid above, whitish tomentose beneath. Capitula 3–4 at the apex of stems and branches, shortly peduncled. Involucre campanulate, 0.75–1 cm diam., phyllaries 5–7-seriate, arachnoid or glabrous, up to 2 cm long, 2.5 mm broad, outer and intermediate ones ovate, apices acuminate, with prominent midribs, spinous, inner ones membranous, unribbed, acuminate, spineless. Flowers purple, rarely white, corollas 13–16 mm long, basal tubes 6–8 mm long, lobes 3.5–6 mm long. Receptacular setae c. 1 cm long. Achenes 4–5 mm long, fawn. Pappus whitish or buff, 12–15 mm long.

D i s t r. Middle and South Europe, SW Asia, Afghanistan and Pakistan.
E c o l. Roadsides and margins of cultivated land, not common. Flowering February (and probably longer).
S p e c i m e n s E x a m i n e d. NUWARA ELIYA DISTRICT: Nuwara Eliya, *Alston 868* (PDA, K).

Tribe M U T I S I E A E

Herbs or shrubs, sometimes climbers. Leaves radical or cauline and alternate. Capitula homogamous but sometimes apparently radiate. Corollas equally 5-lobed or bilabiate with a longer lip of 3 lobes and a shorter lip of two lobes. Anther with long caudate bases. Style branches obtuse, unappendaged, usually connate to near the apex. Pappus capillary or barbellate.

KEY TO THE GENERA

1 Herbs with pinnatifid radical leaves. Corollas bilabiate................**55a. Gerbera**
1 Shrubs with leathery entire leaves. Corollas equally 5 lobed.............**55b. Stifftia**

55a. Gerbera jamesonii Bolus ex Hook., the "Baberton Daisy" from S. Africa, is widely grown in Ceylon gardens. A member of the tribe Mutisieae that is not represented in the native flora, it is characterised by having bilabiate corollas in which the three anterior lobes are fused together and longer than the two free posterior ones. The flower colour varies through white, yellow, orange or red.

55b. Stifftia chrysantha Mikan. from Tropical Eastern South America is another member of the Mutisieae that is reputedly cultivated. It forms a shrub 2 metres tall with evergreen leaves, and orange-yellow flowers that are much exserted from the involucre. The corollas have five equal, revolute lobes and the pappus hairs are as long as the flowers and similarly coloured.

Tribe L A C T U C E A E

Herbs with alternate or sometimes radical rosulate leaves. Capitula homogamous, ligulate, ligules all 5-lobed. Involucre several-seriate. Anther bases sagittate or caudate. Styles thin, rather obtuse. Achenes compressed or terete, sometimes rostrate. Pappus capillary or plumose, hairs sometimes of varying thicknesses.

KEY TO THE GENERA

1 Pappus plumose. Receptacle bearing thin, slender paleae............**57. Hypochoeris**
1 Pappus capillary. Receptacle naked
  2 Dwarf (peduncles less than 5 cm tall) stoloniferous perennial herbs. Coastal sandbanks
  ....**60. Launaea**
  2 Taller herbs without stolons
    3 Capitula solitary on leafless scapes. Achenes tuberculate above and rostrate........
    ....**58. Taraxacum**
    3 Capitula several on branching leafy stems. Achenes otherwise
      4 Setae of pappus dimorphic, consisting of fine hairs and finer down
        5 Achenes compressed. Capitula 5–10 mm diam.....................**59. Sonchus**
        5 Achenes angular. Capitula 2–3 mm diam........................**60. Launaea**
      4 Setae of pappus consisting uniformly of fine hairs
        6 Stems ± densely leafy. Achenes compressed.................... .....**58a. Lactuca**
        6 Stems with few leaves. Achenes terete or angular..................**56. Youngia**

56. YOUNGIA

Cass., Ann. Sci. Nat. Bot. 1, 23: 88. 1831. Type species: *Y. japonica* (L.) DC. (= *Y. lyrata* Cass.).

Annual or perennial herbs. Stems elongate, erect. Leaves subpinnatifid or lyrate-pinnatifid. Inflorescence cymose or corymbiform. Capitula small to medium, 10–20 flowered. Involucre cylindric, dark green, glabrous, 2-seriate; inner bracts subequal; outer involucral bracts few, short. Flowers yellow, ligulate, 5-toothed at the apex. Anthers commonly green, caudate-acuminate at the base. Styles yellow, filiform. Receptacle naked. Achenes fusiform, 11–14-ribbed, unequal, 2–5 ribs more prominent, spiculate. Pappus 1- or 2-seriate, bristles united at the base.

KEY TO THE SPECIES

1 Annuals; capitula fairly numerous, c. 5 mm long; pappus white..........**1. Y. japonica**
1 Perennials; capitula 2–10 in cymes, c. 8 mm long; pappus greyish......**2. Y. fuscipappa**

1. Youngia japonica (L.) DC., Prod. 7: 194. 1838; Babc. & Stebbins. The Genus Youngia 94, fig. 28. 1937.

Prenanthes japonica L., Mant. 107. 1767. Type: Habitat in Japonica, *Kleyn-hoff* (Herb. LINN. 952/6).
Crepis japonica Benth., Fl. Hongk. 194. 1861; Hook. f., Fl. Br. Ind. 3: 395. 1881; Trimen, Handb. Fl. Ceylon 3: 51. 1895; Alston, Kandy Fl. 54. 1938.
Youngia lyrata Cass., Ann. Sci. Nat. Bot. 1, 23: 88. 1831; Thw., Enum. Pl. Zeyl. 168. 1860. Type: Mauritius, *Bouton* (P).

Stems up to 60 cm tall, glabrous. Leaves mostly radical, oblanceolate, simple or lyrate, pinnatifid, up to 18 cm long, 4.5 cm broad, usually shortly petiolate at the base, lateral segments somewhat irregular, 0–3 pairs, glabrous or puberulent on both surfaces; cauline leaves few, smaller. Capitula numerous in cymose corymbs; involucres urceolate-cylindric, 2 mm diam. at base; outer phyllaries c. 5, very small, inner ones linear-lanceolate, pubescent on the inner surface, glabrous without, midrib thickened near the base. Flowers 10–20 per capitulum; corollas orange-yellow, 6 mm long. Achenes 1.5–2 mm long, compressed, c. 12-ribbed. Pappus uniseriate, 3.5 mm long.

Chromosome number. n = 8 (Shetty in Taxon 16: 572. 1967).

D i s t r. Japan and Korea to Western China; Malay Peninsula to Northwestern India; Philippines and Malay Archipelago.

E c o l. Weed of cultivation and roadsides at mid elevations, very common. Flowering September–June.

S p e c i m e n s E x a m i n e d. WITHOUT PRECISE LOCALITY: *C.P. 1747* annotated "Hantane and Kotmale, *Gardner*; Rambodde Oct. 1853" (PDA, K, BM unannotated). KANDY DISTRICT: Peradeniya, *J.M. Silva 181* (PDA); Madugoda, *Simpson 9435* (K, BM); above Marutenne, near Laksapana Falls, *Grierson 1052* (E, US, PDA, BR, CANB). NUWARA ELIYA DISTRICT: Hakgala, 6 Mar. 1906, *A.M. Silva s.n.* (PDA); near Talawakelle, *Simpson 8914* (PDA, BM); BADULLA DISTRICT: Craig Estate, Bandarawela, 25 Mar. 1906, *Willis s.n.* (PDA). WITHOUT LOCALITY: *Walker 32* (PDA, K).

2. Youngia fuscipappa Thw., Enum. Pl. Zeyl. 168. 1860; Babc. & Stebbins. The Genus Youngia 63, fig. 4. 1937. Type: *Thwaites C.P. 1748*.

Crepis fuscipappa (*Thw.*) C.B. Clarke, Comp. Ind. 254. 1876; Hook. f., Fl. Br. Ind. 3: 395. 1881; Trimen, Handb. Fl. Ceylon 3: 51. 1895.

Rootstocks rhizomatous. Stems 25–50 (–75) cm tall, glabrous, simple. Basal leaves oblanceolate, coarsely sinuate-dentate or runcinate-pinnatifid, 10–20 (–30) cm long, 1–2 cm broad, acuminate at the apex, attenuate into a petiole 3–20 cm long at the base, glabrous or puberulent on both surfaces, margin narrowly revolute; cauline leaves smaller and narrower, becoming linear. Capitula 3 or more in racemose corymbs, branches brownish pubescent bearing up to 10 capitula; involucres cylindrical or suburceolate, 3–4 mm diam. at base; outer phyllaries 5, ovate, 1–2 mm long, inner ones 8, lanceolate, 7–8 mm long, scarious-margined, glabrous, midribs prominent. Flowers 11-14 per capitulum; corollas 9–10 mm long, pubescent on the tubular portion. Achenes fusiform, subcompressed, 3 mm long, 5-ribbed, each rib having 3 minor ribs. Pappus greyish, c. 4.5 mm long, 2-seriate.

D i s t r. Endemic.

E c o l. On moist patanas 5500–7500 ft, quite common. Flowering January–September.

Specimens Examined. WITHOUT PRECISE LOCALITY: *s. coll. C.P. 1748* annotated Maturata, Aug. 1853; Haputala, 1856 (PDA; BM, K, unannotated). NUWARA ELIYA DISTRICT: Nuwara Eliya, 6000 ft, 1847, *Gardner 427* (K, BM); Horton Plains, Sept. 1890, *Trimen?* *s.n.* (PDA); Sita Eliya, Mar. 1922, *A. de Alwis s.n.* (PDA); Horton Plains, Pattipola track, *Simpson 9527* (BM); Near Ambawela railroad station on road to Horton plains, 1830 m, *Mueller-Dombois & Comanor 67070818* (US, PDA); New Farm, Horton Plains, *Cooray 68051724 R* (US, PDA); Horton Plains, 1 mile from Farr Inn, 2400 m, *Gould & Cooray* 13821 (E, US, PDA); between Nuwara Eliya and Kande Ela Reservoir, Elk Plains, *Mueller-Dombois 68051727* (US, PDA); Pidurutalagala, 7500 ft, *Grierson 1062* (E, US, PDA, BR, CANB).

57. HYPOCHOERIS

L., Gen. Pl. ed. 5. 352, 1754. Type species: *H. radicata* L.

Perennial herbs. Leaves radical, rosulate, runcinate-pinnatifid. Stems scapiform or sparsely branched, bracteate above. Capitula medium sized, homogamous. Involucre campanulate, phyllaries 3–4 seriate, imbricate. Receptacle flat or convex, paleae narrow, hyaline. Flowers yellow, ligulate, 5-dentate at the apex. Anther bases sagittate, acuminate; style branches thin, obtuse. Achenes oblong-linear, ± terete, c. 15-ribbed, narrowed into a thin rostrum at the apex. Pappus 2-seriate, inner hairs plumose, the outer ones shorter, simple.

Hypochoeris radicata L., Sp. Pl. 811. 1753; Alston in Trimen, Handb. Fl. Ceylon 6: 172. 1895; Bond, Wild Fls. Ceylon Hills 118, t. 61. 1953. Type: Herb. Hort Cliff. (BM).

Flowering stems 15–25 or more cm tall, simple or branched, glabrous, leafless with scattered ovate-lanceolate scales c. 2 mm long, bearing a solitary terminal capitulum. Leaves sinuate-dentate or runcinate-pinnatifid, oblanceolate in outline, 4–10 cm long, 0.5–1.5 cm broad, bearing up to 4 pairs of lateral segments up to 1.3 cm long, covered with simple hairs especially on the upper surface. Capitulum campanulate, 5–6 mm diameter, involucre 4–5 seriate, imbricate, phyllaries lanceolate, outer ones 3 mm long, inner ones 12 mm long, black tipped, glabrous or pilose along the mid rib. Flowers yellow, ligulate, ligules 10–12 mm long, greyish beneath, spreading to form a circle 2.5–3.5 cm diameter. Receptacular paleae linear-lanceolate, acuminate, scarious, c. 10 mm long. Achenes c. 3 mm long, brown; rostrum c. 5 mm long. Pappus hairs 8 mm long, creamy or dirty white.

Chromosome number. 2n=8 (Gadella & Kliphuis, Proc. Roy. Neth. Acad. Sci. Ser. C. 69, 541–556. 1966), n=4 (Powell & King, Amer. J. Bot. 56 (1) 116–121. 1969).

D i s t r. Native of Europe also found in Nilgiri Hills, India and in Khasia Hills, Assam.

E c o l. In moist grassy banks and meadows above 5000 ft elevation, common. Flowering December–July.

S p e c i m e n s E x a m i n e d. KANDY DISTRICT: Nursery, Royal Botanic Garden Peradeniya, April 1899, Trimen? 654 (PDA). NUWARA ELIYA DISTRICT: Nuwara Eliya, *Alston 874* (PDA), *Amaratunga 224* (PDA); Elk Plains, 1 mile S of Kande Ela Reservoir, 1860 m, *Mueller-Dombois & Comanor 67070807* (US, PDA); *Comanor 930* (E, US, PDA); Route A5 near 45 milestone, 6000 ft, *Grierson 1058* (E, US, PDA, BR, CANB); Horton Plains near Farr Inn, 2400 m, *Gould & Cooray 13853* (E, US, PDA).

58. TARAXACUM

Wiggers, Prim. Fl. Hols. 56. 1780. nom. cons. non Zinn, 1757. Type: *T. officinale* Wiggers (*Leontodon taraxacum* L.).

Acaulous perennial herbs. Leaves radical, simple and dentate or runciante-pinnatifid. Scapes aphyllous, monocephalous, homogamous, liguliflorous. Involucre campanulate, several-seriate, inner series longer, subequal, outer ones shorter. Receptacle flat, naked. Corollas yellow, ligulate, 5-dentate at the apex. Anther bases sagittate, shortly setaceous, acuminate. Style branches thin, ± obtuse. Achenes oblong, terete, 4–5 angled, narrowing abruptly into a short cusp or pyramidal section which tapers finally into the rostrum. Pappus uniseriate, bristles minutely barbellate.

Taraxacum javanicum v. Soest, Wentia 10: 56, fig. 27. 1963. Type: W. Java, Tji Kadjan, S of Garoet, 1200 m, *Beguin s.n.* (L.).

Taraxacum officinale auct. non Wiggers: Hook. f., Fl. Br. Ind. 3: 401. 1881; Trimen, Handb. Fl. Ceylon 3: 51. 1895.
Taraxacum vulgare auct. non Schrank : Alston in Trimen, Handb. Fl. Ceylon 6: 173. 1931.

Leaves oblanceolate, 5–15 cm long, tapering at the base into a petiole about a third as long, simple with irregularly dentate margins or runcinate-pinnatifid with 3–4 pairs of lateral lobes up to 3 cm long, terminal lobe hastate or deltoid, obtuse or subacute, sparsely araneose on both surfaces. Scapes 10–15 (–25) cm tall, araneose below the capitulum at first, glabrescent, involucre c. 6 mm diam., outer phyllaries reflexed spreading, inner ones erect, lanceolate, 10–12 mm long, shortly horned near the apex on the outer surface, margins scarious. Corollas yellow, ligules 10–12 mm long, greyish violet beneath. Anthers and styles yellow. Achenes 3.5–4 mm long (including cusp), yellowish brown, spinulose at the apex, cusp conical, 0.75–1 mm long. Rostrum 6–7 mm long; pappus white, 5 mm long.

D i s t r. Java, India.

E c o l. Grassy banks at about 6000 ft, locally common. Flowering January–August (and probably longer).

S p e c i m e n s E x a m i n e d. NUWARA ELIYA DISTRICT: Hakgala Botanic Garden, August 1883, *Trimen s.n.* (PDA); Nuwara Eliya, 6100 ft, *Grierson 1117* (E, US, PDA, BR, CANB).

N o t e s. I am indebted to Professor J.L. van Soest who has kindly examined and determined my material. According to him, this taxon is placed in Sect. *Ceratophora* Dahl. and does not belong to the groups of species indigenous to Europe, whence Trimen assumed it to have originated. *T. javanicum* has now been found in several parts of India and in the Nilgiri Hills; thus the possibility exists of its being an indigenous species. In Java, however, it has been found associated with tea plantations and it may be through this industry that it owes its introduction to Ceylon. Contrary to Trimen's expectations, it does not appear to have become widespread "in the hill country".

58a. Lactuca sativa L., the European Culinary Lettuce has been cultivated in Ceylon for many years. It was recorded by Moon (Cat. p. 57) and no doubt does escape from time to time. The yellow-flowered capitula are arranged in corymbs the branches of which bear sagittate, cordate bracts. *L. heyneana*, which Trimen (Handb. p. 52) recorded, has been transferred to *Launaea*.

59. SONCHUS

L., Sp. Pl. 794. 1753; Gen. Pl. ed. 5. 347. 1754. Type species: *S. oleraceus* L.

Annual or perennial herbs or subshrubs. Stems erect, branched, foliose or leafless. Leaves alternate, simple or pinnately divided, often semiamplexicaul and auriculate at the base. Capitula several in cymose corymbs, homogamous, liguliflorous. Involucre ovoid, campanulate or urceolate, phyllaries several-seriate, imbricate, becoming swollen at the base at maturity. Flowers numerous, yellow, ligules linear-lanceolate. Anther bases sagittate, caudate-acuminate. Style branches thin. Receptacle flat, convex or concave. Achenes usually homocarpous, oblanceolate, obovate or oblong, ± compressed, erostrate with 1–4 ribs on each face. Pappus white, heteromorphic, consisting of thin soft hairs and coarser bristles, coherent in a ring at the base.

KEY TO THE SPECIES

1 Achenes strongly compressed and narrowly winged, 3-ribbed on each face, ± smooth; tube of corolla longer than ligule; leaf margins coarsely and subpungently toothed....
....**1. S. asper**
1 Achenes weakly compressed, unwinged with a variable number of ribs on each face, surface rough or wrinkled; tube of corolla longer or shorter than ligule.............
  2 Corolla tube and ligule ± equal in length; involucre glandular setose or eglandular but otherwise glabrous; cauline leaves usually runcinate with well-developed auricles....
....**2. S. oleraceus**
  2 Corolla tube almost twice as long as ligule; involucre glandular setose and tomentose; cauline leaves elliptic-lanceolate, entire or shallowly pinnatifid, auricles small........
....**3. S. wightianus**

1. Sonchus asper (L.) Hill, Br. Herb. 1: 47, t. f. 2. 1756; Alston in Trimen, Handb. Fl. Ceylon 6: 174. 1931.

Sonchus oleraceus var. *asper* L., Sp. Pl. 794. 1753. Type: herb. LINN (949/7?).

Annual herbs, 25–100 cm tall, glabrous. Lower leaves oblanceolate or spathulate, undivided or lobed, mid-cauline leaves often runcinate-pinnatifid, sometimes entire and similar to basal leaves, up to 15 cm long, 5 cm broad, usually with 7 triangular acuminate segments 1–2 cm long, coarsely dentate or more commonly subspinose dentate, auricles well developed, rounded at the margin, uppermost leaves lanceolate, entire, subspinose dentate. Capitula (4–) 10–20, borne on glandular peduncles. Involucres c. 7.5 mm diam.; phyllaries ovate-lanceolate, 3.5–12 mm long, 1.5–3 mm broad, membranous, glabrous. Corolla basal tube c. 8 mm long, pubescent, ligules 6–7 mm long. Achenes obovate, 2.5–3 mm long, brown. Pappus 7–8 mm long.

Chromosome number. 2n = 18 (See Boulos in Bot. Not. 113: 408. 1960).

D i s t r. Europe, SW Asia, N Africa, introduced in North and South America and Australia.

E c o l. Roadsides, railway embankments and margins of cultivated ground, not common. Flowering April–May and probably longer.

S p e c i m e n s E x a m i n e d. BADULLA DISTRICT: Ohiya, *Simpson 9572* (PDA, BM). NUWARA ELIYA DISTRICT: Horton Plains, New Farm, *Cooray 68051708R* (PDA). RATNAPURA DISTRICT: Hatton, 1906—fide Alston.

2. Sonchus oleraceus L., Sp. Pl. 794. 1753 excl. vars; Moon, Cat. 57. 1824; Thw., Enum. Pl. Zeyl. 168. 1860; Hook. f., Fl. Br. Ind. 3: 414. 1881; Trimen, Handb. Fl. Ceylon 3: 52. 1895 in nota; Alston in Trimen, Handb. Fl. Ceylon 6: 174. 1931 et Kandy Fl. 55. 1938. Type: Herb. LINN (949/6).

Annual herbs 30–100 cm tall, glabrous. Basal leaves ovate, mid-cauline leaves usually runcinate-pinnatifid, up to 15 (or sometimes 20) cm long with 1–3 pairs of lateral segments 1–5 cm long and large deltoid or hastate terminal segments 3–10 cm broad, margins coarsely (but not subspinously) dentate, auricles acute, spreading, uppermost leaves generally undivided, lanceolate. Capitula c. 10, peduncles glandular or eglandular, glabrous. Involucre campanulate, 6–8 mm diam., phyllaries lanceolate, membranous, 0.4–1.2 cm long, glabrous (or cottony in the bud), sometimes glandular. Corolla basal tubes 6–7 mm long, pubescent, ligules 5–6 mm long. Achenes oblanceolate, brown, compressed, 3-ribbed on each face, transversely rugose. Pappus 7–8 mm long.

Chromosome number. 2n = 32 (Boulos, Bot. Not. 113: 409. 1960).

D i s t r. Europe, SW Asia, N Africa, introduced in North and South America, South Africa, India, China, Australia.

E c o l. Common at roadsides and on cultivated ground in the montane region. Flowering throughout the year.

V e r n. Gal-potu-kola (S).

S p e c i m e n s E x a m i n e d. NUWARA ELIYA DISTRICT: Nuwara Eliya (*Gardner*) *C.P. 3631* (PDA); between Hakgala and Nuwara Eliya, 6 Mar. 1906, *A.M. Smith s.n.* (PDA); Horton Plains on Ohiya road, 2160 m, *Mueller-Dombois & Comanor 67070925* (PDA); ibid., *Grierson 1107* (E, US, PDA, BR, CANB). BADULLA DISTRICT: Below Ohiya Station, 1690 m, *Mueller-Dombois 68051846* (PDA); Bogawantalawa-Boralanda road 1575 m, *Comanor 1059* (E, US, PDA); between Haputale and Boralanda, *Amarantunga 471* (PDA). WITHOUT LOCALITY: *Wight 545* (E); *Walker 358* (K), *1704* (E).

3. Sonchus wightianus DC., Prod. 7: 187. 1838.

Sonchus arvensis auct. non L.: Hook. f., Fl. Br. Ind. 3: 414. 1881; Alston in Trimen, Handb. Fl. Ceylon 6: 174. 1931, Kandy Fl. 54. 1938. Type: "in Peninsula Indiae orientalis, legit cl. *Wight*".

Perennial, rhizomatous herbs, 30–100 cm tall, glaucous, glabrescent below, tomentose above in the inflorescence. Leaves linear-oblanceolate, 5–20 (–30) cm long 0.2–3 (–8) cm broad, often undivided, sometimes undulate and shallowly, rarely deeply, pinnatifid, with 4–5 pairs of lobes or segments, attenuate at the base to rounded auricles, acute or acuminate at the apex, margins sharply dentate or denticulate, glabrous above, glaucous and at first weakly pilose beneath, glabrescent. Capitula 3–10 or more on glandular and, at first tomentose, peduncles. Involucres urceolate, c. 1 cm diam.; phyllaries linear, 4–12 mm long, 1.5–2 mm broad, margins scarious, glandular setose and at least at the base, tomentose. Corolla basal tubes 6–7.5 mm long, sparsely pubescent, ligules 3.5–4 mm long. Achenes narrowly ellipsoidal, tetragonous, somewhat compressed, 2.5–3 mm long, pale brown, transversely rugose. Pappus 6–7.5 mm long.

D i s t r. India, China.

E c o l. Weed of roadsides and in the mortar of bridges and embankments in the lower montane zone, locally quite common. Flowering January–June and probably throughout the year.

V e r n. Val-dun-Kola (S); Poilaip-pillu, Musal-katha (T).

S p e c i m e n s E x a m i n e d. KANDY DISTRICT: Royal Botanic Garden, Peradeniya, weed, 6 Feb. 1953, *Appulay s.n.* (PDA); Parragalla between Gampola and Dolosbage, 300 m, *Grierson 1007* (E, US, PDA, BR, CANB). BADULLA DISTRICT: Bogawantalawa-Boralanda road, 1400 m, *Comanor 1087* (E, US, PDA); Koslande, *Simpson 8348* (BM).

N o t e s. According to Alston (l.c.) this species was "introduced before 1715", a statement which raises two points. Firstly, *S. wightianus* may not be an alien, Ceylon possibly falling within the natural distributional range of the species. Secondly, I have seen no specimens of it earlier than 1915 (PDA, without collector), nor do I understand the significance of 1715; this is not an important date in the history of the Flora according to Boulger (in Trimen, Handb. Fl. Ceylon 5: 367–381, 1900). Probably Alston's reference is in error for 1915.

60. LAUNAEA

Cass., Dic. Sc. Nat. 25: 321. 1822. Type species: *L. sarmentosa* (Willd.) Sch. Bip. ex Kuntze (syn. *L. bellidifolia* Cass.).

Annual or perennial herbs. Stems erect or prostrate and stoloniferous. Leaves alternate or rosulate, oblanceolate and sinuate-dentate or runcinate-pinnatifid, margins subspinulous. Capitula solitary or few on short peduncles or in sessile axillary groups in branched spike-like inflorescences, homogamous, liguliflorous. Involucres urceolate-campanulate; phyllaries 3–4 seriate, imbricate, appressed, membranous, outer ones shorter than the inner ones and with narrow scarious margins. Flowers ligulate, 5-toothed at the apex. Anther bases shortly fimbriate caudate. Style branches thin, somewhat flattened. Achenes narrow, 4–5 angular, truncate or tapering and rostrate at the apex. Pappus ± as long as the involucre, consisting of setae alone or intermixed with finer hairs, fused at the base into a ring and deciduous with it.

KEY TO THE SPECIES

1 Tall erect annual herbs. Pappus heterogeneous, consisting of fine setae and fine down-like hairs...**2. L. intybacea**
1 Prostrate stoloniferous herbs. Pappus homogeneous, of fine setae only.............. ....**1. L. sarmentosa**

1. Launaea sarmentosa (Willd.) Sch. Bip. ex Kuntze, Rev. Gen. Pl. 1: 350. 1891; Alston in Trimen, Handb. Fl. Ceylon 6: 173. 1931; Grierson in Ceylon J. Sci., Biol. Sci. 60. 1972. Type: "Habitat in Africa et India orientale", D. Klein, Herb. Willd. (B, iso E?).

Prenanthes sarmentosa Willd., Phytogr. 10, t. 6, f. 2. 1794; Sp. Pl. 3: 1540. 1803; Moon, Cat. 57. 1824.
Launaea pinnatifida Cass., Ann. Sci. Nat. Paris 23: 85. 1831; Hook. f., Fl. Br. Ind. 3: 416. 1881; Trimen, Handb. Fl. Ceylon 3: 52. 1895; Gamble, Fl. Pres. Madras 2: 733. 1921.
Microrhynchus sarmentosa DC., Prodr. 7: 181. 1839; Wight, Ic. Pl. Ind. Or. t. 133. 1846; Thw. Enum. Pl. Zeyl. 168, 1860.

Perennial, prostrate, stoloniferous herbs. Stolons long, glabrous; leaf rosettes 8–15 cm apart, rooting at each rosette. Leaves rosulate, 1.5–9 cm long, 2–15 mm broad, oblanceolate or spathulate, pinnatifid with 2–4 pairs of lobes, acute or obtuse at the apex, attenuate at the base, margins denticulate, teeth indurated white, glabrous on both surfaces, glaucous, somewhat fleshy. Capitula solitary, borne on short bract-covered peduncles 0.5–3 cm long. Involucre urceolate-campanulate, 3–5 mm diam. at base, 0.9–1.6 cm long; phyllaries 3–4 seriate, often purplish, glabrous with pale whitish scarious margins, outer phyllaries ovate, inner ones lanceolate. Flowers yellow, ligules c. 7–10 cm long, basal tubes 4–5 mm long. Achenes black, 3–6.25 mm long, thickly 4–5 ribbed, glabrous, minutely wrinkled, truncate or narrowed but scarcely beaked at the apex. Pappus homogeneous, white, 6.5–10 mm long.

D i s t r. India, Malaysia, E. Africa, Mauritius.

E c o l. On sandy sea shores above the high tide mark, common. Flowering July–May and probably throughout the year.

There are two variants of this species in Ceylon:

A. From the West Coast, North and North-East (around Trincomalee), smaller plants with leaves up to 3 × 1.2 cm; involucres 9–10 mm long, 3 mm broad at base on peduncles about 1 cm long; ligules fully extended form circle c. 1.75 cm diam.; achenes 3 mm; pappus 6.5 mm long. This form is widespread throughout Old World Tropics.

S p e c i m e n s E x a m i n e d. WITHOUT PRECISE LOCALITY: *C.P. 1746* annotated "Jaffna, *Gardner*, Batticaloa, 1868" (PDA), unannotated (K, BM). JAFFNA DISTRICT: Karativoe Island, Aug. 1883, *Trimen s.n.* (PDA); Jaffna, Feb. 1890, *Trimen s.n.* (PDA); Punkudativu, *Grierson 1118* (E, US, PDA). MANNAR DISTRICT: Talaimannar, 16 July 1916, *J.M. Silva s.n.* (PDA). PUTTALAM DISTRICT: Chilaw, *Simpson 8171* (BM). COLOMBO DISTRICT: Uswetakeiyawa near Negombo, *Amaratunga 100* (PDA), *Amaratunga 844* (PDA); Colombo, *Macrae 111* (K). TRINCOMALEE DISTRICT: Trincomalee, *Harvey s.n.* (E). VAVUNIYA DISTRICT: S of Mullaitivu, *Fosberg & Balakrishnan 53532* (US, E, PDA). ANURADHAPURA DISTRICT: Wilpattu Nat. Park, Kollankanatta, *Cooray 69092805* (US, E, PDA).

B. From the South coast and southern part of the East coast, larger plants with leaves up to 9 × 1.5 cm; involucres 1.3–1.6 cm long, 5 mm diam., at base, on peduncles 1–3 cm long; ligules fully extended form circle 2.5 cm diam., achenes 6.25 mm long, pappus 10 mm long. Similar specimens are known from Madras and Andaman islands.

Chromosome number. n = 9 (Mitra & Datta, Taxon 16: 461. 1967).

Specimens Examined. GALLE DISTRICT: Between Matara and Galle, Highway A2 at mile marker 81/1, *Comanor 346* (US, PDA). HAMBANTOTA DISTRICT: Ruhuna Nat. Park, Buttuwa, *Grierson 1143* (E, US, PDA); Ruhuna Nat. Park, Patanagalla, *Cooray 69042204R* (E, US, PDA). AMPARAI DISTRICT: Beach in front of Resthouse, Pottuvil, *Mueller-Dombois & Comanor 67072601* (US, PDA).

2. Launaea intybacea (Jacq.) Beauv., Bull. Soc. Bot. Geneve Ser. 2, 2: 114. 1910; Jeffrey, Kew Bull. 18: 472. 1966. Type: Cultivated at Vienna, Seed from Central America (W).

Lactuca intybacea Jacq., Ic. Pl. Rar. 1: 16, t. 12. 1784.
Lactuca runcinata DC. in Wight, Contrib. 26. 1834; Alston in Trimen, Handb.
  Fl. Ceylon 6: 173. 1931. Type: *Wight 1502*.
Brachyramphus sonchifolia DC., Prod. 7: 177. 1838; Thw., Enum. Pl. Zeyl.
  168. 1860. Type: *Wallich 3144* (K).
Lactuca heyneana DC., Prod. 7: 140. 1838; Hook. f., Fl. Br. Ind. 3: 403. 1881;
  Trimen, Handb. Fl. Cey. 3: 52. 1895. Type: *Wallich 3286* (K).
Prenanthes sonchifolia Willd., Sp. Pl. 3: 1541. 1803; Moon, Cat. 57. 1824.
  Type: *Klein*, Herb. Willd. (B).

Erect annual herbs. Stems terete, glabrous, up to 1.5 m tall, branched. Radical leaves runcinate-pinnatifid, up to 15 cm (–30) long, 5 cm (–10) broad, with 3–5 pairs of triangular lateral lobes up to 2 cm (–6) long, terminal segment ± hastate, up to 6 cm long, acute or acuminate, margins ± irregularly and finely subspinulose dentate, teeth whitish, indurated, glabrous, glaucous on both surfaces; upper leaves similar, narrower, semiamplexicaul, auriculate, auricles rounded with long fine points. Capitula numerous, in distant clusters of 1–3, on long leafless upper branches; involucre c. 1 cm long, 3 mm diam. at the base, 3–4 seriate; phyllaries with pale membranous margins, outer ones ovate, 2–3 mm long, inner ones lanceolate, c. 10 mm long, glabrous. Flowers yellow, c. 25–30 per capitulum; ligules 3.5–4 mm long, basal tubes c. 7 mm long. Achenes blackish, 3 mm long, elliptic and somewhat compressed, indistinctly 4–5 ribbed, minutely papillate, narrowed and shortly rostrate at the apex. Pappus white, c. 6 mm long, heterogeneous, consisting of two thicknesses of hairs.

Chromosome number. 2n = 18 (Copde, Sci. & Cult. 31: 30. 1965).

D i s t r. North-western and western India.

E c o l. In low country, principally in the dry region, on roadsides and old walls, rare. Flowering August–March.

S p e c i m e n s E x a m i n e d. GALLE DISTRICT: *Gardner*, 1862, *C.P. 2827* (PDA). JAFFNA DISTRICT: Jaffna, Feb. 1890, *Trimen s.n.* (PDA); Delft Isl., *Grierson 1122* (E, US, PDA, BR, CANB). ANURADHAPURA DISTRICT: Anuradhapura, Oct. 1883, *Trimen s.n.* (PDA), Aug. 1885, *Trimen s.n.* (PDA).

CONNARACEAE

(by Deva Duttun Tirvengadum*)

Type genus: *Connarus* L.

Trees or shrubs, often scandent. Leaves alternate, exstipulate, imparipinnate or unifoliate (apparently simple in *Ellipanthus*). Base of petiole and petiolules pulvinate. Leaflets alternate or subopposite, entire. Inflorescence in axillary, pseudoterminal or terminal paniculate racemes or cymes. Flowers pentamerous, hypogynous, regular, bisexual or unisexual, bracteate. Calyx deeply 5-lobed or sepals slightly confluent at the base only, imbricate or subvalvate. Petals imbricate, often glandular hairy. Stamens 5 or 10, inner ones shorter, epipetalous and sometimes staminodial or sterile, slightly connate at base; filament usually glandular pubescent; anthers 2-celled, introrse. Pistils 5 (4 often abortive), free, or solitary; ovary 1-celled; ovules 2, collateral; styles filiform; stigmas capitately lobed. Fruit usually of 1 or rarely 2 one-seeded follicles, dehiscing ventrally. Seed arillate with or without endosperm; testa often thick.

A family of 16 genera and about 300 to 350 species, circumtropical, well developed in Africa, generally few in the moist subtropics (Assam, Yunnan, Asia, Natal, S. America). The genus *Connarus* is the most widely distributed of the family. It is represented in Ceylon by 3 genera and 4 species of which two are endemic, *Connarus championii* and *Ellipanthus unifoliatus*. Most Ceylonese Connaraceae are confined to low altitude extending to the lower montane zone, chiefly in the wet regions, except for *Connarus monocarpus* which occurs exclusively in the low dry region.

In Ceylon and in South-East Asia, a few species are used for making very strong ropes.

The family Connaraceae has much affinity with the Dilleniaceae, the Sapindaceae and the Rosaceae-Leguminosae. It has often been confused with the latter, especially with the genus *Derris* from which it differs by the absence of stipules, 2 or more carpels and the ovules which are collateral and not serial as in the Leguminosae. The genus *Ellipanthus* bears superficial resemb-

*Museum National d' Hitoire Naturelle, Paris.

The revision of this family has been prepared under the supervision of Dr. J.E. Vidal, Laboratoire de Phanérogamie, Paris.

lance to *Dichapetalum* and is sometimes confused with it.

For a complete treatment of the taxonomy, morphology and subdivision of the family, see P.W. Leenhouts (1958—Fl. Mal. sér. 1, 5 (4): 495–497).

KEY TO THE GENERA

1 Leaves pinnate. Inflorescence always bisexual. Sepals imbricate. Pistils 5 or 1. Seeds without endosperm
  2 Calyx accrescent, clasping the base of the fruit. Stamens 10, all perfect. Pistils 5....
....**1. Rourea**
  2 Calyx not accrescent, clasping the stalk of the stipitate fruit. Stamens usually 5 fertile, 5 staminodial, rarely all fertile. Pistil 1.............................**2. Connarus**
1 Leaves 1-foliolate. Inflorescence sometimes unisexual. Sepals valvate. Pistil 1. Seeds with endosperm...**3. Ellipanthus**

1. ROUREA

Aubl., Hist. Pl. Guiane Fr. 1: 467, t. 187. 1755, nom. cons. Type species: *Rourea frutescens* Aubl.

Kiridiwael Hermann, Mus. Zeyl. 10. 1717.
Santaloides L., Fl. Zeyl.: 192. 1747; Schellenberg, Pflanzenr. H. 103: 119. 1938.
Kalawael (non Hermann, Mus. Zeyl. 10. 1717) Adans., Fam. Pl. 2: 344. 1763.

Semiscandent trees or shrubs. Leaves imparipinnate. Leaflets entire. Inflorescence in axillary or pseudoterminal panicles. Flowers bisexual. Sepals deeply 5-lobed, distinctly imbricate, much enlarged in fruit and clasping its base. Petals much longer than the calyx. Stamens 10, slightly connate at base, episepalous ones longer, all perfect. Pistils 5, distinct; ovary pubescent; style slender; stigma faintly 2-lobed. Fruit 1 (rarely 2) per flower, follicular, opening by ventral suture; pericarp coriaceous. Seed 1, erect, with a basal arillode; endosperm absent.

A genus of about 90 species in the tropical regions of Central and S. America, Africa, Madagascar, S.E. Asia, S. India, Malay Islands, N.E. Australia and Melanesia. It is represented in Ceylon by 1 species.

For a good discussion of the typification and subdivision of the genus, see Leenhouts (1958—Fl. Mal. Ser. 1, 5 (4): 511–512).

Of the three subgenera recognised by Leenhouts, viz., subg. *Jaundea*, subg. *Rourea* and subg. *Palliatus* Leenh., only the last is represented in Ceylon.

1. Rourea minor (Gaertn.) Alston (*"minus"*) in Trimen, Handb. Fl. Ceylon 6: 67. 1931. Type: Based on *Aegiceras minus* Gaertn. (*König s.n.*). This specimen is represented by a few fruits in the Carpological collection in Leiden, no. *1163*.

Aegiceras minus Gaertn., Fruct. 1: 216, t. 46. 1788 (non Willd., Sp. Pl. 1: 1184. 1797 et auct.).

Connarus santaloides, Vahl, Symb. 3: 87. 1794; Moon, Cat. 49. 1839.

Rourea santaloides Wight & Arn., Prod. 144. 1834; Moon, Cat. 49. 1834; Thw., Enum. Pl. Zeyl. 80. 1858; Hook. f., Fl. Br. Ind. 2: 47. 1876; Trimen, Handb. Fl. Ceylon 1: 1. 1894. Type: Ceylon, *Wight 539*. Isotype (MH). I have not seen the holotype which according to Wight & Arnott l.c., is in Rottler's herbarium Colombo.

Rourea caudata Planch., Linnaea 23: 419. 1850; Hook. f., Fl. Br. Ind. 2: 48. 1876.

Rourea javanica Blume, Ann. Mus. Bot. Lugduno Batavum 1: 262. f. 59. 1850.

Rourea minor (Gaertn.) Leenhouts, Fl. Mal. Ser. 1, 5 (4): 514. 1958; Vidal, Fl. Thailand 2 (2): 122. 1972.

This species possesses an extensive synonymy, because of the wide distribution and the wide range of variability. Only those closely related to the Ceylon Flora are cited here. For a complete list of synonymy, see Leenhouts l.c.

Powerful liana reaching up to 30 m tall. Mature stem up to 25 cm in diameter, closely fluted. Outer bark smooth, greyish brown; inner bark salmon pink. Twigs glabrous, blackish-brown. Axillary buds ferrugineous-hirtellous. Rachis + petiole up to 10 cm long, subpulvinate at base, slender, curved, glabrous. Leaflets subopposite, sometimes closely alternate, oval-lanceolate, shortly accuminate at apex, more or less rounded at base, terminal one largest, 8 cm long, 3 cm broad; lateral ones 6.5 cm long, 2.5 cm broad; upper surface shining, olive green; lower surface paler with prominent reticulate venation; younger leaves greenish pink with very distinct venation on both surfaces. Petiolule 2 to 4 cm long. Flowers in axillary or pseudoterminal cymose or racemose panicles, up to 5.5 cm long or in clusters of 4 to 5, central one longer, up to 10 cm long. Bracts pubescent. Pedicel jointed, 2 mm long, slender, greenish white. Sepals broadly ovate or orbicular, up to 3 mm long, slightly pubescent outside. Petals oval-oblong, up to 5 mm long, translucent with prominent nerves, yellowish. Stamens erect, in 2 whorls of 5 each, slightly exerted; filaments slightly connate at base, longer ones 7 mm long, shorter ones 1.75 mm long, white; anthers globose with parallel pale yellow cells. Pistils distinct; ovary more or less ovoid, densely hirsute; ovules 2; style about 6 mm long, spreading, pubescent at base. Calyx, corolla, stamens and styles covered with stipitate glands. Fruit a follicular structure, 2 cm long, 0.7 cm broad, woody, with accrescent calyx, clasping the base of the fruit; valves opening along the ventral suture, glabrous on both sides with longitudinal ridges on the outer surface, tipped with remnant of style. Seed oboval up to 1 cm long; testa membranous; pericarp woody.

D i s t r. In South and East India, Andaman & Nicobar Islands; South China (Hong-Kong), Hainan and Kotosyo Isl., Malaysia, N.E. Queensland, New Caledonia, New Hebrides, Fiji and Samoa. In Ceylon, in the low country up to an altitude of 1000 m.

E c o l. Found along borders of primary and secondary rain forests, near river banks or streams. Flowers pinkish white. Flowering from September to December.

U s e s. In Ceylon, strong ropes are made by twisting the stems, and used for various purposes.

V e r n. Kirindi-wel or Goda-Kirindi (S).

N o t e. Vidal (1962—Fl. Camb. Laos & Vietn. 39–40) distinguishes three subspecies in the Sino Indian region and in South East Asia: Ssp. minor (leaflet 6.5 cm by 3 cm); Ssp. monadelpha (Roxb. ex DC.) Vidal (leaflet 15 cm by 7 cm) and Ssp. microphylla (Hook. & Arn.) Vidal (leaflet 4 cm by 1.5 cm). The Ceylon species belongs to the intermediate form, i.e. Ssp. minor.

I l l u s t r. Brandis, Indian Trees 211, f. 92. 1906 (*Rourea santaloides*); Blume, Ann. Mus. Bot. Lugduno Batavum 1: 262, f. 59. 1850; Vidal, Fl. Camb. Laos & Vietn. 2: 43, Pl. 4. f. 1–10. 1962.

S p e c i m e n s   E x a m i n e d. ANURADHAPURA DISTRICT: Summit of Ritigala, *s. coll. s.n.* 24.3.1905 (PDA). KANDY DISTRICT: Hantane, *s. coll. C.P. 749* (BM, K, P, PDA); between Mahiyangana and Kandy, *Tirvengadum & Jayasuriya 158* (K, MAU, P, PDA, US); between Panwila and Madulkele, mile marker 16/2, near stream, *Tirvengadum & Balasubramaniam 349* (MAU, PDA, US); Gammaduwa, *Alston 665* (K, PDA). COLOMBO DISTRICT: dans le voisinage de Colombo, terrain sablonneux, *Leschenault s.n.* (P), *Cinghol 496* (K); Herb. Pen. Ind. Or., April 1, 1896, *s. coll. s.n.* (K). RATNAPURA DISTRICT: Maratenna, *Balasubramaniam 291* (PDA, US), in secondary wet evergreen forest, vicinity of stream, *Tirvengadum, Cramer & Balasubramaniam 175* (G, K, L, MAU, P, PDA, US). GALLE DISTRICT: s. loc., *Gardner 195* (BM, K); low country, s. loc., *Walker 539* (K, MH). LOCALITY UNKNOWN: *Kelaart s.n.* in 1843 (P); *Mackenzie s.n.* (PDA); Herb. Ceylon, collect. *Stathouderienne 54* (P); *Alston s.n.* (CAL); *s. coll. s.n.* in 1831 (K).

2. CONNARUS

L., Fl. Zeyl. 112, n. 248. 1747; Gen. Pl. ed. 5. 305. 1754. Type species: *Connarus monocarpus* L.

Omphalobium Gaertn., Fruct. 1: 217, t. 46, f. 3. 1788.

Scandent shrubs. Leaves imparipinnate; leaflets usually 5, sometimes 3 or 7, entire, more or less glandular-punctate. Inflorescence in axillary and terminal panicles or terminal paniculate cymes. Flowers bisexual; sepals, petals

and stamens glandular-punctate. Sepals slightly confluent at the base, imbricate, not enlarged and accrescent in fruit, persistent. Petals free, imbricate,
slightly coherent in the middle just before anthesis. Stamens 10, connate at
the base, epipetalous ones always included, all fertile or some sterile; filaments
often glandular pubescent; anthers often glandular at base. Pistil 1; ovary
ovoid or subglobose, densely pubescent; style pilose at base, glandular pubescent in the upper-half; stigma capitate. Fruit a pod-like follicle opening
length-wise along the ventral suture, sometimes also along the dorsal suture,
usually nearly straight on the dorsal, curved on the ventral suture which is
also gibbous in *Connarus championii*; base shortly stalked or narrowed into a
long and slender stalk; remnant of style usually shifted to the dorsal side;
pericarp woody or coriaceous. Seed 1; testa dark purple, shiny, basal part
enveloped by a fleshy yellow lobulate arillode; endosperm absent.

A genus of about 100 species, pantropical especially in S. America, S.E.
Asia and Malaysia. Represented by one species in Australia and two species
in Melanesia. Two representatives in Ceylon, one species in the dry coastal
regions and one species extending to the moist central region.

KEY TO THE SPECIES

1 Leaflets 3 or 5. Rachis+petiole up to 4.5 cm, obscurely pulvinate and wrinkled at base.
  Inflorescence in terminal paniculate cymes. Stamens all fertile. Fruit tapering gradually
  to a stalk about 5 mm long, curved but not gibbous along the ventral suture. Valves
  with longitudinal striations outside, glabrous inside...............**1. C. monocarpus**
1 Leaflets 5 or 7. Rachis+petiole up to 17.5 cm, distinctly pulvinate and wrinkled at base.
  Inflorescence in axillary and terminal panicles. Stamens not all fertile. Fruit abruptly
  stalked (stalk 2 mm long), curved and very gibbous along the ventral suture. Valves
  with oblique striations outside, puberulous inside...................**2. C. championii**

1. Connarus monocarpus L., Sp. Pl. 675. 1753; Thw., Enum. Pl. Zeyl. 80.
1858; Hook. f., Fl. Br. Ind. 2: 50. 1876; Trimen, Handb. Fl. Ceylon 2: 2.
1894; Schellenb. in Pflanzenr. H. 103: 284, f. 47. 1938. Syntype: Herb. Hermann, Cat. 3, page 8 & cat. 4, page 77 (BM). Lectotype: Cat. 3, page 8 (BM).

Rhus zeylanicus trifoliatus, Burm., Thes. Zeyl. 199, f. 89, 1737.
Rhus radaelijawael Miller, Gard. Dict. ed. 8: n. 13. 1768.
Connarus pinnatus Lam., Enc. 2 (1): 95. 1786; Ill. t. 572. 1797; Moon, Cat. 49.
  1824.
Omphalobium indicum Gaertn., Fruct. 1: 217, t. 46, f. 3. 1788.
Canarium zeylanicum Blume, Mus. Bot. Lugduno Batavum 1: 218. 1850.
See Leenhouts (1958—Fl. Mal. ser. 1, 5: 538) for complete list of synonymy.

Scandent shrub up to 5 m tall. Outer bark reticulate, striate, minutely
pustular with numerous lenticels; inner bark beef-red with a watery-coloured
exudate; sap-wood mottled-pale pink. Young parts ferrugineous tomentose.

Leaf scars very prominent. Leaf rachis + petiole 4.5 cm long, obscurely pulvinate and wrinkled at base. Leaflets 3 or 5, ovate oblong, 12.4 cm long, 4.4 cm broad, more or less obtuse or rounded at base, subacuminate to caudate at tip, often twisted at the apex, glabrous, shiny dark-green above, paler and with many minute browny scales beneath; young flush coppery brown; venation reticulate and prominent. Petiolule up to 5 mm long. Flowers in terminal erect, irregularly pyramidal paniculate cymes, ferrugineous-tomentose. Bracts less than 1 mm long. Pedicel 3 to 5 mm long, puberulous. Sepals narrowly triangular or oblong, up to 3.5 mm long, outer surface puberulous, margin ciliate. Petals linear-oblanceolate, up to 8 mm long, cuneate to tapering at base, acute to slightly rounded at tip, a few stipitate glands present on the inner surface, margin ciliate. Stamens in 2 whorls, both fertile; outer filaments up to 8 mm long, shorter ones up to 2 mm long; anthers subglobose, up to 0.5 mm in diameter. Ovary subglobose, densely pubescent, brownish. Style slender. Fruit an irregularly obovoid follicle, fusiform, compressed, 4.5 cm long, 2 cm broad, more or less falcate when dried, apiculate, tapering below into a narrow stalk, up to 5 mm long, surrounded at base by the persistent calyx and petals; valves leathery, naviculate, outer surface rather coarse with longitudinal striations, green through yellow to scarlet red; inner surface glabrous, pale cream. Seed single, conspicuous, ovoid, 2 cm long, 1.2 cm broad, compressed, reniform, shining, purplish-black, surrounded at base with a large lobulate, pulpy, bright yellow aril.

D i s t r. In Ceylon, very common in the dry regions, in sandy places; rather rare in the moist low country. Also in South India (W. Deccan).

E c o l. Often found growing in sandy soils or dunes, or low secondary jungles, often along seaward slopes of hill. Flowering from July to September.

The ripe follicles, with the black seeds, are very pretty objects at the ends of branches and form a very conspicuous part of the landscape.

V e r n. Radaliya (S); Chettupulukodi (T).

I l l u s t r. Burm., Thes. Zeyl. f. 89, l.c.; Brandis, Indian Trees 211, f. 93, 1906; Schellenb., in Pflanzenr. H. 103, f. 47, l.c.

N o t e. Leenhouts l.c. distinguishes two subspecies, Ssp. *monocarpus*, described above and a second subspecies *malayensis* Leenh. which occurs in the Malay Peninsula, the Moluccas, Nicobars and Andamans. It is characterized by its stiff leaflets, slender ascending nerves, rather inconspicuous venation, its spindle-shaped fruits, and by the non-ferrugineous tomentum covering the young parts and inflorescence.

S p e c i m e n s   E x a m i n e d. ANURADHAPURA DISTRICT: Wilpattu Nat. Park, North East of Kuruttu Pandi Villu, *Koyama & Herat 13402* (PDA, US); *Wirawan, Cooray & Balakrishnan 68091008* (K, PDA, US); At Dangala in plot W32, *Mueller-Dombois, Wirawan & Balakrishnan 69042812*

(PDA, US); Altitude 30–150 m, *Robyns 6974* (K, PDA, US); In open scrub forest on sandy terrain, *Tirvengadum & Jayasuriya 252* (G, K, L, MAU, P, PDA, US), *253* (K, L, MAU, P, PDA, US), *254* (K, MAU, P, PDA, US); By Manavila pond, *Tirvengadum & Jayasuriya 255* (G, K, L, MAU, P, PDA, US); 3 miles West of Office, *Meijer 356* (PDA, US); *C.F. & R.J. Van Beusekom 1612* (PDA, US). AMPARAI DISTRICT: Lahugala Tank, East side close to large rock outcrop, altitude 36 m, *Mueller-Dombois & Comanor 67072522* (PDA, US). COLOMBO DISTRICT: Près de Colombo, terrain sablonneux, *Leschenault s.n.* BATTICALOA DISTRICT: Batticaloa, *Walker 201* (PDA); Vandaramulai, among fence post along Batticaloa-Vallaichena road, *Tirvengadum, Cramer & Balasubramaniam 233* (G, K, L, MAU, P, PDA, US). MONERAGALA DISTRICT: Bibile, *Silva s.n.* (PDA); BADULLA DISTRICT: Gurulupota, near mile marker 37/2, *Tirvengadum & Jayasuriya 157* (K, MAU, P, PDA, US). MATARA DISTRICT: *Alston 1222* (PDA); GALLE DISTRICT: Pointe de Galles, *Pierre 39* (P); Galle, Buena Vista Hill, *Meijer 249* (PDA, US); Devundera, *s. coll. s.n.* (PDA); Along seaward slopes of hill, *Cramer 3010* (PDA, US); Low secondary jungle near Kimbulapitiya, *Simpson 8591* (BM). LOCALITY UNKNOWN: *Blume s.n.* (P); *Burmann s.n.* in 1773 (G); *Burmann 85* (G); *Burmann s.n.* (G); *Hermann s.n.* (BM); *Macrae 240* (BM, K); *Thwaites C.P. 323* (BM, G, P, PDA); *Walker 19, 121* (K); *Walker s.n.* in 1830 (G); *Jonville s.n.* in 1800 (BM); *John Miers 11* (BM); Collection Stathoudérienne *2, 52, 112* (P).

2. Connarus championii Thw., Enum. Pl. Zeyl. 80. 1858; Hook. f., Fl. Br. Ind. 2: 52. 1876; Trimen, Handb. Fl. Ceylon 2: 3. 1894; Schellenb., in Pflanzenr. H. 103: 281. 1938. Holotype: *Thwaites C.P. 2399* (K); Isotypes: (G, MH, P, PDA).

Scandent shrub. Outer bark vertically striate, lenticellate, pale brown. Young shoots rufous puberulous. Rachis + petiole up to 17.5 cm long, cylindrical, glabrous, wrinkled at base, distinctly pulvinate; pulvinus articulates on annular projection at nodes. Leaflets 5 to 7, oval oblong, 7 to 21 cm long, 4 to 7 cm broad, subacute at base, caudate acuminate at tip, coriaceous, glabrous on both surfaces, shining above; veins 5 to 7 pairs, prominent beneath. Petioles swollen, about 5 mm long. Inflorescence in axillary and terminal much-branched panicles, rufous pilose. Bracts 1 mm long, rufous pilose. Pedicel up to 2 mm long. Sepals boat-shaped, triangular or oval oblong, up to 2.5 mm long, coarsely pilose inside, densely so outside. Petals obovate to oblong lanceolate, up to 1 cm long, acute or obtuse; limb short and narrow, glabrous on both surfaces, not ciliate. Stamens in 2 whorls, distinctly gland-tipped; outer filaments up to 6 mm long, with fertile anthers; shorter ones subulate, up to 1 mm long, sterile or staminodial. Ovary ovoid, densely rufous pilose; style stout, rufous pilose, covered with numerous pale yellow stipitate glands. Fruit an ovoid follicular structure 3.5 cm long, 2 cm broad, subcompressed, abruptly stalked at base (stalk about 2 mm long), surrounded by persistent calyx, very gibbous along ventral suture; valves striate with oblique ridges, especially in the dried fruits, opening by ventral suture, from green through yellow and brown to scarlet; inner surface puberulous; follicle for the most part empty. Seed single on a marginal placenta, ovoid, 9 cm long, 3 cm broad, surrounded by a yellow lobulate arillode, white when immature, pale brown later.

D i s t r. Endemic in Ceylon.
E c o l. Found in fringes of secondary forests, often close to stream. Flowering in January.
V e r n. Wel-radaliya (S).
S p e c i m e n s E x a m i n e d. KANDY DISTRICT: Madulkele, between Panwila and Madulkele, mile marker 16/2, close to stream, *Tirvengadum & Balasubramaniam 348* (K, MAU, P, PDA, US). RATNAPURA DISTRICT: Gilimale, *Tirvengadum & Balasubramaniam 170* (G, K, L, MAU, P, PDA, US). GALLE DISTRICT: Sinharaja, between Deniyaya and Ensalwatta, near mile marker 54/4, *Tirvengadum & Balasubramaniam 330* (MAU, P, PDA, US); between Rakwana & Kalawana, near bridge, *Tirvengadum & Balasubramaniam 341 & 342* (G, K, L, MAU, P, PDA, US); in the jungle, 400 ft altitude, *Balakrishnan, NBK 249* (PDA, US). LOCALITY UNKNOWN: *Walker 16* (G); *Thwaites C.P. 2399* (G, K, MH, P, PDA); *Champion s.n.* (K); *Mackenzie s.n.* (K); *Kelaart s.n.* in 1843 (P).

3. ELLIPANTHUS

Hook. f. in Benth. & Hook. f., Gen. Pl. 1: 434. 1862. Type species: *Ellipanthus unifoliatus* (Thw.) Thw.

Small trees or shrubs. Leaves unifoliolate, entire. Petiole articulate. Flowers in short axillary racemes, bisexual or unisexual. Calyx deeply 5-lobed, lobes valvate, persistent but not enlarged in fruit. Petals free, imbricate. Stamens 10, connate at base into a tube, episepalous ones fertile, epipetalous ones sterile, much smaller, tooth-like. Pistil 1, pilose; ovary ovoid, oblique; style short, stigma capitate. Fruit a follicular structure, strongly dorsally geniculate, the basal part constricted into a long stipe with persistent calyx, fertile part opening lengthwise by a slit, densely tomentose outside, glabrous within; pericarp woody. Seed solitary, arillate; endosperm not abundant.

A genus with about 10 species; 3 in Africa, 2 in Madagascar, the others in S.E. Asia (Deccan to Hainan), the Andamans & Malaysia. In Ceylon, it is represented by 1 species which is endemic and rare.

Ellipanthus unifoliatus (Thw.) Thw., Enum. Pl. Zeyl. Add. 410. 1864; Schellenb., in Pflanzenr. H. 103: 183. 1938. Type: Based on *Connarus unifoliatus* Thw.

Connarus unifoliatus Thw., Enum. Pl. Zeyl. 80. 1858. Type: Ceylon, *Thwaites C.P. 2443*. Holotype (K); Isotypes (BM, G, MH, P, PDA).
Ellipanthus thwaitesii Hook. f., Fl. Br. Ind. 2: 55. 1876; Trimen, Handb. Fl. Ceylon 2: 3. 1894. Type: Based on *Connarus unifoliatus* Thw.

A small tree 7 to 10 m tall. Branches slender, smooth, purplish-black; young twigs puberulous. Leaves simple, unifoliate (reduced to 1 leaflet), up to 10 cm long, up to 3 cm broad, elliptic-oblong, acute to rounded at base, caudate-acuminate at tip, coriaceous, glabrous, with prominent reticulate venation, articulated on the short petiole. Inflorescence in axillary racemes, up to 2 cm long, pubescent. Flowers bisexual, sometimes unisexual, articulated on short pubescent pedicels. Bracts deciduous. Calyx tube short; calyx lobes triangular, thick, pubescent. Petals twice the length of the sepal, obtuse, tomentose outside, glabrous inside. Staminal tube glabrous outside, densely pilose inside; filaments up to 0.5 mm long, subulate, villous at the base; anthers up to 1 mm long, sagittiform. Ovary ovoid, densely pilose, attenuate into a short style and capitate stigma. Fruit 2.5 to 3 cm long, much falcate when young, tapering into a narrow stipe at base, acute at tip, compressed, woody, covered with a yellowish-brown tomentum. Seed 0.5 to 2 cm long, basal part covered with a thin, pinkish, pulpy tomentum.

D i s t r. Endemic in Ceylon. Reported in the Midlands and Uplands up to an elevation of 1700 m by Trimen l.c. Flower pale green.

E c o l. Flowering time January. Very rare, probably due to clearings and deforestations around Kandy District.

N o t e. Although Thwaites referred to this plant as a rather rare taxon, it must have thrived fairly well in various places in the Central Province since Trimen gave a number of localities where it had been collected. It has, however, not been seen by any recent collector.

S p e c i m e n s E x a m i n e d. KANDY DISTRICT: Maskeliya, *Alexander s.n.* in 1888 (PDA); alt. 3000–4000 ft, Hunasgiriya, Deltota, Gampola, *Thwaites C.P. 2443* (BM, G, K, MH, P, PDA); 3000 to 4000 ft, *s. coll. s.n.* (MH).

CONVOLVULACEAE

(by Daniel F. Austin*)

Type Genus: *Convolvulus* L.

Herbs, vines, lianas, shrubs or trees, the sap milky in some species; the rootstocks sometimes large, otherwise fibrous; sometimes parasitic. Leaves mostly simple, pinnately lobed or pectinate, palmately compound in some species, or reduced to scales in *Cuscuta*; exstipulate. Inflorescences axillary, dichasial, solitary, racemose or paniculate. Flowers perfect or imperfect (some African species), regular or slightly zygomorphic, small and inconspicuous to large and showy but mostly wilting quickly; sepals 5, free, imbricate, equal or unequal, persistent, occasionally accrescent in fruit; corolla sympetalous, tubular, funnelform, campanulate, urceolate or salverform, the limb with 5 lobes or teeth or almost entire, with plicae and interplicae, in bud mostly induplicate; stamens 5, distinct, the filaments inserted on the corolla tube base alternate with corolla lobes, the anthers mostly linear or oblong, 2-celled, extrorse; disc annular or cupuliform, sometimes 5-lobed occasionally absent; ovary superior, of 2 to 4 carpels, usually 2- or 3-locular, each locule biovulate, rarely 4- or 6-ovulate or unilocular with 4 ovules, the style filiform, simple or bifid or 2 distinct styles present, the stigma capitate or bilobate or the stigmas 2 and linear, ellipsoid, branched or globose. Fruits 1- to 4-locular, capsular, dehiscent by valves, transversely dehiscent, irregularly dehiscent or indehiscent and baccate or nut-like; seeds 1–4, commonly fewer than ovules, glabrous or pubescent, the endosperm absent or scanty, cartilaginous, the cotyledons mostly foliaceous.

A family of 40 or more genera and about 1200 species, these plants are most abundant in the tropics and sub-tropics. In Ceylon there are 16 genera, 2 of which are known only from cultivation (*Porana & Turbina*). Three species are endemic: *Argyreia hancorniaefolia*, *A. populifolia* and *Ipomoea jucunda*. About 18 of the species known to occur have been introduced from the Western Hemisphere. The other taxa show a close relationship with the Indo-Malaysian region, and, to a lesser extent, with Africa.

The family is probably most closely related to the Polemoniaceae. Some have thought the Convolvulaceae more closely related to the Solanaceae, but

*Florida Atlantic University, U.S.A.

this is not likely. Within the family most have found generic limits difficult. All of the genera recognized in this treatment are distinct enough that, with a little practice, they can be easily recognized. *Operculina* is separable from *Merremia* in some cases only if fruiting material is available. *Rivea* is the most poorly defined taxon discussed. Van Ooststroom and others have considered this small group of species distinct from *Argyreia*. Differences largely appear to be the adaptation to moth pollination in *Rivea* vs. bee pollination in *Argyreia*, but without detailed study of all the species I am not prepared to initiate changes in nomenclature. The genera found in Ceylon are grouped in the following tribes:

Subfamily Convolvuloideae
    Tribe **Erycibeae**:   *Erycibe*
    Tribe **Cresseae**:   *Bonamia, Cressa*
    Tribe **Convolvuleae**:   *Evolvulus, Jacquemontia*
    Tribe **"Merremioids"**:   *Aniseia, Merremia, Hewittia, Operculina*
    Tribe **Ipomoeeae**:   *Ipomoea*
    Tribe **Argyreieae**:   *Argyreia, Rivea, Stictocardia, Turbina*
    Tribe **Poraneae**:   *Porana*
Subfamily Cuscutoideae
    Tribe **Cuscuteae**:   *Cuscuta*

Economically the most important species in the family is the sweet potato (*Ipomoea batatas*) or "batala" in Sinhala. This species provides a supplement to the basic rice diet, and also provides nutrition absent from rice. Most of the homes in the wet zone have at least a small bed of "batala". Many of the dry zone homes also have the plants in their gardens. Of minor importance in the island diet is "kankun" (*Ipomoea aquatica*). The stems and leaves of this vine are eaten in a "mallun" with so many chillies that its taste is often lost. Perhaps the two most common ornamentals are *Argyreia nervosa* and *Merremia tuberosa*. Of secondary importance are *Ipomoea indica* and *I. cairica*; these last two have become naturalized so widely that cultivation and spontaneous occurrence are difficult to determine. *Stictocardia, Turbina, Porana, Ipomoea alba* and *Ipomoea quamoclit* are cultivated occasionally.

Although the family is not noted for many active chemical compounds, several of the species are used in local ayurvedic medicines. The best known is "trastawalu" (*Operculina turpethum*), long noted for its laxative roots. This species along with "vishnu-kranti" (*Evolvulus alsinoides*) and "kaladana" (*Ipomoea nil*) show a strong Indian influence in local medicines. In addition several of the *Argyreia* species, *Ipomoea carnea, Ipomoea obscura, I. pescaprae, Merremia tridentata* and others are used locally.

To make this treatment as useful as possible genera and species have been alphabetized. This may obscure some relationships between species, but most users will probably want to identify their plants and not delve into phylogeny within the family. Furthermore, I have included cultivated with native and naturalized species in the text. Notes are given as to the status of each but I thought it more utilitarian to not treat the cultivated plants separately.

KEY TO THE GENERA

1 Leafless, parasitic plants. Stems yellow to orange, without chlorophyll. Flowers small, in clusters or short racemes. Corollas mostly with 5 epipetalous fimbriate scales inside
....**5. Cuscuta**
1 Leafy, non-parasitic (autotrophic) plants. Stems green or brown, at least the young chlorophyllous. Flowers large to medium, rarely small, in compound inflorescences or solitary. Corollas without scales
   2 Styles absent; stigma 1, conical or semiglobular, 5–10-rayed. Corolla lobes bifid. Ovary 1-celled. Fruit fleshy or woody, indehiscent. Woody twiners or straggling shrubs..**6. Erycibe**
   2 Styles present; stigmas 1 to 2 or 4, globose, ellipsoid or linear. Corolla lobes subentire to entire. Ovary 1-celled, less commonly 2-celled or incompletely 4-celled. Fruits fleshy to chartaceous, dehiscent or indehiscent. Woody or herbaceous twiners, subshrubs or shrubs
      3 Sepals accrescent in fruit, patent, scarious, falling with the fruit. Flowers 5–6 mm long, white. Corolla limbs shallowly lobed..........................**13. Porana**
      3 Sepals not or rarely accrescent in fruit, falling with the fruit or not. Flowers usually 10 mm or much larger, variously colored. Corolla limbs shallowly lobed to subentire
         4 Styles 2, free or united near the base
            5 Styles united below; stigmas globose to peltate. High twiners........**3. Bonamia**
            5 Styles free, each branch forked; with 4 filiform or slightly clavate stigmas. Small herbaceous plants, never twining...................................**7. Evolvulus**
         4 Styles 1, entire, or with 2 inconspicuous branches hidden by the stigmas
            6 Herbs, subshrubby, much-branched, perennial. Leaves to 1 cm long, sessile. Plants of xeric regions...**4. Cressa**
            6 Herbs, vines or lianas, perennial or annual. Leaves mostly over 1 cm long, petiolate. Plants of hydric or mesic regions, rarely xeric
               7 Stems and leaves with stellate trichomes. Stigmas ellipsoid to oblong...........
               ....**10. Jacquemontia**
               7 Stems and leaves with bilobed or simple trichomes or glabrous. Stigmas globose or capitate
                  8 Outer 2 or 3 sepals enlarged, much longer and broader than inner
                     9 Outer sepals decurrent on the pedicel. Corolla white. Leaves rounded to acute at base...**1. Aniseia**
                     9 Outer sepals not decurrent on the pedicel. Corolla white or cream-yellow with a purple center, rarely without colored center. Leaves cordate to truncate at base
                     ....**8. Hewittia**
                  8 Outer and inner sepals equal or unequal but the outer not markedly longer and broader than the inner
                     10 Corollas broad-funnelform or campanulate, usually yellow or yellowish with a red or purple eye, or white. Pollen smooth, colpate
                        11 Capsule circumscissile, the upper part of the epicarp separating from the lower part. Corolla usually white or yellow throughout. Stems terete or often winged
                        ....**12. Operculina**
                        11 Capsule opening by 4 valves or irregularly. Corolla white to yellow, often with a red or purple center. Stems terete....................**11. Merremia**

10 Corollas funnelform to salverform, rarely campanulate, variously colored but often
   purple. Pollen spinose, porate
   12 Calyx accrescent, completely enclosing the ripe fruit. Leaf blades with minute black
      glands below. Flowers mauve, scarlet or crimson, campanulate-funnelform.........
      ....**15. Stictocardia**
   12 Calyx not accrescent, not enclosing fruit. Leaf blades without black glands below
      (except *Ipomoea jucunda*). Flowers mostly purple or purplish, less commonly yellow,
      white or red, funnelform to salverform
      13 Fruit capsular, thin-walled, opening by valves or irregularly dehiscent. Herbaceous
         or rarely woody, twining or prostrate or rarely erect plants. Corolla usually glabrous
         outside..**9. Ipomoea**
      13 Fruit indehiscent, fleshy, woody or leathery. Suffrutescent to woody twining plants.
         Corolla mostly pubescent outside, at least on the midpetaline bands (interplicae)
         14 Corolla white, salverform. Stamens attached near the middle of the tube. Stigmas
            linear-oblong. Fruits nearly dry.....................................**14. Rieva**
         14 Corolla white, purple or rose, funnelform to campanulate-funnelform. Stamens
            attached below the middle of the tube. Stigmas globose or biglobose. Fruits fleshy,
            leathery or dry and with a thin woody pericarp.
            15 Flowers white, with a dark base inside the tube. Fruits dry, woody and distinctly
               mucronate by the style base. Seeds puberulent....................**16. Turbina**
            15 Flowers purple to rose, rarely white. Fruits fleshy or leathery, not or indistinctly
               mucronate by the style base. Seeds glabrous or pilose at the hilum....**2. Argyreia**

1. ANISEIA

Choisy, Mem. Soc. Phys. Genève 6: 481. 1834. Type Species: *Aniseia martinicensis* (Jacq.) Choisy.

Herbaceous vines. Leaves linear to ovate or elliptic, often mucronate,
entire. Flowers axillary, solitary or in few-flowered dichasia; sepals 5, herbaceous, unequal, the 3 outer sepals larger, often decurrent on the pedicel;
corolla white, campanulate, the limb 5-dentate or sub-entire, with 5 pubescent
interplicae; stamens and style included, the pollen pantocolpate; ovary
glabrous, 2-locular, the locules 2-ovulate; the disc small or absent; style 1,
slender, the stigma biglobose. Fruits capsular, globose to ovoid, 2-celled, 4-
valvate; seeds 4, glabrous.

The genus contains 4 or 5 species, all of New World origin. One species
has been introduced throughout the Old World tropics.

Aniseia martinicensis (Jacq.) Choisy, Mem. Soc. Phys. Genève 8: 66. 1838.
Type: West Indies, Martinique, "vicum Roberti" (no specimen found).

Convolvulus martinicensis Jacq., Sel. Stirp. Amer. 26. t. 17. 1763.
Convolvulus uniflorus Burm. f., Fl. Ind. 47. t. 21. f. 2. 1768.
Aniseia uniflora (Burm. f.) Choisy, Mem. Soc. Phys. Genève 6: 483. 1834;
   Thw., Enum. Fl. Zeyl. 212. 1860.
Ipomoea uniflora (Burm. f.) Roem. & Schult., Syst. Veg. 4: 247. 1819; Clarke

in Hook. f., Fl. Br. Ind. 4: 201. 1883; Trimen, Handb. Fl. Ceylon 3: 215. 1895.

Vines; the stems herbaceous, at least above, glabrous to sparsely pubescent. Leaves narrowly lanceolate, 4–8 cm long, obtuse to acute basally, obtuse and mucronate apically, entire, glabrous. Inflorescences axillary, flowers usually solitary but occasionally cymose. Flowers with peduncles to 5 cm long; sepals broadly ovate, the outer 2 broader than the inner 3, 12–17 mm long, acuminate; corolla white, campanulate, 25–30 mm long. Fruits capsular, ovoid, 2 cm long, subtended by the enlarged calyx; seeds black, glabrous.

D i s t r. A species originally from the tropics of Central and South America, now pantropical.

E c o l. Found in low country on moist or swampy ground; 50–90 meters or less in altitude. The plants are not uncommon weeds in the rice fields of Kalutara and Galle Districts. They might interfere with paddy cultivation more if they were not eaten by the cultivators. Leaves, which are somewhat thicker than American populations, are used in a "mallun".

V e r n. Potu-pala (S); "potu"—bark, "pala"—vine.

S p e c i m e n s E x a m i n e d. KALUTARA DISTRICT: Kalutara, *s. coll. s.n. anon.*, in 1882 (PDA); Agalawatte, *s. coll. s.n.* in 1893 (PDA). GALLE DISTRICT: Wakwella, *Austin et al. 6261* (FAU, PDA, US); Koggala Airport, *Austin et al. 6265* (FAU, PDA, US); Galle, *s. coll.* in 1853. *C.P. 3006* (PDA). LOCALITY UNKNOWN: *s. coll. C.P. 3006* (G, L); *Fraser s.n.* in 1850 (US).

2. ARGYREIA

Lour., Fl. Cochinch. 134. 1790. Type Species: *Argyreia obtusifolia* Lour.

Lettsomia Roxb., Fl. Ind. ed. Carey and Wall. 2: 75. 1824. Type: Not chosen. *Moorcroftia* Choisy, Mem. Soc. Phys. Genève 6: 431. 1833. Type: Not chosen.

Lianas, perennial. Leaves petioled, variable in size and shape, glabrous to pubescent. Flowers in axillary few- to many-flowered cymes; sepals 5, herbaceous to subcoriaceous, variable in shape and size, often hairy outside, slightly to much enlarged in fruit, in the latter case often red inside; corolla small to large, campanulate, funnelform or tubular, purple, red, pink, or white, the limb nearly entire to deeply lobed, the interplicae pubescent; stamens 5, included or exserted, the stigma biglobular. Fruits ellipsoid or globose, fleshy, leathery, or mealy berries, purplish, red, orange, or yellowish; seeds 4 or fewer, glabrous, rarely pilose at the hilum.

This genus contains about 90 species, all of which are native to tropical continental Asia, Malaysia and northern Australia. Little study of the group has been done in recent times with the exception of van Ooststroom and Hoogland's studies in Malaysia (Fl. Mal. 4: 494–512. 1953). No recent study has been made of the Indian species and these are virtually all distinct from the Malaysian plants.

KEY TO THE SPECIES

1 Corolla less than 2 cm long. Stamens_exserted. Fruit 5–9 mm long, red.............
....6. A. osyrensis
1 Corolla 2 cm long or larger. Stamens included. Fruits mostly over 1 cm long, usually yellow, rarely red
 2 Leaves densely silver-white pubescent below
  3 Base of leaves cordate. Flowers 5–7 cm long. Fruits brownish, mealy...5. A. nervosa
  3 Base of leaves acute to ovate. Flowers 2–3 cm long. Fruits red, fleshy.............
  ....9. A. splendens
 2 Leaves glabrous or pubescent below, if pubescent then yellowish to brownish
  4 Sepals linear, acute. Leaves densely pubescent on both sides, oval-oblong.........
  ....1. A. choisyana
  4 Sepals oval, obtuse. Leaves glabrous to pubescent, cordate to elliptic
   5 Leaves cordate basally, usually about as wide as long, the secondary veins palmate at least basally
    6 Bracts linear-subulate, 7–9 mm long.............................11. A. sp. A.
    6 Bracts oblong, elliptic to lanceolate, mostly 1.5–3.5 cm long
     7 Leaves densely pubescent above and below with yellowish or reddish trichomes. Plants of altitudes above 2000 feet.............................4. A. hirsuta
     7 Leaves glabrous or remotely pubescent. Plants of lower altitudes from sea level to about 2000 feet elevation...................................8. A. populifolia
   5 Leaves truncate, cuneate or acute basally, always longer than wide, the secondary veins pinnate, emerging directly from the midvein at obtuse or acute angles
    8 Leaves coriaceous, in appearance much like *Ficus*. Fruits ellipsoid to oblong-ovoid, 2.5–3 cm long...3. A. hancorniaefolia
    8 Leaves herbaceous to chartaceous, not appearing like *Ficus*. Fruits globose to depressed-globose or oblong-globose, 10–20 mm long
     9 Bracts caducous in fruit. Secondary veins of leaves purplish when living. Fruits globose to somewhat ovoid, 10–11 mm long. Plants of submontane forests 2000–4000 feet in elevation...2. A. elliptica
     9 Bracts persistent. Secondary veins greenish when living. Fruits globose to depressed-globose, 10–20 mm long. Plants of low country, usually below 1000 feet
      10 Outer 2 sepals shorter than the inner. Flowers on pedicels up to 3 mm long. Plants of the dry zone.......................................7. A. pomacea
      10 Outer 2 sepals equal to or longer than the inner. Flowers sessile. Plants of the wet zone...10. A. thwaitesii

1. Argyreia choisyana Wight ex Clarke in Hook. f., Fl. Br. Ind. 4: 190. 1883; Trimen, Handb. Fl. Ceylon 3: 208. 1895. Type: India, *Wight 1961* (K).

Batatas choisyana Wight in Thw., Enum. Pl. Zeyl. 210. 1860, nomen nudum. *Ipomoea atropurpurea* Choisy in DC., Prod. 9: 366. 1845. Type: India, *Wallich 1345* (G-DC).

Lianas (?); the stems apparently twining, covered with spreading brownish-yellow trichomes. Leaves ovate-oblong to elliptic-oblong, 2.5–2.8 cm long, basally truncate to slightly rounded, the apex obtuse to subacute, apiculate, densely pubescent on both surfaces with spreading brownish-yellow trichomes. Inflorescences of 1–3-flowered cymes; bracts narrowly oblong to linear-lanceolate, pubescent. Flowers with 5–6 mm peduncles; sepals lanceolate to linear-lanceolate, 18–20 mm long, tapering, apically acuminate, pubescent with spreading trichomes of a brownish-yellow; corolla probably lavender or purplish, funnelform, about 4 cm long. Fruits not seen.

D i s t r. Found only in southern India and Ceylon. This is apparently a rare plant in India and has not been found in Ceylon since the 1850's.

E c o l. Very little about the plant is known. The specimen from Ceylon was collected somewhere in the dry zone of Batticaloa.

N o t e. Insufficient study has been made of the Indian species and the limits of several species are in question. This population is similar to *Argyreia bracteata* Choisy.

S p e c i m e n s E x a m i n e d. BATTICALOA DISTRICT: Batticaloa, *s. coll.* Mar. 1858. *C.P. 3647* (PDA).

2. Argyreia elliptica Choisy, Mem. Soc. Phys. Genève 6: 330. 1834; Choisy in DC., Prod. 9: 330. 1845 (pro parte). Type: India, *Wallich 1417, 1380, 1381* (G-DC).

Lettsomia elliptica Wight, Ic. Pl. Ind. Or. 4 (2): 12. 1850; Clarke in Hook. f., Fl. Br. Ind. 4: 192. 1883; Trimen, Handb. Fl. Ceylon 3: 209. 1895.

Lianas; the stems herbaceous toward the tips, woody on older growth, glabrous or with erect, scattered, stiff trichomes. Leaves oblong-lanceolate to ovate-lanceolate, occasionally ovate, 5–17 cm long, cuneate, obtuse or rarely slightly rounded basally, acute, cuneate to acuminate apically, scattered appressed trichomes on both surfaces. Inflorescences axillary, of 2–6-flowered cymes; bracts caducous, rarely present in fruit, narrowly lanceolate. Flowers with peduncles 3–10 cm long, enlarged in fruit; sepals ovate, 3–4 mm long, acute, pubescent without; corolla lavender, with a darker purple tube, funnelform, 2.5–3 cm long. Fruits fleshy, indehiscent, globose to somewhat ovoid, 10–11 mm long, glabrous; seeds not seen.

D i s t r. Known only from southern India and the Central Province of Ceylon.

E c o l. Found in the hills of the wet zone between about 2000 and 4000 feet elevation. The plants are common in some sites near roadsides and in disturbed sites and margins of submontane forests. Unlike *Argyreia hancorniaefolia*, which is found in the same zone, *A. elliptica* appears able to survive as a pioneer plant on roadsides.

N o t e. This is an easy species to recognize in the living state because of the purplish secondary veins on the leaves. No other member of the family on the island has this character. When dried the plants may be confused with a lowland species from the Districts of Galle, Kalutara, Kegalle and Ratnapura, listed below as *Argyreia thwaitesii*. To distinguish these two see the discussion under *A. thwaitesii*.

S p e c i m e n s E x a m i n e d. KANDY DISTRICT: Hantane, *Gardner 614* (K, PDA); Hantane, *Gardner s.n., C.P. 1933* (PDA). BADULLA DISTRICT: Uma-Oya off Ettampitiya, *Jayasuriya & Townsend 1174* (K, PDA); Lunugala, *s. coll. s.n.* Jan. 1888 (PDA). LOCALITY UNKNOWN: *s. coll. C.P. 1933* (K); *s. coll.* in 1862, *C.P. 1933* (K).

3. Argyreia hancorniaefolia Gardner in Thw., Enum. Pl. Zeyl. 210. 1860. Type: Kandy District: Hantane, *s. coll.* in 1851. *C.P. 1924* (holotype PDA).

Lettsomia hancorniaefolia (Gardner) Clarke in Hook. f., Fl. Br. Ind. 4: 196. 1883; Trimen, Handb. Fl. Ceylon 3: 210. 1895.

Lianas; the stems mostly woody, herbaceous at the tips, glabrous or with sparse appressed fulvous indument when young. Leaves ovate, elliptic to oblong-ovate, 5–12 cm long, obtuse, truncate or slightly rounded basally, acute to abruptly acuminate apically, coriaceous, with prominent parallel secondary veins, glabrous. Inflorescences terminal or subterminal or on lateral branches, solitary or axillary or short-racemose; bracts inconspicuous, subulate-triangular. Flowers on short peduncles, usually 6–8 mm long, pedicels as long or somewhat longer; sepals ovate to broadly-ovate, 4–6 mm long in flower, enlarging to 7–8 mm in fruit, obtuse, minutely fulvous-pubescent; corolla rose-pink (fide Trimen), funnelform, 2–2.5 cm long. Fruits indehiscent, baccate, somewhat leathery, oblong-ovoid to ellipsoid, 2.5–3 cm long, glabrous, ripe fruits not seen, probably yellowish, immature fruits green, turning black when dried, the sepals only slightly spreading, supporting; seeds 1 or 2, glabrous, oblong to ellipsoid.

D i s t r. These lianas are endemic to the submontane forest slopes of the Central Province of Ceylon.

E c o l. Plants of the submontane forests, these lianas have been collected recently only between about 2400 and 3000 feet. The forests where these plants grow are being cut for cultivation and they are increasingly endangered. Even in Trimen's time they were considered "very rare".

N o t e. This is a liana of the mature or at least maturing forest in the hill country. At present only two plants are known to remain, but large areas have been little studied botanically and the species will perhaps be found elsewhere. The species looks little like the others on the island. Characteristic are the leathery leaves which are flushed with red on the new branches. Fruits are berries with abundant white latex. This latex oxidizes quickly on exposure to the air to a yellow-brown colour.

Specimens Examined. KANDY DISTRICT: road to Hantane, *Ferguson s.n.* (PDA); Hunnasgiriya, *Austin et al. 6206* (FAU, PDA, US); between Hunnasgiriya and Madugoda, *Jayasuriya 359* (K, PDA, US); Nugatenne, *Alston s.n.*, Sept. 1928 (PDA); LOCALITY UNKNOWN: *s. coll. C.P. 1924* (G, K); *Gardner 607* (K); *Wallich 149* (K).

4. Argyreia hirsuta Arn., Nova Acta Phy. Med. Acad. Caes. Leop. Carol. Nat. Cur. 18: 365 c. 1836. Type: India, in montibus Peninsulae australioribus, *Wight 2254* (not seen).

Rivea zeylanica var. *β hirsuta* Thw., Enum. Pl. Zeyl. 209. 1860. Type: Ceylon, Central Province, Kandy District, Hewahetta, *s. coll.* Oct. 1853, *C.P. 1944* (PDA, lectotype here chosen).
Argyreia hirsuta var. *coacta* Clarke in Hook. f., Fl. Br. Ind. 4: 189. 1883. Type: based on *Rivea zeylanica* var. *β hirsuta* Thw.
Argyreia populifolia var. *coacta* (Clarke) Trimen, Handb. Fl. Ceylon 3: 208. 1895.
Argyreia coacta (Clarke) Alston, Ann. R. Bot. Gard. Perad. 11: 209. 1929.

Lianas; the stems herbaceous at the tips, woody toward the base, pubescent with a whitish woolly or arachnoid indument. Leaves cordate, 8–23 cm long, basally cordate to somewhat truncate-cordate, apically acute to obtuse, often acuminate, pubescent on both surfaces with appressed yellowish or reddish trichomes, more densely pubescent below than above. Inflorescences of compound cymes clustered into pseudo-capitula, several-flowered; bracts 1–4 cm long, lanceolate to elliptic, with pubescence like leaves; peduncles (8−) 10–30 cm long. Flowers on pedicels up to 5 mm long; sepals ovate, 5–6 mm long, acute, mucronulate, pubescent; corolla lavender to purple, 4–5.5 cm long, funnelform. Fruits baccate, yellow, usually 1 cm long; seeds mostly less than 4, white, glabrous.

Distr. Known only from the Nilgiri Mountains of southern India and the hill country of Ceylon.

Ecol. This species occupies the same kinds of habitats as *A. populifolia* in that they are disturbed sites. In contrast, *A. hirsuta* is a highland species rarely found below 2000 feet. Most of the plants seen were in the 2000–3500 foot elevation range.

Specimens Examined. MATALE DISTRICT: Dambulla, *s. coll.* Apr. 1852, *C.P. 1944* (in part) (PDA). KANDY DISTRICT: Doluwa, *Austin & Austin 6143* (FAU, PDA, US); Hantane, *Gardner s.n. C.P. 1944* (in part) (PDA); Mahiyangana-Kandy Road, *Austin et al. 6192* (FAU, PDA, US); Nugateene, *Alston 484* (PDA); Peradeniya, *Wirawan 623* (PDA); Pussellawa, *Austin et al. 6131* (FAU, PDA, US). NUWARA ELIYA DISTRICT:

Pundaluoya, *Austin et al. 6128* (FAU, PDA, US); Ramboda, *Austin et al. 6130* (FAU, PDA, US). BADULLA DISTRICT: Bandarawella, *anon.*, Sept., 1890 (PDA); Diyatalawa, *Mueller-Dombois 68051914* (PDA); Haputale, *Austin et al. 6123* (FAU, PDA, US); Haputale, *A. Silva s.n.*, May 1906 (PDA).

5. Argyreia nervosa (Burm. f.) Bojer, Hort. Maurit. 224. 1837; van Ooststroom, Fl. Mal., ser. 1, 4: 499. 1953. Type: E. India, *Roxburgh s.n.* (isotype K).

Convolvulus nervosus Burm. f., Fl. Ind. 48, t. 20, f. 1. 1768.
Convolvulus speciosus L. f., Suppl. 137. 1781. Type: Brazil, *Vandelli* (not seen).
Ipomoea speciosa (L. f.) Pers., Syn. Pl. 1: 183. 1805.
Lettsomia nervosa (Burm. f.) Roxb., Fl. Ind. ed. Carey & Wall. 2: 78. 1824.
Argyreia speciosa (L. f.) Sweet, Hort. Br. 289. 1827; Trimen, Handb. Fl. Ceylon 3: 207. 1895.
Rivea nervosa (Burm. f.) Hall. f., Bull. Herb. Boissier 5: 381. 1897.

Lianas; the stems herbaceous toward the tips, woody at the base, younger branches densely white pubescent, glabrate with age. Leaves cordate, 18–27 cm long, apically acute to obtuse, entire, densely white pubescent below, glabrous above. Flowers in cymes on long white-tomentose peduncles; sepals ovate to broadly ovate, 1.5–2 cm long, white-tomentose; corolla with lavender limb and darker throat, 6–6.5 cm long, pubescent outside at least on the tube and interplicae. Fruits indehiscent, dry-baccate, subglobose, 1–1.5 cm long; seeds dark to fairly light brown, glabrous.

D i s t r. Native in India from Assam and Bengal to Belgaum and Mysore; cultivated in other tropical countries around the world.

E c o l. Known only from cultivation in the wet zone.

V e r n. Maha-dumudu (S); "maha"—large, "dumudu"—meaning unknown.

N o t e. While this plant is not common throughout the wet zone, it is cultivated in several districts including Colombo, Kalutara and Galle. The specimen cited by Trimen (*C.P. 2849*) has not been located.

S p e c i m e n s E x a m i n e d. KURUNEGALA DISTRICT: near Kurunegala, *Austin et al. 6221* (FAU, PDA, US). KANDY DISTRICT: Peradeniya, *Austin et al. 6134* (FAU, PDA, US).

6. Argyreia osyrensis (Roth) Choisy, Mem. Soc. Phys. Genève 6: 427. 1834; Choisy in DC., Prod. 9: 333. 1845; van Ooststroom, Blumea 5: 380. 1943. Type: *Wallich 1362* (G-DC).

Ipomoea osyrensis Roth, Nov. Pl. Sp. 117. 1821.
Lettsomia aggregata Roxb., Fl. Ind. ed. Carey & Wall. 2: 76. 1824.
Argyreia aggregata (Roxb.) Choisy, Mem. Soc. Phys. Genève 6: 427. 1834.

Lettsomia aggregata var. *osyrensis* (Roth) Clarke in Hook. f., Fl. Br. Ind. 4: 192. 1883; Trimen, Handb. Fl. Ceylon 3: 209. 1895.

Lianas; the stems woody except at the youngest growth, covered with a dense whitish indument. Leaves cordate to ovate or oblong-ovate, 3–9.5 cm long, cordate to truncate basally, obtuse to rounded or rarely emarginate apically, glabrous or sparsely appressed pubescent above, densely covered below with appressed whitish indument. Inflorescences mostly congested capitate or racemose cymose clusters along a terminal branch, occasionally sub-paniculate; bracts mostly deltoid, some rounded to ovate, 6–8 mm long and broad, densely whitish pubescent. Flowers sessile to subsessile, on peduncles about as long as the leaves; sepals broadly ovate to rounded, 5–6 mm long in flower, enlarging to 7–8 mm in fruit, obtuse to rounded, with dense whitish indument outside; corolla violet to red-purple, funnelform, 8–10 mm long, the stamens exserted. Fruits baccate, globose, 6–10 mm long, shiny red, subtended and partially surrounded or at least supported by the enlarged sepals which are red-brown on the inner surface; seeds gray, glabrous.

D i s t r. Known from southern India to Burma; van Ooststroom reported the species from Sumatra.

E c o l. These lianas grow in almost any disturbed site on the northeastern side of the central hill country down to near the coast. The fruits are undoubtedly spread widely by birds and the plants appear in abundance along fences and in abondoned chenas. They are also common plants on roadsides.

V e r n. Dumbada (S).

S p e c i m e n s E x a m i n e d. ANURADHAPURA DISTRICT: Habarane, *Alston 508* (PDA). POLONNARUWA DISTRICT: Polonnaruwa, *Ripley 266* (PDA); Sigiriya-Polonnaruwa Jungle Road, *Austin et al. 6163* (FAU, PDA, US). TRINCOMALEE DISTRICT: Trincomalee, *Gardner s.n.*, *C.P. 1945* (in part) (PDA). MATALE DISTRICT: Dambulla, *s. coll. C.P. 1945* (in part) (PDA); Dambulla, *Balakrishnan 595* (PDA), *Kostermans 23546* (PDA); Sigiriya, *Austin et al. 6156* (FAU, PDA, US); Sigiriya Tank, *Nowicke et al. 369* (PDA, US), *Nowicke et al. 357* (PDA, US). KANDY DISTRICT: Kandy-Mahiyangana Road, *Austin et al. 6203* (FAU, PDA, US); Raxawa, *s. coll.* Feb. 1854, *C.P. 1945* (in part) (PDA); Yatawatta, *Simpson 8857* (PDA). BADULLA DISTRICT: lower Badulla road, *s. coll.* July 1856. *C.P. 1945* (in part) (PDA). LOCALITY UNKNOWN: *Wallich 281* (K); *Wallich 268* (K); *s. coll. C.P. 1945* (K, PDA); Ooma-oya, *s. coll. s. n.* April 1883 (L).

7. **Argyreia pomacea** Choisy in DC., Prod. 9: 329. 1845; Clarke in Hook. f., Fl. Br. Ind. 4: 188. 1883; Trimen, Handb. Fl. Ceylon 3: 208. 1895. Type: India, *Wight 1419* (G-DC, holotype).

Argyreia leschenaultii Thw., Enum. Pl. Zeyl. 210. 1860, non Choisy (1845).

Argyreia pomacea var. *triflora* Clarke in Hook. f., Fl. Br. Ind. 4: 188. 1883. Type: Ceylon, *s. coll. C.P. 1932* (K, holotype).

Lianas; the stems woody below, herbaceous at the tips, with somewhat scattered reddish-brown trichomes either appressed or erect. Leaves ovate, or ovate-lanceolate, 3.5–12 (– 15) cm long, basally obtuse to rounded, apically acute, glabrous or remotely pubescent above, strigose to somewhat remotely pubescent below. Inflorescences in dense pseudo-capitate cymose clusters, the peduncles shorter than the leaves; bracts oblong to oblong-ovate, obtuse or apiculate, pubescent. Flowers on pedicels up to 3 mm long, usually shorter; sepals unequal, the outer 2 shorter, 5 mm long, the 3 inner 6–7 mm long, ovate, the apex obtuse, mucronulate, glabrous or remotely appressed pubescent; corolla lavender, often with an almost white limb, the tube darker, funnelform, 4–5.5 cm long. Fruits baccate, ovoid, apiculate with the persistent style base, 15–20 mm long, yellow, glabrous; seeds 1–3, glabrous.

D i s t r. Known only from southern India and from the island of Ceylon.
E c o l. The plants are found only in the dry zone of northeastern Ceylon. No site has been found where the vines are abundant, instead they are occasional throughout the region. Plants have been found in disturbed sites such as vacant lots, abandoned paddy fields and roadside scrub.
V e r n. Unam-Kodhy (T).
S p e c i m e n s E x a m i n e d. POLONNARUWA DISTRICT: Habarane, *Austin et al. 6168* (FAU, PDA, US). TRINCOMALEE DISTRICT: Trincomalee, *s. coll. s.n.* Aug. 1885 (PDA). BATTICALOA DISTRICT: Batticaloa, *Gardner C.P. 1932* (PDA); Chenkaladi, *Austin et al. 6179, 6180* (both FAU, PDA, US). AMPARAI DISTRICT: Maha-oya, *Austin et al. 6187* (FAU, PDA, US).

8. Argyreia populifolia Choisy in DC., Prod. 9: 329. 1845. Type: Ceylon, Colombo, *Wallich 1414* (G-DC, holotype).

Convolvulus fastigatus Wall., Cat. 2258. 1830. nom. nud., non Sweet (1826). Type: *Wallich 2258* (G-DC).
Ipomoea zeylanica Gaertn, Fruct. 2: 482. t. 178, f. 1. 1791.
Rivea zeylanica (Gaertn.) Thw., Enum. Pl. Zeyl. 209. 1860.
Argyreia populifolia var. *fastigata* (Wall.) Clarke in Hook. f., Fl. Br. Ind. 4: 187. 1883.

Lianas; the stems herbaceous toward the tips, woody near the base, glabrous to remotely appressed pubescent. Leaves cordate, 7-15 cm long, basally cordate, rounded to subtruncate, apically obtuse and then abruptly short-acuminate, glabrous above and below. Inflorescences in dense cymose clusters, usually 7-flowered, the peduncles 6–18 cm long; bracts elliptic to obovate, 1–3 cm long, glabrous or remotely appressed pubescent. Flowers on pedicels

3–4 mm long, the central flower of a cyme sessile; sepals ovate, 4–5 mm long, minutely and densely appressed pubescent throughout, the apex obtuse, the inner sepals broader than the outer; corolla variable, usually the limb lavender but often almost white, the tube always darker, usually purple, lighter outside, funnelform, 3–5 cm long. Fruits baccate, globose to depressed-globose, rarely ovoid, minutely apiculate, 12–15 mm long, often wider than long, yellow, glabrous; seeds whitish, glabrous, 1–4, often 3.

D i s t r. Endemic to the wet zone of Ceylon.

E c o l. These vines may be found in almost any sunny or disturbed site within their range. On cleared ground it is common to find seedlings of a dozen or more plants beginning within a few feet of each other. The seeds are undoubtedly spread by birds. People also spread the plants since the fruits are occasionally eaten. The fruits are not very popular, however, and human distribution must be minor.

S p e c i m e n s E x a m i n e d. ANURADHAPURA DISTRICT: Medawachi-Anuradhapura Road, *Balasubramanium* (*Austin 6197*) (US). KURUNEGALA DISTRICT: Galagedera, *Austin et al. 6211* (FAU, PDA, US); Kurunegala, *s. coll.* Aug. 1926, *C.P. 1943* (in part) (PDA). MATALE DISTRICT: Matale, *Austin et al. 6145* (FAU, PDA, US); Sigiriya, *Nowicke et al. 372* (PDA, US). KANDY DISTRICT: Gampola, *Austin et al. 6133* (FAU, PDA, US). KEGALLE DISTRICT: Mawanella, *Austin et al. 6083* (FAU, PDA, US). COLOMBO DISTRICT: Colombo, *Austin et al. 6244* (FAU, PDA, US), *Austin et al. 6246* (FAU, PDA, US); Negombo, *Silva, s. n.*, July 1930 (PDA); Nittambuwa, *Austin et al. 6088* (FAU, PDA, US). KALUTARA DISTRICT: Kalutara, *Austin et al. 6240* (FAU, PDA, US); Paiyagala South, *Austin et al. 6091* (FAU, PDA, US).

9. Argyreia splendens (Roxb.) Sweet, Hort. Br. ed. 2. 373. 1830; Thw., Enum. Pl. Zeyl. 210. 1860; Clarke in Hook. f., Fl. Br. Ind. 4: 186. 1883; Trimen, Handb. Fl. Ceylon 3: 207. 1895. Type: India (not seen).

Lettsomia splendens Roxb., Hort. Beng. 13. 1814.

Lianas; the stems herbaceous toward the tips, woody at the base, appressed silky pubescent. Leaves ovate, 15–24 cm long, rounded to obtuse basally, acuminate apically, glabrous on the upper surface, densely pubescent with silvery-white to slightly brownish-white appressed trichomes on the lower surface. Inflorescences 2-(or more?) flowered, cymose; bracts caducous. Flowers on peduncles longer than the petioles but shorter than the leaves, 11–12 cm long; sepals ovate to rounded, subequal, 5–6 mm long, obtuse to rounded, densely whitish to yellowish-white tomentose; corolla not seen, fide Clarke and Trimen 2.5–3 cm long, the interplicae pubescent outside, probably funnelform. Fruits baccate, red, glabrous; seeds not seen.

D i s t r. The species has been reported from India, Burma and Ceylon.

E c o l. Apparently a low moist montane species since the plants from India were collected in the Khasia and Chittagong Mountains and the only collection from Ceylon was from Hantane. This would suggest that the species occurs between about 2000 and 3000 feet in elevation, probably as a submontane forest liana.

S p e c i m e n s E x a m i n e d. KANDY DISTRICT: Hantane, *Gardner s.n. C.P. 2845* (PDA).

10. Argyreia thwaitesii (Clarke) D. Austin, comb. et stat. nov. Type: Colombo, *s. coll.* in 1861, *CP. 1943* (in part) (K, lectotype; PDA, isolectotype).

Argyreia populifolia var. *thwaitesii* Clarke in Hook. f., Fl. Br. Ind. 4: 187. 1883; Trimen, Handb. Fl. Ceylon 3: 208. 1895.

Lianas or more commonly vines; the stems often prostrate or climbing, hirsute or glabrescent. Leaves ovate, 5–18 cm long, basally obtuse, rounded or slightly cordate, rarely acute, apically acute to obtuse, at least when prostrate the leaves secund, hirsute with scattered yellowish-brown trichomes on both surfaces. Inflorescences in subcapitate or fairly lax compound cymes; bracts lanceolate or oblong-lanceolate, 1.5–2 (– 3.5) cm long. Flowers sessile or subsessile; sepals subequal or the outer 2 slightly longer, 5–6 mm long, ovate-triangular to ovate, acute; corolla lavender, the tube darker purple, 5–6 cm long. Fruits baccate, yellowish, globose or oblong-globose, 10–12 mm long, glabrous; seeds glabrous, roundish, white when mature.

D i s t r. This species is endemic to the river basins and low country of Ceylon's southwestern wet zone.

E c o l. Plants may be found in several types of disturbed sites such as roadsides, stream margins, fences and garden margins. In contrast to *A. populifolia*, with which it has been confused, the species has a marked preference for wet sites in the lowland.

S p e c i m e n s E x a m i n e d. MATALE DISTRICT: Matale East, *s. coll.* June 1863, *C.P. 1943* (PDA). KANDY DISTRICT: Ginigathena Road, *Simpson 8546* (PDA). KEGALLE DISTRICT: Dehiowita-Eheliyagoda Road, *Austin et al. 6226* (FAU, PDA, US). RATNAPURA DISTRICT: Bulutota Pass, *Simpson 9977* (PDA); Pussella, *Austin et al. 6229* (FAU, PDA, US). COLOMBO DISTRICT: Colombo, *Ferguson* in 1859, *C.P. 1944* (PDA); Hanwella, *Alston 880* (PDA). KALUTARA DISTRICT: Horana-Bandaragama Road, *Austin et al. 6236* (FAU, PDA, US); Ingiriya, *Austin et al. 6234* (FAU, PDA, US); Matugama, *Balakrishnan 1013* (PDA); Morapitiya Forest Reserve, *Meijer 460* (PDA). GALLE DISTRICT: between Galle & Wakwella, *Austin et al. 6258* (FAU, PDA, US); Kanneliya, *Austin et al. 6255* (FAU, PDA, US), *Waas 64* (PDA); Kotawa Forest Reserve, *Alston 1302*

(PDA). MATARA DISTRICT: Weligama, *Austin et al. 6103* (FAU, PDA, US).

11. Argyreia sp. A.

Lianas (?); the stems herbaceous toward the tips, densely appressed pubescent. Leaves ovate-cordate, basally cordate or only rounded, apically obtuse, 6–11 cm long, remotely pubescent above with scattered appressed trichomes, densely appressed pubescent below. Inflorescences in lax compound cymes, 3–5-flowered, the peduncles shorter than the leaves; bracts linear-subulate, 7–9 mm long, remotely pubescent. Flowers on 2–3 mm pedicels; sepals unequal, the outer 2 shorter than the inner, 4 mm long, ovate, apically acute, the inner 5–6 mm long, broadly ovate, apically obtuse, some emarginate-mucronulate, with scarious margins at the apex, glabrous; corolla pale red (fide collector), funnelform, 3.5 cm long, pubescent on tube and interplicae. Fruits not seen.

This specimen does not match the other species found on the island nor does it match anything in the Indian floras. Probably it is a new species but I am not prepared to describe it from a single collection.

Specimens Examined. MONERAGALA DISTRICT: Bibile, 2 June 1971, *Kostermans 24384* (PDA).

3. BONAMIA

Thouars, Hist. Veg. Isl. France 1: 33. 1804. nom. cons. Type Species: *Bonamia madagascariensis* Poir.

Breweria R. Br., Prod. 487. 1810. Type: *Bonamia linearis* (R. Br.) Hall. f.
Trichantha Karst. & Triana, Linnaea 28: 437. 1856, non Hook. (1844). Type:
    T. ferruginea Karst. & Triana = *Bonamia trichantha* Hall. f.

Lianas to small scrambling shrubs or herbaceous vines, mostly perennial, glabrous to pubescent. Leaves entire, lanceolate to ovate. Inflorescences of solitary flowers or few-flowered dichasia or panicles; the bracts small. Flowers with the sepals obtuse to acute, subequal, the outer ones larger and suborbicular; corolla campanulate or funnelform, the limb plicate, the interplicae ferrugineous; stamens included, the filaments filiform, mostly triangular-dilate and glandular-pubescent at the base, the anthers oval or oblong, the pollen 3-colpate; ovary 2-locular, 4-ovulate, the style filiform, bifid to almost entire, or the styles 2 and free, the stigmas capitate, subglobose. Fruits capsular, 4-valvate, pericarp membranaceous to coriaceous; seeds 4 or fewer by abortion, glabrous or pubescent.

A genus of about 40 species widely spread in the tropics of both hemispheres. Much confusion has surrounded the delimitation of *Bonamia* against *Breweria*. Recently this generic difficulty was discussed by Myint and Ward (Phytologia 17: 121–239. 1968) and their conclusions appear the best yet proposed. There is only one species in Ceylon.

Bonamia semidigyna (Roxb.) Hall. f., Bot. Jahrb. Syst. 16: 528. 1893. Type: India, grown from seeds sent by Capt. *Hardwicke* (not found).

Convolvulus semidigynus Roxb. (Hort. Beng. 13. 1814, nomen nudum) Fl. Ind. ed. Carey & Wall. 2: 47. 1824.
Breweria cordata Blume, Bidjr. 722. 1825; Clarke in Hook. f., Fl. Br. Ind. 4: 223. 1883; Trimen, Handb. Fl. Ceylon 3: 227. 1895.
?*Convolvulus malabaricus* sensu Moon, Cat. 13. 1824.
Breweria roxburghii Choisy, Mem. Soc. Phys. Genève 6: 493. 1834.

Vines; the stems suffruticose or herbaceous, densely brown to reddish-brown tomentose. Leaves ovate, 6.5–15 cm long, cordate to rarely truncate basally, shortly acuminate to cuspidate apically, pubescent on both surfaces, more densely below, the upper surface glabrescent. Inflorescences 2–5-flowered umbellate cymes. Flowers with variable length peduncles; sepals ovate, ovate-oblong to broadly ovate, subequal or the inner slightly shorter, 8–14 mm long, acute to acuminate, tomentose; corolla white, campanulate to funnelform, 3–4 (– 5) cm long. Fruits capsular, broadly ovoid to subglobose, 10–12 mm long, apically pubescent, the valves splitting into segments; seeds black, glabrous, 5–6 mm long.

D i s t r. Madagascar, India, Indo-China, Siam and Malaysia have been recorded as sites for the species.

E c o l. These vines grow at fairly low altitudes, usually from sea level to about 700–800 feet. Plants have been found on the edges of secondary forests, thickets, hedges, waysides and riverbanks throughout its range. No recent collections have been made in Ceylon and the plants must be considered very rare.

V e r n. Bu-wasa-thel-kola (S); "bu"—pubescent, "wasa"—poison, "thel"—oil, "kola"—leaf.

S p e c i m e n s E x a m i n e d. COLOMBO DISTRICT: Colombo, *s. coll. C.P. 2853* (in part) (PDA). GALLE DISTRICT: Galle, *s. coll. C.P. 2853* (in part) (PDA). LOCALITY UNKNOWN: *Wallich 1405* (K); *Walkers 66* (K); *Walkers s.n.* (K).

4. CRESSA

L., Sp. Pl. 233. 1753; Gen. Pl. ed. 5. 104. 1754.

A much-branched, short-lived, perennial, subshrubby herb. Leaves small, sessile, entire. Flowers small, subsessile, in bracteate clusters at the tips of the branchlets; sepals obovate, subequal, imbricate; corolla tube campanulate, the lobes ovate, imbricate, spreading; stamens and styles exserted, the filaments filiform, the ovary 2-locular, 4-ovulate, the styles 2, distinct to the base, the stigmas large, capitate. Fruits capsular, 2–4-valved, usually 1-seeded; seeds glabrous and shining, dark brown.

A small genus of one or perhaps two species. Found in the tropical xeric regions of both hemispheres. The plants are remarkable because of their adaptation to arid, saline conditions.

1. Cressa cretica L., Sp. Pl. 223. 1753; Clarke in Hook. f., Fl. Br. Ind. 4: 225. 1883; Trimen, Handb. Fl. Ceylon 3: 228. 1895; Verdcourt, Fl. Trop. E. Africa 33. 1963. Type: Crete, specimen 317.1 (LINN, lectotype not seen; microfiche seen).

Evolvulus capitatus sensu Moon, Cat. 23. 1824; Thw., Enum. Pl. Zeyl. 213. 1860.

Stems basally woody, much-branched above, the branches pilose. Leaves closely condensed, sessile, ovate-lanceolate to ovate, 2.5–9 mm long, 1–6 mm wide, apically acute, basally cuneate, rounded or subcordate, gray-green, pubescent with appressed indument. Inflorescence of compacted, subsessile bracteate flower clusters at the tips of the branchlets. Flowers sessile in the upper leaf axils, forming short compact spikes; sepals ovoid, 3–4 mm long, abruptly acute, silky pubescent; corolla 5–6 mm long, white with a pink flush on the lobes, campanulate, the tube and oblong-ovate lobes about equal in length; styles and stamens exserted from the tube for 2–4 mm. Fruits capsular, ovoid, 3–4 mm long; seeds usually 1, glabrous and shining, dark brown.

D i s t r. Found in the tropics of Africa, Pakistan and in other dry sites in Asia.

E c o l. These plants are found on coastal dunes, salt pans and other places which tend to be salty and sandy; usually found near sea level. In the drier parts of northern Ceylon these plants become troublesome in paddy fields. The species is common in certain parts of the Northern Province but rare elsewhere.

V e r n. Panittanki (T); "panit"—dew, "tanki"—resting place. The name refers to the ability of these plants to collect the morning dew in the northern dry zone. Dew collected on these and other plants in the northern dry zone is used by some of the Tamil people as a remedy for eye problems.

S p e c i m e n s E x a m i n e d. JAFFNA DISTRICT: Jaffna, *s. coll. C.P. 1925* (in part) (K, PDA); Jaffna, *Thwaites s.n.* in 1890 (in part) (PDA). VAVUNIYA DISTRICT: Kokoli (Kokkilai?), *s. coll. C.P. 1925* (in part) (K,

PDA). MANNAR DISTRICT: Illupaikedavai, *Thwaites, s.n.* in 1890 (in part) (PDA); Mannar-Mantai Road, *Balasubramanium (D.F. Austin 6194)* (FAU, PDA, US). TRINCOMALEE DISTRICT: Trincomalee, *s. coll. C.P. 1925* (in part) (K, PDA). PUTTALAM DISTRICT: Wilpattu National Park: Periya Uppa Villu, *Mueller-Dombois et al. 69042712* (US). HAMBANTOTA DISTRICT: Ruhuna National Park, Uda Gajabawa, *Cooray 68060601* (K, PDA, US). LOCALITY UNKNOWN: *s. coll. C.P. 1925* (US).

5. CUSCUTA

L., Sp. Pl. 124. 1753; Gen. Pl., ed. 5. 60. 1754. Type Species: *Cuscuta europaea* L.

Vines without chlorophyll; the stems twining, filiform, yellow or orange or rarely greenish, attached to host plants by haustoria; roots withering and absent from mature plants. Leaves reduced to minute scales. Inflorescences cymose, composed of small whitish flowers; calyx gamosepalous, 5-lobed, the sepals rarely almost free; corolla urceolate or campanulate, the 5 lobes various, usually with basal scale-like appendages inside opposite the stamens, forming a corona; the pollen 3-colpate; ovary 2-locular, locules biovulate, styles 2, distinct or rarely united, terminal, the stigmas capitate to linear. Fruit capsular, often circumscissile near the base; the seeds (1–3) –4, smooth or roughened.

The number of species in this genus have been estimated recently at 140 or 165. Yuncker, the last student of the whole group, considered more species to exist. I must agree with Verdcourt (Fl. Trop. E. Afr. 4. 1963) that Yuncker had a narrow concept of species. The genus has been variously dissected into subgenera and sections (Yuncker, Univ. Ill. Biol. Monog. 6: 1–142. 1921, Mem. Torrey Bot. Club 18: 111–331. 1932; van Ooststroom, Fl. Mal., ser. 1, 4: 392. 1953). There are only two species in Ceylon, the majority of the genus apparently being concentrated in the Americas.

KEY TO THE SPECIES

1 Stems slender, less than 0.4 mm in diameter. Corolla yellowish, somewhat globular, 3–3.5 mm long...**1. C. chinensis**
1 Stems coarse, up to 2.5 mm in diameter. Corolla white or cream, campanulate-tubular, 6–10 mm long ....**2. C. reflexa**

1. Cuscuta chinensis Lam., Enc. 2: 229. 1786; Clarke in Hook. f., Fl. Br. Ind. 4: 227. 1883; Trimen, Handb. Fl. Ceylon 3: 229. 1895; Yuncker, Mem. Torrey Bot. Club 18: 209. 1932. Type: Specimen in Paris from seeds from China, *Lamarck* (P-LAM, not seen; photograph K).

Cuscuta reflexa sensu Moon, Cat. 12. 1824, non Roxb. (1798).

Stems slender, less than 0.4 mm in diameter, yellow. Inflorescences of dense glomerules. Flowers sessile or shortly pedicellate; sepals loose around the corolla, the lobes triangular-ovate, barely reaching the sinuses of the corolla, thickened and fleshy near the tips and forming a carina, slightly over-lapping, obtuse or acute; corolla yellowish, somewhat globular, 3–3.5 mm long, remaining on the developing capsule, the tube about 2 times as long as the lobes, the lobes triangular-ovate to oblong-ovate, acute to obtuse, spread-ing and the tips mostly inflexed; filaments longer than the ovoid anthers; corolla scales oblong, fimbriate above, bridged below; ovary globose; style about equal in length to the ovary, the stigmas rounded. Fruits capsular, de-pressed-globose, circumscissile; seeds 1.25 mm long.

D i s t r. Reported from Abyssinia, Sokotra, Afghanistan and eastward to Ceylon, Australia and China.

E c o l. Found on a variety of hosts but often on *Mikania*. When Trimen studied the flora of the island he considered the plants very rare. Alston noted an increase by his time. Today the parasitic plants may be found in almost any paddy margin throughout the southern two-thirds of the island. The increase may be due, in large part, to an increase in imports of rice from China.

V e r n. Aga-mula-neti-wel (S); "aga"—tip, "mula"—base, "neti"—with-out, "wel"—creeper—thus, a creeper without beginning or end.

S p e c i m e n s E x a m i n e d. KURUNEGALA DISTRICT: Mawata-gama, *Austin et al. 6218* (FAU, PDA, US). MATALE DISTRICT: Nalanda, *Austin et al. 6150* (FAU, PDA, US). KANDY DISTRICT: Mahiyangana, *Austin et al. 6191* (FAU, PDA, US); Peradeniya, *s. coll. s.n.* (PDA); Perade-niya, *s. coll. s.n.* July 1915 (PDA). MONERAGALA DISTRICT: Wellawaya-Haputale Road, *Austin et al. 6119* (FAU, PDA, US). KEGALLE DISTRICT: Dehiowita, *Austin et al. 6225* (FAU, PDA, US). COLOMBO DISTRICT: Colombo, *Drieberg s.n.*, June 1915 (PDA); Colombo, *Ferguson s.n.*, Nov. 1892 (PDA); Colombo, *Gardner in 1855, C.P. 611* (PDA); Colombo, *Rama-chandra Rao 4* (PDA). KALUTARA DISTRICT: between Horana & Ban-daragama, *Austin et al. 6237* (FAU, PDA, US).

2. **Cuscuta reflexa** Roxb., Pl. Corom. 2: 3. t. 104. 1798; Thw., Enum. Pl. Zeyl. 213. 1860; Clarke in Hook. f., Fl. Br. Ind. 4: 226. 1883; Trimen, Handb. Fl. Ceylon 3: 229. 1895; Yuncker, Mem. Torrey Bot. Club 18: 259. 1932; van Ooststroom, Fl. Mal. ser. 1, 4: 393. 1953. Type: A specimen at K is sup-posedly the type. The sheet contains four different collections including 2 species. One of the species conforms with the present and past concepts of *C. reflexa*.

Stems coarse, up to 2.5 mm in diameter, pale green or yellowish-green.

Inflorescences of small subglobose groups or racemose. Flowers sessile or very shortly pedicellate; sepals in a cupulate calyx, the lobes orbicular, obtuse, overlapping, the outside verrucose-carinate; corolla white or cream, campanulate-tubular, 6–10 mm long, remaining for a while on the developing capsule, the tube 2.5–3 times as long as the lobes, the lobes narrow-ovate to ovate-triangular, obtuse to subacute, crenate or entire, erect, spreading or reflexed; filaments very short, inserted just below the sinus; corolla scales ovate to oblong, fimbriate; ovary ovate-conical; style shorter than the elongate stigmas. Fruits capsular, globose-conical, circumscissile near the base; seeds 3–3.5 mm long, black.

D i s t r. Found from Afghanistan through India, Ceylon, China, Siam and Malaysia.

E c o l. Parasitic on a wide variety of plants in the upper montane zone from about 3000–5400 feet.

V e r n. Aga-mula-neti-wel (S); Dodder (E).

S p e c i m e n s E x a m i n e d. NUWARA ELIYA DISTRICT: Pidurutalagala, *s. coll. s.n.* April 1881 (PDA); Pidurutalagala, *Simpson s.n.*, April 1906 (PDA). WITHOUT LOCALITY: *Gardner 616* (K, PDA); *s. coll. s.n.*, Dec. 1867, *s. coll. C.P. 1922* (K, PDA). LOCALITY UNKNOWN: *s. coll., C.P. 1922* (K); *Thompson s.n.* in 1845 (K).

6. ERYCIBE

Roxb., Pl. Corom. 2: 31, t. 159. 1798. Type Species: *Erycibe paniculata* Roxb.

Fissipetalum Merr., J. Straits Branch R. Asiat. Soc. 85: 168. 1922. Type: *Fissipetalum borneense* Merr.

Lianas; the stems climbing or creeping, rarely trees. Leaves petiolate, simple, entire, mostly ovate to elliptic, usually acuminate apically. Inflorescences terminal or axillary, paniculate, rarely solitary; bracts usually minute, caducous. Flowers fragrant, the pedicels usually with 2 minute, caducous bracteoles; sepals 5, free, usually pubescent outside, glabrous within, the 2 outer sepals usually somewhat different in shape from the inner 3; corolla deeply 5-lobed, the tube glabrous outside, each lobe with 2 lateral lobules; stamens 5, inserted slightly above corolla base, with short somewhat triangular or laterally concave filaments, the anthers usually obtuse to acuminate apically, cordate basally; pollen smooth, 3-colpate; ovary ellipsoid, glarbous to pubescent, 1-celled, 4-ovulate, the style absent, the stigma usually conical, with 5 or 10 longitudinal, straight or slightly contorted ridges on the stigma. Fruits baccate, slightly fleshy, ellipsoid or rarely obpyriform, glabrous, smooth or pubescent; seeds usually 1, with plain or strongly folded cotyledons.

A genus of about 70 species found almost exclusively in Asia. The species occur from S. Japan to western India and south through Malaysia with one species in Queensland, Australia. Only one species is known from Ceylon.

Erycibe paniculata Roxb., Pl. Corom. 2: 31. pl. 159. 1798; Thw., Enum. Pl. Zeyl. 213. 1860; Clarke in Hook. f., Fl. Br. Ind. 4: 180. 1883; Trimen, Handb. Fl. Ceylon 3: 205. 1895. Type: India (not seen).

Erycibe paniculata var. *wightiana* (Grah.) Clarke in Hook. f., Fl. Br. Ind. 4: 180. 1883.
Erycibe wightiana Grah., Cat. Bombay Pl. 137. 1839; Gamble, Fl. Pres. Madras 930. 1923; Alston in Trimen, Handb. Fl. Ceylon 6: 201. 1931.

Lianas; the stems woody or herbaceous at the tips, when young covered with reddish-brown indument, glabrescent, the older stems reaching a diameter of 6–8 cm. Leaves ovate, obovate, elliptic, oblong or oblong-lanceolate, 4–10 cm long, cuneate to acute basally, obtuse-acuminate to acute-acuminate apically, coriaceous, glabrous. Inflorescences of clustered or solitary racemose groups. Flowers with pedicels 1–2 mm long; sepals ovate to rounded, subequal, 1.5–2 mm long, obtuse to rounded, densely brown-tomentose; corolla white, campanulate-rotate, 5–6 mm long. Fruits sub-baccate, somewhat leathery, ovoid to ellipsoid, 10–14 mm long, glabrous; seeds solitary, glabrous.

D i s t r. Restricted to India, Ceylon and the surrounding regions; it does not occur in Malaysia as reported by several authors (van Ooststroom & Hoogland, Fl. Mal. ser. 1, 4: 406. 1953).

E c o l. These lianas are found from almost sea level to about 3000 feet. While plants have been found in the inner fringe of the *Pandanus* zone near the coast, they are more common at the higher altitudes in submontane forests. Plants persist after the forests have been cut around them in the central mountains. The flowers are white to creamy white and extremely sweet-scented; they must be pollinated by bees although none have been seen visiting. Flowers open early in the day, apparently between 7:00 and 8:00 a.m., and remain open until at least 3:00 p.m.

V e r n. Eta-miriya, Etambiriya (S); "eta"—seed, "miriya"—sweet—a reference to the edible, sweet pulp around the seed.

S p e c i m e n s E x a m i n e d. BATTICALOA DISTRICT: Bintenne, *s. coll. C.P. 1881* (in part) (L, PDA). KURUNEGALA DISTRICT: Doluwa Kanda, *s. coll. s.n.* in 1911 (PDA). KANDY DISTRICT: Hantane, *s. coll. C.P. 1881* (in part) (L, PDA); Kandy-Mahiyangana Road, *Austin et al. 6202, 6204, 6207* (all in FAU, PDA, US); Madugoda, *Simpson 8838* (PDA); Maskeliya Valley, *Jayasuriya et al. 749* (PDA); Utuwankande, *Moon C.P. 1881* (in part) (L, PDA). RATNAPURA DISTRICT: Bulutota, *Alston 1693* (K,

PDA). GALLE DISTRICT: Bentota, *s. coll. C.P. 1881* (in part) (L, PDA); Galle, *s. coll. C.P. 1881* (in part) (L, PDA), *Austin et al. 6248* (FAU, PDA, US); Udugama, *Balakrishnan 527* (PDA, US), *Cramer 3388* (US). LOCALITY UNKNOWN: *s. coll. C.P. 1881* (US); *Gardner 617* (K); *Walker 200, 240, 129* (all K).

7. EVOLVULUS

L., Sp. Pl., ed. 2. 391. 1762; Gen. Pl., ed. 6. 152. 1764. Type Species: *Evolvulus nummularius* L.

Herbs or small suffrutescent shrubs, annual or perennial, not twining but sometimes creeping. Leaves usually small, ovate to almost linear, entire. Flowers in axillary, pedunculate, 1- to several-flowered dichasia or solitary, pedunculate or sessile in the leaf axils; sepals 5, free, equal or subequal; corolla small to medium, conspicuous blue or inconspicuous faded bluish-white, rotate, funnelform or salverform, the limb plicate, mostly subentire, the interplicae pilose outside; stamens 5, the filaments filiform, inserted within the corolla tube, the anthers ovate to oblong or linear, pollen pantocolpate; ovary 2-loculate, each locule biovulate, sometimes 1-locular and 4-ovulate; styles 2, free or basally united, each style deeply bifid for at least half its length, stigmas long, terete, filiform to subclavate. Fruits capsular, globose to ovoid, 4-valvate, (1-) 4-seeded; seeds small, smooth or minutely verrucose, the cotyledons almost flat, the radicle incurved.

A genus of perhaps 100 species, almost all of which are found only in the Americas. Two species have been introduced into the Old World and both of these are in Ceylon.

KEY TO THE SPECIES

1 Plants ascending to trailing. Stems with woolly, erect pubescence. Corolla shallowly lobed. Capsules 2-locular..**1. E. alsinoides**
1 Plants creeping and prostrate. Stems glabrous or sparsely appressed tomentose. Corolla deeply lobed. Capsules 1-locular.................................**2. E. nummularius**

1. Evolvulus alsinoides (L.) L., Sp. Pl. ed. 2. 392. 1762; Moon, Cat. 23. 1824; Thw., Enum. Pl. Zeyl. 213. 1860; Clarke in Hook. f., Fl. Br. Ind. 4: 220. 1883; Trimen, Handb. Fl. Ceylon 3: 227. 1895; van Ooststroom, Fl. Mal., ser. 1, 4: 395. 1953; Verdcourt, Fl. Trop. E. Africa 18. 1963. Type: Ceylon, specimen in Hermann Herb. 3: 55 (BM, lectotype fide Verdcourt).

Convolvulus alsinoides L., Sp. Pl. ed. 1. 157. 1753.

Herbs; the stems and indument unusually variable, either annual or perennial, trailing or prostrate but the flowering shoots ascending, mostly covered with silky indument. Leaves elliptic to linear-oblong, 8–26 mm long, subsessile to shortly petioled, acute to rounded at both ends, silky pilose on both surfaces. Inflorescences with 1 to 5 flowers. Flowers on peduncles 6–40 mm long; sepals ovate-lanceolate, 4–5 mm long, usually 1 mm wide, acute; corolla blue, rarely white, campanulate to sub-rotate or less commonly broadly funnelform, 5–6 mm long and wide. Fruits capsular, globose, 3–4 mm long, glabrous; seeds usually 4, pale brown to black, ovoid, 1.5–1.7 mm long.

D i s t r. A species of the American tropics which is now widely spread and pantropical.

E c o l. The species is usually found in grassland areas of various plant associations. Plants have been found in thorn scrub, along roads in the sub-montane forest zone, near beaches and in cultivated fields. The plants may be expected in almost any dry, sunny site but are much more abundant in the dry zone.

U s e s. These small plants play an important role in the ayurvedic medi-cines of the island. A water extract from the stems and roots has been used to cure almost everything from depression to dysentery. The root is consider-ed a febrifuge; smoking the leaves is said to be a remedy for asthma. One man in Galle said that a decoction of the mashed plant and sesame oil "cools the brain". This apparently means that there is a calming effect.

V e r n. Visnu-kranti (S), "visnu"—the guardian deity of Sri Lanka, "kranti"—halo; Vichnukiranti (T), "vichnu"—orthographic variant of above, "kiranti"—halo or divine emission.

N o t e. van Ooststroom has recognized 16 or 17 varieties of this species throughout its range. Most of these intergrade and I prefer to consider the species in the broad sense. My field studies suggest that many of the named populations are autogamous variants from the ancestral allogamous stock. There are two basic forms of the plants on the island if one wishes to apply formal names. The ascending to erect plants not having the leaves in two distinct rows are *Evolvulus alsinoides* var. *alsinoides*. Plants with the stems essentially prostrate and having the leaves in two distinct rows are *Evolvulus alsinoides* var. *hirsutus* (Lam.) van Ooststroom.

S p e c i m e n s E x a m i n e d. JAFFNA DISTRICT: Jaffna, *Gardner s.n.*, *C.P. 1926* (in part) (PDA); Keerimalai to Point Pedro, *Clayton 5195* (PDA). MANNAR DISTRICT: Madawachchiya-Mannar Road, *Cramer 2900* (PDA); Talai Mannar, *Silva s.n.*, in 1911 (PDA). POLONNARUWA DIST-RICT: Habanara, *Austin et al. 6169* (FAU, PDA, US); Polonnaruwa, *Town-send 73/227* (PDA). TRINCOMALEE DISTRICT: Kantalai-Allai Road, *Austin et al. 6175* (FAU, PDA, US). BATTICALOA DISTRICT: Binpenna, *s. coll.*, *C.P. 1926* (in part) (PDA). AMPARAI DISTRICT: Maha-Oya, *Austin et al. 6188* (FAU, PDA, US). PUTTALAM DISTRICT: Wilpattu, Wilpattu National Park, Kali Villu Plot, *Fosberg et al. 50969* (L). KURUNEGALA DISTRICT: Polgahawela-Narammala Road, *Cramer 3270* (PDA). MATALE

DISTRICT: Sigiriya-Polonnaruwa Jungle Road, *Austin et al. 6160* (FAU, PDA, US). KANDY DISTRICT: Hantane, *s. coll.*, *C.P. 1926* (in part) (PDA); Kandy-Mahiyangana Road, *Austin et al. 6205* (FAU, PDA, US). BADULLA DISTRICT: Bandarawela, *Soysa s.n.*, in 1954 (PDA); Haputale, *Fosberg 51832* (PDA). RATNAPURA DISTRICT: between Delgoda & Karawita, *Lewis & Silva* (PDA). COLOMBO DISTRICT: Colombo, *Gardner s.n.*, *C.P. 1926* (in part) (PDA); Jaela, *Rajapakse s.n.*, in 1913 (PDA); Negombo, *Senaratne s.n.*, in 1940 (PDA). GALLE DISTRICT: Galle, *Austin et al. 6249* (FAU, PDA, US). HAMBANTOTA DISTRICT: Kirinda, *Austin et al. 6108* (FAU, PDA, US); Ruhuna National Park, Andunoruwa Wewa, *Cooray 6911160R* (PDA); Buttawa Plain, *Wirawan 671* (PDA); Gonalabbe Lewaya, *Fosberg 50252* (PDA); Karaugaswala, *Mueller-Dombois & Cooray 67121001* (PDA); Katagamuwa, *Mueller-Dombois et al. 67093036* (PDA); Walaskema, *Mueller-Dombois & Cooray 67100105* (PDA); Uraniya, *Cooray & Balakrishnan 69011006R* (PDA). LOCALITY UNKNOWN: *s. coll.*, *C.P. 1926* (K); *s. coll. C.P. 1927* (K); Herbarium *Burman* no. 4 (L); *Gardner 615* (K); *Wallich 130* (K).

2. Evolvulus nummularius (L.) L., Sp. Pl. ed. 2. 391. 1762; Senaratna, Ceylon J. Sci. Sect. A. Bot. 12: 214. 1947; Abeywick., Ceylon J. Sci., Biol. Sci. 2: 214. 1959; van Ooststroom, Fl. Mal., ser. 1, 4: 558. 1958; Verdcourt, Fl. Trop. E. Afr. 16. 1963. Type: West Indies, Jamaica, *Sloane* (BM-SL, lectotype fide Verdcourt).

Convolvulus nummularius L., Sp. Pl. 157. 1753.
Volvulopsis nummularium (L.) Roberty, Candollea 14: 28. 1952.

Perennial herbs; the stems prostrate, herbaceous, rooting at the nodes, pilose with short trichomes to glabrate. Leaves broadly ovate to orbicular, 4–15 mm long, short-petiolate, rounded to emarginate apically, rounded to subcordate basally, glabrous or somewhat pubescent beneath. Inflorescences of solitary or paired flowers in the leaf axils. Flowers on pedicels 2–6 mm long; sepals elliptic-ovate to ovate-oblong, 2.5–4 mm long, pubescent, glabrescent, ciliate; corolla white, broadly campanulate, 5–7 mm wide. Fruits capsular, globose, 3–4 mm in diameter, reflexed; seeds brown to black, subglobose, slightly muricate.

D i s t r. Originally a species in the American tropics, this plant has been introduced into several Old World regions including Africa, Malaysia and Ceylon.

E c o l. This species usually prefers more moist sites than the previous one. In Ceylon it has been found as a weed on the roadside, in the yard at the University Campus in Colombo, and along the cracks in an abandoned airfield near Sigiriya.

Specimens Examined. MATALE DISTRICT: Sigiriya, *Austin et al. 6159* (FAU, PDA, US). COLOMBO DISTRICT: Colombo, *Austin & Austin 6138* (PDA); Negombo, *Senaratna 3533* (not found).

8. HEWITTIA

Wight & Arn., Madras J. Sci. 1 (5): 22. 1837. Type Species: *Hewittia sublobata* (L. f.) O. Ktze.

Shutereia Choisy, Mem. Soc. Phys. Genève 6: 485, t. 2, f. 11. 1834, non *Shuteria* Wight & Arn., 1834, nom. cons.

Vines; the stems twining or prostrate, herbaceous, pubescent. Leaves petiolate, entire, angular or lobed, ovate to broad-ovate, usually cordate at the base. Flowers on axillary peduncles, in 1- to few-flowered cymes; bracts 2, oblong or linear-lanceolate, acuminate, inserted at some distance from the calyx; sepals 5, mostly acute, herbaceous, the outer 3 larger, ovate, accrescent in fruit, the inner 2 smaller, not accrescent; corolla regular, medium-sized, campanulate, the limb shallowly 5-lobed, the stamens and style included, the filaments adnate to the corolla tube, filiform with a dilated base, the pollen smooth; disc annular; ovary pubescent, 1-celled or imperfectly 2-celled at the apex, 4-ovulate, the style 1, simple filiform, the stigmas 2, ovate-oblong, complanate. Fruits capsular, unilocular, 4-valved; seeds 4 or less, black.

This monotypic genus is widely distributed through the tropics of the Old World; also known from Jamaica.

Hewittia sublobata (L. f.) O. Ktze., Rev. Gen. Pl. 2: 441. 1891; van Ooststroom, Fl. Mal., ser. 1, 4: 438. 1953; Verdcourt, Fl. Trop. E. Afr. 45. 1963. Type: India, no type found.

Convolvulus sublobatus L. f., Suppl. 135. 1781.
Convolvulus bicolor Vahl, Symb. 3: 25. 1794, non Desr. (1791), nomen illegit.
Shutteria bicolor (Vahl) Choisy, Mem. Soc. Phys. Genève 6: 486. 1834; Thw., Enum. Pl. Zeyl. 212. 1860.
Hewittia bicolor (Vahl) Wight & Arn., Madras J. Sci. 5: 22. 1837; Clarke in Hook. f., Fl. Br. Ind. 4: 216. 1883; Trimen, Handb. Fl. Ceylon 3: 226. 1895.

Vines; the stems perennial, mostly prostrate, occasionally rooting at the nodes. Leaves ovate to broadly-ovate, 2.5–16 cm long, cordate, hastate, cuneate or sometimes truncate basally, obtuse to acuminate apically, dentate to entire, pilose to velvety above and below. Inflorescences mostly of axillary solitary flowers but also in several-flowered bracteate cymes. Flowers on peduncles 2.5–12 cm long; sepals lanceolate to ovate, 7–17 mm long, somewhat pubescent, the outer 3 much larger than the inner 2, conspicuously nervose in fruit; corolla pale yellow to white, usually with a conspicuous purple or purplish center, campanulate, 2–2.5 cm long, the interplicae pilose. Fruits capsular, ovoid to subglobose, 8–10 mm long, pilose; seeds glabrous or sparsely pubescent, 5–6 mm long.

D i s t r. Found throughout tropical Africa, Asia, Malaysia and Polynesia; escaped and apparently naturalized in Jamaica.

E c o l. Plants may be found in a variety of disturbed sites such as grass-lands, thickets, forest margins, waste places, roadsides, cultivated field margins. The vines occur from near sea level to about 3000 feet.

U s e s. According to one source the stems of this vine are strong enough that villagers use them for tying fences or the wattle for houses.

V e r n. Wal-trasta-walu (S); 'wal'—wild, 'trasta' & 'walu'—meaning unknown.

S p e c i m e n s E x a m i n e d. POLONNARUWA DISTRICT: Minneri-ya, *Gardner s.n., C.P. 1970* (in part) (PDA). TRINCOMALEE DISTRICT: Trincomalee, *Gould & Cooray 13710* (PDA, US). BATTICALOA DISTRICT: near Tumpalancholai, *Austin et al. 6185* (FAU, PDA, US). KURUNEGALA DISTRICT: Kurunegala, *Austin et al. 6220A* (FAU, PDA, US). MATALE DISTRICT: near Pannampitiya, *Austin et al. 6153* (FAU, PDA, US). KANDY DISTRICT: Kandy, *Austin & Austin 6193* (PDA); Kandy-Mahiyan-gana Road, *Austin et al. 6208* (FAU, PDA, US). BADULLA DISTRICT: Pangaragammana, *Jayasuriya 393* (PDA, US); Uma Oya, *Balakrishnan & Jayasuriya 835* (PDA, US). MONERAGALA DISTRICT: Udawalawe area, *Balakrishnan & Jayasuriya 900* (PDA, US); Wellawaya-Haputale Road, *Austin et al. 6118* (FAU, PDA, US). RATNAPURA DISTRICT: Ratnapura, *Austin et al. 6231* (FAU, PDA, US). COLOMBO DISTRICT: Kadawata, *Austin & Austin 6139* (FAU, PDA, US). KALUTARA DISTRICT: *Moon C.P. 1970* (in part) (PDA). GALLE DISTRICT: Galle, *s. coll. s.n.* Dec. 1853, *C.P. 1970* (in part) (PDA); Wakwella, *Austin et al. 6259* (FAU, PDA, US). LOCALITY UNKNOWN: *s. coll. s.n. C.P. 1970* (K, L); *Deschamps 2/90,* in 1891 (G).

9. IPOMOEA

L., Sp. Pl. 159. 1753; Gen. Pl., ed. 5, 76. 1754. Lectotype Species: *Ipomoea pes-tigridis* L.

Quamoclit Moench, Meth. Bot. 453. 1794. Lectotype: *Ipomoea coccinea* L.
Batatas Choisy, Mem. Soc. Phys. Genève 6: 434. 1834. Lectotype: *B. edulis* Choisy = *Ipomoea batatas* (L.) Lam.
Pharbitis Choisy, Mem. Soc. Phys. Genève 6: 438. 1834. Lectotype: *P. hispida* Choisy = *Ipomoea purpurea* (L.) Roth.

Calonyction Choisy, Mem. Soc. Phys. Genève 6: 441. 1834. Lectotype: *C. speciosum* Choisy = *Ipomoea alba* L.

Exogonium Choisy, Mem. Soc. Phys. Genève 6: 443. 1834. Lectotype: *Ipomoea bracteata* Cav.

Vines, shrubs or trees, usually twining, sometimes prostrate or floating. Leaves mostly petiolate, often variable in shape and size on the same plant, entire, lobed, divided, or rarely compound, the petiole occasionally with pseudostipules. Flowers mostly in axillary 1- to many-flowered dichasia, rarely paniculate; sepals herbaceous or subcoriaceous, variable in size and shape, glabrous or pubescent, often somewhat enlarged in fruit; corolla small to large, regular, or rarely slightly zygomorphic, mostly funnelform or campanulate, less often tubular or salverform, purple, red, pink, white, or yellow, the limb shallowly or rarely deeply lobed, the interplicae well defined by 2 distinct nerves; stamens included or rarely exserted, the filaments filiform, often triangular-dilated at the base, mostly unequal in length; the pollen pantoporate, globose, spinulose; ovary usually 2- or sometimes 4-locular, 4-ovulate, rarely 3-locular, 6-ovulate, glabrous or pubescent, the style simple, filiform, included or rarely exserted, the stigma capitate, entire or often 2 (–3)-globose. Fruits globose or ovoid capsules, mostly 4 (–6)-valved or rarely splitting irregularly; seeds 4, (6, or less), glabrous or pubescent.

Ipomoea is a cosmopolitan genus of probably more than 500 species. While the genus is widespread, the majority of species occur in the Americas and Africa. Asia and Malaysia are comparatively poor in species. Unfortunately the genus is so large that no recent study of all the species has been made. The older studies have mostly considered the genus in the restricted sense and excluded several species groups as separate genera. While there is no concensus on subdivision of *Ipomoea*, the groups recognized by van Ooststroom, Verdcourt and myself do not drastically differ. The classification for the species herein proposed is a result of discussions with both van Ooststroom and Verdcourt. While they may not agree with the levels at which the taxa are placed, I believe we agree on the limits of the species groups.

1. sect. *Ipomoea*. Including: *I. bracteata, I. eriocarpa, I. indica, I. nil, I. pes-tigridis, I. pileata, I. purpurea, I. wightii.*

2. sect. *Batatas*. Including: *I. batatas, I. littoralis, I. triloba.*

3. sect. *Eriospermum*. Including: *I. carnea, I. horsfalliae, I. jucunda, I. macrantha, I. mauritiana.*

4. sect. *Erpipomoea*. Including: *I. aquatica, I. asarifolia, I. pes-caprae, I. stolonifera.*

5. sect. *Orthipomoea*. Including: *I. cairica, I. coptica, I. sepiaria, I. staphylina, I. tuberculata.*

6. sect. *Calonyction*. Including: *I. alba, I. turbinata.*

7. sect. *Quamoclit*. Including: *I. hederifolia, I. quamoclit.*

KEY TO THE SPECIES

1 Corolla salverform, the long narrow tubes only slightly widened near or above the middle, abruptly flaring near summit; anthers exserted (included in *I. macrantha* & *I. jucunda*). Either open during night and closing in the morning (white flowers) or open most
 of the day (red or scarlet flowers)
  2 Sepals acute to obtuse at the apex, often mucronulate (sect. *Eriospermum*)
    3 Corolla red or red-purple. Leaves mostly lobed or dissected into 5–7 parts........
    ....**11. I. horsfalliae**
    3 Corolla white. Leaves mostly entire, very rarely dentate with a few teeth or shallowly
      lobed
      4 Leaf blades with scattered light colored trichomes below. Seeds long comose......
      ....**14. I. jucunda**
      4 Leaf blades glabrous below. Seeds with short, erect indument.....**16. I. macrantha**
  2 Sepals acute to acuminate with at least the outer 2 having long fleshy-caudate apices
    (mucronate only in *I. quamoclit*)
    5 Corolla 2–3.5 cm long, red to orange or yellowish (very rarely white); flowers open
      all day or most of the day (sect. *Quamoclit*)
      6 Leaf blades divided more than halfway to the midrib with linear, acute lobes, the
        leaf appearing pinnately compound.............................**24. I. quamoclit**
      6 Leaf blades entire, angled or 3–7-lobed, the lobes broad or narrow, obtuse, the leaf
        not appearing compound.....................................**10. I. hederifolia**
    5 Corolla 6–14 cm long, the limb and tube white to partially green or lavender; flowers
      open during night and closing in early morning (sect. *Calonyction*)
      7 Flower tube 9–15 cm long. Fruit 2–3 cm long...........................**1. I. alba**
      7 Flower tube 3–6 cm long. Fruit 1.8–2 cm long...................**30. I. turbinata**
1 Corolla funnelform to campanulate (salverform in *I. sepiaria*), the short to long tube
 expanding from below the middle, gradually or abruptly flaring near summit; anthers
 mostly included. Open during morning, closing near noon
  8 Glabrous perennials with procumbent stems, not normally twining. Habitat of coa-
    stal dunes and beaches or inland waterway margins or cultivated wetlands. Leaves
    fleshy or leathery. Sepal elliptic-oblong to orbicular (sect. *Erpipomoea*)
    9 Flowers white, with light or dark throat inside tube
      10 Leaves sagittate..**2. I. aquatica**
      10 Leaves mostly oblong to ovate-oblong, rarely lobed, blades rounded at base......
      ....**27. I. stolonifera**
    9 Flowers pink, lavender or purple (rarely white in *I. asarifolia*)
      11 Leaves rounded-cordate, apically acute to obtuse.................**3. I. asarifolia**
      11 Leaves suborbicular to suborbicular-oblong, apically emarginate...............
      ....**20. I. pes-caprae**
  8 Glabrous or pubescent annuals or perennials with twining or erect stems, not usually
    rooting at the nodes (except in *I. batatas*). Habitat various. Leaves chartaceous to
    fleshy. Sepals acuminate to suborbicular
    12 Sepals herbaceous; sepals, peduncles or pedicels with reflexed or erect trichomes (ex-
      cept *I. indica*). Stigma lobes 3 (usually) and the ovary (2–) 3–4-locular, each locule
      2-ovulate. Corolla blue, red or white or inflorescences sub-capitate or bracteate (sect.
      Ipomoea)
      13 Corolla 5–7 cm long. Sepals soft-pubescent outside with slender trichomes or rarely
        glabrous..**13. I. indica**
      13 Corolla mostly less than 5 cm long. Sepals hispid-pilose outside with long spread-
        ing trichomes

14 Leaves deeply palmately 7–9-lobed, the lobes cut almost to blade base..............
....**21. I. pes-tigridis**
14 Leaves entire, toothed or shallowly 3-lobed, the lobes cut less than halfway to the blade base
  15 Flowers in sub-capitate to capitate inflorescences, occasionally involucrate or strongly bracteate. Corollas 0.7–3 cm long
    16 Inflorescences bracteate, subtended by one or two boat-shaped bracts
      17 Bracts one, boat-shaped, subtending the inflorescence................**22. I. pileata**
      17 Bracts two, somewhat boat-shaped because of the overlapping bases and subtending the inflorescence...**8. I. deccana**
    16 Inflorescences with inconspicuous small bracts or at least not subtending the inflorescence in a boat-like form
      18 Leaves white-arachnoid pubescent below. Inflorescences on peduncles as long or longer than the leaves...**31. I. wightii**
      18 Leaves glabrous or scattered hispid-pilose below. Inflorescences on peduncles shorter than the leaves, at time appearing sessile.......................**9. I. eriocarpa**
  15 Flowers solitary or in open cymose inflorescences. Corollas 4–8 cm long
    19 Sepals with slightly narrowed green tips shorter than to slightly longer than the body ....**23. I. purpurea**
    19 Sepals with very narrow elongate green tips much longer than the body....**18. I. nil**
12 Sepals coriaceous or membranaceous, rarely somewhat herbaceous; the sepals, peduncles and pedicels glabrous or at least without reflexed trichomes. Stigma lobes 2 and the ovary 2 (–3)-locular, each locule 2-ovulate. Corolla mostly lavender, sometimes blue or white, the inflorescences with caducous or squamiform bracts
  20 Sepals mostly coriaceous. Large perennial vines or shrubs. Seeds oblong, woolly at least on the margins. Corollas mostly large, funnelform (sect. *Eriospermum*)
    21 Leaves deeply palmately lobed...................... ....**17. I. mauritiana**
    21 Leaves entire
      22 Sepals 5–8 mm long. Shrubs.....................................**6. I. carnea**
      22 Sepals (7–) 10–18 mm long. Woody vines...................**12. I. campanulata**
  20 Sepals membranaceous to chartaceous. Small annual or perennial vines. Seeds suborbicular to pyriform, glabrous to densely short pubescent. Corollas small to large, funnelform to campanulate
    23 Sepals smooth or pubescent on backs, margins not obviously scarious, mostly oblong, elliptic to lanceolate. Leaves cordate, pandurate or 3-lobed to palmately 5–7-lobed (sect. *Batatas*)
      24 Flowers 1–2 (–2.5) cm long. Inflorescences umbelliform-cymose (rarely solitary). Plants not rooting at the nodes................................**28. I. triloba**
      24 Flowers 3–5 (–7) cm long. Inflorescences few-flowered, cymose. Plants often rooting at the nodes
        25 Outer sepals elliptic to broad-ovate, broadest near the middle, mostly with a single raised central vein. Stamens pubescent on the lower half of the filament.... ....**15. I. littoralis**
        25 Outer sepals sublanceolate to oblong, broadest above the middle, with 3 to 5 large, raised central veins. Stamens glabrous except at the base of the filament. (a commonly cultivated food plant, very variable)..................**4. I. batatas**
    23 Sepals verrucose or cristate on backs, otherwise with obvious scarious margins, mostly oblong or ovate, Leaves deeply lobed to dissected or less commonly entire, cordate (sect. *Erpipomoea*)
      26 Leaves deeply lobed, divided or palmately compound
        27 Leaf segments entire. Pseudostipules (small leaves on the axillary shoot) often present

28 Corolla purplish, mauve, bluish or white..........................**5. I. cairica**
28 Corolla yellow or white with a purple center..................**29. I. tuberculata**
27 Leaf segments coarsely dentate to deeply and irregularly pinnatifid....**7. I. coptica**
26 Leaves entire
  29 Corolla salverform, up to 3–3.5 cm long........................**25. I. sepiaria**
  29 Corolla funnelform to campanulate, to 2.5 cm long
    30 Inflorescences paniculate. Corolla lavender to purplish............**26. I. staphylina**
    30 Inflorescences of solitary flowers or few-flowered cymes. Corolla white to yellow with
      a red purple centre..**19. I. obscura**

1. Ipomoea alba L., Sp. Pl. 161. 1753, van Ooststroom, Fl. Mal., ser. 1, 4: 480. 1953; Verdcourt, Fl. Trop. E. Afr. 130. 1963; Gunn, Brittonia 24: 150–168. 1972. Type: India, Malabar; illustration of *Convolvulus malabaricus flore amplo* etc., in Rheede, Hort. Malab. 11. t. 50. 1692 (designated by Verdcourt as holotype; Gunn did not agree and designated as lectotype).

Convolvulus aculeatus L., Sp. Pl. 155. 1753.
? *Convolvulus grandiflorus* Moon, Cat. 13. 1824.
Calonyction speciosum Choisy, Mem. Soc. Phys. Genève 6: 441. 1834; Thw., Enum. Pl. Zeyl. 211. 1860.
Ipomoea bona-nox L., Sp. Pl. ed. 2. 228. 1762; Clarke in Hook. f., Fl. Br. Ind. 4: 197. 1883 (as to name, not description); Trimen, Handb. Fl. Ceylon 3: 213. 1895.
Calonyction bona-nox (L.) Bojer, Hort. Maurit. 227. 1837.
Calonyction aculeatum (L.) House, Bull. Torrey Bot. Club 31: 590. 1904 (a mixed concept, including both *I. alba* and *I. macrantha*).

Vines; the stems herbaceous at the tips, becoming somewhat woody at the base, smooth or often with short fleshy prickles, occasionally rooting near the nodes, glabrous. Leaves rounded ovate, entire or 3–5 lobed, 5–15 cm long, basally cordate, apically acuminate, glabrous. Inflorescences of 1- to several-flowered cymes. Flowers with pedicels 7–15 mm long; sepals fleshy, ovate to elliptic, 10–20 mm long, apically caudate at least on the outer 2 sepals; corolla white with greenish nectar-guides, the tube 9–15 cm long, the rotate limb 8–10 cm broad. Fruit capsular, ovoid to subglobose, 2–3 cm long, 1–2 cm in diameter, with a 7–10 mm apiculus, mostly dark brown, glabrous; seeds dark brown to black, rarely tan, 8–10 mm long, glabrous.

D i s t r. Pantropical but undoubtedly originally from the New World. During the time Trimen was a studying the Ceylon flora the plants were common on the island, apparently through cultivation only. Now the species is rare.

E c o l. The only plants found on the island and in collections have been cultivated. The white nocturnal flowers of this species open shortly after sundown; they open rapidly and saturate the air with a heavy, sweet odor. Moths are the pollinators in the Western Hemisphere.

V e r n. Alanga (S); a name usually applied to *Alangium salviifolium* (L. f.)

Wangerin. Kalu-alanga (S); "kalu"—black, "alanga"—as above. Moon Flower (E); alluding to the similarity of the open flower and the moon.

Specimens Examined. KEGALLE DISTRICT: between Kegalle & Kadugannawa, *Austin & Austin 6140* (FAU, PDA, US). GALLE DISTRICT: Galle, *Cramer 2495* (L). LOCALITY UNKNOWN: *s. coll., C.P. 3648* (PDA).

2. Ipomoea aquatica Forsk., Fl. Aegypt.-Arab. 44. 1775; Clarke in Hook. f., Fl. Br. Ind. 4: 210. 1883; Trimen, Handb. Fl. Ceylon 3: 221. 1895; van Ooststroom, Fl. Mal., ser. 1, 4: 473. 1953; Verdcourt, Fl. Trop. E. Africa. 120. 1963. Type: Yemen, Zebid, *Forskal* (C, holotype; BM, isotype, fide Verdcourt).

Ipomoea reptans sensu auct. mult., e.g. Moon, Cat. 14. 1824; Thw., Enum. Pl. Zeyl. 211. 1860, non *Convolvulus reptans* L. (1753).

Vines; the stems hollow, rooting at the nodes when floating or procumbent, glabrate. Leaves mostly hastate, the terminal lobe broadly to narrowly triangular or lanceolate, the basal lobes smaller and spreading or almost absent, 4–12 cm long, apically acute or obtuse, glabrescent. Inflorescences of solitary flowers or in few-flowered cymes, glabrous. Flowers on pedicels 2-7 cm long; sepals ovate-oblong, subequal, 7 mm long, obtuse or subacute, mucronulate, glabrous; corolla purple or rarely white, 4–5 cm long, funnelform. Fruits capsular, ovoid to globose, 8–10 mm long; seeds densely softpilose or glabrous.

D i s t r. A native of the Old World tropics, this plant now occurs in several countries in the New World. The introduction into the New World is because of its use as a vegetable. From its common name in Ceylon it has apparently been introduced there from the east, perhaps Malaysia.

E c o l. Plants are restricted to wet sites, particularly tank margins, canals, paddy margins and stream beds. Some are cultivated on drier sites but they usually do poorly. Although cultivated in both the wet and dry zones, the plants appear to be naturalized in the dry zone.

V e r n. Kankun (S); apparently there is no meaning in Sinhalese for this common name although "kan" means ears. Most likely the Sinhalese name was derived from the Malaysian name "kangkung" which is spread through those islands in many of the languages.

Specimens Examined. RATNAPURA DISTRICT: Atakalankorle, *s. coll. s.n.* Sept. 1857 (PDA). HAMBANTOTA DISTRICT: Kirinde, *Simpson 9951* (PDA); Tissamaharama, *Austin et al. 6106* (FAU, PDA, US); Wirawila, *Austin et al. 6114* (FAU, PDA, US). Ruhuna National Park, Katagamuwa tank, *Ripley 270* (US); Situlpahuwa, *Cooray 70032705R* (L, PDA). LOCALITY UNKNOWN: *Meijer 234* (PDA, US).

N o t e. Trimen recognized a new variety based on *C.P. 3941* (Trimen,

1895: 222). Hallier annotated the specimen "*I. gleniei*?" While the specimen has narrower leaves than is normally seen, it appears best kept in *I. aquatica*.

3. Ipomoea asarifolia (Desr.) Roem. & Schultes, Syst. Veg. 4: 251. 1819; van Oostroom, Fl. Mal., ser. 1, 4: 477. 1953. Type: Senegal. *Roussillon* (not seen).

Convolvulus asarifolius Desr. in Lam., Enc. 3: 562. 1789.

Ipomoea repens Lam., Tabl. Enc. 1: 467. 1791, non Roth (1821); Trimen, Handb. Fl. Ceylon 3: 222. 1895.

Ipomoea rugosa (Rottl.) Choisy, Mem. Soc. Phys. Genève 6: 446. 1834; Thw., Enum. Pl. Zeyl. 211. 1860.

Ipomoea beladamboe Roem. & Schultes, Syst. Veg. 4: 233. 1819; Clarke in Hook. f., Fl. Br. Ind. 4: 209. 1883.

Vines; the stems herbaceous, decumbent and the tips twining, rooting at the nodes, glabrous. Leaves rounded-cordate to subreniform, 4–8 cm long, basally cordate, apically rounded, glabrescent. Inflorescences of solitary flowers or in axillary or terminal simple or compound cymes, glabrous or puberulent. Flowers on pedicels 14–24 mm long; sepals unequal, the outer 5–6 mm long, the inner 10–12 mm long, elliptic to ovate, coriaceous, rounded apically, mucronate, glabrous, verrucose; corolla lavender to purple, rarely white, 6–8 cm long, funnelform. Fruits tardily dehiscent capsules, subglobose, 10–12 mm long, brown, glabrous; seeds brown to dark brown, 6–7 mm long, minutely gray-pubescent.

D i s t r. Originally an American species, these plants are now pantropical. Although my studies are incomplete, the original home of this species may have been in the Orinoco River Basin of Venezuela. From there it probably spread to the West Indies from which it was carried in ballast by the early sailing ships to the Old World.

E c o l. Virtually always associated with wetlands, particularly streams, canals and lagoons, this species has been found in only the wet zone. Some plants are associated with paddies also.

S p e c i m e n s E x a m i n e d. PUTTALAM DISTRICT: Wilpattu National Park, Marikaran Villu, *Cooray & Balakrishnan 69050123R* (L, PDA). KURUNEGALA DISTRICT: Weuda, *Austin et al. 6217* (FAU, PDA, US). RATNAPURA DISTRICT: Dewalagawa, *Cramer 3103* (PDA, US); without locality, *s. coll. s.n.* Feb. 1892 (PDA). MATALE DISTRICT: Inamaluwa, *Austin et al. 6154* (PDA, US); Nalanda, *Austin et al. 6151* (FAU, PDA, US). KANDY DISTRICT: Peradeniya, *s. coll. s.n.*, Feb. 1898 (PDA). DISTRICT UNKNOWN: *s. coll. C.P. 2850* (G, L). GALLE DISTRICT: Galle, *Austin et al. 6093* (FAU, PDA, US). LOCALITY UNKNOWN: *s. coll. C.P. 2850* (G, PDA); *Gardner s.n.* (K); *Walker s.n.* (K).

4. Ipomoea batatas (L.) Lam., Ill. 1: 465. 1793; Trimen, Handb. Fl. Ceylon 3: 212. 1895; van Ooststroom, Fl. Mal., ser. 1, 4: 469. 1953; Verdcourt, Fl. Trop. E. Africa 114. 1963; Austin, Ann. Missouri Bot. Gard. 62: 195. 1975. Type: India, *anon.*, specimen 218.12 in LINN (lectotype not seen; microfiche seen).

Convolvulus batatas L., Sp. Pl. 154. 1753.
Convolvulus edulis Thunb., Fl. Japan 84. 1784.
Batatas edulis (Thunb.) Choisy, Mem. Soc. Phys. Genève 6: 435. 1834.

Vines; the stems usually somewhat succulent but sometimes slender and herbaceous; perennial, glabrous or pubescent. Leaves variable, from cordate to ovate, entire, dentate or often deeply lobed, 5–10 cm long, glabrous or sometimes pubescent. Inflorescences of solitary or few-flowered cymes. Flowers absent in some varieties, if present on pedicels 3–12 mm long; sepals oblong, the outer sepals acuminate and cuspidate, (8–) 10–15 mm long, mostly pubescent or only ciliate; corolla with a lavender to purple-lavender limb and darker throat, white in some varieties, 4–7 cm long. Fruits rarely formed, ovoid, glabrous; seeds rotund, glabrous.

D i s t r. Originally from the New World, this food plant is now cultivated over most of the world. Although cultivated in temperate regions it is most common in the tropics.

E c o l. Outside the Americas the sweet potato or "batala" is rarely encountered outside cultivation. Knowledge of non-American plants has led numerous authors to conclude erroneously that the plants do not occur in the wild (cf. Trimen, Handb. Fl. Ceylon 3: 212. 1895). In northern South America and several countries in Central America wild plants are actually common. In Ceylon plants are cultivated on almost all available sites. Perhaps most common are dooryard gardens but it is not uncommon to find plots on roadside margins and occasionally in a road median. Plants are apparently planted and harvested at all times during the year, essentially being controlled by need. At least in the New World the plants are most commonly pollinated by bumblebees (*Bombus*). No pollinator has been observed in Celyon.

V e r n. Batala (S); the Sinhalese word for this plant was undoubtedly derived from the West Indian "batata" through the Portuguese. There is a Sinhalese legend, however, which presents a different interpretation. According to the legend there was once a Sinhalese son who did not like his mother. Because the son neglected the mother she was forced to beg for food. One day the daughter-in-law saw the mother coming begging as she was preparing rice ("bath" for cooked rice in Sinhalese). Quickly hiding the rice she told the old woman that they were so poor there was no food in the house. The old woman knew this to be a lie and put a curse on the household. After she left the daughter-in-law removed the rice from its hiding place to discover it had been turned to blood ("le" in Sinhalese). Disgusted the daughter-in-law threw the blood into the garden. Some dayslater she was surprised to find an unfamiliar vine in the garden, exactly on the spot where she had thrown the cursed rice. Digging up the unfamiliar plant she found it had large red tubers. This led to the modern word for the plant, "bath" plus "le" or "bathle" which finally became "batala."

Vel-kelengu (T), "vel"—creeper, "kelengu"—yam. Sweet potato (E).

S p e c i m e n s   E x a m i n e d. MATALE DISTRICT: Sigiriya, *Austin et al. 6155* (FAU, PDA, US). KANDY DISTRICT: Kandy, *Austin et al. 6136* (FAU, PDA, US). NUWARA ELIYA DISTRICT: between Pussalawa and Nuwara Eliya, *Austin et al. 6129* (FAU, PDA, US). BADULLA DISTRICT: between Welimada and Nuwara Eliya, *Austin et al. 6126* (FAU, PDA, US). KEGALLE DISTRICT: just past Mawanella, *Austin et al. 6086* (FAU, PDA, US). RATNAPURA DISTRICT: Pussella, *Austin et al. 6228* (FAU, PDA, US). GALLE DISTRICT: Walawella, *Austin et al. 6269* (FAU, PDA, US). LOCALITY UNKNOWN: *s. coll. 2305* (L).

N o t e. In addition to the collections cited above, I have eaten or seen sweet potatos in the following districts: Trincomalee, Polonnaruwa, Batticaloa, Amparai, Moneragala, Hambantota, Kurunegala, Colombo and Kalutara.

At present there are over 20 varieties of the species being cultivated in the country. No detailed study of exactly how many varieties exist and so an absolute number is not possible. Many of these varieties have been introduced recently by the Department of Agriculture. My observations in seventeen of the districts suggest that there are three basic common varieties: "kaha-batala" or yellow yam; "sudu-batala" or white yam; and "bola-batala" or ball-shaped yam. Local variants of these basic strains occur, such as the "ratu-batala" or red yam, and those that I have seen appear to be sports of the basic strains. Among the villages classification of the yams (a local English term for any tuberous root) is based primarily on tuber flesh color not skin color. Still the flesh color is recognized by leaf shape and anthocyanin content of leaves, petioles and stems. A secondary category of classification in the villages is based on whether or not the yams are solitary, clustered or at the ends of branch roots.

Virtually every plot of batala is prepared by loosening the soil with a "mammote" (E) or "uddala" (S). The loose soil is most often mounded into a low, flat bed. Some ethnobotanists have suggested that this bed preparation type indicates contact with New World cultivation styles. A labourer in Kandy, however, provided what is probably a more rational explanation: unless the tropical clay soils are loosened and mounded they are so hard that tuber production is limited.

5. Ipomoea cairica (L.) Sweet, Hort. Br. 287. 1827; van Ooststroom, Fl. Mal., ser. 1, 4: 478. 1953; Verdcourt, Fl. Trop. E. Africa 125. 1963. Type: illustration of *Convolvulus aegyptius* Vesling, Obs. in Prosp. Alp. Pl. Aegypt. 75. fig. 1638 (syntype).

Convolvulus cairicus L., Syst. Nat. ed. 10. 922. 1759.
Ipomoea palmata Forsk., Fl. Aegypt.-Arab. 43. 1775; Thw., Enum. Pl. Zeyl. 212. 1860; Clarke in Hook. f., Fl. Br. Ind. 4: 214. 1883; Trimen, Handb. Fl. Ceylon 3: 225. 1895.

Vines; the stems twining or sometimes prostrate, smooth or muricate, glabrous or rarely villous at the nodes; perennial, with a tuberous rootstock. Leaves ovate to orbicular in outline, palmately divided to the base into 5–7 lobes, 3–10 cm long and wide, the lobes lanceolate to ovate or elliptic, acute or obtuse and mucronulate at the apex, 3–5 cm long, the outer lobes sometimes bifid, pseudostipules present. Inflorescences lax, 1- to many-flowered, on peduncles 0.5–8 cm long. Flowers on pedicels 1.2–3 cm long; sepals ovate, 4–6.5 mm long, the outer slightly shorter, obtuse to acute, mucronulate, the edges membranaceous, glabrous, sometimes verruculose; corolla purple, blue-purple or white with a purple centre (red or entirely white fide Verdcourt), funnelform, (3–) 4.5–6 cm long. Fruits capsular, subglobose, 1–1.2 cm long, glabrous; seeds subglobose to ovoid, blackish to tan, 4.2–6 mm long, densely short-tomentose, sometimes with long silky trichomes along the edges.

D i s t r. Found in tropical Africa, from the eastern Mediterranean region through Asia to Formosa and Malaysia; also in the New World tropics. Long considered a species of Old World origin, the original home of the species has actually not been determined. It appears likely that the plants are originally from the Western Hemisphere.

E c o l. Widely cultivated, the species is naturalized in waste places, thickets, hedges, stream banks and cultivated grounds. Most of the plants are self-incompatible and must be cross-pollinated; numerous bees visit and pollinate.

S p e c i m e n s   E x a m i n e d. KANDY DISTRICT: Peradeniya, *s. coll. s.n.* Jan. 1898 (PDA); University Campus, *Comanor 509* (US). NUWARA ELIYA DISTRICT: Ambagamuwa, *s. coll. C.P. 3387*, Mar. 1855 (PDA). BADULLA DISTRICT: Haputale, *Austin et al. 6122* (FAU, PDA, US); Meda Oya, *M. Jayasuriya 398* (PDA, US). KEGALLE DISTRICT: Kegalle-Avissawella Road, Ruwanwella, *Austin et al. 6223* (FAU, PDA, US). GALLE DISTRICT: Galle, *Austin et al. 6254* (FAU, PDA, US). LOCALITY UNKNOWN: *s. coll., C.P. 3387* (K).

6. Ipomoea carnea Jacq. subsp. **fistulosa** (Mart. ex Choisy) D. Austin, Taxon 26: 237, 1977. Type: Brasil, *Martius 2398* (M, lectotype).

Ipomoea carnea Jacq., Enum. Pl. Carib. 13. 1760 as to species, not subspecies.
Ipomoea fistulosa Mart. ex Choisy in DC., Prod. 9: 349. 1845.
Batatas? *crassicaulis* Benth., Voy. Sulphur 5: 134. 1845.
Ipomoea crassicaulis (Benth.) Rob., Proc. Amer. Acad. Arts 51: 530. 1916.

Shrubs to 2.5 m high; the stems woody at the base, the tips herbaceous, hollow, glabrous or minutely puberulent. Leaves ovate to lanceolate, less commonly suborbicular, 10–25 cm long, truncate to shallowly cordate basally, long acuminate apically, pubescent on both surfaces but sometimes glabrescent. Inflorescences cymose-paniculate clusters at the branch tips, 1- to several-flowered. Flowers with pedicels longer than the calyx; sepals suborbicular, 5–6 mm long, subcoriaceous, glabrate or puberulent; corolla deep pink, light pink to rose-purple, the throat darker than the limb, 5–8 cm long, finely tomentose outside. Fruits capsular, ovoid to subglobose, 2 cm long, 1–1.5 cm in diameter; seeds covered with long woolly brown trichomes.

D i s t r. Originally from the American tropics, this species is now circumtropical because of introductions for cultivation with subsequent escape and naturalization.

E c o l. All of the plants yet found in Ceylon have been associated with homes and villages. Some plants were cultivated and used in local remedies; others were said to be wild.

S p e c i m e n s E x a m i n e d. POLONNARUWA DISTRICT: Giritale, *Austin et al. 6164* (FAU, PDA, US). TRINCOMALEE DISTRICT: Kantalai-Allai Road, *Austin et al. 6178* (FAU, PDA, US); Kantalai-Trincomalee Road, *Comanor 766* (K, L, PDA); Tampalakamam, *Austin et al. 6170* (FAU, PDA, US). AMPARAI DISTRICT: Pulaveli, *Austin et al. 6186* (FAU, PDA, US). KURUNEGALA DISTRICT: Mawatagama, *Austin et al. 6220* (FAU, PDA, US). MATALE DISTRICT: Naula, *Austin et al. 6149* (FAU, PDA, US). MONERAGALA DISTRICT: Tanamalwila, *Austin et al. 6117* (FAU, PDA, US). KEGALLE DISTRICT: Mawanella, *Austin et al. 6084* (FAU, PDA, US). RATNAURA DISTRICT: Kuruwita, *Austin et al. 6230* (FAU, PDA, US). COLOMBO DISTRICT: Nittambuwa, *Austin et al. 6087* (FAU, PDA, US). KALUTARA DISTRICT: Horana, *Austin et al. 6235* (FAU, PDA, US). GALLE DISTRICT: Galle, *Austin et al. 6270* (FAU, PDA, US). MATARA DISTRICT: Weligama, *Austin et al. 6102* (FAU, PDA, US). HAMBANTOTA DISTRICT: Tissamaharama-Wellawaya Road, *Austin et al. 6115* (FAU, PDA, US).

7. Ipomoea coptica (L.) Roem. & Schultes, Syst. Veg. 4: 208. 1819; van Ooststroom, Fl. Mal., ser. 1, 4: 479. 1953; Verdcourt, Fl. Trop. E. Africa 128. 1963. Type: Orient, specimen 218. 32 (LINN, not seen; microfiche seen).

Convolvulus copticus L., Mant. 2: 559. 1771.

Ipomoea dissecta Willd., Phytogr. 5. t. 2. 1794; Thw., Enum. Pl. Zeyl. 212. 1860; Clarke in Hook. f., Fl. Br. Ind. 4: 200. 1883; Trimen, Handb. Fl. Ceylon 3: 213. 1895.

Vines; the stems slender, prostrate or twining, glabrous; annual. Leaves orbicular in outline, digitately 5-lobed, 1–7 cm long and wide, the lobes linear to ovate or elliptic, dentate to deeply and coarsely once or twice pinnatifid, up to 6 cm long and 2 cm wide, the two outer lobes often bifid, pseudostipules present. Inflorescences axillary, 1–3-flowered, the peduncle 1–3.5 cm long, narrowly alate. Flowers with pedicels 4–10 mm long; sepals subequal, oblong or elliptic, 4–5 mm long, obtuse or cuspidate, muriculate, echinate or with undulating crests; corolla white, pink or white with a purple throat, funnelform, about 1.2 cm long. Fruits capsular, globose, glabrous, 7–8 mm long; seeds often 6 in 3 locules, 2–3 mm long, densely grayish-tomentose.

Distr. Known from southern India, Ceylon, tropical Africa, and Australia.

Ecol. Found only in the dry zone in sandy places, especially near the coast. A rare species.

Specimens Examined. MANNAR DISTRICT: Madhu Road, *Jayasuriya et al. 594* (PDA); Mantai, *s. coll. s.n.* Feb. 1890 (PDA); Illupaikaduvai, *s. coll. s.n.* Feb. 1890 (PDA). TRINCOMALEE DISTRICT: Trincomalee, *Glenie s.n.*, *C.P. 1928* (in part) (PDA). BATTICALOA DISTRICT: Kalmunai (as Karamoonie), *Gardner s.n.*, *C.P. 1928* (in part) (PDA).

8. Ipomoea deccana D. Austin, nom. nov. Type: India, S. Deccan Peninsula, Quilon, *Wight* (not seen).

Ipomoea bracteata Wight, Ic. Pl. Ind. Or. 4 (2): 14. t. 1374. 1850, non Cav. (1799); Clarke in Hook. f., Fl. Br. Ind. 4: 203. 1883; Trimen, Handb. Fl. Ceylon 3: 216. 1895.

Vines; the stems twining, pubescent with spreading trichomes. Leaves ovate-cordate, 2–4 cm long, basally cordate, apically acute, entire to 5-lobed, the lobes attenuate basally, acute apically, pubescent on both surfaces. Inflorescences in boat-shaped involucrate-bracteate, head-like cymose clusters, the two outer bracts ovate, basally truncate-cordate, apically acute, each separate bract to 1.5 cm long, the inner bracts smaller. Flowers sessile to subsessile; sepals subequal, lanceolate-acuminate, 7–9 mm long, pubescent with spreading trichomes; corolla purplish, funnelform, 1.5–2 cm long. Fruits subglobose, 5 mm long, brown, glabrous; seeds glabrous, brown, 2 mm long.

Distr. Known only from India and Ceylon.

Ecol. No recent collections of the species have been made in Ceylon. Perhaps the species was introduced as an ephemeral weed since it was originally collected on an estate. At any rate the species must still be considered very rare.

Specimens Examined. KALUTARA DISTRICT: Kalutara, *Ferguson s.n.*, in 1880 (PDA). LOCALITY UNKNOWN: *s. coll. C.P. 1942* (PDA).

9. Ipomoea eriocarpa R. Br., Prod. 484. 1810; Clarke in Hook. f., Fl. Br. Ind. 4: 204. 1883; Trimen, Handb. Fl. Ceylon 3: 217. 1895; van Ooststroom, Fl. Mal., ser. 1, 4: 462. fig. 35. 1953; Verdcourt. Fl. Trop. E. Africa 91. 1963. Type: Australia, "New Holland", *Banks & Solander* (BM, holotype fide Verdcourt).

Convolvulus hispidus Vahl, Symb. Bot. 3: 29. 1794.
Ipomoea hispida (Vahl) Roem. & Schultes, Syst. Veg. 4: 238. 1819, non Zucc. (1806).
Ipomoea sessiliflora Roth, Nov. Pl. Sp. 116. 1821; Thw., Enum. Pl. Zeyl. 212. 1860.

Vines; the stems twining, pubescent or hispid with both long and short trichomes; annual. Leaves ovate-cordate to linear-oblong, 2.5–8 cm long, usually subhastate basally with rounded lobes, pilose to glabrescent. Inflorescences 3- to many-flowered, flowers rarely solitary, axillary, subsessile or on peduncles up to 1 cm long. Flowers on pedicels about 5 mm long; sepals ovate, acuminate apically, hispid-pilose, basal part 5 mm long, apical part 4 mm long; corolla lavender, white, pink or white with a lavender centre, 6–9 mm long, 13 mm across. Fruits capsular, 5–6 mm in diameter, subglobose, pubescent; seeds black, finely punctate, glabrous, 2.5 mm long.

D i s t r. The species is known from tropical Africa to Transvaal, Madagascar, Egypt, Pakistan, tropical Asia and northern Australia.

E c o l. A species normally found in rather xeric habitats such as grasslands and thorn scrub. Plants have also been found in hedgerows, and cultivated ground in various parts of the range. Most plants have been found on clay soils.

Specimens Examined. KURUNEGALA DISTRICT: Kurunegala, *Alston 1707* (PDA). MATALE DISTRICT: Wattegoda, *anon.*, Feb. 1854, *C.P. 3107* (in part) (PDA). BADULLA DISTRICT: between Welimada & Ettampitiya, *s. coll. s.n.* Jan. 1888 (PDA); WITHOUT LOCALITY, *s. coll.* Apr. 1854, *C.P. 3107* (in part) (PDA). LOCALITY UNKNOWN: *s. coll. C.P. 3107* (G).

10. Ipomoea hederifolia L., Syst. Nat. ed. 10. 925. 1759; Verdcourt, Fl. Trop. E. Africa 132. 1963. Type: West Indies, illustration of *Ipomoea foliis cordatis* Plumier, Pl. Amer. t. 93. f. 2. (lectotype).

Ipomoea coccinea of authors, e.g., Clarke in Hook. f., Fl. Br. Ind. 4: 199.

326 CONVOLVULACEAE

1883; Trimen, Handb. Fl. Ceylon 3: 215. 1895, non L. (1753).

Ipomoea angulata Lam., Ill. 1: 464. 1793; van Ooststroom, Fl. Mal., ser. 1, 4: 481. 1953.

Ipomoea phoenicea Roxb., Fl. Ind. ed. Carey & Wall. 2: 92. 1824.

Vines; the stems slender and herbaceous; annuals, glabrous to sparsely pubescent. Leaves ovate to suborbicular in outline, 2–15 cm long, entire, dentate, trilobate or less commonly with 5 or 7 lobes, basally cordate, acute to acuminate apically, glabrous or remotely pubescent. Inflorescences few- to several-flowered cymes or flowers solitary. Flowers on pedicels 5–7 mm long or sometimes longer; sepals oblong to elliptic 1.5–3 mm long, apically obtuse or truncate, the outer sepals with a 1.6–6 mm long, subterminal arista, glabrous; corolla red or red-yellow, 2.5–4.5 cm long, the tube 1–2 mm in diameter, often yellow at the throat, the limb 1.8–2.5 cm in diameter. Fruits capsular, subglobose, 6–8 mm long; seeds dark brown or black, pyriform, with usually 2 lines of short dark trichomes on the dorsal surface.

D i s t r. A species originally from the Americas, this vine has been introduced into most of the tropical countries of the world.

E c o l. Plants have thus far been found only in the upland wet zone. The species is associated with various disturbed sites and is perhaps cultivated. Flowers are visited by sunbirds.

S p e c i m e n s E x a m i n e d. KANDY DISTRICT: Urugala, *Austin et al. 6200* (FAU, PDA, US). BADULLA DISTRICT: road to Duhinda Hills, *Balakrishnan & Jayasuriya 869* (PDA, US). KEGALLE DISTRICT: W. of Kadugannawa, *Grupe 206* (PDA, US).

11. Ipomoea horsfalliae Hook., Bot. Mag. t. 3315. 1834; van Ooststroom, Blumea 3: 564 & Fl. Mal., ser. 1, 4: 484. 1953. Type: A specimen cultivated at Kew (K, not seen).

Vines; the stems twining, glabrous, becoming woody with age, lenticellate; perennial. Leaves orbicular in outline, 5–20 cm long and wide, deeply palmately lobed to beyond the middle or to the base into 3–5 segments, middle segment usually larger than laterals, ovate, elliptic or elliptic-oblong, mostly attenuate toward both ends, acuminate apically with an acute or obtuse, mucronulate point, the lateral segments ovate-lanceolate to linear-lanceolate, margins of segments slightly crisped, entire or coarsely dentate to crenate. Inflorescences axillary, few- to several-flowered, widely cymosely branched, the peduncle 1.5–14 cm long. Flowers with pedicels 8–15 mm long; sepals subequal or the outer slightly shorter, elliptic or ovate-elliptic, obtuse, concave, 7–10 mm long; corolla red or red-purple, salverform, the tube about 4 cm long, the limb 4–4.5 cm wide, stamens and style exserted. Fruits not seen.

D i s t r. A native of Jamaica and supposedly also Puerto Rico, this species is now widely cultivated in the tropics of both hemispheres.

E c o l. Apparently the plants rarely if ever produce fruits outside their home in Jamaica. Because of this the vines are encountered only in cultivation and have not escaped.

S p e c i m e n s E x a m i n e d. KANDY DISTRICT: Peradeniya, *Austin et al. 6278* (FAU, PDA, US).

N o t e s. Plants have also been seen cultivated in Kegalle District. The species is perhaps to be found elsewhere.

12. Ipomoea campanulata L., Sp. Pl. 160. 1753; Moon, Cat. 14. 1824; Trimen, Handb. Fl. Ceylon 3: 221. 1895. Type: Adamboe, Rheede, Hort. Mal. 16: 115. t. 56. 1695 (lectotype).

Ipomoea illustris (Clarke) Prain, Beng. Pl. 2: 735. 1903; van Ooststroom, Fl. Mal., ser. 1, 4: 485. 1953; Type: Malay Peninsula: Moulmein. *Parish* (K?, not seen).

Ipomoea campanulata var. *illustris* Clarke in Hook. f., Fl. Br. Ind. 4: 211. 1883.

Lianas; the stems twining, rarely prostrate and rooting, glabrous or pubescent. Leaves ovate to orbicular, sometimes ovate-oblong, 6–16 cm long, shallowly cordate to truncate basally, acuminate apically, with a long acute or obtuse, mucronulate acumen, the margins entire or undulate, surfaces glabrous or the lower pubescent, at least some glandular trichomes on the lower surface. Inflorescences axillary, cymosely 1- to several-flowered, glabrous or rarely pubescent. Flowers on pedicels 1–1.5 (−2.5) cm long; sepals very slightly unequal, the outer somewhat shorter, 7–10 mm long, the inner 10–12 mm long, enlarging in fruit, glabrous or rarely pubescent, coriaceous, with pale thinner margins, orbicular with rounded apices; corolla purple with a darker throat, paler without, apparently rarely white, campanulate-funnelform, mostly 8–10 cm long. Fruits capsular, ovoid, about 1.5 cm long, brown; seeds 8–9 mm long, black, with silky, long trichomes along the margins.

D i s t r. These plants are found in India, Ceylon, Indo-China, Siam, Andamans and Malaysia.

E c o l. Apparently always found near the sea in thickets, along the margins of brackish rivers, in lagoon margins and on sea-shores; found up to 25 m in elevation in Malaysia.

S p e c i m e n s E x a m i n e d. KALUTARA DISTRICT: Paiyagala, *Austin et al. 6273* (FAU, PDA, US); Paiyagala South, *Austin et al. 6092* (FAU, PDA, US); Kalutara, *Austin et al. 6243* (FAU, PDA, US). GALLE DISTRICT: Galle, *s. coll.* Dec. 1853, *C.P. 2847* (PDA).

13. Ipomoea indica (Burm. f.) Merr., Int. Rumph. Herb. Amb. 445. 1917; Fosberg, Micronesia 2: 151. 1967; Bot. Notiser. 129: 35–38. 1976. Type: based on *Convolvulus indicus flore violaceo* Besler, Hort. Eyst. Aest. Ord. 13 vol. 8, fig. 2. 1613 (chosen lectotype by Fosberg, 1976).

Ipomoea acuminata (Vahl) Roem. & Schultes, Syst. Veg. 4: 228. 1819; Verdcourt, Fl. Trop. E. Africa 113. 1963; Austin, Ann. Missouri Bot. Gard. 62: 192. 1975.

Ipomoea leari Paxton, Bot. Mag. 6: 267. 1839; Trimen, Handb. Fl. Ceylon 3: 213. 1895.

Ipomoea congesta R. Br., Prod. 485. 1810; van Ooststroom, Fl. Mal., ser. 1, 4: 465. 1953.

Ipomoea cathartica Poir. in Lam., Enc. Suppl. 4: 633. 1816.

Vines; the stems twining, much branched, herbaceous to somewhat woody near the base, perennial, the stems appressed pubescent to glabrate. Leaves rounded-ovate, commonly with 3 lobes, also entire, 5–9 cm long, basally cordate, apically acuminate, densely pubescent, particularly below, to glabrate or glabrous. Inflorescences of 1- to few-flowered cymes, the cymes usually silky white-pubescent. Flowers on pedicels mostly 1 cm long; sepals lanceolate to ovate or broadly-ovate, 10–20 mm long, apically long acuminate to acuminate, appressed pubescent to glabrate; corolla blue or purple, rarely white, 5–7 cm long, the limb 6–8 cm broad. Fruits capsular, to 1 cm broad, globose or somewhat flattened apically, glabrous; seeds commonly 4, tan to dark brown, glabrous.

D i s t r. Although probably an American tropical species, this population is now pantropical. Several variations occur in the different parts of its range and some of these have had formal names applied.

E c o l. Plants grow in a variety of disturbed sites but are particularly common near villages and towns in the wet zone. As with most members of the family, the vines are heliophylic and grow best in sunny areas; they will grow under low canopy forests if able to climb to the crowns of the trees. The species was commonly cultivated in Trimen's time but has now been replaced by other favorites.

The plants I have studied have an incompatibility system which requires cross-pollination. Flowers are frequented and pollinated by a variety of bees and perhaps some butterflies.

S p e c i m e n s   E x a m i n e d. KURUNEGALA DISTRICT: Road A10, Weuda, *Austin et al. 6215* (FAU, PDA, US). KANDY DISTRICT: Kandy, *Kundu 133* (PDA); Peradeniya, *Comanor 470* (K, US), *507* (US); Pussellawa, *Austin et al. 6132* (FAU, PDA, US). NUWARA ELIYA DISTRICT: northeast of Nuwara Eliya, *Austin et al. 6127* (FAU, PDA, US). BADULLA DISTRICT: Haputale, *Austin et al. 6121* (FAU, PDA, US); Wellawaya-Haputale Road, *Austin et al. 6120* (FAU, PDA, US). KEGALLE DISTRICT: Kegalle-Avissawella Road, *Austin et al. 6222* (FAU, PDA, US). RATNAPURA DISTRICT: near Kiriella, *Austin et al. 6233* (FAU, PDA, US).

COLOMBO DISTRICT: near Nittambuwa, *Austin et al. 6090* (FAU, PDA, US). GALLE DISTRICT: between Galle & Wakwella, *Austin et al. 6257* (FAU, PDA, US).

N o t e. This species has a complicated nomenclatural history which has partially been discussed by Verdcourt (Taxon 6: 231–233. 1957 & 7: 84–85. 1958). The earliest name for the species is *Conovolvulus purpureus* L. (LINN 218.10, not seen; microfiche seen), but Verdcourt has typified the plants in such a manner as to preserve common application. The next name for this population is *Convolvulus indicus* Burm. f. (in Rumph. Herb. Amboinense, Index Universalis 7: [6]. 1755). Various authors have avoided this name in preference to the next name, *I. acuminata* (Vahl) Roem. & Schultes, because the typification of the Burmann name was obscure (van Ooststroom, Blumea 3: 500–503. 1940; O'Donell, Lilloa 29: 134–139. 1959; Verdcourt, Taxon 6: 231–233. 1957; Austin, Ann. Missouri Bot. Gard. 62: 192. 1975). Finally F.R. Fosberg has untangled the imperfectly cited references in the Rumphian treatment and selected a lectotype (Fosberg, Bot. Notiser. 129: 36. 1976).

14. Ipomoea jucunda Thw., Enum. Pl. Zeyl. 211. 1860; Clarke in Hook. f., Fl. Br. Ind. 4: 198. 1883 (under *I. grandiflora*); Trimen, Handb. Fl. Ceylon 3: 214. 1895. Type: Ceylon, Dolosbage District, Thwaites *C.P.* 3448 (PDA, lectotype; syntypes or isotypes K, G-DC).

Stictocardia jucunda (Thw.) Gunn, Brittonia 24: 174. 1972.

Lianas; the stems twining, often slightly tuberculate, glabrous or glabrescent. Leaves ovate to ovate-cordate, 7–13 cm long, basally cordate, apically acute but abruptly acuminate, glabrous or nearly so above, pubescent with appressed and glandular trichomes below or rarely glabrous. Inflorescences axillary, solitary or cymose. Flowers on pedicels 1.5 cm long, enlarging to 2–2.5 cm in fruit; sepals subequal, oblong-ovate, obtuse, mucronulate, 2–2.5 cm long, pubescent at least on the dorsal median portion, often glandular at the base; corolla white, salverform, the tube 4–5 cm long, the limb 7–8 cm in diameter, stamens and style included or the stigma slightly exserted. Fruits capsular, light brown, surrounded by the slightly thickened sepals, ovoid to subglobose, 2.5–3 cm long, apiculate, glabrous; seeds black, 1–1.5 cm long, comose with light brown indument.

D i s t r. Endemic to the hills of Ceylon.

E c o l. Thwaites left behind no information about the ecology of these rare plants but Magdon Jayasuriya has recently rediscovered a small population. The species may be sought between 1000 and 2000 feet (perhaps as high as 3000 feet). The recent collection was found on open rocky, eroded slopes on an isolated hill. Like some other species on the island (*I. alba, I. macrantha*) these plants undoubtedly flower at night; apparently they are adapted for moth pollination.

Specimens Examined. ANURADHAPURA DISTRICT: Riti-
gala Strict Natural Preserve, Andikanda, *Jayasuriya 1063* (PDA, US).
KANDY DISTRICT: Dolosbagie, *s. coll.* Apr. 1855, *C.P. 3448* (PDA).
LOCALITY UNKNOWN: *s. coll. C.P. 3448* (G, K).

15. Ipomoea littoralis Blume, Bidjr. 713. 1825; Thw., Enum. Pl. Zeyl. 211.
1860. Type: Java. *Blume 1710* (holotype L).

Ipomoea denticulata (Desr.) Choisy, Mem. Soc. Phys. Genève 6: 576. 1834,
non R. Br. (1810); Clarke in Hook. f., Fl. Br. Ind. 4: 208. 1883; Trimen,
Handb. Fl. Ceylon 223. 1895.
Ipomoea gracilis of authors, non R. Br. (1810).

Vines; the stems usually prostrate and often rooting, thin and herbaceous;
becoming woody toward base, glabrous or with a few scattered trichomes;
perennial. Leaves coriaceous, broadly ovate to oblong in outline or orbicular
to reniform, very variable in size, 1–10 cm long or rarely longer, the margins
entire, undulate, angular-toothed, 3-lobed, or less commonly 5–7-lobed, basally cordate, apically acute, obtuse or retuse, mucronulate, upper and lower
surfaces glabrous. Inflorescences axillary, flowers usually solitary, less commonly cymose, the peduncles 1–3 (–9) cm long. Flowers on pedicels 10–25
mm long, glabrous; sepals unequal, the outer shorter than the inner, oblong-
elliptic or elliptic-ovate, acute to obtuse, 6–10 mm long, the inner elliptic or
more commonly suborbicular, 8–12 mm long, all mucronulate, the mucrone
subterminal, glabrous, the outer coriaceous, the inner thinner with membranaceous margins; corolla lavender to pinkish-purple, the tube darker, funnelform, 3–4.5 cm long, the filaments glabrous on the upper half, pubescent with
glandular trichomes on the lower half. Fruits capsular, depressed-globose,
brown, 9–10 mm long; seeds black or brown, glabrous, 3.5–4 mm long.

Distr. Coasts of the Indian and Pacific Oceans: Mauritius Islands, Seychelles, Madagascar, southern Asia, Malaysia, east to Fiji, Hawaii and the
other Pacific Islands; also Mexico.

Ecol. Found on sandy beaches and in thickets near the sea shore or
along bays and lagoons off the shore. Occasionally found twining up shrubs
and trees, but most often prostrate. Rarely found above 15 m altitude. Trimen considered the species rare but now the plants are locally common along
the southwestern coast.

Vern. Tel-kola (S); "tel"—oil, "kola"—leaves. This name is most commonly applied to *Ipomoea obscura*. As with vernacular names everywhere
they vary from region to region.

Specimens Examined. KALUTARA DISTRICT: Beruwala,
Austin et al. 6272 (FAU, PDA, US); Beruwala, *Balakrishnan 1024* (K, PDA,
US); Kalutara, *Gardner s.n., C.P. 1939* (in part) (PDA). GALLE DISTRICT:

Ahangama, *Austin et al. 6100* (FAU, PDA, US); Galle, *s. coll* in 1860, *C.P. 1939* (K), *Austin et al. 6095* (FAU, PDA, US), *Austin et al. 6263* (FAU, PDA, US), *Gardner s.n., C.P. 1939* (in part) (PDA); Talpe, *Austin et al. 6098* (FAU, PDA, US). LOCALITY UNKNOWN: *s. coll.* Dec. 1860, *C.P. 1939* (in part) (PDA); *anon., C.P. 1936* (K); *Cuming s.n.,* in 1863, *C.P. 1936* (G); *Gardner 610* (K).

16. Ipomoea macrantha Roem. & Schultes, Syst. Veg. 4: 251. 1819; Gunn, Brittonia 24: 158. 1972. Type: based on *I. longiflora* R. Br., non Willd.

Ipomoea longiflora R. Br., Prod. 484. 1810, non Willd. (1809). Type: Australia, Queensland, *Brown 2741* (BM, holotype, not seen).
Ipomoea tuba (Schlecht.) G. Don, Gen. Hist. 4: 271. 1837; van Ooststroom, Fl. Mal., ser. 1, 4: 487. 1953.
Calonyction tuba (Schlecht.) Colla, Mem. Nouva Sp. Calon. 15. 1840.
Ipomoea grandiflora sensu authors, e.g. Clarke in Hook. f., Fl. Br. Ind. 4: 198. 1883, pro parte; Trimen, Handb. Fl. Ceylon 3: 214. 1895, non Lam. (1791).

Vines; the stems twining over beach plants or up brackish lagoon margin plants; perennial, glabrous. Leaves broadly ovate to reniform-ovate, 8–16 cm long, usually entire but rarely few-toothed, cordate basally, acute to broadly acuminate apically, glabrous. Inflorescences of mostly solitary flowers but occasionally 2–3 (–4) in a cymose cluster. Flowers with pedicels 1–3 cm long; sepals ovate to ovate-elliptic, 1.5–2.5 cm long, obtuse apically, glabrous, corolla white, the tube 6–8 (–10) cm long, the limb campanulate to rotate. Fruits capsular but tardily dehiscent, ovoid to subglobose, 2–2.5 cm in diameter; seeds dark brown, pubescent with short stiff trichomes.

D i s t r. A species of pantropical distribution; the region of origin is not known.

E c o l. Normally a sea shore plant found above the high tide line; occasionally found farther inland. Also found along the margins of brackish rivers and lagoons. The plants that Gunn grew produced few capsules; those that I have studied fruited well even when not pollinated by hand. At least some of the populations are autogamous.

S p e c i m e n s E x a m i n e d. JAFFNA DISTRICT: Jaffna, *Gardner C.P. 3536* (PDA). GALLE DISTRICT: Galle, *Austin et al. 6264* (FAU, PDA, US); Koskada, *Balakrishnan 998* (PDA). MATARA DISTRICT: Dikwella, *s. coll.* Sept. 1857, *C.P. 3536* (PDA); Gandara, *Austin et al. 6105* (FAU, PDA, US). LOCALITY UNKNOWN: *s. coll. C.P. 3536* (G, K).

17. Ipomoea mauritiana Jacq., Collect. 4: 216. 1791; Hort. Schoenbr. 2: 39. t. 200. 1797; van Ooststroom, Fl. Mal., ser. 1, 4: 483. 1953; Verdcourt, Fl. Trop. E. Africa 135. 1963. Type: a plant from Mauritius cultivated in Vienna, probably not preserved. The plate published in Hort. Schoenbr. t. 200. 1797 chosen as lectotype.

Ipomoea digitata of authors, e.g., Clarke in Hook. f., Fl. Br. Ind. 4: 202. 1883; Trimen, Handb. Fl. Ceylon 3: 212. 1895, non L. (1759).
Batatas paniculata (L.) Choisy, Mem. Soc. Phys. Genève 6: 436. 1834; Thw., Enum. Pl. Zeyl. 210. 1860.

Vines; the stems woody below, herbaceous nearer the tips, glabrous. Leaves orbicular in outline, palmately lobed with (3–) 5–7 (–9) lobes, rarely entire, 5–8 cm long, cordate or truncate basally, the lobes ovate, acuminate apically, glabrous or with scattered trichomes. Inflorescences of few-flowered to many-flowered cymose clusters. Flowers with pedicels 9–25 mm long; sepals orbicular or elliptic, 6–12 mm long, markedly convex and clasping the corolla, subcoriaceous, glabrous; corolla reddish-purple to rose pink, 4–6 cm long. Fruits capsular, ovoid, 1.2–1.4 cm long, glabrous; seeds black, comose.

D i s t r. The original home of this pantropical species has not been determined but its closest relatives are found in the West Indies and South America.

E c o l. A plant of various habitats, being found in lowland forests, riverine forest, secondary bushland, cultivated field margins and savannas. The vines are also frequently encountered on or near beaches throughout the range. Plants have been found cultivated in Kegalle District.

V e r n. Kiribadu (S); "kiri"—milk, "babu"—meaning unknown.

S p e c i m e n s E x a m i n e d. ANURADHAPURA DISTRICT: Ratmale, *s. coll. C.P. 499* (L, PDA). KANDY DISTRICT: Galagedera, *Austin et al. 6210* (FAU, PDA, US). COLOMBO DISTRICT: Colombo, *Ferguson s.n., C.P. 499* (PDA); Henaratgoda, *J. Silva s.n.*, Aug. 1958 (PDA). KALUTARA DISTRICT: Beruwala, *Austin et al. 6271* (FAU, PDA, US). GALLE DISTRICT: Wakwella, *Austin et al. 6260* (FAU, PDA, US). PROVINCE UNKNOWN: Kiri Caddire (Kire Caddre), *s. coll. 78* (L).

18. Ipomoea nil (L.) Roth, Cat. 1: 36. 1797; van Ooststroom, Fl. Mal., ser. 1, 4: 465. 1953; Verdcourt, Fl. Trop. E. Africa 113. 1963. Type: illustration of *Convolvulus caeruleus hederaceo*.... Dill., Hort. Elth. t. 80. f. 91. 1732 (syntype).

Convolvulus nil L., Sp. Pl. ed. 2. 219. 1762.
Ipomoea hederacea of authors, e.g., Clarke in Hook. f., Fl. Br. Ind. 4: 199. 1883; Trimen, Handb. Fl. Ceylon 3: 1895, non Jacq. (1786).
Pharbitis nil (L.) Choisy, Mem. Soc. Phys. Genève 6: 439. 1834; Thw., Enum. Pl. Zeyl. 210. 1860.

Vines; the stems and other plant parts often covered with dense or scattered large trichomes; annual. Leaves ovate to suborbicular, 5–15 cm long, entire or 3 (– 5)-lobed, basally cordate, the lobes apically acute to acuminate, pubescent. Inflorescences of 1–5-flowered, often dense cymose clusters. Flowers on pedicels 5–10 mm long; sepals long-lanceolate, 15–25 mm long with linear-lanceolate apices, densely to sparsely long-hirsute at least on the basal part of the sepal; corolla blue, purple or almost scarlet, the throat often white, the Ceylon plants with a blue limb, 3–5 cm long, the limb 4–5 cm broad. Fruits capsular, subglobose to globose, surrounded by the sepals, 8–12 mm long; seeds pyriform, densely pubescent with short trichomes.

D i s t r. This American species is now pantropical. Numerous varieties have been developed and cultivated under various names in several countries. Perhaps the most famous is the "Japanese Morning Glory." The plants in Ceylon are the typical feral forms also found in Mexico, the United States and South America near towns and villages.

E c o l. Usually found in settlements of various sizes near vacant lots or roadside margins. These are typical plants of disturbed areas. Occasional to commonly found in the wet zone.

V e r n. Kaladana (S); no apparent meaning in Sinhalese, perhaps because the name was adapted from India. Kalamaruva (S); meaning unknown. Tail (T); literally a "lady's necklace."

N o t e. Verdcourt (1963) and earlier has pointed out an early misinterpretation of Linnaeus' species *I. nil* and *I. hederacea*. Because of this early mistake, many authors appear to have the species confused. Verdcourt has typified the taxa to maintain a minimal amount of disturbance in the majority of literature. The seeds of *I. nil* are a drastic laxative and were formerly on the official Pharmacopoeia, known a "Kaladana." Probably they still play a part in ayurvedic medicine.

Specimens Examined. JAFFNA DISTRICT: Jaffna, *Gardner s.n., C.P. 1938* (in part) (PDA). POLONNARUWA DISTRICT: Polonnaruwa, *s. coll.* Mar. 1857, *C.P. 1938* (in part) (PDA). KURUNEGALA DISTRICT: Weuda, *Austin et al. 6216* (FAU, PDA, US). MATALE DISTRICT: Matale, *Austin et al. 6147* (FAU, PDA, US); Nalanda, *Alston 2455* (PDA). KANDY DISTRICT: Kandy-Mahiyangana Road, *Austin et al. 6199* (FAU, PDA, US); Peradeniya, *Alston 1303* (PDA). KALUTARA DISTRICT: Kalutara, *Austin et al. 6241* (FAU, PDA, US). HAMBANTOTA DISTRICT: Ruhuna National Park, Rakinawala, *Cooray 69011701R* (US). LOCALITY UNKNOWN: *s. coll. C.P. 1938* (G).

19. Ipomoea obscura (L.) Ker-Gawl, Bot. Reg. 3: t. 239. 1817; Clarke in Hook. f., Fl. Br. Ind. 4: 207. 1883; Trimen, Handb. Fl. Ceylon 3: 220. 1895; van Oost-stroom, Fl. Mal., sér. 1, 4: 471. fig. 44. 1953; Verdcourt, Fl. Trop. E. Africa 116. 1963. Type: Java, Batavia: illustration of *Convolvulus flore minore lac-teo*.... Dill., Hort. Elth. t. 83, fig. 95. 1732 (syntype).

Convolvulus obscurus L., Sp. Pl. ed. 2. 220. 1762; Moon, Cat. 13. 1824; Thw., Enum. Pl. Zeyl. 212. 1860.

Ipomoea obscura var. *indica* Hall. f., Bot. Jahrb. Syst. 28: 39. 1899.

Vines; the stems slender, twing or less commonly prostrate, pilose or more commonly glabrescent; perennial. Leaves ovate to cordate, 2.7–9 cm long, cordate basally, acute, acuminate or apiculate apically, pubescent or glabrescent on both surfaces. Inflorescences 1- or less commonly several-flowered, the peduncles 3.5–4 cm long. Flowers on pedicels 1–2 cm long; sepals ovate, ovate-orbicular or ovate-lanceolate, 4–8 mm long, acute or apiculate, somewhat verrucose, glabrous or pilose; corolla yellow, orange, cream or white, usually with a white limb and yellowish nectar-guides, the throat purplish or brownish, 1.4–2.5 cm long, campanulate. Fruits capsular, globose, glabrous, 8–12 mm long; seeds ovoid, black, appressed pubescent or velvety, 5–5.5 mm long.

D i s t r. Found in tropical Africa, Madagascar, through tropical Asia to Queensland and Fiji; also China, Formosa and Polynesia.

E c o l. Essentially plants of any disturbed site such as grassland, thickets, forest margins, waste ground, hedges and at times on sandy soil near the sea.

U s e s. At least some of the people on the island use the leaves of this plant mashed and mixed with "ghee" oil to cure boils.

V e r n. Tel-kola (S); "tel"—oil "kola"—leaves.

S p e c i m e n s E x a m i n e d. POLONNARUWA DISTRICT: Sigiriya-Polonnaruwa Jungle Road, *Austin et al. 6161* (FAU, PDA, US). TRINCOMALEE DISTRICT: Welcombe Hotel drive, *Austin et al. 6171* (FAU, PDA, US). KURUNEGALA DISTRICT: Galgedera, *Austin et al. 6213* (FAU, PDA, US). MATALE DISTRICT: Dambulla, *s. coll.*, Mar. 1868, *C.P. 1935* (PDA); Naula, *Austin et al. 6152* (FAU, PDA, US); Naula-Elahera Road, *Jayasuriya 315* (PDA). KANDY DISTRICT: Hantane, *Gardner s.n.*, *C.P. 1935* (PDA); Peradeniya, *Alston 1305* (PDA); Peradeniya, *Austin & Austin 6144* (FAU, PDA, US). BADULLA DISTRICT: Boralande, *Austin et al. 6124* (FAU, PDA, US). RATNAPURA DISTRICT: Embilipitiya, *Nowicke & Jayasuriya 382* (US). KALUTARA DISTRICT: Kalutara, *Austin et al. 6242* (FAU, PDA, US). HAMBANTOTA DISTRICT: Palatupana, *Austin et al. 6109* (FAU, PDA, US). LOCALITY UNKNOWN: *Deschamps s.n.* in 1891 (G); *Fraser s.n.* (US).

20. Ipomoea pes-caprae (L.) R. Br. in Turkey, Narr. Exped. R. Zaire 477. 1818; Sweet, Hort. Suburb. Lond. 35. 1818, redundant combination; van Ooststroom, Fl. Mal., sér. 1, 4: 475. 1953; Verdcourt, Fl. Trop. E. Africa 121. 1963. Type: India, specimen 218. 59 (LINN, lectotype not seen; microfiche seen).

Convolvulus pes-caprae L., Sp. Pl. 159. 1753; Moon, Cat. 14. 1824; Thw., Enum. Pl. Zeyl. 211. 1860.

Ipomoea biloba Forsk., Fl. Aegypt.-Arab. 44. 1775; Clarke in Hook. f., Fl. Br. Ind. 4: 212. 1883; Trimen, Handb. Fl. Ceylon 3: 224. 1895.

Vines; the stems long-trailing and often rooting at the nodes; perennial with a thickened taproot, glabrous. Leaves often secund, ovate, obovate, elliptic, orbicular, or transverse-elliptic to reniform, 3–10 cm long, rarely, longer, basally cuneate to truncate, attenuate or cordate, apically mostly emarginate, rarely truncate, mucronulate, fleshy, glabrous. Inflorescences mostly 1-flowered, occasionally cymose. Flowers on pedicels 10–30 mm long, rarely longer; sepals unequal or subequal, the outer 8–9 mm long, the inner 12–13 mm long, ovate to broadly elliptic with the inner often orbicular, obtuse and mucronulate, glabrous, subcoriaceous to coriaceous; corolla limb pink to lavender-purple, the throat darker purple within, 5–7 cm long. Fruits capsular, ovoid to depressed-globular, 12–17 mm long, glabrous; seeds dark brown to black, densely brownish-tomentose, 6–10 mm long.

D i s t r. The species is circumtropical; subspecies *pes-caprae* occurs from Arabia through tropical Asia, but principally in the Indian Ocean.

E c o l. Almost invariably this plant is found on coastal beaches and dunes. Occasionally plants are found inland but most of these appear to have been introduced accidentally with soil movement and are ephemeral populations.

U s e s. Both the roots and leaves are used in remedies in India, Ceylon and Malaysia. The leaves are mostly used as a poultice to relieve external infections; roots are used as a laxative or diuretic in treating dropsy.

V e r n. Mudu-bin-tamburu (S); "mudu"—sea or ocean; "bin"—earth, "tamburu"—creeper; thus the creeper on the earth by the sea.

S p e c i m e n s   E x a m i n e d. MANNAR DISTRICT: Talaimannar, *J. Silva s.n.* July 1916 (PDA). TRINCOMALEE DISTRICT: Irrakkakandi, *Comanor 787* (PDA, US). BATTICALOA DISTRICT: Kalkudah, *Mueller-Dombois 68041906* (PDA, US). AMPARAI DISTRICT: Pottuvil, *F. Silva s.n.* Mar. 1929 (PDA). PUTTULAM DISTRICT: Wilpattu National Park, Pallwgaturai, *Fosberg et al. 50898* (L, PDA, US). GALLE DISTRICT: Galle, *Austin et al. 6094* (FAU, PDA, US), *Austin et al. 6251* (FAU, PDA, US), *Gardner s.n.* Dec. 1853, *C.P. 1934* (PDA); Hikkaduwa, *Fosberg 36767* (US). HAMBANTOTA DISTRICT: Hambantota, *van Steenis 19535* (L); Ruhuna National Park, Patanagala, *Cooray 69012401R* (PDA); *Fosberg 50348* (PDA, US); Yala, *Comanor 645B* (PDA, US).

N o t e. Two taxa have been recognized within the species: the eastern subsp. *pes-caprae* and the mostly western subsp. *brasiliensis*. After having studied both populations in the living state I agree that they are distinct. Moreover, I agree with the subspecific status recognized by van Ooststroom and Verdcourt and not with Prof. H. St. John who has concluded that they are distinct species (St. John, Bot. Jahrb. Syst. 89: 563–583. 1970). Subspecies *pes-caprae* has somewhat larger flowers but the most distinctive characteristic is the more deeply lobed leaf (see: van Ooststroom, Fl. Mal., sér. 1, 4: 476, fig. 50. 1953).

21. Ipomoea pes-tigridis L., Sp. Pl. 162. 1753; Moon, Cat. 14. 1824; Thw., Enum. Pl. Zeyl. 212. 1860; Clarke in Hook. f., Fl. Br. Ind. 4: 204. 1883; Trimen, Handb. Fl. Ceylon 3: 216. 1895; van Ooststroom, Fl. Mal., sér. 1, 4: 467. 1953; Verdcourt, Fl. Trop. E. Africa 108. 1963. Type: Ceylon, *Hermann herbarium* 4: 82 (BM, lectotype fide Verdcourt).

Vines; the stems slender or stout, trailing or less commonly twining, covered with long spreading yellow bristly trichomes; annual. Leaves palmately 7–9-lobed, often almost to the base of the blade, to 10.5 cm long and 13 cm wide in outline, the lobes narrowly oval to obovate, narrowed above and below, subacute apically, 1.6–7 cm long, 1–2.8 cm wide, thinly pubescent to strigose on both surfaces. Inflorescences of few-flowered, bracteate heads on pubescent peduncles up to 14 cm long, the bracts foliaceous, oblong to oblong-lanceolate, pubescent outside, the outer to 5 cm long and 6 mm wide, the inner narrower and shorter. Flowers subsessile; sepals lanceolate to narrowly lanceolate, 8–12 mm long, pubescent; corolla white, pink or purple, if colored then with a darker throat, funnelform, 3.5–5 cm long. Fruits capsular, brown, ovoid, 8–9 mm long, glabrous; seeds black, 4 mm long, grey pubescent.

D i s t r. Found throughout tropical Africa and Asia.

E c o l. Plants occur in disturbed sites such as grasslands, bushlands, cultivated ground and roadsides. Studies of this species by A. Jones with the Department of Agriculture (Charleston, South Carolina, U.S.A.) indicate that the species is self-compatible and autogamous (Jones, unpublished).

V e r n. Divi—adiya, Divi—pahuru (S),—"divi"—leopard, "adiya" —footprint, "pahura"—scratching.

S p e c i m e n s E x a m i n e d. JAFFNA DISTRICT: Jaffna, *s. coll. C.P. 1942* (in part) (PDA). MANNAR DISTRICT: Illupaikaduvai, *s. coll.* Feb. 1890 (PDA); Tampanaikkulam, *Jayasuriya et al. 604* (PDA, US). POLONNARUWA DISTRICT: Polonnaruwa, *Senaratne 3497* (PDA). TRINCOMALEE DISTRICT: Kantalai-Allai Road, *Austin et al. 6174* (FAU, PDA, US). BATTICALOA DISTRICT: Batticaloa. *s. coll. C.P. 1942* (in part) (PDA); Chenkaladi, *Austin et al. 6181* (FAU, PDA, US). MATALE DISTRICT: Matale, *s. coll. C.P. 1942* (L). KANDY DISTRICT: Peradeniya, *Gardner s.n. C.P. 1942* (in part) (PDA). HAMBANTOTA DISTRICT: Ruhuna National Park, Buttawa Bungalow, *Cooray & Balakrishnan 69010902R* (PDA); Karaugaswala, *Mueller-Dombois & Cooray 67121067* (PDA); Patanagala, *Cooray 70031602R* (PDA); *Fosberg 50225* (PDA, US); Yala Bungalow, *Fosberg et al. 51117* (US).

22. Ipomoea pileatea Roxb., Fl. Ind. ed. Carey & Wall., 2: 94. 1824: Thw.,

Enum. Pl. Zeyl. 212. 1860; Clarke in Hook. f., Fl. Br. Ind. 4: 203. 1883; Trimen, Handb. Fl. Ceylon 3: 215. 1895; van Ooststroom, Fl. Mal., sér. 1, 4: 467. 1953; Verdcourt, Fl. Trop. E. Africa 105. 1963. Type: a plant cultivated at Calcutta from Chinese seed, *Wallich 1376* (K, holotype; isotype G-DC.).

Vines; the stems twining, pubescent; annual. Leaves ovate, up to 9 cm long, cordate basally, acute to acuminate apically, pubescent. Inflorescences few- to many-flowered, enclosed in a pubescent boat-shaped involucre, 2–5.5 cm broad, on peduncles 1–5 cm long. Flowers on very short pedicels enclosed within the involucre; sepals ovate, 1.4–1.6 cm long, villous, obtuse apically; corolla pink or white, funnelform, the tube 2.5 cm long, 1.5–2 mm wide at the base, the limb 1.5 cm wide. Fruits capsular, ovoid, 6 mm long, glabrous; seeds ovoid, black, glabrous except for slight indument around the hilum, 3.5–4 mm long.

D i s t r. Found in tropical Africa, India to China and Malaysia.

E c o l. Throughout its range the plants have been found in lowland rainforest, bushland, grassland, rocky and cultivated ground. According to Trimen the flowers open "punctually at 5 p.m." This would suggest that the plant is pollinated by moths in the same manner as *Mirabilis jalapa*.

S p e c i m e n s E x a m i n e d. MATALE DISTRICT: Dambulla, *s. coll.* in 1868, *C.P. 3501* (in part) (PDA); Dambulla Rock, *s. coll. s.n.* in 1893 (PDA). KANDY DISTRICT: Peradeniya, *s. coll.* in 1856, *C.P. 3501* (in part) (PDA), *s. coll. s.n.* in 1889 (PDA). LOCALITY UNKNOWN: *s. coll. C.P. 3501* (L.).

23. Ipomoea purpurea (L.) Roth, Bot. Abh. 27. 1787; Clarke in Hook. f., Fl. Br. Ind. 4: 200. 1883; van Ooststroom, Fl. Mal., sér. 1, 4: 465. 1953; Verdcourt, Fl. Trop. E. Africa 114. 1963. Type: U.S.A., illustration of *Convolvulus follio cordato glabro flore violaceo* Dill., Hort. Elth. t. 84. f. 97. 1732 (syntype).

Convolvulus purpureus L., Sp. Pl. ed. 2. 219. 1762.
Pharbitis diversifolius Lindley. Bot. Reg. 23: t. 1988. 1837.
Ipomoea purpurea var. *diversifolius* (Lindl.) O'Donell, Lilloa 26: 385. 1953.

Vines; the stems slender and herbaceous; annual, pilose hirsute with spreading trichomes. Leaves broadly ovate to cordate, 2–10 cm long, entire or trilobate, pubescent on both surfaces. Inflorescences of 1–5 flowered cymose clusters. Flowers on pedicels 8–15 mm long, recurved in fruit; sepals oblong-lanceolate, 8–16 mm long, apically abruptly acute, hirsute on the basal portion; corolla blue, purple, pink, or with stripes of these colors on a white background, the stripes occasionally broken, throat white, 3–5 cm long. Fruits capsular, depressed-globose, 10 mm long; seeds black, pyriform, glabrous.

D i s t r. Although now pantropical this is a native of the American tropics, probably Mexico.

E c o l. The only plants found in Ceylon were growing on a bank below a house. Apparently the seed had been introduced accidentally as a contaminant of others since the inhabitants of the house claimed they had not cultivated the vines. These plants are often spread in such a manner and appear in a variety of disturbed sites.

S p e c i m e n s E x a m i n e d. BADULLA DISTRICT: Welimada-Palugama Road, *Austin et al. 6125* (FAU, PDA, US).

24. Ipomoea quamoclit L., Sp. Pl. 159. 1753; Clarke in Hook. f., Fl. Br. Ind. 4: 199. 1883; Trimen, Handb. Fl. Ceyl. 3: 215. 1895; van Ooststroom, Fl. Mal., sér. 1, 4: 482. 1953. Type: India, Linn. 219. 1 (LINN, not seen; microfiche seen).

Quamoclit vulgaris Choisy, Mem. Soc. Phys. Geneve 6: 434. 1834.
Quamoclit pinnata Bojer, Hort. Maurit. 224. 1837.

Vines; the stems slender, herbaceous; annual, glabrous. Leaves 1–9 cm long, ovate to elliptic in outline, deeply pinnatisect with 9–19 alternate or opposite pairs of linear lobes, glabrous. Inflorescences with solitary flowers or 2–6-flowered cymes. Flowers with pedicels 9–20 mm long; sepals elliptic to oblong, 4–7 mm long, obtuse apically, with a 0.25–0.75 mm long mucro, glabrous; corolla red or rarely white, 2–3 cm long. Fruits capsular, ovoid, 6–8 mm long; seeds dark brown to black, with dark patches of short trichomes scattered somewhat irregularly.

D i s t r. Originally from tropical America, now widely cultivated and naturalized in the Old World tropics.

E c o l. Cultivated in gardens as an ornamental; naturalized in thickets and other disturbed sites. The flowers are adapted for bird pollination as are those of *I. hederifolia*. Although Sunbirds have been seen visiting that species, they have not been seen on *I. quamoclit*. Perhaps due to a long period of cultivation the plants are autogamous.

V e r n. Bambu (fide Hermann), Rata-pamba (S); "rata"—red, "pamba"— meaning unknown.

S p e c i m e n s E x a m i n e d. BATTICALOA DISTRICT: Karadyanaru, *Austin et al. 6184* (FAU, PDA, US). RATNAPURA DISTRICT: Ratnapura, *Austin et al. 6232* (FAU, PDA, US). GALLE DISTRICT: Galle, *Austin et al. 6252* (FAU, PDA, US). LOCALITY UNKNOWN: Hermann herbarium 1: 5 (L).

25. Ipomoea sepiaria Roxb., Fl. Ind. ed. Carey & Wall., 2: 90. 1824; Clarke in Hook. f., Fl. Br. Ind. 4: 209. 1883; Trimen, Handb. Fl. Ceylon 3: 220. 1895; Verdcourt, Fl. Trop. E. Africa 117. 1963. Type: Roxburgh Icones No. 570 (K, lectotype).

Convolvulus maximus of authors, non L. (1781).
Ipomoea maxima of authors (e.g. van Ooststroom, Fl. Mal., sér. 1, 4: 472.
1953), non (L.) Sweet.

Vines; the stems slender, twining, usually with erect pilose indument but
also glabrous; perennials from a woody tuberous rootstock. Leaves ovate-
cordate, triangular, oblong-triangular or lanceolate, 1–12 cm long, truncate,
sagittate, hastate or with rounded lobes at the base, apically acute to acuminate, glabrous except for the margins which are often puberulent. Inflorescences few- to many-flowered, often subumbellate-cymose, the peduncle
1.5–23 cm long. Flowers on pedicels 0.75–1.2 cm long, enlarging in diameter
in fruit; sepals elliptic-oblong to ovate, 4–8 mm long, obtuse to acute, glabrous but verrucose at least on the outer two; corolla lavender to pink or
almost white, the throat dark purple, 2–6 cm long, subsalverform to salverform or funnelform-salverform, the tube gradually enlarging from the base
to the subrotate limb, the stigma and sometimes the stamens exserted. Fruits
capsular, globose, 6–7 mm long, glabrous; seeds pale, 3–4 mm long, densely
tomentose and often also with long trichomes at least along the margins.

Distr. Found in tropical Africa, tropical Asia and Malaysia to Formosa
and Queensland, Australia.

Ecol. Usually found in moist areas such as swamp margins, river banks
and habitats near the sea; probably most common in the dry zone but also in
the wet zone. Found in most disturbed sites.

Vern. Rasa-tel-kola (S); "rasa"—sweet, "tel"—oil, "kola"—leaf. Tali
(T); "tali"—literally, a lady's necklace.

Specimens Examined. JAFFNA DISTRICT: Jaffna, *Gardner s.n.*,
C.P. 1937 (in part) (PDA). MANNAR DISTRICT: Uyilankulam, *Balasubra-
manium (Austin 6195)* (FAU, PDA, US). POLONNARUWA DISTRICT:
Gallale *Kundu & Balakrishnan 244* (PDA); Giritale, *Austin et al. 6165* (FAU,
PDA, US). TRINCOMALEE DISTRICT: Kantalai-Allai Road, *Austin et al.
6176* (FAU, PDA, US). BATTICALOA DISTRICT: Batticaloa, *Kundu &
Balakrishnan 186* (PDA); Chenkaladi, *Austin et al. 6182* (FAU, PDA, US);
Kalmunai, *s. coll. C.P. 1937* (in part) (PDA). AMPARAI DISTRICT: Maha-
oya, *Austin et al. 6189* (FAU, PDA, US). KURUNEGALA DISTRICT:
Kurunegala, *s. coll.* June 1853, *C.P. 2859* (PDA); *s. coll. s.n.* in 1888 (PDA);
Weuda, *Austin et al. 6214* (FAU, PDA, US). MATALE DISTRICT: Sigiriya,
Austin et al. 6157 (FAU, PDA, US). COLOMBO DISTRICT: Colombo,
Austin et al. 6247 (FAU, PDA, US). GALLE DISTRICT: Talpe, *Austin et al.
6097, 6099* (both FAU, PDA, US). MATARA DISTRICT: Weligama, *Aust-
in et al. 6104* (FAU, PDA, US). HAMBANTOTA DISTRICT: Hambantota,
Alston s.n., Dec. 1926 (PDA); Tissamaharama, *Austin et al. 6107* (FAU, PDA,
US); Tissamaharama-Kataragama Road, *Austin et al. 6113* (FAU, PDA,
US); Ruhuna National Park, Andronoruwa Vela, *Fosberg et al. 51123* (PDA);

Komawa Wewa, *Cooray 70032505R* (PDA); *Cooray 70032510R* (PDA); Kumana, *Cooray 69073124R* (PDA); Patanagala, Fosberg 50371 (PDA); Salt Lake and Uda Potana Lewaya, *Cooray* 67100203 (PDA); Yala Plain, *Comanor 869* (PDA). DISTRICT UNKNOWN: Fort Kails, *s. coll.* Sept. 1897 (PDA). LOCALITY UNKNOWN: *s. coll. C.P.* 1937 (G); *s. coll. C.P.* 2859 (PDA).

N o t e. Van Ooststroom (1953) and Verdcourt (1963) disagree on the identity of *I. maxima* (L. f.) Don ex Sweet and *I. sepiaria*. Verdcourt has discussed the problem in detail in Kew Bulletin (15: 7. 1961). Several other authors have also misidentified this species with *Ipomoea sagittata* Poir. resulting in a complex synonymy. These two species are entirely distinct. Varietal names are available if desired. Trimen (Handb. Fl. Ceylon 3: 220) recognized *I. sepiaria* var. *β stipulacea* Clarke (in Hook. f., Fl. Br. Ind. 4: 209. 1883) on the basis of *C.P. 2859*. This specimen is entirely within the normal variation of the species and I prefer to recognize no taxa below species.

26. Ipomoea staphylina Roem. & Schultes, Syst. Veg. 4: 249. 1819; Clarke in Hook. f., Fl. Br. Ind. 4: 210. 1883; Trimen, Handb. Fl. Ceylon 3: 219. 1895. Type: India oriental (not seen, no specimen cited).

Lianas or scrambling shrubs; the stems scrambling or twining at the tips, glabrous. Leaves ovate to elliptic-ovate, (4–) 6–11 cm long, basally truncate to cordate, apically acute, glabrous. Inflorescences axillary and terminal, lax, paniculate-cymose. Flowers on pedicels 4–5 mm long; sepals broadly ovate to rounded, 4–5 mm long, glabrous; corolla white, purple in the tube fide Trimen, campanulate-funnelform, 2.5–3 cm long. Fruits not seen, said to be ovoid, glabrous; seeds not seen, said to be comose.

D i s t r. Found in Assam, China, Ceylon and India.

E c o l. This species has not been found since Trimen's time. No information is given on the original collection but the country around Kurunegala is low and moist.

S p e c i m e n s E x a m i n e d. KURUNEGALA DISTRICT: Kurunegala, *s. coll. s.n.* Dec. 1883 (PDA).

27. Ipomoea stolonifera (Cyrill.) Gmelin, Syst. Nat. ed. 13. 2: 345. 1791; van Ooststroom, Fl. Mal., sér. 1, 4: 478. 1953. Type: based on Cyrill., Pl. Rar. Neap. 1: 14· t. 5. 1788 (lectotype).

Convolvulus littoralis L., Syst. Nat. ed. 10. 924. 1759.
Convolvulus stoloniferus Cyrill., Pl. Rar. Neap. 1: 14. t. 5. 1788.
Ipomoea littoralis Boiss., Fl. Orient. 4: 112. 1879, non Blume (1826).
Ipomoea carnosa R. Br., Prod. 485. 1810; Clarke in Hook. f., Fl. Br. Ind. 4: 213. 1883.

Vines; the stems trailing and rooting at the nodes; perennial, glabrous. Leaves variable in shape, often linear, lanceolate, ovate to oblong and the margins entire or undulate all on the same plant, also 5–7-lobed, 1.5–4 (–8) cm long, the size varying greatly with habitat, basally obtuse, truncate to cordate, apically obtuse, emarginate or occasionally bilobate, glabrous. Inflorescences of usually solitary flowers in the leaf axils. Flowers with pedicels 8–15 mm long; sepals oblong, the inner sepals 10–15 mm long, the outer shorter, acute to obtuse, mucronulate, glabrous, subcoriaceous; corolla with the limb white, the throat yellow (basally purple in the New World plants), 3.5–5 cm long. Fruits capsular, globular, rarely ovoid, 10 mm long; seeds light brown, short-tomentose and with longer woolly trichomes on the margins, 8–9 mm long.

D i s t r. Although pantropical in distribution, this species occurs mostly in Atlantic coastal areas. While not previously found in Ceylon, this species may be sought in other coastal areas.

E c o l. While always associated with coastal dunes this species occupies a zone behind that where *I. pes-caprae* is found. *Ipomoea pes-caprae* is normally a part of the high action outer dune vegetation while *I. stolonifera* is most often found behind the major dune crest where the substrate is more stable.

S p e c i m e n s   E x a m i n e d. HAMBANTOTA DISTRICT: near Palatupana, at Amaduwa, *Austin et al. 6110* (FAU, PDA, US).

28. Ipomoea triloba L., Sp. Pl. 161. 1753; van Ooststroom, Fl. Mal., ser. 1, 4: 468. 1953. Type: based on Sloane, Jam. pl. 97. f. 1. (lectotype).

Convolvulus dentatus Blanco, Fl. Filip. ed. 1. 89. 1837, non Vahl (1794).
Ipomoea blancoi Choisy in DC., Prod. 9: 389. 1845.

Vines; the stems twining or rarely prostrate, very rarely rooting at the nodes, glabrous or somewhat pubescent; annual. Leaves broadly ovate to orbicular in outline, 2.5–8 cm long, entire, coarsely dentate or deeply 3-lobed, less commonly 5–7-lobed, cordate basally, the basal lobes rounded or angular to lobed, both surfaces glabrous or sparsely pilose. Inflorescences axillary, usually sub-umbelliform cymose, flowers rarely solitary, the peduncles 1–12 cm long, usually somewhat verruculose. Flowers on pedicels 2.5–8 mm long, minutely verruculose, glabrous; sepals slightly unequal, 7–8 mm long, rarely somewhat longer, the outer 2 a little shorter than the inner 3, oblong to elliptic-oblong, obtuse to acute, mucronate with a long mucro, usually sparsely pubescent on the back, less commonly glabrous, but with the margins always distinctly ciliate; corolla lavender, the throat darker, 18–20 mm long, funnelform. Fruits capsular, subglobose, 5–6 mm long, bristly pubescent, brown; seeds glabrous, subrotund, 3–3.5 mm long.

Distr. An American species whose major region of distribution is the West Indian Islands; now a pantropical vine found throughout Malaysia, the Pacific Islands and tropical Asia.

Ecol. Normally this is an island species, being found on almost every island in the Caribbean and Malaysia. In Ceylon it is most common climbing plants in the margins of paddy fields; also found in fencerows, cultivated lots and other disturbed sites. Due to the common association with paddies, it is likely that the species was introduced as a contaminant in seed rice. The species is autogamous, although facultatively allogamous, and seed-set is always high even without pollination.

Specimens Examined. TRINCOMALEE DISTRICT: Kantalai-Allai Road, *Austin et al. 6173* (FAU, PDA, US). KURUNEGALA DISTRICT: Galagedera, *Austin et al. 6212* (FAU, PDA, US). MATALE DISTRICT: Matale *Austin et al. 6146* (FAU, PDA, US). KANDY DISTRICT: Kandy, *Austin et al. 6135* (FAU, PDA, US). Peradeniya, *Comanor 717* (PDA). COLOMBO DISTRICT: Colombo, *Austin et al. 6245* (FAU, PDA, US); Nittambuwa, *Austin et al. 6089* (FAU, PDA, US). KALUTARA DISTRICT: between Horana & Bandaragama, *Austin et al. 6238* (FAU, PDA, US).

29. Ipomoea tuberculata Ker-Gawl. in Edwards, Bot. Reg. 1. t. 86. (Feb.) 1816; Verdcourt, Fl. Trop. E. Africa 123. 1963. Type: a plant cultivated from seed sent from Calcutta (no specimen found). The plate (t. 86) chosen as lectotype.

Ipomoea dasysperma Jacq., Eclog. Pl. 1: 132. t. 89. (Aug.) 1816; Clarke in Hook. f., Fl. Br. Ind. 4: 215. 1883; Trimen, Handb. Fl. Ceylon 3: 225. 1895.

Vines; the stems slender, smooth or tuberculate; annual, glabrous. Leaves round in outline, biternately or digitately 5–9-lobed, up to 12 cm long, the lobes linear-lanceolate to elliptic, acute, 3–8 cm long, 1–4 cm wide, with pseudostipules. Inflorescences 1–3-flowered, on peduncles 2.5–7 cm long. Flowers with pedicels up to 1 cm long, woody, clavate; sepals orbicular to elliptic ovate, obtuse, smooth or verruculose, somewhat unequal, the outer 3 shorter and broader, 6–12 mm long, gibbous and 1–2-tuberculate at the base; corolla yellow or white with a purple centre, funnelform to almost salverform, with a narrowed tube, 5–10 cm long. Fruits capsular, globose, 6–11 mm long; seeds subglobose-trigonous, brown, 5 mm long, with appressed pubescence and occasionally with long trichomes on the angles.

Distr. Found in tropical Africa, extending to India and Ceylon.

Ecol. Known from deciduous thickets and bushlands in Africa; in Ceylon found growing in the thicket near a house. The original C.P. collection has not been found but Trimen states that it was collected in the Northern Province. Thus, the species appears to be a dry zone plant.

Specimens Examined. HAMBANTOTA DISTRICT: near Kirinda, *Austin et al. 6111* (FAU, PDA, US).

30. Ipomoea turbinata Lag., Gen. Sp. Pl. 10. 1816; Gunn, Brittonia 24: 163. 1972. Type: based on *Ipomoea muricata* (L.) Jacq.

Convolvulus muricatus L., Mant. Pl. 44. 1767. Type: India, Suratt, *Braad*, LINN 218. 18 (LINN, not seen; microfiche seen).
Ipomoea muricata (L.) Jacq., Hort. Schoenb. 3 (2): 40. t. 323. 1798 (1803), non Cav. 1799 (1794); Trimen, Handb. Fl. Ceylon 3: 214. 1895.
Calonyction muricatum (L.) G. Don, Gen. Hist. 4: 264. 1837.

Vines; the stems twining, usually muricate; annual, glabrous. Leaves ovate to orbicular, 7–18 cm long, cordate basally, acute to more commonly acuminate apically, glabrous. Inflorescences 1- to few-flowered, the peduncles 3–6 cm long, muricate. Flowers on pedicels 1–2 cm long; sepals subequal, ovate to oblong, the outer 6–7 mm long with a fleshy-caudate awn 4–6 mm long, the inner 7–8 mm long, the awn somewhat shorter; corolla nocturnal, lavender to purplish, 5–7.5 cm long, the tube narrow and cylindric, 3–6 cm long, the limb funnelform or salverform. Fruits capsular, ovoid, 1.8–2 cm long; seeds ovoid, black, glabrous, 9–10 mm long.

D i s t r. Pantropical, adventive in the temperate zones, especially the United States.

E c o l. Frequently cultivated, often escaped and naturalized on dumps, cultivated fields and other disturbed sites. Plants are perhaps not as common in Ceylon as in Trimen's time, but I have not had a chance to visit the Northern Province. As in India, the plants are mostly cultivated for the swollen fleshy pedicels of the fruits which are eaten. Trimen cited *C.P. 3580* but this specimen has not been located. The flowers have a faint scent similar to that of *I. alba*. Since the flowers of both are nocturnal they appear to be adapted for moth pollination in *I. turbinata* as well. Those plants that I have cultivated were autogamous.

Specimens Examined LOCALITY UNKNOWN: *Deschamps 3/90*, in 1891 (G).

N o t e. Gunn (1972) appeared to be of the opinion that this species was native to the Old World, as is, he thinks, *I. alba*. Data that I have collected over the past six years (1969–1975) suggest that both are originally from the New World, almost certainly from Mexico.

31. Ipomoea wightii (Wall.) Choisy, Mem. Soc. Phys. Genève 6: 470. 1834; Thw., Enum. Pl. Zeyl. 212. 1860; Clarke in Hook. f., Fl. Br. Ind. 4: 203. 1883; Trimen, Handb. Fl. Ceylon 3: 216. 1895; Verdcourt, Fl. Trop. E. Africa

110. 1963. Type: India, cultivated at Calcutta from seed from Nilgiri Hills,

Wight in Wallich 1406 (K, holotype; isotype G-DC).
Convolvulus wightii Wall., Pl. As. Rar. 2: 55. 171. 1831.

Vines; the stems twining or prostrate, covered with more or less spreading yellowish indument; perennial. Leaves ovate-cordate, 5–11 (–13) cm long, entire (fide Verdcourt), dentate or shallowly to deeply 3-lobed, green above and pilose, usually densely covered with a white-cottony tomentum below. Inflorescences few- to many-flowered, dense to somewhat lax head-like cymose clusters, very rarely solitary, the peduncles 7–29 cm long. Flowers apparently subsessile or on pedicels up to 5 mm long; sepals linear to ovate-lanceolate, 6–16 mm long, obtuse or more commonly acuminate, with an indument of white-cottony trichomes, appressed or spreading yellow bristly trichomes and glands, one or more of these indument types may be absent; corolla magenta or mauve, 2–4 (–5) cm long, funnelform. Fruits capsular, globose, 6–7 mm long, slightly to densely bristly pubescent above or with inconspicuous white tomentum; seeds ovoid, black, with scattered lines of short and long white trichomes, 4 mm long.

D i s t r. Plants have been reported from tropical Africa, Madagascar, India and Ceylon.

E c o l. Not a great deal is known about the plants in Ceylon. Trimen indicates that they have been found between 2000 and 4000 feet. Verdcourt (1963) states that they have been found as low as 150 feet in Africa. Plants in Ceylon have been collected mostly in submontane forest zones; these have now been severely cut over. Elsewhere the plants have been found in open forest, and scrub.

S p e c i m e n s E x a m i n e d. KANDY DISTRICT: Hantane, *s. coll.* Feb. 1857, *C.P. 2851* (in part) (PDA). NUWARA ELIYA DISTRICT: Ramboda, *Gardner s.n., C.P. 2851* (in part) (PDA). BADULLA DISTRICT: between Welimade & Ettampitiya, *s. coll. s.n.* Jan. 1888 (L, PDA). LOCALITY UNKNOWN: *s. coll. C.P. 2851* (G).

10. JACQUEMONTIA

Choisy, Mem. Soc. Phys. Genève 6: 476. 1834. Lectotype species: *Convolvulus pentanthus* Jacq. =*Jacquemontia pentantha* (Jacq.) G. Don.

Thyella Raf., Fl. Tell. 4: 84. 1838. Lectotype: *T. tamnifolia* (L.) Raf. =*Jacquemontia tamnifolia* (L.) Griseb.

Herbs or suffrutescent procumbent shrubs, glabrous or densely pubescent. Leaves petiolate, mostly cordate at the base, entire, dentate or lobate. Flowers axillary, solitary, in scorpioid cymes or in umbelliform or head-like cymes;

small or medium-sized; the bracts small and linear to lanceolate or large and foliose; sepals 5, equal or unequal; corolla campanulate or funnelform, blue, lilac, or white (red in one species), deeply lobed, 5-dentate or almost entire; stamens and style included (exserted in one species), the pollen pantocolpate; style one, filiform, the 2 stigmas ellipsoid or oblong and complanate, ovary 2-locular, 4-ovulate, the disc small or none. Fruits capsular, globose to subglobose, 2-celled, with 4 or rarely 8 valves, 4-seeded; seeds glabrous, tuberculate, winged or pilose.

A genus of 100 or more species, for the most part American, but also with a few in tropical Africa, Asia and Australia. No recent revision of all the species in the genus has been done although K.R. Robertson (Thesis, Washington University, St. Louis, Missouri, U.S.A.) has studied the American species from Panama north. Trimen, Alston and more recent authors have considered this genus synonymous with *Convolvulus*. These two genera are most easily distinguished by stigma shape: filiform in *Convolvulus* and ellipsoid or oblong in *Jacquemontia*. There are several other differences including pollen. Certainly *Convolvulus* and *Jacquemontia* are closely related, but I cannot consider them synonymous.

KEY TO THE SPECIES

1 Corolla to 1 cm long; outer sepals 5–6 mm wide; bracts to 5 mm long..............
....**1. J. paniculata**
1 Corolla 1.5–2 cm long; outer sepals to 4 mm wide; bracts 5–10 mm long............
....**2. J. pentantha**

1. Jacquemontia paniculata (Burm. f.) Hall. f., Bot. Jahrb. Syst. 16: 541. 1893; van Ooststroom, Fl. Mal., ser. 1, 4: 432. fig. 19. 1953; Verdcourt, Fl. Trop. E. Africa 34. 1963. Type: Java, Batavia, *Kleynhoff* in *Burmann 413 (88)* (G, holotype fide Verdcourt. Several specimens of this species were found but none matching the citation given by Verdcourt).

Ipomoea paniculata Burm. f., Fl. Ind. 50. t. 21. f. 3. 1768.
Convolvulus parviflorus Vahl, Symb. Bot. 3: 29, 1794, non Dest. (1791), nom. illegit.; Clarke in Hook. f., Fl. Br. Ind. 4: 220. 1883; Trimen, Handb. Fl. Ceylon 3: 226. 1895.

Vines; the stems pubescent with whitish tomentum; supposedly annual but the plants in Peradeniya appear to be perennial. Leaves ovate-cordate, 4–8 cm long, cordate basally, acuminate apically, glabrescent above and either sparsely pubescent below on the nerves or densely tomentose on both sides. Inflorescences of axillary few- to several-flowered cymose clusters. Flowers on peduncles up to 5.5 cm long, pubescent; sepals ovate to broadly ovate, 6–9 mm long, 5–6 mm wide, acute, pubescent; corolla white, pink or pale blue, campanulate to broadly funnelform, 8–10 mm long. Fruits capsular, globose, 4–6 mm long, straw colored to brown; seeds brownish to blackish, minutely verrucose, glabrous, 1.5–2 mm long.

D i s t r. Reported from Africa, Madagascar to southeastern Asia, Malaysia, tropical Australia, New Caledonia and Polynesia.

E c o l. Found on sandy soil in the dry zone in grasslands, thickets and cultivated lands.

S p e c i m e n s E x a m i n e d. KURUNEGALA DISTRICT: Vetakeyapota, *Alston s.n.*, Jan. 1927 (K). KANDY DISTRICT: *s. coll. s.n.* May 1899 (PDA). HAMBANTOTA DISTRICT: Bundala, *s. coll. s.n.*, Dec. 1882 (PDA); Tissamaharama, *s. coll. s.n.* Dec. 1882 (PDA).

2. Jacquemontia pentantha (Jacq.) G. Don, Gen. Syst. 4: 283. 1838; van Oost-stroom, Fl. Mal., ser. 1, 4: 435, 1953; Austin, Ann. Missouri Bot. Gard. 62: 172. 1975. Type: in the herb. *Jacquin* (W, lectotype).

Convolvulus pentanthus Jacq., Coll. Bot. 4: 210. 1780.
Convolvulus violaceus Vahl, Symb. Bot. 3: 29. 1794, non Spreng. (1824).
Jacquemontia azurea (Desr.) Choisy, Mem. Soc. Phys. Genève 6: 467. 1834.
Jacquemontia violacea (Vahl) Choisy, Mem. Soc. Phys. Genève 8: 139. 1839.

Vines; the stems herbaceous, pubescent to glabrate; perennial. Leaves ovate to broadly ovate, 3–6 cm long, broadly cordate, apically acuminate, glabrate. Inflorescences cymose, mostly with 1–2 flowers open at any time. Flowers on peduncles mostly longer than the leaves; sepals ovate to lanceolate, 7–8 mm long, 4 mm broad, acute to acuminate, pubescent; corolla usually blue, sometimes white, campanulate to occasionally subrotate, 2 cm long. Fruits capsular, globose, 4 mm long, glabrous; seeds brown, 2.5 mm long, glabrous.

D i s t r. A New World species occurring from Florida into South America. Also found in Malaysia and Ceylon. Often cultivated in the Asian area as an ornamental.

E c o l. One collection from Ceylon that I have made is doubtfully wild. Plants were growing in the margin of a yard and, although the inhabitants of the house said they were wild, appeared to be cultivated. In the Western Hemisphere the species grows in a variety of disturbed sites.

S p e c i m e n s E x a m i n e d. KANDY DISTRICT: Peradeniya, *Austin & Austin 6281* (FAU, PDA, US). GALLE DISTRICT: Galle, *Austin et al. 6262* (FAU, PDA, US).

11. MERREMIA

Dennstedt, Schluss Hort. Malab. 34. 1818. Type Species: *Merremia convolvulacea* Dennst. ex Hall. f. = *M. hederacea* (Burm. f.) Hall. f.

Skinnera Choisy, Mem. Soc. Phys. Genève 6: 487. 1834, non Forst. (1776).
   Type: *S. caespitosa* Choisy = *Merremia hirta* (L.) Merr.
Spiranthera Bojer, Hort Maurit. 226. 1837, nomen nudum, non St. Hil.
   (1823).

Vines or lianas; usually herbaceous, some lignescent, small or large. Leaves entire, lobed, or palmately compound with 3–7 leaflets, glabrous or pubesent. Flowers solitary and axillary, in few-flowered dichasia or subumbellate, the bracts linear or lanceolate; sepals subequal, oblong to elliptical; corolla campanulate, large or small, white, yellow or purple; the filaments equal or subequal, mostly glabrous at the base, the anthers spirally twisted with complete dehiscence, the pollen 3-colpate or rarely pantocolpate; ovary usually glabrous, 2–3 carpellate, 4–5 ovulate, the style filiform, the stigma globose or biglobose, included. Fruits capsular, 2–4 celled, longitudinally dehiscent by 4–6 valves or irregularly, the pericarp thin and fragile; the seeds 4–6, glabrous or pubescent.

This genus is thought to have about 80 species widely distributed in the tropics of both hemispheres. Many authors have either included it in *Ipomoea* or suggested that it was not very distinct. Several characters separate the two, including spiraled anthers and smooth pollen in *Merremia* versus straight anthers and spinulose pollen in *Ipomoea*. Many of the other characters are best seen in living material but may be detected in good herbarium specimens. Various authors have pointed out that yellow corollas are unusual in *Ipomoea*; this color is frequent in *Merremia*.* In addition, the corollas of *Merremia* are campanulate. This shape is rare in *Ipomoea* (*I. obscura* being an exception) where the shape is usually funnelform or somewhat less commonly salverform. There is occasionally a somewhat transitional funnelform-campanulate corolla such as in *Ipomoea campanulata* but the shape is well distinct from *Merremia*. Notable exceptions occur, but there is a trend for *Merremia* to open its flowers well after dawn, often near 10:00 or 11:00 a.m. while *Ipomoea* flowers almost invariably open at or before dawn. Some *Ipomoea* are adapted for moth pollination (*I. alba, I. jucunda, I. macrantha*) and open at dusk or dark.

KEY TO THE SPECIES

1 Leaves palmately 5–7 lobed to palmately compound with 5 leaflets
   2 Leaves palmately compound
      3 Sepals deltoid, 12–17 mm long.....................................**1. M. cissoides**
      3 Sepals oblong, 17–25 mm long.....................................**2. M. dissecta**
   2 Leaves palmately lobed, but not compound
      4 Plants glabrous. Leaves divided to below the middle of the blade, the 5–7 segments entire, oblong-lanceolate...**6. M. tuberosa**

*The following species of *Ipomoea* in Ceylon have yellow flowers: *I. obscura* and *I. tuberculata*.

4 Plants pubescent. Leaves 5–7-lobed, the lobes broadly triangular to lanceolate, coarsely dentate to crenate or subentire....................................8. M. vitifolia
1 Leaves entire, crenate, or at most 3-lobed
5 Corolla pilose on the upper portion of the plicae, 2–3.5 cm long, yellow or rarely white. Inflorescence subumbelliform.............................7. M. umbellata
5 Corolla glabrous outside, 5–15 (–20) cm long, yellow or yellow with red to purple eye or with nectar guides only purplish. Inflorescences loosely cymose or flowers solitary
6 Peduncle very short or nearly absent. Leaves reniform to broadly ovate. Prostrate herbs..3. M. emarginata
6 Peduncle longer, at least as long as the flower. Leaves variable but usually not reniform. Sprawling or twining vines, rarely prostrate
7 Inner sepals acute, attenuate-acuminate. Leaves linear, linear-oblong to oblanceolate, spathulate or subquadrate................................5. M. tridentata
7 Inner and outer sepals obtuse. Leaves ovate or broadly ovate, rarely narrow-ovate to oblong in outline, more rarely nearly reniform...............4. M. hederacea

1. Merremia cissoides (Lam.) Hall. f., Bot. Jahrb. Syst. 16: 552. 1893; van Ooststroom, Fl. Surinam 84. 1932; O'Donell, Lilloa 6: 520. 1941. Type: French Guiana, Cayenne (P not seen).

Convolvulus cissoides Lam., Tabl. Enc. 1: 462. 1791.
Ipomoea cissoides (Lam.) Griseb., Fl. Br. W. Ind. Isl. 473. 1861; Trimen, Handb. Fl. Ceylon 3: 212. 1895; Alston, in Trimen, Handb. Fl. Ceylon 6: 202. 1931.

Vines; the stems slender, herbaceous, twining; perennials from a woody rootstock, glandular pubescent. Leaves broadly ovate to suborbicular in outline, compound, usually with 5 leaflets, the leaflets ovate to ovate-lanceolate, basally acute to obtuse, apically long-acuminate, the middle leaflet largest, (2–)3–5 cm long, the other leaflets shorter, the margins dentate, covered with scattered glandular trichomes. Inflorescences axillary, flowers solitary or in 2–3-flowered cymes, the peduncles 2–4 cm long, glandular. Flowers on glandular pubescent pedicels 2–3 mm long; sepals broadly rhomboid-ovate to ovate, the body 5–7 mm long, with a 7–10 mm long acuminate apex, with spreading whitish-yellow trichomes and glandular indument; corolla white, campanulate, 1.5–2 cm long. Fruits capsular, globose, 6–7 mm long, light brown, glabrous; seeds subrotund, dark brown to black, glabrous, 2–3 mm long.

D i s t r. Originally from the tropics of the New World, this species has been reported from Africa and Ceylon.

E c o l. All of the populations thus far studied in Ceylon were growing in disturbed sites such as roadsides, fencerows, and cultivated ground.

S p e c i m e n s E x a m i n e d. ANURADHAPURA DISTRICT: Medawachi, *Balasubramaniam* (*Austin 6196*) (FAU, PDA, US). POLONNARUWA DISTRICT: Minneriya, *Austin et al. 6166* (FAU, PDA, US). KANDY DISTRICT: Kandy, *Austin & Austin 6198* (FAU, PDA, US).

2. Merremia dissecta (Jacq.) Hall. f., Bot. Jahrb. Syst. 16: 552. 1893; van Ooststroom, Fl. Mal., ser. 1, 4: 448. 1953. Type: grown in Vienna from seeds collected by Jacquin in "America" (no specimen found).

Convolvulus dissectus Jacq., Obs. Bot. 2: 4. t. 28. 1767.
Ipomoea sinuata Ortega, Hort. Matr. Dec. 7: 84. 1798; Clarke in Hook. f., Fl. Br. Ind. 4: 214. 1883.

Vines; the stems herbaceous, sparsely hirsute to glabrous. Leaves palmately divided almost to the base, the 7–9 lobes sinuate to sinuate-dentate, usually glabrous, the entire leaf suborbicular in outline. Inflorescences axillary, 1-to few-flowered, cymose, the peduncles 5–10 cm long, hirsute, glabrescent on the upper portion. Flowers on pedicels 1.5–2 cm long, thickened toward the calyx, glabrous; sepals oblong, 18–25 mm long, mucronate, glabrous; corolla white with a purple centre, broadly campanulate, 3–4.5 cm long. Fruits capsular, depressed-globose, 1–2 cm in diameter, subtended and partially surrounded by the accrescent calyx; seeds black, subrotund, glabrous.

D i s t r. Native to the Americas from Florida to Argentina and Uruguay, introduced elsewhere in the tropics including India, Ceylon and Malaysia.

E c o l. The plants in Ceylon escaped from cultivation, perhaps first in Colombo. Those vines found in Colombo occur on fences, in vacant lots, and other disturbed sites. Elsewhere they have been found on roadsides and climbing among other cultivated vines.

S p e c i m e n s E x a m i n e d. KANDY DISTRICT: Kandy, *Austin & Austin 6277* (FAU, PDA, US). COLOMBO DISTRICT: Colombo, *Austin & Austin 6137* (FAU, PDA, US). GALLE DISTRICT: Galle, *Austin et al. 6253* (FAU, PDA, US).

3. Merremia emarginata (Burm. f.) Hall. f., Bot. Jahrb. Syst. 16: 552. 1893; van Ooststroom, Fl. Mal., ser. 1, 4: 444. 1953; Verdcourt, Fl. Trop. E. Africa 55. 1963. Type: India (according to Verdcourt the specimen in LINN may be the isotype).

Evolvulus emarginatus Burm. f., Fl. Ind. 77. t. 30. fig. 1. 1768.
Convolvulus reniformis Roxb., Fl. Ind. ed. Carey & Wall., 2: 67. 1824.
Ipomoea reniformis (Roxb.), Choisy, Mem. Soc. Phys. Genève 6: 446. 1834; Thw., Enum. Pl. Zeyl. 211. 1860; Clarke in Hook. f., Fl. Br. Ind. 4: 206. 1883; Trimen, Handb. Fl. Ceylon 3: 218. 1895.

Vines; the stems prostrate, rooting at the nodes; perennial, sparsely pubescent, glabrescent. Leaves reniform to broadly ovate, 0.5–3 cm long, often slightly wider, cordate basally with a broadly rounded sinus and rounded basal lobes, obtuse to broadly rounded or somewhat emarginate apically, coarsely crenate or entire, glabrous or sparsely appressed pilose. Inflorescences axillary, solitary or in 2–3-flowered cymose groups. Flowers with very

short or apparently absent peduncles; sepals obovate to orbicular or subquadrate, the outer 2.5–3 mm long, obtuse with a cucullate and distinctly mucronate apex, the inner 3–4 (–6) mm long, deeply emarginate, all pubescent on
the back and ciliate; corolla yellow with a paler tube, campanulate, 5–9 mm
long. Fruits capsular, subglobose, 5–6 mm long, longitudinally sulcate, glabrous, brownish-black or black; seeds grayish-brown, glabrous, dotted, 2.5
mm long.

D i s t r. Reported from tropical Africa, tropical Asia and Malaysia.

E c o l. Found in the dry zone. These plants have a preference for soils
where there is a tendency toward waterlogging in the wet season and yet also
having a long dry season. Throughout its range the species has been collected
in open grasslands, cultivated ground and waste places. Trimen indicated
that the species preferred sandy soils in Ceylon; van Ooststroom and Verdcourt suggest heavy clay soils.

S p e c i m e n s E x a m i n e d. MANNAR DISTRICT: Mannar, *Simpson
9326* (PDA). ANURADHAPURA DISTRICT: Kekirawa, *s. coll. s.n.* July
1887 (L, PDA). TRINCOMALEE DISTRICT: Trincomalee, *Glenie s.n.*,
C.P. 3579 (in part) (PDA) (cited in error in Trimen as *C.P. 3597*). BATTI-
CALOA DISTRICT: Batticaloa, *s. coll.* Mar. 1858, *C.P. 3579* (in part) (PDA)
(cited in error in Trimen as *C.P. 3597*). HAMBANTOTA DISTRICT: Ruhuna National Park, Andronoruwa Vela, *Fosberg et al. 51137* (PDA);
Komawa Wewa, *Cooray 68052901R* (PDA).

4. Merremia hederacea (Burm. f.) Hall. f., Bot. Jahrb. Syst. 18: 118. 1893; van
Ooststroom, Fl. Mal., ser. 1, 4: 441. 1953; Verdcourt, Fl. Trop. E. Africa 54.
1963. Type: East Indies, Java, *D. Pryon* (G, not found).

Evolvulus hederaceus Burm. f., Fl. Ind. 77. t. 30. fig. 2. 1768.
Ipomoea chryseides Ker-Gawl., Bot. Reg. 4. t. 270. 1818; Clarke in Hook. f.,
Fl. Br. Ind. 4: 206. 1883; Trimen, Handb. Fl. Ceylon. 3: 219. 1895.
Convolvulus flavus Moon, Cat. 13. 1824, non Willd. (1797); Thw., Enum. Pl.
Zeyl. 212. 1860.
Merremia convolvulacea Hall. f., Bot. Jahrb. Syst. 16: 552. 1893.
Ipomoea zebrina Choisy in DC., Prod. 9: 382. 1845.
Merremia gemella of authors, non (Burm. f.) Hall. f. (1893).

Vines; the stems twining or prostrate, if prostrate then sometimes rooting
at nodes or internodes, smooth or minutely tuberculate, glabrous or sparsely
pubescent. Leaves ovate in outline, 1.5–5 cm long, broadly cordate basally,
usually obtuse and mucronulate apically, the margins entire, crenate, shallowly
lobed or deeply 3-lobed, glabrous or sparsely pubescent. Inflorescences 1- to
several-flowered, dichasial and often also monochasial; peduncles 1–10 cm
long, mostly glabrous. Flowers with sepals broadly obovate to spathulate,

broadly notched at the apex, mucronulate, the outer two 3.5–4 mm long, the inner 5 mm long, glabrous or occasionally somewhat pilose on the back and along the margins; corolla yellow, campanulate, 6–10 (–12) mm long. Fruits capsular, broadly conical to depressed-globose, somewhat 4-angled, 5–6 mm long, the valves wrinkled either transversely or reticulately; seeds blackish, short-pubescent or nearly glabrous over the whole surface, or with longer tri-chomes along the edges, sometimes also on the sides, 2.5 mm long.

D i s t r. Tropical Africa, Madagascar, tropical Asia to China, Malaysia, Queensland and some Pacific islands.

E c o l. Thickets, open banks, grasslands, sandy places; found in the wet and dry zones, but apparently more common in the dry zone.

V e r n. Kaha-tel-kola (S); "Kaha"—yellow, "tel"—oil, "kola"—leaves.

S p e c i m e n s E x a m i n e d. ANURADHAPURA DISTRICT: Anu-radhapura, *Kundu & Balakrishnan 563* (PDA). TRINCOMALEE DISTRICT: Kantalai-Allai Road, *Austin et al. 6177* (FAU, PDA, US); Mahaweli Ganga North Forest Reserve, *Jayasuriya et al. 639* (PDA); Trincomalee, *s. coll. C.P. 1940* (in part) (PDA). KANDY DISTRICT: Hantane, *Gardner C.P. 1940* (in part) (PDA); Peradeniya, *Alston 1702* (PDA). KALUTARA DISTRICT: Kalutara, *s. coll.* in 1855; *C.P. 1940* (in part) (PDA). HAMBANTOTA DIS-TRICT: Hatagala, *s. coll. s.n.* in Dec. 1882 (PDA); Ruhuna National Park, Komama Wewa, *Cooray 69030901R* (PDA); Meynet Wewa Junction, *Cooray 70032308R* (PDA). LOCALITY UNKNOWN: *s. coll. C.P. 1940* (L, PDA); *Graham s.n.* (in part) (PDA).

5. Merremia tridentata (L.) Hall. f., Bot. Jahrb. Syst. 16: 552. 1893; van Oost-stroom, Fl. Mal., ser. 1, 4: 445. 1953; Verdcourt, Fl. Trop. E. Africa 51. 1963. Type: Rheede, Hort. Mal. 11: 133. t. 65 (lectotype).

Convolvulus tridentatus L., Sp. Pl. 157. 1753; Moon, Cat. 13. 1824; Thw., Enum. Pl. Zeyl. 211. 1860.
Ipomoea tridentata (L.) Roth, in Roem., Arch. Bot. 1 (2): 38. 1798; Roth, Cat. 2: 19. 1800; Clarke in Hook. f., Fl. Br. Ind. 4: 203. 1883; Trimen, Handb. Fl. Ceylon 3: 218. 1895.
Ipomoea angustifolia Jacq., Ic. Pl. Rar. 2: 10. t. 317. 1786-93; Jacq., Collect. 2: 367. 1789; Thw., Enum. Pl. Zeyl. 211. 1860; Clarke in Hook. f., Fl. Br. Ind. 4: 205. 1883; Trimen, Handb. Fl. Ceylon 3: 217. 1895.
Convolvulus hastatus Desr. in Lam., Enc. 3: 542. 1791, non Forsk. (1775).
Merremia hastata (Desr.) Hall. f., Bot. Jahrb. Syst. 16: 552. 1893.
Merremia tridentata subsp. *hastata* (Desr.) van Ooststroom, Blumea 3: 317. 1939.
Convolvulus filicaulis Vahl, Symb. Bot. 3: 24. 1794.
Ipomoea filicaulis (Vahl) Blume, Bijdr. 721. 1826.

Ipomoea denticulata R. Br., Prod. 485. 1810.

Merremia tridentata subsp. *angustifolia* (Jacq.) van Ooststroom, Blumea 3:
   323. 1939.

Vines; the stems prostrate to twining, glabrous or pubescent; an extremely
variable perennial. Leaves linear or lanceolate to oblong, 2.5–10 cm long,
truncate, hastate or auriculate basally, the lobes often 1- to several-toothed,
acuminate to emarginate and mucronulate apically, glabrous or pubescent.
Inflorescences axillary, often solitary, sometimes few-flowered and cymose;
slender peduncles, 2.5–4 cm long. Flowers with sepals oblong, ovate-oblong
or lanceolate, 4–10 mm long, the outer 2 usually shorter, obtuse, attenuate-
acuminate or cuspidate, sometimes winged and crisped; corolla pale yellow,
cream, or white, often with a reddish or purplish eye, campanulate, 10–20 mm
long. Fruits capsular, globose, 4–9 mm long; seeds black, glabrous, 2–3 mm
long.

D i s t r. Tropical and south Africa, Mascarene Islands, tropical Asia to
Formosa, Malaysia, Australia and Micronesia.

E c o l. Found in a variety of disturbed sites including roadsides, grasslands, cultivated ground and rocky land; especially common in the dry region
but also in the wet zone.

V e r n. Hin-madu (S); "hin"—a variant of "heen"—narrow, "madu"—
milky creeper, Hawari-madu (S); "hawari"—a long wig, "madu"—milky
creeper. Mudiyakuntal (T); meaning unknown.

S p e c i m e n s E x a m i n e d. MANNAR DISTRICT: Mantai, *s. coll.
s.n.* Jan. 1890 (L). POLONNARUWA DISTRICT: Ambagaswewa, *Austin et
al. 6167* (FAU, PDA, US); Minneri, *s. coll.* Mar. 1858, *C.P. 1929* (in part)
(PDA). BATTICALOA DISTRICT: Batticaloa, *Gardner s.n. C.P. 1930*
(PDA); Chenkaladi, *Austin et al. 6183* (FAU, PDA, US); Kalkudah, *Cramer
2757* (PDA). PUTTALAM DISTRICT: Wilpattu National Park, Kali Villu,
Cooray & Balakrishnan 1008 (PDA). KURUNEGALA DISTRICT: Kurune-
gala, *Alston 1456* (K, PDA); Mawatagama, *Austin et al. 6219* (FAU, PDA,
US). KANDY DISTRICT: Doluwa, *Austin & Austin 6142* (FAU, PDA, US);
Gampola-Dolosbage Road, *Grupe 149* (PDA); Peradeniya, *Comanor 700*
(PDA); Peradeniya-Kandy River Road, *Austin & Austin 6082* (FAU, PDA,
US). RATNAPURA DISTRICT: Pussella, *Austin et al. 6227* (FAU, PDA,
US). COLOMBO DISTRICT: Colombo, *Moon s.n., C.P. 1929* (in part)
(PDA). KALUTARA DISTRICT: Kalutara, *Austin et al. 6239* (FAU, PDA,
US); Matugama-Kalutara Road, *Kundu & Balakrishnan 449* (PDA). GALLE
DISTRICT: *Balakrishnan 968* (PDA); Galle, *Austin et al. 6250* (FAU, PDA,
US); Ahangama, *Austin et al. 6101* (FAU, PDA, US). HAMBANTOTA
DISTRICT: Kirinda, *Austin et al. 6112* (FAU, PDA, US); Ruhuna National
Park, Buttawa Bungalow, *Mueller-Dombois et al. 69010538* (PDA); *Cooray
70031906R* (PDA); Karaugaswala, *Mueller-Dombois & Cooray 67121072*

(PDA); Patanagala, *Wirawan 689* (PDA). LOCALITY UNKNOWN: *s. coll. C.P. 1929* (K); *s. coll. C.P. 1930* (K); *Burmann*, in 1644 (G); *Wight s.n.* (K).

N o t e. A number of authors have unsuccessfully attempted to divide this polymorphic complex into subspecies and varieties. Van Ooststroom and Verdcourt have different interpretations. After studying the living plants in Ceylon I believe that the small-flowered, narrow leaf forms are ecopheno-types adapted to seashore conditions. The larger-flowered, broader leaf forms are common inland. There seems to be no correlation between these and the morphological characters used by van Ooststroom and Verdcourt to distinguish taxa. I prefer to consider the species in the broad sense. If subspecies or varietal names are desired, they are available.

6. Merremia tuberosa (L.) Rendle, Fl. Trop. Africa 4 (2): 104. 1905; van Ooststroom, Fl. Mal., ser. 1, 4: 447. 1953; Verdcourt, Fl. Trop. E. Africa 60. 1963. Type: Jamaica?, specimen 219.4 (LINN, syntype not seen; microfiche seen).

Ipomoea tuberosa L., Sp. Pl. 160. 1753; Clarke in Hook. f., Fl. Br. Ind. 4: 213. 1883; Trimen, Handb. Fl. Ceylon. 3: 224. 1895.
Operculina tuberosa (L.) Meisn. in Mart., Fl. Bras. 7: 212. 1869.

Lianas; the stems herbaceous toward the tips, basally woody, glabrous. Leaves orbicular in outline, usually 7-lobed, at times almost to the base, at least to below the middle of the blade, the lobes lanceolate to elliptic, 6–16 cm long, acuminate, entire, glabrous. Inflorescences axillary few—to several-flowered, occasionally solitary, cymose; peduncles 4–20 cm long. Flowers with sepals unequal, the outer oblong, 25–30 mm long, obtuse, mucronate, the inner 12–20 mm long, acute; corolla yellow, campanulate, 5–6 cm long. Fruits capsular but irregularly dehiscent, subglobose, 30–35 mm long, the sepals somewhat accrescent and subtending the fruits; seeds black, densely short tomentose, 16–17 mm long.

D i s t r. Of tropical American origin, now in tropical Africa, India, Ceylon, Malaysia; mostly cultivated in the Old World, occasionally escaped.

E c o l. In the Eastern Hemisphere these plants are rarely encountered outside cultivation. Plants in Ceylon appear at times to be wild, but those that I have inquired about were cultivated. The vines are grown on fences, temple arches and shrine arches, and occasionally on pergolas. For some reason unknown to me van Ooststroom (1953: 448) says that the flowers open in the early morning. All plants that I have seen over the past several years opened between 11:00 a.m. and noon. In fact, most of the species in the genus bloom near mid-day.

S p e c i m e n s E x a m i n e d. KANDY DISTRICT: Kandy, *Austin & Austin 6141* (FAU, PDA, US); Peradeniya, *Austin & Austin 6080* (FAU, PDA, US). COLOMBO DISTRICT: Seeduwa, *Jayasuriya 1398* (PDA, US).

N o t e. In addition to the specimens cited, I have seen plants cultivated in the following districts: Trincomalee, Polonnaruwa, Matale, Kurunegala, Kegalle, Kalutara and Galle.

7. Merremia umbellata (L.) Hall. f., Bot. Jahrb. Syst. 16: 552. 1893; van Ooststroom, Fl. Mal., sér. 1, 4: 449. 1953; Verdcourt, Fl. Trop. E. Africa 54. 1963. Type: West Indies, Martinique, Hispaniola & Jamaica (no specimens in LINN).

Convolvulus umbellatus L., Sp. Pl. 155. 1753.
Convolvulus cymosus Desr. in Lam., Enc. 3: 556. 1791.
Ipomoea cymosa (Desr.) Roem. & Schultes, Syst. Nat. 4: 241. 1819; Clarke in Hook. f., Fl. Br. Ind. 4: 211. 1883; Trimen, Handb. Fl. Ceylon 3: 219. 1895.
Convolvulus bifidus sensu Moon, Cat. 13. 1824; Thw., Enum. Pl. Zeyl. 212. 1860.
Merremia umbellata var. *orientalis* Hall. f., Versl. 'sLands Pl.-tuin 1895: 132. 1896.
Merremia umbellata subsp. *orientalis* (Hall. f.) van Ooststroom, Fl. Mal., ser. 1, 4: 449. 1953.

Vines; the stems herbaceous above, the older parts becoming woody, twining or prostrate and rooting, mostly glabrous but occasionally softly pubescent. Leaves entire, narrowly triangular to broadly ovate, mostly long-acuminate, 4–12 cm long or rarely larger, basally truncate, cordate to has-tate, densely pubescent on some plants but more often glabrous or at least glabrescent. Inflorescences umbelliform-cymose, rarely 1-flowered; peduncles 1–7 cm long, often pubescent. Flowers with sepals oblong, 6–8 mm long, rounded apically, the margins scarious, glabrous or pubescent; corolla yellow, in Asia more commonly white, funnelform, 3–3.5 cm long. Fruits capsular, ovoid to conical, 10–12 mm long, glabrous or sparsely pubescent; seeds dark brown, densely pubescent with short, erect trichomes, 5 mm long.

D i s t r. The species as a whole is pantropical. There are, however, as Hallier and van Ooststroom have pointed out, two distinctive populations. A population in tropical America is best known as subsp. *umbellata* (the var. *occidentalis* of Hallier f.). Plants in tropical East Africa, the Seychelles, India, Ceylon to China, Indo-China and Malaysia belong to subsp. *orientalis*. Van Ooststroom (1953: 450) has given a good discussion of the differences bet-ween these taxa.

E c o l. Found in thickets, forest edges, grasslands, fields, roadsides and other disturbed sites. In some areas these plants are extremely common, forming loose nets of vines on the ground and across other vegetation.

V e r n. Kiri-madu (S); "kiri"—milk, "madu"—a milky creeper. Maha-madu (S); "maha"—large, "madu"—as above.

Specimens Examined. AMPARAI DISTRICT: near Padiyat-
talawe, *Austin et al. 6190* (FAU, PDA, US). MATALE DISTRICT: between
Madumana & Galgedewela, *Jayasuriya 347* (PDA, US). KANDY DIST-
RICT: Colombo-Kandy Road, *Comanor 803* (PDA); Kandy, *Alston 1304*
(PDA); Madugoda, *Jayasuriya et al. 504* (PDA, US). KEGALLE DIST-
RICT: Dambatenna, Kitugala, *Silva 210* (K). KALUTARA DISTRICT:
Pelawatte, *Cramer 2814* (PDA). GALLE DISTRICT: Bona Vista, *Balakrish-
nan 1153* (PDA). LOCALITY UNKNOWN: *s. coll., C.P. 1931* (PDA);
Gardner s.n. (K); *Gardner 612* (K).

8. Merremia vitifolia (Burm. f.) Hall. f., Bot. Jahrb. Syst. 16: 552. 1893; van
Ooststroom, Fl. Mal., ser. 1, 4: 448. 1953. Type: not located.

Convolvulus vitifolius Burm. f., Fl. Ind. 45. t. 18. f. 1. 1768.
Ipomoea vitifolia (Burm. f.) Blume, Bijdr. 709. 1825; Sweet, Hort. Br. ed. 2.
372. 1830; Thw., Enum. Pl. Zeyl. 426. 1860; Clarke in Hook. f., Fl. Br. Ind.
4: 213. 1883; Trimen, Handb. Fl. Ceylon 3: 224. 1895.

Vines; the stems herbaceous at the tips, apparently becoming woody at
the base, glabrous or hirsute with patent, white or fulvous trichomes. Leaves
orbicular in outline, 5–16 cm long and broad, basally cordate, palmately 5–7-
lobed, the lobes broad-triangular to lanceolate, more or less acuminate to
acute or obtuse at the apex, coarsely dentate to crenate, rarely subentire,
sparsely to densely pubescent on both sides, sometimes glabrous above. Inflorescences axillary, 1–3- or several-flowered, cymose; peduncles 1–15 cm long
or longer, patently hirsute. Flowers with sepals oblong to ovate-oblong,
12–20 mm long, obtuse to acute, the outer more or less hirsute, glabrescent,
the inner glabrous, all with glandular pellucid trichomes; corolla yellow, paler
toward the base, campanulate, 4–6 cm long. Fruits capsular, subglobose,
12 mm long, papery, straw-colored, the fruiting sepals 20–25 mm long, thick,
subcoriaceous, whitish inside; seeds dull black to blackish-brown, glabrous,
6–7 mm long.

Distr. Found from India and Ceylon to Indo-China eastward throughout Malaysia.
Ecol. Plants have been reported from grasslands, thickets, margins of
forests, on riverbanks and other disturbed sites. The only population I have
seen occupied several miles along the roadside between Mawanella and
Kegalle. These plants were covering the roadcut, climbing over roadside
shrubs and small trees.
Specimens Examined. KEGALLE DISTRICT: near Mawanella,
Austin et al. 6085 (FAU, PDA, US). COLOMBO DISTRICT: Colombo, *s.
coll.* Dec. 1860, *C.P. 3685* (K, PDA).

12. OPERCULINA

S. Manso, Enum. Subst. Bras. 16. 1836. Type Species: *Operculina convolvulus* S. Manso.

Lianas to small herbaceous vines, the stems, petioles, and pedicels often winged. Leaves entire to lobed, often cordate. Flowers axillary, in few-flowered cymes or solitary; sepals large, glabrous, enlarging in fruit and becoming coriaceous, often irregularly erose on the margins; corolla large, broadly campanulate, funnelform, or salverform, white, yellow, or reddish; stamens included, the anthers twisted at least in age, the pollen 3-colpate; ovary glabrous, bilocular, each locule biovulate, the style included, filiform, the stigma biglobose. Fruits dehiscent at or above the middle by a circumscissile epicarp, the upper part more or less fleshy and separating from the lower part and from the endocarp, 2-locular, 4-seeded; the seeds glabrous or pubescent.

A genus of about 15 species found throughout the tropics of both hemispheres. Flowering specimens are difficult to distinguish from *Merremia*; the group is well characterized only if restricted to species whose fruits are dehiscent as described above. The entire assemblage has the same facies as *Merremia* and perhaps should be considered a subdivision of that genus.

Operculina turpethum (L.) S. Manso, Enum. Subst. Bras. 16. 1836; van Ooststroom, Fl. Mal., ser. 1, 4: 456. 1953; Verdcourt, Fl. Trop. E. Africa 61. 1963. Type: Ceylon, *Hermann* Herb. 2: 68 (BM, lectotype fide Verdcourt; a specimen which is probably an isolectotype is in the *Hermann* Herb. 2: 135 in Leiden).

Convolvulus turpethum L., Sp. Pl. 155. 1753; Moon, Cat. 13. 1824.
Ipomoea anceps (L.) Roem. & Schultes, Syst. Nat. 4: 231. 1819; Thw., Enum. Pl. Zeyl. 212. 1860.
Ipomoea turpethum (L.) R. Br., Prod. 485. 1810; Clarke in Hook. f., Fl. Br. Ind. 4: 212. 1883; Trimen, Handb. Fl. Ceylon. 3: 222. 1895.

Vines; the stems perennial, herbaceous at the tips, narrowly 3–5-winged, sulcate or angular, glabrous or sparsely pilose, the younger parts sometimes tomentose; the roots long, fleshy, much-branched. Leaves variable in shape, orbicular, broadly ovate, ovate-lanceolate or lanceolate, 5–15 cm long, basally cordate to hastate, apically acuminate, acute or obtuse to rounded, the margins entire or more commonly coarsely dentate to shallowly lobed, the upper surface glabrous or appressed-pilose, lower surface pubescent. Inflorescences cymosely 1- to few-flowered. Flowers with peduncles 2–18 cm long, terete or sometimes winged like the stems, glabrous or pubescent; sepals ovate or broadly ovate, the outer 1.5–2.5 cm long, the inner 2 cm long, acute or shortly acuminate, the outer pubescent, the inner glabrous; corolla white or white with a yellowish base, campanulate to broadly funnelform, 3–4.5

cm long, glabrous or with yellowish glandular indument outside. Fruits capsular, depressed-globose, 1.5 cm long; seeds dull black, glabrous, 6 mm long.

D i s t r. Reported from tropical Africa, Madagascar, southern Asia to Australia, Polynesia; introduced into the West Indies.

E c o l. Found in wet sites, thickets, waste places, and farmland. Trimen was of the opinion that the species was cultivated and not wild on the island. Admittedly most plants are cultivated, but some are naturalized.

V e r n. Trastawalu (S); a word derived from Sanskrit or Pali, the meaning in Sinhalese is now lost.

N o t e. This plant has long been associated with man because of the latex in the root which has been used as a laxative. According to most authorities the specific name was taken from the Arabic "turbith" which referred to roots containing drugs. The species figures prominently in ayurvedic medicine on the island and may be seen cultivated in many areas. In addition to the collections cited belew, I have seen sterile plants cultivated in Trincomalee and Kurunegala districts.

S p e c i m e n s E x a m i n e d. MATALE DISTRICT: Sigiriya, *Austin et al. 6155A* (US). KANDY DISTRICT: Kandy, *s. coll. s.n.* June 1894 (PDA). MONERAGALA DISTRICT: Tanamalwila, *Austin et al. 6116* (FAU, PDA, US).

13. PORANA

Burm. f., Fl. Ind. 51. t. 21. f. 1. 1758; van Ooststroom, Blumea 3: 85. 1938.

Large woody or herbaceous twiners. Leaves petioled, ovate, mostly cordate at the base and palmately nerved, rarely penninerved, entire, herbaceous. Inflorescences racemose or paniculate, rarely flowers solitary; bracts leaf-like, or minute and subulate, or none; sepals 5, small in flower, the 3 outer ones or all in fruit much accrescent, scarious, reticulately veined, spreading, often spathulate, falling off with the fruit; corolla regular, white, small, campanulate or funnel-shaped, rarely larger and funnel- or salver-shaped, the limb subentire or 5-lobed; stamens and style included, rarely exserted, stamens 5, filaments adnate to the corolla, filiform, glabrous, or glandular or pubescent at the base; pollen smooth; disk annular or none; ovary mostly glabrous, 1-celled, 2-ovuled, or 1–2-celled, 4-ovuled; style 1, simple, or bifid with unequal branches; stigma globose or 2-lobed, solitary, or one on each branch. Capsule small, sub-globose to oblong, 2-valved, or indehiscent; seed usually 1, glabrous.

This tropical and subtropical genus has about 20 species in Asia, Africa and one in Australia. Species have been attributed to the Americas but they all appear to be members of *Calycobolus*. The single species in Ceylon is originally from N. India and is cultivated in several tropical countries.

Porana paniculata Roxb., Pl. Corom. 3. 1819; Clarke in Hook. f., Fl. Br. Ind. 4: 222. 1883; Trimen, Handb. Fl. Ceylon 3: 227. 1895; van Ooststroom, Fl. Mal., ser. 1, 4: 404. 1953. Type: Java. *Kleinhof* (not found).

Lianas; the stems herbaceous at the tips, woody at the base, grayish tomentellous throughout. Leaves ovate, 4–9 cm long, cordate basally, obtuse, acute, acuminate or shortly cuspidate apically, pubescent on both surfaces but more densely below. Inflorescences lateral or terminal, paniculate. Flowers usually on pedicels 1–2 mm long; sepals linear, 1–1.5 mm long, densely tomentellous; corolla white, funnelform, 5–6 mm long. Fruits indehiscent, ovoid-globular, 5–6 mm long, the outer 3 sepals enlarged in fruit, wing-like; seeds ovoid, brown.

D i s t r. Native to northern India and Upper Burma; cultivated in Ceylon, Malaysia, Africa and the New World tropics.

N o t e. This attractive large woody vine produces a profusion of small white flowers; thus it is widely cultivated throughout the regions free of frost. van Ooststroom noted that the species does not fruit where it has been introduced in Malaysia. Plants grown in the Americas do not fruit either.

S p e c i m e n s E x a m i n e d. KANDY DISTRICT: Peradeniya, *Austin & Austin 6081* (US).

14. RIVEA

Choisy, Mem. Soc. Phys. Genève 6: 407. 1834. Type Species: *Rivea hypocrateriformis* (Desr.) Choisy.

Lianas; the stems with a silvery-whitish appressed indument, at least when young. Leaves cordate to ovate-cordate, petiolate, silky-whitish pubescent below, some glabrescent. Inflorescences on axillary peduncles, 1–3-flowered, cymose, mostly with a single flower open at any time; bracts narrow, shorter than the sepals. Flowers with corollas white, salverform; sepals ovate to oblong, equal or unequal; stamens included, inserted on the tube mostly near the middle; ovary 4-celled, 4-ovulate, the style filiform, the stigmas with two lobes, linear-oblong. Fruits indehiscent, nearly dry, sometimes dehiscent and breaking irregularly; seeds 1–4, enclosed within a mealy pulp at least when dry, glabrous.

This poorly defined genus has about 6 species in the tropics of Asia. Very little distinguishes the group of species from *Argyreia* except for the corolla shape and stigmas. Perhaps the species are most closely related to *Argyreia* and have diverged from that group by adaptation to moth pollination.

Rivea ornata Choisy, Mem. Soc. Phys. Genève 6: 409. 1834; Thw., Enum. Pl. Zeyl. 209. 1860; Clarke in Hook. f., Fl. Br. Ind. 4: 183. 1883; Trimen,

Handb. Fl. Ceylon 3: 205. 1895. Type: India, *Wallich 1369* (G-DC, holotype).

Lianas; the stems herbaceous at the tips, woody below, covered with appressed silky-white indument. Leaves broadly ovate to reniform, 3.5–10 cm
long, cordate basally, obtuse to very abruptly and shortly acuminate apically,
glabrous above, somewhat densely white-silky pubescent below. Inflorescences terminal or at least terminal on lateral branches, cymose. Flowers with
peduncles 2–3 cm long, each peduncle usually with a solitary flower; sepals
oblong-ovate, 18–20 mm long, subequal or the inner slightly shorter, acute to
obtuse, densely whitish-tomentose outside; corolla white, salverform, 6–9 cm
long, the tubes mostly 4 cm long. Fruits becoming dry, indehiscent, globose
to ellipsoid, 1–1.5 cm long, brown; seeds black, glabrous, 6–7 mm long.

D i s t r. Reported only from southern India and Ceylon.
E c o l. These lianas are frequent to common in the coastal areas of the
dry zone. In these sites they may be found climbing over rocks, in thickets,
on roadsides, or climbing with cultivated plants. The flowering season is
restricted to the period between December and March. Occasional flowers
are produced outside this time, but rarely. Flowers on the plants are nocturnal, at first white when they open and later pale cream and yellow when closing. These characteristics and the sweet fragrance mentioned by Trimen
suggest moth pollination.
S p e c i m e n s E x a m i n e d. MANNAR DISTRICT: Illupaikaduvai,
s. coll. s.n. in 1890 (PDA). TRINCOMALEE DISTRICT: Trincomalee,
Gardner s.n., C.P. 1946 (in part) (PDA). MONERAGALA DISTRICT:
Nilgala, *s. coll.* in 1858, *C.P. 1946* (in part) (PDA); between Bibile & Ekiriyankumbura, *Trimen s.n.*, in 1888 (L, PDA). HAMBANTOTA DISTRICT:
Kirinde *s. coll. s.n.*, in 1882 (PDA); Kirinde, *Austin et al. 6111A* (US). LOCA-
LITY UNKNOWN: *Thwaites C.P. 1946* (K).
N o t e. Choisy (in DC., Prod. 9: 326. 1845) listed *Rivea hypocrateriformis*
for Trincomalee. Apparently Choisy based this on the upper part of the
fourth specimen in the DeCandolle Herbarium. This sheet is numbered 1368
and the upper specimen on the sheet is from Trincomalee. Although the
sepals are slightly smaller, the plants are undoubtedly the same species.

15. STICTOCARDIA

Hall. f., Bot. Jahrb. Syst. 18: 159. 1894. Type Species: *Convolvulus tiliifolia*
Desr. = *Stictocardia tilifolia* (Desr.) Hall. f.

Vines to about 4 m in length, perennial; stems puberulent, glabrate, the
older stems with exfoliating bark. Leaves petiolate, cordate, apically acuminate, entire, glabrate above but covered with small black glandular trichomes
beneath. Flowers in 1–3-flowered axillary cymes; sepals subequal, orbicular

with black glandular trichomes, becoming coriaceous and clasping in fruit; corolla funnelform, red, scarlet, purplish-red or mauve, the limb usually entire; stamens included, the filaments glandular-pubescent at the base, filiform above, the anthers oblong, pollen pantoporate, spheroidal, spinulose; ovary bilocular, the style longer than stamens, the stigma capitate, biglobose. Fruits indehiscent, thin-walled, surrounded by enlarged fleshy sepals, subspheroidal; seeds 4, ovoid, grayish brown, minutely pubescent.

A genus of 6–12 species. Several authors have indicated its distribution as circumtropical apparently on the basis of a single species introduced into the New World. Perhaps the group originated in Africa or Asia. Apparently the species in the genus are adapted for pollination by birds.

KEY TO THE SPECIES

1 Corolla scarlet and yellow, 5.5–7 cm long; sepals unequal, the inner about 2 cm long, the outer about 1.5 cm . . . . **2. S. macalusoi**
1 Corolla reddish-purple with a darker centre, 8–10 cm long; sepals subequal, 1–2 cm long . . . . **1. S. tiliifolia**

1. Stictocardia tiliifolia (Desr.) Hall. f., Bot. Jahrb. Syst. 18: 159. 1894; van Ooststroom, Fl. Mal., ser. 1, 4: 491. 1953. Type: Mauritius: *Comerson* (P, not seen).

Convolvulus tiliafolius Desr. in Lam., Enc. 3: 544. 1792.
Rivea tiliaefolia (Desr.) Choisy, Mem. Soc. Phys. Genève 6: 407. 1834; DC., Prod. 9: 325. 1845; Thw., Enum. Pl. Zeyl. 209. 1860.
Argyreia tiliaefolia (Desr.) Wight, Ic. Pl. Ind. Or. 4: 12. t. 1358. 1848; Clarke in Hook. f., Fl. Br. Ind. 4: 184. 1883; Trimen, Handb. Fl. Ceylon 3: 206. 1895.
Rivea campanulata sensu House, Muhlenbergia 5: 72. 1909.
Stictocardia campanulata sensu Merr., Philipp. J. Sci. 9: 133. 1914; Gunn, Brittonia 24: 169. 1972.
Argyreia campanulata sensu Alston in Trimen, Handb. Fl. Ceylon 6: 201. 1931.

Lianas; the stems herbaceous at the tips, becoming woody with age, puberulent but glabrescent. Leaves cordate to cordate-ovate, 8–25 cm long, basally cordate, apically acute to short-acuminate, glabrate above and below, with numerous scattered pellucid-glandular dots on the lower surface. Inflorescences mostly of solitary flowers in the leaf axils, occasionally cymose and 1–3-flowered. Flowers on peduncles mostly shorter than the leaves; sepals suborbicular, 1–2 cm long, subequal, puberulent, glabrescent; corolla reddish-purple with a darker center, funnelform, 8–10 cm long. Fruits indehiscent, globose, 2.5–3 cm long, surrounded by the accrescent calyx which eventually disintegrates leaving the vascular framework; seeds obovoid, grayish-brown, pubescent with minute trichomes, 8–9 mm long.

D i s t r. Circumtropical, apparently originally from Asia or Africa; cultivated widely and introduced into the New World.

E c o l. Previous reports indicate that the plants always occur on or near the sea shore throughout its range. Those plants that I have seen in Ceylon suggest that this is correct. Plants have been seen on dunes, in the margin of brackish lagoons, climbing shrubs and small trees and similar habitats in the wet zone.

V e r n. Ma-banda (S); "ma"—a shortened form of "maha" or large, "banda"—refers to tying. This name is given to an *Argyreia* inland, perhaps by settlers from the coast.

S p e c i m e n s   E x a m i n e d. KANDY DISTRICT: Haragama, *s. coll.* in 1853, *C.P. 2847* (in part) (PDA); Kandy, *s. coll.*, in 1859, *C.P. 2848* (in part) (PDA). GALLE DISTRICT: Kosgoda, *Balakrishnan 998* (US); Unawatuna, *Austin et al. 6256* (FAU, PDA, US). LOCALITY UNKNOWN: *s. coll.*, in 1860, *C.P. 2848* (K); *s. coll.*, in 1862, *C.P. 2848* (K).

N o t e. This species has been confused with *Ipomoea campanulata*, another plant of brackish coastal areas. The glandular dots on the lower leaf surface are usually enough to distinguish *Stictocardia*, but there are other differences. Basal leaf lobes of *I. campanulata* diverge from the petiole at an acute to obtuse angle while they diverge from *Stictocardia* for a short distance and curve to parallel the petiole; there are (5 –) 7–8 pairs of secondary veins in *Stictocardia*, and 10–15 pairs in *I. campanulata*. Fruits and seeds are also different in the two: dehiscent and comose seeds in *I. campanulata*; indehiscent with short pubescent seeds in *Stictocardia*.

2. Stictocardia macalusoi (Mattei) Verdcourt, Kew Bull. 15: 6. 1961; Verdcourt, Fl. Trop. E. Africa 68. 1963. Type: Somali Republic, Merca, Giumbo, *Macaluso 80* (not found).

Ipomoea macalusoi Mattei, Bol. R. Ort. Bot. Palermo 7: 106. 1908.
Stictocardia tiliifolia (Desr.) Hall. f. subsp. *macalusoi* (Mattei) Verdcourt, Webbia 13: 322. 1958.

Lianas; the stems twining, yellow, ridged, pubescent and glabrescent. Leaves broadly ovate to suborbicular, 6–11 cm long, deeply cordate-emarginate basally, obtuse, shortly acuminate or rounded apically, glabrous or more often pubescent at least on the veins below, densely punctate glandular below. Inflorescences axillary, (1 –) 2- to several-flowered, often somewhat umbellate-cymose, on peduncles up to 5 mm long, or sessile. Flowers on pedicels up to 2.5 cm long; sepals oval, unequal, the outer 2 about 1.5 cm long, the inner mostly 2 cm long, mucronate, glabrous; corolla bright red to scarlet, the tube yellow with red nectar guides, yellow outside, funnelform, 5.5–7 cm long. Fruits capsular globose, yellowish-brown, indehiscent, 1.8 cm long; seeds subglobose, brown, shortly pubescent, 6–7 mm long.

D i s t r. Apparently originally from the southern Somali Republic in Africa, now cultivated sparingly in both hemispheres.

E c o l. In Africa the plants are found on dunes near the sea; they have not become naturalized elsewhere but are cultivated. In Ceylon the flowers are visited by Sunbirds. Since these birds are too small to enter the flowers "correctly" and take nectar, they pierce the corolla just above the base. Flowers open on the plants at dawn and close near sunset, thus supplying a display throughout the day.

S p e c i m e n s E x a m i n e d. KANDY DISTRICT: Kandy, *Austin & Austin 6209* (FAU, PDA, US).

16. TURBINA

Raf., Fl. Tellur. 4: 81. 1838. Type Species: *Turbina corymbosa* (L.) Raf.

Legendrea Webb & Berth., Hist. Nat. Iles Canaries, Bot. 3, 2: 26. 1844. Type:
   L. mollissima Webb & Berth. = *Turbina corymbosa* (L.) Raf. var.; van Ooststroom, Blumea 5: 355. 1943.

Lianas; often high climbing, pubescent or glabrous. Leaves petiolate, cordate and entire. Flowers white, greenish, pink or crimson, solitary or on many-flowered axillary or terminal inflorescences; sepals ovate or lanceolate, the outer sphaecelate, often unequal, accrescent in fruit; corolla funnelform or salverform; the filaments filiform with glandular-pubescent, dilated bases; the pollen pantoporate, spheroidal, spinulose; ovary glabrous, 2-locular, the style single, the stigmas 2, globose. Fruits indehiscent, dry, mostly ligneous to subligneous, ellipsoid to subglobose, 1-locular, mostly 1-seeded; the seeds pubescent.

This genus contains about 12 species in the tropics of the Old and New World. Although there is a common facies to the species included, they are mostly placed in the genus because of indehiscent ovoid-oblong or ellipsoid fruits, usually with a single seed. While the genus may not be natural, its inclusion in other recognized genera would make them too heterogeneous.

Turbina corymbosa (L.) Raf., Fl. Tellur. 4: 81. 1838; van Ooststroom, Fl. Mal., ser. 1, 4: 493. 1953; Verdcourt, Fl. Trop. E. Africa 152. 1963. Type: based on Plumier, Pl. Amer. 78. t. 89. f. 2 (lectotype).

Convolvulus corymbosus L., Syst. Nat. ed. 10. 923. 1759.
Rivea corymbosa (L.) Hall. f., Bot. Jahrb. Syst. 16: 157. 1893.
Ipomoea sidaefolia (H.B.K.) Choisy, Mem. Soc. Phys. Genève 6: 459. 1834;

Clarke in Hook. f., Fl. Br. Ind. 4: 216. 1883; Trimen, Handb. Fl. Ceylon 3: 220. 1895.

Convolvulus zeylanicus Moon ex Wall., Cat. n. 1379, nom. nud.

Lianas; the stems herbaceous at the tips, woody at the base, glabrous to glabrescent. Leaves ovate-cordate, 4–10 cm long, apically acute to shortly acuminate, glabrous or rarely pubescent. Inflorescences of axillary or terminal thyrses. Flowers on pedicels 1–1.5 cm long; sepals oblong, 8–12 mm long, glabrous; corolla white with a dark brown to purplish base inside the tube, 2.5–3 cm long, the filaments with yellowish trichomes at their base. Fruits indehiscent, ovoid-oblong, 1–1.5 cm long, the sepals somewhat accrescent; seeds 1, rarely 2 per fruit, pubescent with short trichomes.

D i s t r. Originally a species of the American tropics, this plant has been introduced into many countries as an ornamental. Although rarely becoming established, it has naturalized in the Philippines.

E c o l. In Ceylon the plants are occasionally cultivated for the profusion of white flowers produced in November and December. Bees, particularly the genus *Apis*, are efficient pollinators in the Americas and presumably in Ceylon also.

S p e c i m e n s   E x a m i n e d. LOCALITY UNKNOWN: British E. Indies, *Wallich 1379* (L).

DIPTEROCARPACEAE

(by P.S. Ashton*)

(ut Dipterocarpeae) Blume, Bijdr. 222. 1825. Type genus: *Dipterocarpus* Gaertn. f.

Trees, usually tall, with crowns becoming sympodial, often emergent, all at first monopodial and a few remaining so. All parts sometimes hairy; hairs mainly unicellular, acicular and usually fascicled or stellate, peltate or emarginate and single; frequently also with more or less caducous multicellular long-stalked (*Vateria*) or capitate (*Dipterocarpus*) hairs. Leaves alternate, entire, usually coriaceous, stipulate, usually prominently penninerved, frequently with domatia in the axils of the nerves, usually evergreen. Inflorescences paniculate or sometimes cymose (some *Vatica*), terminal or axillary to ramiflorous, with small caducous bracts; flowers hermaphrodite, actinomorphic, 5-merous, frequent. Calyx imbricate or rarely subvalvate, frequently united into a short or long tube free or adnate to the ovary; corolla contorted, often connate at the base on falling; stamens 5, 10, 15 or many, centrifugal, usually connate at least at base, frequently adnate to base of petals, with applanate more or less tapering filaments, connective extended into a more or less prominent appendage, and 2-locular latrorse or rarely (*Stemonoporus*) end-porous anthers; ovary superior or semi-inferior (*Dipterocarpus*), (2–) 3-locular, each cell with 2 anatropous or pendulous ovules; style columnar, entire or trifid, frequently on a stylopodium; stigmas usually small, often obscure, 3- or 6-lobed. Fruit a usually 1-seeded nut, with a persistent calyx frequently more or less enclosing it, or reflexed, often with some of the lobes accrescent into contorted wings. Embryo usually without endosperm at maturity; cotyledons small and photosynthetic or large, ruminate and reddish, often unequal, often twisted, lobed or laciniate, enclosing the radicle. Pericarp splitting irregularly or along 3 loculicidal sutures at germination; first 2 pairs of leaves opposite, with interpetiolar stipules.

Subfamily DIPTEROCARPOIDEAE

Androecium without gynophore; anthers basifixed; with intracellular resin canals and multiseriate rays.

*Arnold Arboretum, Harvard University, U.S.A.

15 genera, 580 species, Asian tropics, mostly in the humid zone. 45 species in Ceylon, all but one endemic; confined mainly to the wet zone, except *H. brevipetiolaris*, *H. cordifolia*, *V. obscura*, and *D. zeylanicus* (see under species descriptions). Occurring only in primary forest below 1600 m alt., where several species together often comprise a high proportion of all canopy trees. Single species may dominate in the submontane forests, while some others form local gregarious aggregations—'drifts'—in the lowlands.

No full monograph of the family has appeared since that of Brandis (J. Linn. Soc. Bot. 31: 1. 1895), who defined 5 tribes. These are not now considered to be natural divisions, and no suprageneric taxa are recognised here. Further, genera based on the absence of aliform fruit sepals (e.g., *Balanocarpus*, *Isoptera*) are not recognised, as their species otherwise fall clearly into well-known genera. The genus *Shorea* is now considered as a larger entity including 10 more or less well-defined sections, based on characters of the flower and particularly of the stamens, though often also with characteristic wood and bark anatomy, and sometimes leaf morphology. The present generic concept leads to the reduction of *Balanocarpus* to *Hopea*, and of *Isoptera* and *Doona* to *Shorea*; *Shorea* section *Doonae* (Thw.) Ashton is endemic to the island. For these and other taxonomic changes preparatory to this account see Ashton, Blumea 20, 2: 357–366. 1972.

Two basic chromosome numbers are known: 7 (*Shorea*, *Dryobalanops*, *Neobalanocarpus*, *Hopea*), and 11 (*Dipterocarpus*, *Vatica*, *Anisoptera*, *Stemonoporus*); polyploidy appears to be rare.

KEY TO THE GENERA

1 Base of the calyx fused into a tube at least half enclosing the nut; 2 calyx lobes prolonged and aliform; leaves plicately folded in bud; stipules amplexicaul..............
....**2. Dipterocarpus**
1 Base of calyx not united into a tube; leaves not plicate in bud; stipules not amplexicaul
  2 Fruit sepals imbricate, with a thickened saccate base appressed to the nut
    3 Fruit with 3 aliform sepals, or all short and flower with more than 20 stamens......
    ....**4. Shorea**
    3 Fruit with 2 aliform sepals, or all short and flower with 15 stamens........**3. Hopea**
  2 Fruit sepals valvate, without thickened base
    4 Anthers end-porous...**5. Stemonoporus**
    4 Anthers latrorse
      5 Anthers broadly oblong; stigma prominently conical....................**7. Vatica**
      5 Anthers linear; stigma obscure
        6 Stamens c. 50, anthers prolonged apically into a recurved awn.........**6. Vateria**
        6 Stamens less than 30; anthers not as above.....................**1. Cotylelobium**

1. COTYLELOBIUM

Pierre, Fl. Cochinch. 15: sub tab. 235. 1890. Type species: *C. melanoxylon* (Hook. f.) Pierre.

Dyerella Heim, Rech. Dipt. 123. 1892.
Hemiphractum Heim, l.c.

Medium sized or large trees. Buttresses low, rounded, similar to *Vatica*. Crown hemispherical, dense, rather small. Bark surface greyish, at first smooth, hoop-marked; becoming irregularly flaked; inner bark and wood as in *Vatica*. Stipules fugaceous. Lamina elliptic to oblong or ovate, lanceolate, coriaceous, margin more or less revolute; undersurface lepidote, nerves arched, hardly raised, very slender, bifurcating towards the margin and anastomosing to form a looped intra-marginal nerve, with shorter indistinct intermediates similarly bifurcating; intercostals reticulate, indistinct; midrib depressed above. Petiole comparatively short, hardly geniculate. Inflorescence paniculate, many-flowered; flower buds lanceolate; sepals more or less valvate, subequal; petals cream, more or less broadly elliptic-oblong, pubescent on parts exposed in bud, falling separately; stamens 15, subequal, in 3 verticils, pairs alternating with single stamens; filaments short, deltoid, connate at base; anthers narrowly oblong, with 4 pollen sacs, the inner 2 shorter than the outer 2; appendage to connective less than half the length of anther, columnar, or very short. Ovary free from calyx, more or less globose; stylopodium absent; style filiform, slender, many times longer than ovary, shortly pubescent towards base; stigma small, trifid, slightly broader than style. Fruit as in *Vatica*; or sepals unequal, 2 accrescent, aliform.

D i s t r. 6 species: Ceylon (2), South Thailand (1), Malaya and Riouw (2), Borneo (3).

E c o l. Found typically on rather acid well-drained soils on ridge-tops and rocky plateaux in the wet zone.

V e r n. Mendora, Na-Mendora.

U s e s. The wood is hard and fine-grained, with pale sapwood and dark brown heart. It is suitable for construction and flooring.

KEY TO THE SPECIES

1 Fruit sepals equal, shorter than the nut, becoming reflexed at maturity; lamina undersurface densely pale ocherous puberulent; main nerves c. 10 pairs, hardly raised below
....1. C. lewisianum
1 Fruit sepals unequal, erect, 2 long, oblong to spatulate and 3 short, more or less ovate; lamina undersurface sparsely puberulent; nerves c. 20 pairs, distinctly raised..........
....2. C. scabriusculum

1. Cotylelobium lewisianum (Trimen ex Hook. f.) Ashton, Blumea 20, 2: 358. 1972. Lectotype: *Lewis s.n.*, Apr. 1893 (PDA).

Stemonoporus lewisianus Trimen ex Hook. f., Handb. Fl. Ceylon 5: 383. 1900; Lewis, Trees and Fl. Pl. of W. and Sab. Prov. 37. 1902.

Vatica lewisiana (Trimen ex Hook. f.) Livera, Ann. R. Bot. Gard. Perad. 9: 97. 1924.

Vateria? *lewisiana* (Trimen ex Hook. f.) Alston in Trimen, Handb. Fl. Ceylon 6: 25. 1931.

Hemiphractum lewisianum (Trimen ex Hook. f.) Heim, Rech. Dipt. 123. 1892.

Large unbuttressed tree, –35 m tall, –4 m girth, with irregular open crown pale yellow from below; bark surface pale grey, becoming irregularly flaky. Twigs, buds, petioles, midrib below, inflorescences and parts of perianth exposed in bud densely buff puberulent; ovary and nut fulvously so; base of sytle villous; lamina undersurface pale buff cinereous. Leaf buds minute, ovoid, acute. Twig c. 2 mm diam. apically, slender, smooth, terete. Lamina 4–12.5 × 2–6.5 cm, ovate to lanceolate, coriaceous, with broadly cuneate to obtuse base and –6 mm long, short slender tapering acumen; main nerves c. 8–10 pairs, unraised above, obscurely elevated beneath. Petiole 8–11 mm long. Panicle –10 cm long, –2 mm diam. at base in fruit, terminal or axillary, rigid, with –2 cm long short cymose branches bearing –5 flowers. Flower buds –8 × 4 mm; staminal appendage almost half as long as abaxial anther cells, anthers glabrous, flowers otherwise typical. Fruit pedicel –8 mm long, slender; nut (immature?) c. 6 × 6 mm, globose, verruculose, subtended by –4 × 2 mm subequal deltoid reflexed sepals. Sapling lamina –20 × 7 cm, with subcordate base, –2 cm long acumen, and –18 pairs of main nerves; petiole –2 cm long.

D i s t r. Endemic. Ratnapura District: base of Adam's Peak range, Bambarabotuwa F.R., and hills immediately south of Pelmadulla.

E c o l. In majestic gregarious stands at 550–1800 m alt. on rocky ridges. Flowering in January. Fruiting in April–May.

S p e c i m e n s E x a m i n e d. RATNAPURA DISTRICT: Hunawal Kande, near Pelmadulla, *Lewis s.n.*, January 1893 (PDA, K), *s.n.*, April 1893 (PDA); Kiribatgalle near Kahawatte, *Livera s.n.* (PDA), *Ashton 2116, 2117* (PDA, US).

N o t e. The previous incorrect placing of this species was partially because undue emphasis was placed on the value of characters of the fruit calyx, and partially because the number of stamens was miscounted as 25 in the original description.

2. **Cotylelobium scabriusculum** (Thw.) Brandis, J. Linn. Soc. Bot. 31: 114. 1895; Trimen, Handb. Fl. Ceylon 5: 383. 1900; Alston in Trimen, Handb. Fl. Ceylon 6: 25. 1931; Worthington, Ceylon Trees 66. 1959. Lectotype: *C.P. 3708*, Hewesse (PDA).

Vateria scabriuscula Thw., Enum. Pl. Zeyl. 404. 1864.

Vatica scabriuscula A. DC., Prod. 16. 2: 620. 1868; Dyer, in Hook. f., Fl. Br. Ind. 1: 303. 1872.

Dyerella scabriuscula Heim, Bull. Soc. Bot. France 39: 153. 1892; Rech. Dipt. 123. 1892.

Sunaptea scabriuscula Trimen, Cat. 9. 1885; Handb. Fl. Ceylon 1: 126. 1893;
Lewis, Trees and Fl. Pl. of W. and Sab. Prov. 34. 1902.

Medium sized tree, –35 m tall, –1.5 m girth, sometimes coppicing. Crown
compact, oblong to hemispherical. Twigs, buds, petioles, lamina undersurface, inflorescence, bracts, fruit calyx and parts of perianth exposed in bud
more or less sparsely tawny pubescent, freshly expanding parts and ovary
densely so. Leaf bud –3 × 2 mm, ovoid, subacute. Twig c. 2 mm diam. apically, slender, terete, smooth. Lamina 7.5–22 × 2.4–8 cm, narrowly oblong to
lanceolate, with broadly cuneate to obtuse base and –1.8 cm long slender
acumen; nerves 17–23 pairs, slender but distinctly raised beneath as also the
intermediates and reticulate intercostals, obscure above; petiole 1.3–1.6 cm
long, c. 2 mm diam. Mature panicles unknown, terminal or axillary; bracts
–7 × 4 mm, narrowly ovate, obtuse. Flowers (very young) typical. Fruit pedicel –8 mm long, slender; calyx lobes unequal; 2 longer lobes –5.5 × 1.5 cm,
lorate, obtuse, tapering to c. 4 mm broad at base; 3 shorter lobes –2.5 × 7
mm, lanceolate, acute; nut –1 cm diam., subglobose, verruculose, surmounted by an –6 mm long persistent style remnant. Sapling lamina –35 × 8 cm,
with –1.7 cm long stout petiole.

D i s t r. Endemic. SW corner of the wet zone: From Kottawa F.R. northwards to Opata and north-westwards to Hewesse and Pelawatta in Pasdun
Korale; including Hiniduma, Nellowe, and Kanneliya F.R.

E c o l. Locally frequent on the deep leached soils which characterise the
broad ridges below 300 m in that area. Flowering in late April and May, at
long intervals.

S p e c i m e n s E x a m i n e d. GALLE DISTRICT: Kunelli Mukulana,
Hiniduma, *Worthington 2238* (K); Kottawa natural arboretum, *Worthington
6014* (K), *Ashton 2033, 2034* (PDA, US), *s. coll. 294* (PDA); Kanneliya F.R.,
Worthington 6032 (K), *Ashton 2085, 2087* (PDA, US); Kanneli Ella, Hiniduma, *Ashton 2097* (PDA); Hiniduma, *s. coll. C.P. 3452* (PDA, K); Udugama, *s. coll. 2129* (PDA). KALUTARA DISTRICT: Lenegal Kande &
Hewesse, Pasdun Korale, *s. coll. C.P. 3708* (PDA, K).

2. DIPTEROCARPUS

Gaertn. f., Fruct. 3: 50. 1805. Type species: *D. costatus* Gaertn. f.

Large emergent trees. Bole tall, straight, cylindrical, with little taper.
Buttresses thick, rounded, usually small and concave, sometimes tall and
straight. Crown becoming dome-shaped, sometimes rather open, with a few
large strongly ascending branches. Bark surface pale or dark grey to orange-
brown, sometimes pink-brown; shallowly patchily flaked, more or less prominently densely verrucose lenticellate; outer bark dark rust-brown, brittle,

of varying thickness; inner bark pale yellow-brown to dark rust-brown, hard, becoming paler at the cream cambium; sapwood yellow, gradually merging into the pale or dark rust or pink-brown heart. Resin not exuding on healthy boles but more or less rapidly exuding on freshly cut surfaces. Twigs with distinct, usually pale and swollen, amplexicaul stipule scars. Stipules large, hastate to lorate, obtuse, more or less succulent, caducous, characteristically carpeting the forest floor at times of fresh leaf. Lamina coriaceous, margin somewhat sinuate towards the apex; nerves prominent beneath, straight, curved only towards the margin, with traces of the plicate vernation remaining persistently between them, giving the lamina a corrugated appearance; intercostals scalariform. Petiole prominently geniculate. Racemes short, stout, zig-zag, few-flowered, somewhat irregularly sparingly branched; bracts as stipules, but smaller, fugaceous. Buds and flowers large, buds ellipsoid. Calyx united round the fruit into a tube, fused to it in the basal half only; lobes valvate, with 2 long, oblong to spathulate, more or less distinctly 3-nerved, and 3 short. Petals large, narrowly oblong, strongly contorted, loosely adhering at base on falling, cream with a more or less prominent pink stripe down the centre. Stamens 15-many, persisting in a ring round the ovary after the petals fall; filaments of variable length, broad, compressed, connate at base, tapering gradually and filiform below the anther; anthers long, linear, tapering apically, with 4 pollen sacs, the inner 2 somewhat shorter than the outer 2; appendage to connective short, stout, to long, filiform, slender, glabrous. Ovary enclosed in the calyx tube, the apex ovoid to conical, densely puberulent; stylopodium cylindrical to filiform, densely puberulent, narrowing imperceptibly or abruptly into the glabrous filiform style. Fruit large; calyx tube becoming distinctly constricted into a distal neck as the nut expands; lobes as in flower, but greatly expanded; nut ovoid, with a short acute apical style remnant. Germination hypogeal, the cotyledons remaining within the fruit and the plumule freeing itself by elongation of the cotyledonary petioles.

D i s t r. c. 75 species: From Ceylon and India eastwards to Indo-china, Sumbawa, Borneo and the Philippines. 4 species in Ceylon.

E c o l. Occurring, in some cases gregariously, in evergreen forests below 1300 m, and generally below 1000 m alt. in the wet zone, and in isolated localities where the soil has a permanently high moisture content in the intermediate zone (D. zeylanicus).

U s e s. The wood is heavy, hard and resinous, and used for heavy construction and for railway sleepers; it takes preservatives easily. The resin of some species (especially D. glandulosus) is tapped by cutting a cavity in the trunk and periodically firing it until the tree is inevitably destroyed; it is used as a varnish and as a base, mixed with brick dust, for brass-workers to hammer onto.

V e r n. Hora, Dorana.

KEY TO THE SPECIES

1 Shortly deciduous tree; lamina large, cordate, densely persistently golden hispid beneath; fruit calyx tube without ribs or wings.................................**2. D. hispidus**
1 Evergreen trees; lamina scabrous pubescent to glabrous beneath; base not cordate; tube typically (not always in *D. zeylanicus*) ribbed or winged
  2 Lamina with at least 14 pairs of nerves; fruit calyx tube ribbed or occasionally smooth ....**4. D. zeylanicus**
  2 Lamina with at most 13 pairs of nerves; fruit calyx tube winged
   3 Leaf glabrous but for petiole; calyx tube fusiform, wings exceeding 5 mm wide and adnate to pedicel...**3. D. insignis**
   3 Lamina scabrid beneath; calyx tube becoming globose, wings at most 2 mm wide and not or hardly adnate to the pedicel...........................**1. D. glandulosus**

1. Dipterocarpus glandulosus Thw., Enum. Pl. Zeyl. 34. 1858; Dyer in Hook. f., Fl. Br. Ind. 1: 297. 1872; Trimen, Handb. Fl. Ceylon 1: 115. 1893; Alston in id. 6: 23. 1931; Lewis, Trees and Fl. Pl. of W. and Sab. Prov. 28. 1902; Worthington, Ceylon Trees 47. 1959. Type: *C.P. 2590*.

Dipterocarpus scabridus Thw., l.c.; Dyer, id. 298; Trimen, l.c.; Lewis, l.c.; Alston, id. 22. Lectotype: *C.P. 2692* (PDA).

Large evergreen trees, –45 m tall, –3 m girth, with low rounded concave buttresses and large emergent spreading crown. Bark surface pale orange-brown, verrucose-lenticellate, thinly irregularly flaky. Buds, stipules, twigs, leaf nerves and midrib on both surfaces and petiole, raceme, flower calyx, parts of petals exposed in bud, and nut densely persistently golden-brown scabrid pubescent, intercostals below and fruit calyx sparsely so. Twig c. 2 mm diam. apically, slender. Leaf bud –10 × 3 mm, falcate-lanceolate, acute. Stipule –3.5 × 1 cm, lanceolate. Lamina 6.5–13 × 3–6.5 cm, narrowly elliptic to lanceolate, coriaceous, relatively applanate, with cuneate base and –1 cm long slender tapering acumen; nerves 9–13 pairs, slender but prominent below, evident but unraised above as also the midrib, straight, ascending; intercostals slender, densely subscalarifom; petiole 1.5–2.5 cm long, c. 2 mm diam., slender, prominently geniculate. Raceme –5 cm long, c. 2 mm diam., slender, few-flowered, little branched; flower bud –15 × 5 mm, fusiform; stamens 15; appendage to connective equal to anthers; style and stylopodium columnar, pubescent in the basal half. Fruit pedicel –8 mm long but variable, slender; 2 longer calyx lobes –10 × 2 cm, oblanceolate, obtuse, tapering to c. 6 mm wide above the tube; 3 shorter lobes –11 × 5 mm, ovate; tube –1.8 cm diam., subglobose, with 5, –2 mm wide, narrow ribs. Sapling lamina –35 × 10 cm, with narrowly obtuse base, –4 cm long slender acumen, more or less prominently dentate distal margin, and –22 pairs of nerves.

D i s t r. S.W. Ceylon, widespread; Ambagamuwa, Kitulgala, Siyane Korale, Kuruwita Korale, Karawita, Ratnapura, Kanneliya, Bambarabotuwa, Balangoda, Rakwana, Kottawa.

E c o l. Scattered in Mixed Dipterocarp forest on deep well-drained soils below 1000 m alt. Exterminated by tappers in many forests. Flowering in March and April, at long intervals.

U s e s. Tapped for its oily resin, Dorana Tel.

V e r n. Dorana.

S p e c i m e n s E x a m i n e d. RATNAPURA DISTRICT: Ambaga-muwa and Ratnapura, *s. coll. C.P. 2590* (K, B, PDA); Kandagama, Ratna-pura, *s. coll. C.P. 2692* (PDA, K); Gilimale, *Worthington 3185* (K); Eknali-goda Kande, Karawita, *Ashton 2008* (PDA, US). GALLE DISTRICT: West of Gin Ganga, Hiniduma, *Worthington 2297* (K); Naunkita Ella, Kanneliya F.R., *Worthington 3701, 4150* (K); Galle, *s. coll. 2115* (PDA); Haycock, *Meijer 566* (PDA); Kanneliya, *Meijer 539* (PDA, US), *Cramer 3070* (PDA, US), *s. coll. 292* (PDA); Kottawa natural arboretum, *Ashton 2036, 2037* (PDA). MATARA DISTRICT: Dediyagala Forest Reserve, *Ponnudurai 203* (PDA). KANDY DISTRICT: Base of Adam's Peak, *Meijer 503* (PDA, US).

N o t e. The type of *D. scabridus* consists of leafy twigs from sapling and young trees of this species, with a few fallen fruit of this mixed with some of *D. zeylanicus.*

2. Dipterocarpus hispidus Thw., Enum. Pl. Zeyl. 33. 1858; Dyer in Hook. f., Fl. Br. Ind. 1: 296. 1872; Trimen, Handb. Fl. Ceylon 1: 114. 1893; Alston in id. 6: 22. 1931; Lewis, Trees and Fl. Pl. of W. and Sab. Prov. 27. 1902; Worthington, Ceylon Trees 48. 1959. Lectotype: *C.P. 2903* (PDA).

Dipterocarpus oblongifolius sensu Thw., l.c., non Bl. Type: *C.P. 3405.*
Dipterocarpus oblongus A. DC., Prod. 16: 608. 1868.

Very large tree, –45 m tall –4 m girth, with low rounded buttresses and irregularly dome-shaped large-leaved crown, shortly deciduous and character-istically fresh pale green in February–March. Bark surface orange-brown, flaky. All parts but for stipules within at first densely long golden-brown hispid, fugaceous on upper surface of lamina, caducous on fruit calyx, and becoming scabrid on lamina undersurface. Twigs c. 5–11 mm diam. apically, stout, dark brown. Leaf bud –20 × 12 mm, ovoid, subacute. Stipules –20 × 8 cm, large, oblong-elliptic, obtuse. Lamina (11.5–) 18–50 × (6.5–) 9–26 cm, large, oblong-ovate, somewhat chartaceous and floppy, with cordate base and –12 mm long tapering acumen; nerves 14–24 pairs, ascending, straight, pro-minent below, shallowly depressed above but evident as also the midrib and frequently intercostals; petiole 2–7 cm long, 3–5 mm diam. Flower bud –3.5 × 2 cm, ellipsoid-oblong; stamens 15; appendage to connective shorter than the long slender anthers; style and stylopodium enlarged in the basal half, relatively long pubescent except in the distal third. Raceme –10 cm long, hardly or not branched, bearing –5 distichous shortly pedicellate fruit. Fruit calyx tube –3 cm diam., subglobose, smooth, tapering into the –8 mm long tapering pedicel; 2 longer calyx lobes –17 × 4 cm, spatulate, obtuse; 3 shorter lobes –15 × 9 mm, broadly elliptic, obtuse. Sapling lamina very large, narrowly elliptic-oblong to obovate.

D i s t r. Endemic. Widespread in the wet zone: Kitulgala, Kuruwita, Gilimale, Ratnapura, Kiribatgala, Udakarawita, Rakwana, Kottawa, Kanneliya, Kukul Korale, Sinha Raja Forest, Pasdun Korale, Valley of the Gin Ganga beyond Deniyaya.

E c o l. Locally common in Mixed Dipterocarp forest on undulating land below 1000 m, particularly abundant in moist places. Flowering in April, at long intervals.

V e r n. Bu Hora.

S p e c i m e n s E x a m i n e d. RATNAPURA DISTRICT: Kuraipilai Kanda, *s. coll. C.P. 2903* (PDA, K); Ratnapura, *s. coll. C.P. 3405* (PDA, K); Kitulgala, *Worthington 413, 414A* (K), *Ashton 2005* (PDA, US); Rakwana, Orangefield Estate, *Worthington 2141* (K); Gilimale F.R., *Meijer 421* (PDA, US). GALLE DISTRICT: Nellowe-Pelwatte Road, Ashton *2078* (PDA); Kottawe, *Wijesinghe 80* (PDA), *s. coll. 291* (PDA).

N o t e. The type of *D. oblongifolius* Thw. consists of fallen fruit of *D. hispidus*, with leafy twigs with very young fruit which are atypical for this species in the relatively small size of the lamina (in parentheses in the description), hardly raised intercostals and obtuse base. This, plus the evident ribs on the calyx tube, suggests that the specimen may have been collected from a hybrid with possibly *D. glandulosus*. I consequently chose the fruit only as the lectotype.

3. Dipterocarpus insignis Thw., Enum. Pl. Zeyl. 34. 1858; Dyer in Hook. f., Fl. Br. Ind. 1: 298. 1872; Trimen, Handb. Fl. Ceylon 1: 116. 1893. Type: *C.P. 3406*.

Very large evergreen tree, –45 m tall, –4.5 m girth, with –2 × 2 m almost straight rounded buttresses. Bark surface pale chocolate-brown, becoming thickly flaky, pale lenticellate. Leaf and stipule outside densely persistently rufous hispid, young twig, petiole and sometimes bud caducously so; lamina nerves and midrib below and base of raceme sparsely caducously so; petals outside densely buff pubescent; otherwise glabrous. Twig c. 4 mm diam. apically, stout, pale brown, verruculose, much branched. Leaf bud –6 × 5 mm, stoutly ellipsoid, obtuse. Lamina 7–12 × 4–6 cm, ovate to elliptic, coriaceous, with narrowly to broadly obtuse base and –8 mm long tapering acumen; margin sinuate in the distal half; nerves 10–12 pairs, straight, ascending especially distally, prominent beneath, shallowly depressed between the subpersistent plicate folds of the lamina above as also the midrib; intercostals very slender, densely scalariform; petiole 1.5–2.3 cm long, c. 2 mm diam. Raceme –8 cm long, axillary, lax, hardly branched; flower buds –3.5 × 1 cm, ellipsoid; calyx glabrous, winged; stamens c. 37, very slender and long, the appendage shorter than the anthers; style and stylopodium long and slender, columnar, shortly puberulent except at apex. Fruit pedicel –4 mm long, c. 2 mm diam.; 2 longer fruit calyx lobes –9.5 × 2 cm, lorate, hardly tapering at base and to the obtuse apex; 3 shorter lobes –5 × 6 mm, sinuate; calyx tube –3 × 2 cm including the wings, fusiform, the wings –7 mm wide, continuing below the base and adnate with the –7 mm long pedicel. Seedling lamina –18 × 5 cm, oblanceolate, with cuneate base and –3 cm long caudate acumen; petiole c. 1 cm long. Young tree lamina –24 × 11 cm, narrowly elliptic, with –17 pairs of nerves.

D i s t r. Endemic. Scattered and widespread but never common in the wet zone; Gilimale; Ratnapura; Hewesse; Pasdun Korale; Kanneliya F.R.; Hiniduma; Nellowe.

E c o l. In Mixed Dipterocarp forest on undulating land, often on soils with a high water table. Flowering in April at infrequent intervals.

S p e c i m e n s   E x a m i n e d. RATNAPURA DISTRICT: Ratnapura, *s. coll. C.P. 3406* (PDA, B, K); Gilimale, *Ashton 2019* (PDA,US). GALLE DISTRICT: Hiniduma, West of Gin Ganga, *Worthington 2296* (K); Kanneliya F.R., *Ashton 2049* (PDA, US); Nellowe-Pelawatte Road, *Ashton 2076* (PDA, US).

N o t e. The sapling twig mounted on some sheets of *C.P. 3406* belongs to *D. zeylanicus.*

4. Dipterocarpus zeylanicus Thw., Enum. Pl. Zeyl. 33. 1858; Dyer in Hook. f., Fl. Br. Ind. 1: 297. 1872; Trimen, Handb. Fl. Ceylon 1: 114. 1893; Alston in id. 6: 22. 1931; Lewis, Trees and Fl. Pl. of W. and Sab. Prov. 27. 1902; Worthington, Ceylon Trees 49. 1959. Lectotype: *C.P. 1921*, Deltotte (PDA).

Dipterocarpus turbinatus sensu Moon, Cat. 42. 1824, non Gaertn. f.

Large evergreen tree, –40 m tall, –4 m girth, with low rounded buttresses; crown densely hemispherical, tending to remain oblong and monopodial if isolated. Bark surface pale orange-brown, at first smooth, pale verrucose lenticellate, becoming thickly patchily irregularly flaky. Young parts more or less densely shortly evenly buff pubescent, caducous on midrib below, petiole, twig and raceme, persistent on buds, stipule outside, ovary and parts of corolla exposed in bud, elsewhere fugaceous. Twig c. 6–10 mm diam. apically, stout, becoming dark brown with prominent pale amplexicaul stipule scars. Leaf bud –15 × 6 mm, lanceolate, acute. Stipule –13 × 3 cm, spatulate, obtuse. Leaves clustered round the twig apices; lamina 10–25 × 7.5–14 cm, fairly large, thickly coriaceous, ovate to elliptic (young trees), drying purplish brown, with obtuse to subcordate base and –6 mm long, broad tapering acumen; nerves 15–18 pairs, straight, ascending, close, prominent beneath, narrowly depressed above; petiole 2–5 cm long, c. 2–3 mm diam. long. Raceme –14 cm long, –3 mm diam. at base when in fruit, axillary, with long branches, hanging in dense pendant masses from near the ends of the twigs; flower bud –25 × 8 mm, fusiform; stamens 15, appendages shorter than anthers; style and stylopodium columnar, pubescent in the basal two-thirds. Fruit calyx tube –2.5 cm diam., subglobose, with 5 more or less prominent ribs or becoming smooth on drying; 2 longer lobes –13 × 3 cm, lorate, obtuse, tapering to c. 8 mm wide at the subauriculate base; 3 shorter lobes –3 × 2 cm, relatively large, oblong, obtuse. Young tree lamina –45 × 16 cm, elliptic; nerves –22 pairs; nerves and midrib beneath, petiole and twig persistently pubescent.

D i s t r. Endemic. Wet and intermediate zones. Widespread below 1000 m alt. in the wet zone, as far north as the base of the Knuckles massif; common.

E c o l. In Mixed Dipterocarp forest on hillslopes and more particularly river banks and well drained alluvium, where it is often gregarious and defines a characteristic forest type; often left standing after removal of the forest for cultivation. Occurring also in a few scattered localities on well drained but permanently moist soils in the intermediate zone, including Lunugala and Moneragala in Uva and Madulkelle, Hatale, in Central Province. Flowering in February, fairly regularly.

U s e s. An important timber tree.

V e r n. Hora.

S p e c i m e n s E x a m i n e d. KANDY DISTRICT: Battegodde and Deltota, *s. coll. C.P. 1921* (B, PDA, K); Royal Botanic Garden, *Alston s.n.*, 26.1.26 (PDA); Peradeniya, *Worthington 6734* (K). MONERAGALA DISTRICT: Moneragala, Potuvil road, mile 28 culvert 3, *Worthington 5439* (K); Siyabalanduwa, *Kanagasabapathy, 886a* (PDA). COLOMBO DISTRICT: Indikada, *Pathirana 1485* (PDA). BADULLA DISTRICT: Lunugala, *Worthington 4084* (K). KEGALLE DISTRICT: Atale, Peradeniya estate, *Meijer 392* (PDA). RATNAPURA DISTRICT: Udakarawita, *Ashton 2023* (PDA, US); Rumbukpitiya, Nawalapitiya-Kitulgala Road, mile 4 culvert 10, *Ashton 2002* (PDA, US); Opatha, *Worthington 6056* (K). GALLE DISTRICT: Kottawe, *s. coll. 256* (PDA). MATARA DISTRICT: Kekanadura, Matara, *d'Almeida 29* (PDA). LOCALITY UNKNOWN: *Ferguson s.n.* (PDA); *s. coll. C.P. 2398* (PDA). DISTRICT UNKNOWN: Handamunawake, *Pereira 115* (PDA).

N o t e. The only flowering collection known to me, *C.P. 2398*, has an unribbed calyx (which occasionally occurs in this species in fruit), and has been identified previously with *D. indicus* Brandis; it is impossible to be certain that it belongs here.

3. HOPEA

Roxb., Pl. Corom. 3: 7. 1819. Type species: *H. odorata* Roxb.

Hopea Roxb., Hort. Beng. 42. 1814, nomen nudum.
Balanocarpus Beddome, For. Man. Bot. 236 bis, 1873.
Doona sensu Burck, Ann. Jard. Bot. Buitenzorg 6: 233. 1877, pro parte,
quoad *D. micrantha* (Hassk.) Burck, *D. javanica* Burck, *D. odorata* (Roxb.)
Burck, non Thw.

Small to large trees; bole sometimes tall but often branching low; buttresses (Ceylon spp.) concave, rounded; crown in small species persistently lanceolate, monopodial, the branches more or less pendant, becoming densely evenly hemispherical in large trees, with many small straight branches radiating from the bole apex, or dense, oblong, and irregular. Bark surface at first smooth, chocolate and grey mottled, hoop-marked, remaining so or becoming cracked and flaked, often irregular-section fissured; inner bark yellow-brown or red-brown, close-textured; sapwood pale or dark yellow, soft or hard; heart chocolate-brown (Ceylon spp.). Parts with or without an indumentum of broad or narrow lobed hairs. Twig slender, usually branching horizontally; stipule scars small, inconspicuous. Stipules acicular, fugaceous. Lamina small- to medium-sized; nerves scalariform (Ceylon spp.) with scalariform or reticulate intercostals; petiole hardly geniculate. Inflorescence paniculate, slender, terminal or axillary; flower buds small, ovoid; sepals imbricate, the outer 2 more or less obtuse, thickened, the 3 inner suborbicular, frequently mucronate, thin at the margins; petals oblong, connate and urceolate at the base, falling in a rosette; stamens (10–) 15, subequal in 3 verticils, falling with the petals; filaments broad and compressed at the base, tapering medially and filiform below the anthers; anthers subglobose, tapering apically, with 4 pollen sacs, the outer pair somewhat the larger; appendage to connective slender, glabrous; ovary ovoid to conical, with indistinct stylopodium, tapering into a generally short style (Ceylon spp.) with minute stigma. Fruit relatively small; 2 outer fruit calyx lobes prolonged, spatulate, 3 inner lobes short, or 5 short, subequal; lobes thickened and saccate at base as in *Shorea*; nut ovoid, apiculate, with thin pericarp (Ceylon spp.). Pericarp splitting irregularly at germination (Ceylon spp.); germination epigeal; cotyledons subequal, photosynthetic; first pair of leaves opposite, followed by a whorl of 3 or spiral leaves.

D i s t r. c. 110 species, from Ceylon eastwards to New Guinea and the Louisiade archipelago but avoiding drier areas. 4 species in Ceylon, occurring, each with its own characteristic ecological and geographical distribution, both in the wet and intermediate zones, often very commonly, below 1000 m altitude.

Ethnobotanical and economic information is included under each species.

Note. The type section and subsection is the only one represented in Ceylon.

KEY TO THE SPECIES

1 Fruit sepals not accrescent in fruit, shorter than the nut; intercostals reticulate........
....1. H. brevipetiolaris
1 2 fruit sepals accrescent in fruit, aliform
  2 Lamina base cordate or peltate; intercostals reticulate...............2. H. cordifolia
  2 Lamina base cuneate, intercostals scalariform
    3 Nerves at least 5 pairs; lamina undersurface coppery lepidote..........3. H. discolor
    3 Nerves 3–4 pairs; lamina undersurface glabrous.....................4. H. jucunda

1. Hopea brevipetiolaris (Thw.) Ashton, Blumea 20 (2): 359. 1972. Type: *C.P. 4008*.

Shorea brevipetiolaris Thw. in Trimen, J. Bot. 23: 205. 1885; Worthington, Ceylon Trees 69. 1959.

Balanocarpus (?) *zeylanicus* Trimen, J. Bot. 27: 161. 1889; Handb. Fl. Ceylon 1: 130. 1893.

Balanocarpus brevipetiolaris (Thw.) Alston in Trimen, Handb. Fl. Ceylon 6: 26. 1931.

Medium sized tree, –35 m tall, –3 m girth, coppicing at base; bole of irregular shape, branching low, with a few large ascending branches and dense irregular crown, with semi-pendant twigs; buttresses low, concave, rounded. Bark surface becoming tawny brown, irregularly scaly; outer bark thin, tawny brown; inner bark pale yellow-brown; sapwood dark yellow, heart chocolate-brown, hard. Young parts densely buff puberulent, fugaceous except on panicles and fruit. Twigs c. 1–2 mm diam. apically, slender. Leaf bud minute. Lamina 5–14 × 3–7 cm, coriaceous, lustrous, drying tawny-brown, with subequal obtuse to typically cordate base and –3 cm long slender acumen; nerves 5–7 pairs, slender, arched, somewhat sinuate and frequently bifurcating apically, slender but prominent beneath, obscurely depressed above; intercostals reticulate, more or less obscure; midrib prominent beneath, evident but shallowly depressed above; petiole 4–13 mm long, c. 2 mm diam., typically short. Panicles –18 cm long, c. 1 mm diam. at base, slender, terminal or axillary, singly branched, spreading, the branches –5 cm long bearing –8 small pale yellow flowers; flower buds –3 × 3 mm, ovoid; sepals subequal, broadly ovate, subacute; corolla at anthesis –6 mm diam., petals oblong-ovate; stamens 10 or 15 (on the same plant), anthers subglobose, connectival appendage slender, as long as the anther; ovary ovoid-conical, tapering into the short style. Fruit pedicel –3 mm long, slender; fruit –13 × 10 mm, ovoid, apiculate, subtended by –6 × 5 mm subequal elliptic obtuse sepals. Sapling twigs and petiole densely persistently buff pubescent; lamina somewhat bullate between the nerves; petiole as short as 2 mm, very short, stout.

D i s t r. Known only from Doluwe Kande, Dunkande and adjacent hills N.E. of Kurunegala, in the intermediate zone.

E c o l. Common along the upper parts of the ridge in semi-evergreen forest between 500–700 m. Flowering in April, apparently regularly.

U s e s. As its name suggests, the resin is much sought after.

V e r n. Dunmala.

S p e c i m e n s E x a m i n e d. KURUNEGALA DISTRICT: Doluwa Kande, *s. coll. C.P. 4008* (PDA, K), *s. coll. s.n.*, in September 1888 (PDA), *Ashton 2053* (PDA), *Jayasuriya* and *Balasubramaniam 537, 540* (PDA), *Meiier 372* (PDA); Dunkande, Arankele, Kurunegala, *Jayasuriya* and *Balasubramaniam 527* (PDA). KANDY DISTRICT: Royal Botanical Gardens, Peradeniya, cultivated, *de Silva s.n.*, 26.8.18 (PDA), *s. coll. s.n.*, April 1884 (K), *de Silva 49, 51* (PDA), *s. coll. s.n.*, January 1888 (PDA), *Livera s.n.*, June 1923 (PDA), *Worthington 6821* (K), *Ashton 2105* (PDA), *Meijer 819* (PDA).

N o t e. The type is from a young plant, hence Trimen's caution in identifying it with material collected later, presumably by himself. The name *Balanocarpus zeylanicus* was coined by Trimen when he transferred the species from *Shorea*, presumably on the basis of the unnumbered material collected in 1888, in the Peradeniya herbarium.

2. Hopea cordifolia (Thw.) Trimen, Handb. Fl. Ceylon 1: 126. 1893; Alston in id. 6: 25. 1931; Lewis, Trees and Fl. Pl. of W. and Sab. Prov. 34. 1902; Worthington, Ceylon Trees 63. 1959. Type: *C.P. 3726.*

Vatica (?) *cordifolia* Thw., Enum. Pl. Zeyl. 404. 1864; Dyer in Hook. f., Fl. Br. Ind. 1: 303. 1872.
Isauxis cordifolia Hook. f., Fl. Br. Ind. 1: 722. 1874.

Large tree, –30 m tall, –3 m girth, with crooked or straight bole, low rounded buttresses, and dense oblong to irregular crown with a few large spreading branches; bark surface grey-brown, becoming prominently irregular-section fissured and flaking in small oblong pieces; outer bark thick, dark brown to pale brown at the rhytidome; sapwood hard, dark yellow, heart chocolate-brown. Leaf bud, twig and petiole densely pale tawny puberulent, caducous on petiole; parts of corolla exposed in bud persistently pubescent; otherwise glabrous. Twig c. 2–3 mm diam. apically, terete, becoming dark brown. Leaf buds minute, ovoid. Lamina 8–21 × 4.5–12.5 cm, ovate-falcate, coriaceous, more or less lustrous, drying pale chocolate-brown, with prominently cordate base and tapering subacute to –2 cm long broadly acuminate apex; nerves 6–9 pairs, the first 2–3 pairs arising together from the base, arched, slender but prominent below, elevated above, with a few short intermediates; intercostals subreticulate, slightly elevated on both surfaces; midrib prominent beneath, evident but applanate to slightly elevated above; petiole

1.5–2.5 cm long, c. 3 mm diam., stout. Panicles –10 cm long, –2 mm diam. at base, –2 axillary, with –5 cm long branches bearing –6 secund flowers; flowers pale yellow; buds –6 × 4 mm, ovoid; sepals ovate, acute to subacuminate, at first equal; corolla at anthesis –8 mm diam., petals oblong-ovate; stamens 15, with slender connectival appendages twice as long as the anthers; ovary ovoid-conical, glabrous, tapering into the short glabrous style. Fruit pedicel –2 mm long, short; 2 longer sepals –9.5 × 2.5 cm, broadly spatulate, obtuse, tapering to c. 6 mm broad above the –7 × 6 mm ovate saccate thickened base; 3 shorter lobes –12 × 8 mm, ovate, obscured by larger lobes; nut completely enclosed in calyx, –12 × 7 mm, narrowly ovoid, tapering into the prominent style remnant. Sapling and young tree lamina peltate, with frequently shorter petiole and prominently pubescent petiole, and nerves and midrib below.

D i s t r. Endemic. Locally abundant in gallery forest along the Walawe and Kirindi Oyas and their tributaries in the dry zone of Uva; particularly in the Tanamalwila and Kuda Oya area on the Kirindi, and Uggalkaltota on the Walawe.

E c o l. Flowering in April, apparently regularly.

U s e s. Not apparently used as timber, though the resin is collected.

V e r n. Mendora, Uva Mendora.

S p e c i m e n s   E x a m i n e d. MONERAGALA DISTRICT: Wellawaya road near Doonking, *s. coll. C.P. 3726* (PDA, K); Kirinelli ganga, Tanamalwila, *Broun s.n.* May 1891 (PDA); Tanamalwila, Kuda Oya, *Worthington 2992* (K), *Andiris 1033* (PDA); Kirindi Oya, *Worthington 2996, 5692* (K), *Ashton 2079, 2080, 2081* (PDA, US), *Meijer 190* (PDA, US), *A.G.W. de Silva 741* (PDA); Uda Walawe, *Balakrishnan & Jayasuriya 898* (PDA, US). RATNAPURA DISTRICT: Walawe Oya at Uggalkaltota, *Worthington 3311* (K). DISTRICT UNKNOWN: Beligantota F.R. *B.F.O. 1038* (PDA). LOCALITY UNKNOWN: *Lewis s.n.*, August 1900 (PDA); *Lewis s.n.*, 6.5.1912 (PDA, K).

3. Hopea discolor Thw., Enum. Pl. Zeyl. 36. 1858; Dyer in Hook. f., Fl. Br. Ind. 1: 310. 1872; Trimen, Handb. Fl. Ceylon 1: 125. 1893; Alston in id. 6: 25. 1931; Lewis, Trees and Fl. Pl. of W. and Sab. Prov. 33. 1902. Lectotype: *C.P. 3125.*

Elegant large tree, –45 m tall, –4 m girth, with diffuse dome-shaped crown coppery from below especially in fresh leaf, with many slender straight radiating branches; buttresses –2 m tall, –1.5 m long, concave, thin. Bark surface dark reddish brown with grey lichen dappling on old surfaces, deeply irregular-section fissured at c. 2 cm intervals, the intervening ridges flaky; outer bark dark brown with paler areas towards the rhytidome layer; inner bark red-brown, fibrous; sapwood hard, dark straw-yellow; heartwood dark brown. Twigs, leaf buds, petiole and lamina undersurface pinkish coppery lepidote, parts of petals exposed in bud pubescent, otherwise glabrous. Twig c. 1 mm diam. apically, slender but much branched, becoming black. Leaf bud minute. Lamina 4–7 × 1.3–3.5 cm, ovate-lanceolate, coriaceous, drying chocolate-brown above, pale pinkish beneath with black nerves and midrib, with revolute margin, broadly cuneate subequal base and –2 cm long slender acumen; nerves 6–7 pairs, ascending, relatively straight, slender but prominent beneath, obscurely depressed above; intercostals obscurely densely scalariform; midrib prominent beneath, evident but depressed above; petiole 6–10 mm long, c. 1 mm diam., slender. Panicles –5 cm long, c. 1 mm diam. at base, terminal or axillary, with –1 cm long branches bearing –3 flowers. Flower buds –3 × 3 mm, ovoid; sepals deltoid, subacute, subequal; petals oblong-ovate; stamens 15, with connectival appendage almost twice as long as anthers; ovary ovoid-conical, glabrous, tapering into the short style. Fruit pedicel –4 mm long, slender; 2 longer fruit sepals –6 × 1.4 cm, spatulate, subacute, tapering to c. 2 mm broad above the –6 × 4 mm ovate saccate thickened base; 3 shorter lobes –8 × 5 mm, ovate, acuminate; nut –10 × 7 mm, ovoid, apiculate, exceeding shorter sepals and with the apex exposed. Sapling lamina –11 × 4 cm, chartaceous, not lepidote; petiole 4–8 mm long, short.

D i s t r. Endemic: Rare; Bambarabotuwa Eknaligoda and Kiribatgala, Ratnapura district; Hiniduma Pattuwa.

E c o l. In small groups with plentiful regeneration on ridges and shallow acid soils in Mixed Dipterocarp forest between 300 and 800 m alt. Flowering in April, gregariously at irregular intervals.

U s e s. Popular as a construction timber.

V e r n. Rata Dun, Peely Dun.

S p e c i m e n s E x a m i n e d. RATNAPURA DISTRICT: Eknaligoda near Ratnapura, *s. coll. C.P. 3125* (PDA, K, B); Kiribatgala, Pelmadulla, *Ashton 2118, 2119* (PDA, US); Karawita kande, *Ashton 2261* (PDA); Bambarabotuwe F.R. *Meijer 431* (PDA, US); GALLE DISTRICT: Hiniduma kanda, *Worthington 2288, 2289* (K); Kanneliya F.R., *Meijer 560* (PDA).

N o t e. *C.P. 2970*, quoted in the original description, consists of fallen fruits of *H. jucunda*, with a single fallen leaf which is not from a Dipterocarp.

4. Hopea jucunda Thw., Enum. Pl. Zeyl. 403. 1864; Dyer in Hook. f., Fl. Br. Ind. 1: 310. 1872; Trimen, Handb. Fl. Ceylon 1: 125. 1893; Alston in id. 6: 25. 1931; Lewis, Trees and Fl. Pl. of W. and Sab. Prov. 33–34. 1902. (ssp. *modesta*); Worthington, Ceylon Trees 65. 1959. Type: *C.P. 3709*.

Medium-sized tree, –25 m tall, –2 m girth; crown dense, more or less oblong, with branches sometimes somewhat pendant; buttresses low, rounded, concave; bark surface becoming purplish brown, flaky; inner bark pale brown, sapwood pale yellow, moderately soft, with pale brown heart. Twigs, buds and petioles caducous buff puberulent; parts of petals exposed in bud persistently pubescent. Twig c. 1 mm diam., slender, becoming blackish. Lamina 3.5–11 × 1.5–5.5 cm, ovate, with broadly cuneate subequal base and –2 cm long slender caudate acumen; nerves 3–4 pairs, arched, ascending, slender but more or less prominent beneath, obscurely depressed above, with prominent pubescent axillary domatia; intercostals very slender, obscure, densely scalariform; midrib prominent beneath, evident but more or less applanate above; petiole 5–12 mm long, 1–2 mm diam., relatively short and slender. Panicles –11 cm long, –2 mm diam. at base, with –1.5 cm long branches bearing –4 flowers; sepals broadly ovate, subacute; corolla at anthesis –1 cm diam., petals lanceolate; stamens 15, with long slender connectival appendage; ovary ovoid, with more or less prominent columnar style. Fruit pedicel –2 mm long, short; 2 longer sepals –8 × 2.5 cm, obtuse, tapering to c. 3 mm broad above the –10 × 6 mm ovate, saccate, thickened base; 3 shorter lobes –6 × 6 mm, broadly ovate, mucronate; nut –15 × 10 mm, ovoid, apiculate, often resincoated. Sapling leaves as in mature tree.

D i s t r. Widespread on the lowland hills of the wet zone below 1000 m altitude.

E c o l. Flowering in April, gregariously at irregular intervals.

Two ecotypic subspecies are recognised:

1. ssp. **jucunda**

Lamina never smaller than 6 × 3.5 cm; connectival appendage c. 5 times as long as anther; style twice as long as ovary; otherwise as in description.

D i s t r. Throughout the range of the species.

E c o l. Locally frequent, especially by streams and on hillsides in deep shade.

V e r n. Rat beraliya.

S p e c i m e n s E x a m i n e d. GALLE DISTRICT: Hiniduma, Naunkita Ella, *Worthington 4153* (K); Kanneliya F.R., Hiniduma, *Worthington 6038* (K), *Ashton 2042* (PDA, US); Nellowe-Pellawatte road, *Ashton 2067* (PDA, US); Nakiyadeniya, *de Rosayro 1422* (PDA). KALUTARA DISTRICT: Hewesse, Maraipalai, Pasdun Korale, *s. coll. C.P. 3709*, (PDA, K, B). KEGALLE DISTRICT: Kitulgala forest, *Ashton 2004* (PDA, US). RATNA-PURA DISTRICT: 2 miles S.W. of Ratnapura Kanda, *Worthington 6473* (K); Sinha Raja Forest at Veddagala, *Ashton 2029* (PDA, US), *Meijer 904* (PDA, US); Sinha Raja Forest, *de Rosayro 1424, 1429* (PDA). KANDY DISTRICT: Peradeniya, Royal Botanical Gardens, *Worthington 6823, 4218, 4039* (K), *de Silva 62, 70, 81* (PDA, K), *Meijer 382* (PDA, US); Amba-gamuwa (leaf excepted), *s. coll. C.P. 2970* (PDA). COLOMBO DISTRICT:

Labugama catchment forest, *Ashton 2057* (PDA, US); Indikade Mukulana, *Pieris 1245* (PDA), *de Rosayro 2017* (PDA). LOCALITY UNKNOWN: *Lewis s.n.*, 26. 7. 1912 (PDA).

2. ssp. modesta DC., Prod. 16 (2): 633, 1868. Type: *C.P. 3710.*

Small smooth-barked tree. Lamina never exceeding 7 × 3.5 cm with the nerves hardly elevated beneath; panicles not exceeding 9 cm long, very slender; corolla at anthesis –6 mm diam.; staminal appendage up to twice as long as anther; style shorter than ovary; 2 longer fruit sepals –4.5 × 0.8 cm, nut –7 × 5 mm.

D i s t r. S.W. part of wet zone; Karawita Kande, Yagirella F.R., Pasdun Korale, Hiniduma Pattuwa, Kottawe F.R.

E c o l. More or less confined to relatively light conditions on ridge tops on leached and skeletal soils.

V e r n. Pini beraliya.

S p e c i m e n s E x a m i n e d. KALUTARA DISTRICT: Lihinigala, Hewesse, Pasdun Korale, *s. coll. s.n.* March 1887 (PDA); Haycock, *Cramer 3083* (PDA, US). KANDY DISTRICT: Peradeniya, Royal Botanical Gardens, *Worthington 4219* (K), *de Silva 61, 64* (PDA, K), *Meijer 384* (PDA, US). RATNAPURA DISTRICT: Karawita, F.R., *Ashton 2136* (PDA, US); Base of Adam's Peak, *Worthington 5516* (K). GALLE DISTRICT: Hiniduma, Kunaliella, *Worthington 2322* (K); Nellowe, *Ashton 2077* (PDA, US); Nellowe-Pelawatte road, *Ashton 2093* (PDA, US); Kottawe Natural Arboretum, *Ashton 2035* (PDA, US), *Rajalingam 172* (PDA); Beraliya F.R. *Illeperuma 507* (PDA); Kanneliya F.R., *Meijer 970* (PDA, US). LOCALITY UNKNOWN: *s. coll. C.P. 3710* (PDA, K, B).

N o t e. The two appear not to hybridise, but young trees are sometimes difficult to identify and mixed populations exist.

4. SHOREA

Roxb. ex Gaertn. f., Fruct. 3: 48. 1805. Type species: *S. robusta* Roxb.

Doona Thw., Hook. J. Bot. 4: 7. 1852. Type species: *D. zeylanica* Thw.
Isoptera Scheff. ex Burck, Med. Lands Pl. Tuin. 3: 27. 1886. Type species:
 Isoptera borneensis Scheff. ex Burck.

Medium sized to large more or less buttressed trees. Mature crown typically large, hemispherical or dome-shaped, sympodial. Bark surface (Ceylon ssp.) flaky or sometimes appearing fissured (*S. stipularis, S. pallida*). Inflorescence paniculate, flowers secund. Sepals free to the receptacle; 3 outer lobes thicker, somewhat longer, narrower, than the 2 inner lobes in flower. Petals usually connate at base on falling (excl. sect. subsect. *Shorea*). Stamens 15 or many (Ceylon spp.), filaments applanate, more or less tapering; anthers subglobose to narrowly oblong, glabrous (Ceylon spp.), sometimes apiculate; connectival appendage short and stout or long and acicular (Ceylon spp.). Ovary glabrous or tomentose, style with or without a distinct stylopodium. Fruit sepals accrescent and aliform, the 3 outer longer and broader than the 2 inner, or short and subequal; base of lobes thickened, expanded, saccate, appressed to the fruit. Fruit free, pericarp splitting irregularly at germination. Germination various.

D i s t r. c. 200 species; Ceylon, southern and eastern India, Chittagong, Burma, Thailand, Indo-China, and Malesia eastwards to Buru. 14 species in Ceylon.

E c o l. With the genus *Dipterocarpus*, dominating the emergent canopy of the primary wet zone forests, where single species often form small gregarious stands—'drifts'—of several hectares extent; a few species (*S. trapezifolia*, *S. zeylanica*, *S. gardneri*) forming pure stands in mid-mountain forests—1800 m altitude, where their majestic crowns often dominated the skyline before they were mostly destroyed in the 19th century; one species (see *S. dyeri*) in the intermediate zone.

None flower annually; each has its own characteristic flowering time and periodicity; though sporadic flowering occurs every year (mostly between March and June) certain years witness heavy gregarious flowering. The fruits resulting from sporadic flowering are almost entirely eaten by parakeets, squirrels and pigs, and destroyed.

U s e s. The genus provides some of the best construction and plywood timbers in the wet zone (see under section and species descriptions).

V e r n. Dun is applied to all species in this genus (and often *Hopea* too). Other names, such as Beraliya, Yakahalu, are applied to different species in different localities.

KEY TO THE SPECIES

1 Petals falling separately; stamens at least 20; connectival appendage setose; style shorter than ovary; inner bark not laminated; flushes of young leaves pale green.............
....Section 1 and Subsection **Shorea**
  2 Fruit sepals subequal, shorter than fruit; lamina thickly coriaceous, lustrous, very broad, with prominently revolute margin and nerves depressed above..**2. S. lissophylla**
  2 Fruit sepals unequal, aliform, exceeding fruit; lamina not as above
    3 Lamina white lepidote beneath, with minute pore-like domatia; bark deeply fissured, dark brown...**4. S. pallescens**
    3 Lamina generally lustrous beneath; domatia not as above; bark flaky, yellow-brown
      4 Lamina oblong-ovate, with cordate base and prominent nerves below.............
....**3. S. oblongifolia**
      4 Lamina lanceolate, with broadly cuneate to obtuse base and very slender nerves hardly raised below...**1. S. dyeri**

1 Petals falling in a loose rosette; stamens 15; connectival appendage glabrous; style and stylopodium columnar, at least twice as long as ovary; flushes of young leaves red to violet; inner bark more or less distinctly laminated

    5 Connectival appendage acicular, at least thrice as long as anthers; corolla prominently imbricate and contorted, urceolate at base; stipules large, subpersistent..............
....Section 2. **Anthoshoreae 5. S. stipularis**

    5 Connectival appendage clavate, shorter in length than anther; corolla hardly imbricate or contorted, base not urceolate; stipules fugaceous in mature trees....Section 3. **Doona**

      6 Midrib raised above in mature tree...............................**8. S. cordifolia**

      6 Midrib obscure, depressed above, in mature trees

       7 Margin prominently revolute at base

        8 Lamina ovate, with obtuse to cordate base (if unrolled) and tapering acumen; main nerves with single short intermediates; intercostals scalariform; twigs ascending...
....**10. S. gardneri**

        8 Lamina lanceolate, with cuneate base (if unrolled) and slender caudate acumen; main nerves with 1 long and 2 short intermediates between each; intercostals reticulate; twigs pendant.......................................**15. S. zeylanica**

       7 Margin, if revolute, not more so at the base than elsewhere

        9 Lamina small, lanceolate; nerves very slender, with many intermediates the longer ones of which almost equal to main nerves; intercostals subreticulate............
....**6. S. affinis**

        9 Lamina ovate to elliptic; nerves, if slender, with not more than 3, short, intermediates between each; intercostals scalariform

         10 Lamina small, chartaceous, broadly ovate, caudate............**12. S. ovalifolia**

         10 Lamina more or less coriaceous, not caudate

          11 Lamina distinctly trapeziform, with very slender but distinctly elevated nerves and intercostals almost equally elevated on both surfaces; midrib below slender but sharply ribbed; sapling petiole and twigs prominently pubescent..........
....**13. S. trapezifolia**

          11 Lamina elliptic-oblong, nerves not as above; midrib stout, more or less terete not sharp below; saplings glabrous

           12 Mature tree lamina exceeding 12×5.5 cm...............**11. S. megistophylla**

           12 Mature lamina -11×4.5 cm

            13 Young twigs and inflorescences persistently golden pubescent..**9. S. disticha**

            13 Young twigs and inflorescences glabrescent

             14 Leaf drying coppery brown; inner bark pale brown......**14. S. worthingtoni**

             14 Leaf drying purplish-brown; inner bark meat red........**7. S. congestiflora**

Section and subsection S H O R E A

Flower buds elongate, lanceolate; petals linear, falling separately; stamens 20–60, in several verticils; appendage to connective shorter than length of anther, with a few bristles; ovary including stylopodium short, ovoid-conical, tomentose, style glabrous, very short. Stipules and bracts fugaceous, small. Bark with pale thick conspicuous phelloderm; expansion tissue in short fingers, more numerous towards outer surface.

D i s t r. Throughout the range of the genus. 4 species in Ceylon, in Mixed Dipterocarp forest, on land not subject to flooding, in the lowlands –1000 m.

This section provides a hard heavy close-grained dark brown wood suitable for construction and decking.

1. Shorea dyeri Thw. in Trimen, J. Bot. 23: 204. 1885; Trimen, Handb. Fl. Ceylon 1: 117. 1893; Worthington, Ceylon Trees 50. 1959. Type: *C.P. 4010*.

Hopea discolor sensu Worthington, id. 64, non Thw.

Large tree, –50 m tall, –4 m girth, with spreading hemispherical emergent crown fresh pale green at leaf change (March); bole tall, straight; buttresses concave, thin, frequently prominent; bark surface pale tawny, irregularly thinly flaky. Twig apices, leaf buds, stipules, panicles, calyx, parts of corolla exposed in bud and ovary densely persistently pale buff puberulent; petiole and lamina midrib and nerves beneath sparsely caducously so, fruit sepals sparsely persistently so. Twig c. 1 mm diam. apically, slender, smooth, becoming dark brown. Leaf bud c. 3 × 1 mm, narrowly ellipsoid, acute. Stipule –7 × 3 mm, ellipsoid, subacute, fugaceous. Lamina 5–13 × 2–5.5 cm, lanceolate-falcate, thinly coriaceous, more or less lustrous, drying mauve-brown above, tawny-brown beneath, with cuneate to obtuse subequal base and –2.5 cm long slender tapering acumen; nerves 11–13 pairs, ascending, very slender and hardly elevated beneath, obscure and applanate to slightly depressed above; intercostals obscure, densely scalariform; midrib slender and prominent below, more or less evident but depressed above; petiole 8–15 mm long, c. 1 mm diam., slender. Panicles –14 cm long, c. 2 mm diam. at base in fruit, slender, terminal or axillary, twice branched, the branchlets short, bearing –4 secund flowers; flower buds –5 × 3 mm, fusiform; sepals ovate, the 3 outer obtuse, the 2 inner subacute; corolla –1 cm diam. at anthesis, hardly contorted, petals oblong-ovate; stamens c. 60, unequal, with densely setose appendage slightly shorter than the anthers, densely clustered around the ovoid ovary; ovary tapering into the stylopodium and short glabrous style. Fruit pedicel 1 mm long, short; 3 longer sepals –7.5 × 1.2 cm, narrowly spatulate, obtuse, tapering to c. 4 mm broad above the –7 × 6 mm ovate saccate thickened base; 2 shorter sepals –3.5 × 0.5 cm, otherwise similar; fruit –10 × 8 mm, small, ovoid, apiculate. Seedlings with long geniculate petioles; sapling lamina –16 × 7 cm, ovate, chartaceous, with more prominent nervation, otherwise similar.

D i s t r. Widespread on the lowland hills of the wet zone from Madulkelle and Kegalle southwards and occurring at Lunugala in Uva.

E c o l. Often common, particularly on skeletal soils on ridge tops, and steep hillsides and spurs and rocky places below 1000 m altitude. Flowering apparently in January, gregariously at long intervals.

V e r n. Yakahalu Dun.

S p e c i m e n s E x a m i n e d. KANDY DISTRICT: Madulkelle, Arratenne, *Worthington 2021* (K); Peradeniya R. Bot. Gardens, cultivated, *Jaya-*

---

wardena 9829, de Silva 65, 75, 87 (PDA, K), *Worthington 3382, 3783* (K); Peak Wilderness, Laxapana, *Worthington 5515* (K). BADULLA DISTRICT: Lunugala, *Worthington 4080, 4081, 2957, 2958* (K), *s. coll. s.n.*, January 1888 (PDA). RATNAPURA DISTRICT: Latpandura-Kalawana Road, mile 30, culvert 1, *Worthington 4622* (K); Ratnapura, *Conservator of Forests, s.n.* January 20, 1919 (PDA); Kuttapitiya, *Worthington 6443* (K); Gilimale forest, *Worthington 3174* (K); Rakwana, Orange Field Estate, *Worthington 3621* (K); Kuruwita, Keragala Estate, *Worthington 3341, 3342, 3343* (K); Bambarabotuwa Forest Reserve, *Ashton 2013* (PDA, US); Kalawana Road, mile 15, culvert 19, *Ashton 2025* (PDA, US); Ratnapura, mile 15, Kadugama Rd., *Meijer 452* (PDA, US). COLOMBO DISTRICT: Indikade Mukalana, Waga, *Worthington 3546, 3547* (K); Labugama Reservoir, *Worthington 3475, 3476, 4383* (K). MATARA DISTRICT: Deniyaya forest *Worthington 3703* (K). GALLE DISTRICT: Nellowe—Pelawatte Road, *Ashton 2070* (PDA, US). DISTRICT UNKNOWN: South of Island, *s. coll. C.P. 4010* (PDA, K).

N o t e. Confused with *Doona cordifolia* by Trimen apparently, at least in herbarium annotations, and with *H. discolor* by Worthington.

2. Shorea lissophylla Thw., Enum. Pl. Zeyl. 402. 1864; Dyer in Hook. f., Fl. Brit. Ind. 1: 307. 1872; Trimen, Handb. Fl. Ceylon 1: 117. 1893; Lewis, Trees and Fl. Pl. of W. and Sab. Prov. 29. 1902; Worthington, Ceylon Trees 51. 1959. Type: *C.P. 3407*.

Isoptera lissophylla (Thw.) Livera, Ann. R. Bot. Gard. Perad. 9: 93. 1924; Alston in Trimen, Handb. Fl. Ceylon 6: 23. 1931.

Curious small tree, –20 m tall, –1 m girth, with crooked bole often branching from the base; crown irregular, dense, dark green, shiny, with twisted branches; buttresses low, concave. Bark surface dark chocolate-brown, coming away in small rectangular flakes. Young twig, leaf bud, stipule, panicle, calyx, parts of petals exposed in bud and ovary densely persistently pale greyish buff puberulent, leaf nervation below and petiole sparsely fugaceously so, inside of petals villous. Twig c. 2–3 mm diam., much branched. Leaf bud c. 3 × 2 mm, small, ovoid-falcate, acute. Stipule –8 × 5 mm, oblong, acute, fugaceous. Lamina 6–17 × 4–10 cm, very variable in size in relation to shade even on one tree, broadly ovate to suborbicular, thickly coriaceous, lustrous, drying mauve-brown above and tawny-brown below, with more or less revolute margin, obtuse to cordate base, and obtuse, mucronate, or –12 mm long acuminate apex; nerves 5–12 pairs, spreading, more or less prominent below, applanate to somewhat depressed above; intercostals more or less obscure, densely scalariform; midrib prominent beneath, evident and elevated to depressed above; petiole 6–12 mm long, c. 3 mm diam., stout. Panicles –10 cm long, c. 2 mm diam. at base, terminal or axillary to ramiflorous, singly branched, the branchlets –3 cm long, bearing –5 secund flowers; flower bud −6 × 3 mm, fusiform; sepals ovate, the 3 outer acute, the 2 inner subacuminate; corolla −1 cm diam. at anthesis, hardly contorted, petals linear-lanceolate, narrowly obtuse, cream; stamens c. 47–52, connectival appendage shorter than the anthers, stout with but 1 (−2) prominent bristles; ovary broadly ovoid, surmounted by a short glabrous style. Fruit pedicel −2 mm long, short; fruit sepals −10 × 7 mm, subequal, ovate, acuminate, loosely clasping but not exceeding the −10 × 9 mm ovoid nut with prominent −4 mm long stylopodium. Seedlings with long geniculate petioles; sapling lamina −18 × 10 cm, oblong-ovate, with nerves very prominent below and −2 cm long petiole.

Distr. Endemic. Very local, from Yagirella F.R. and the Sinha Raja Forest southwards; Karawita; Udagama and Nellowe in Hiniduma Pattu; Maddegatte, S. Province.

Ecol. Occurring in groves, with abundant regeneration, on skeletal soils overlying sheet rock, often hanging over cliffs and more or less permanent water courses. Flowering in April, gregariously at infrequent intervals.

Uses. Too small and of too poor form to be useful.

Vern. Once recorded as Malmora.

Specimens Examined. KANDY DISTRICT: Peradeniya R. Bot. Gardens, cultivated, *Worthington 6822, 6364* (K), *Ashton 2103* (PDA, US), *Livera s.n.* (PDA), *de Silva 53, 60, 96* (PDA), *Meijer 381* (PDA). RATNAPURA DISTRICT: Sinharaja forest, *s. coll. C.P. 3407* (PDA, B, K); Between Maddegatte and Weddagalle, *s. coll. s.n.* (PDA); Karawita F.R., *Ashton 2134* (PDA, US); Karawita kande, *de Silva s.n.* (PDA). KALUTARA DISTRICT: Yagirella, *Broun s.n.* (PDA). GALLE DISTRICT: Beraliya F.R., *Forest Department, 442, 443* (PDA).

Note. Broun's comment that this species was the commonest Dipterocarp on the banks of the Bentota river could not have been correct, for though it occurs, apparently rather uncommonly, in Yagirella F.R., the alluvium which borders the river, now cultivated, could never have been a suitable habitat.

3. **Shorea oblongifolia** Thw., Enum. Pl. Zeyl. 36. 1858; Dyer in Hook. f., Fl. Br. Ind. 1: 307. 1872; Trimen, Handb. Fl. Ceylon 1: 116. 1893; Lewis, Trees and Fl. Pl. of W. and Sab. Prov. 29. 1902; Worthington, Ceylon Trees 52. 1959. Type: *C.P. 3005.*

Doona oblonga sensu Worthington, Ceylon Trees 58. 1959, non Thw.

A large tree, −40 m tall, −5 m girth, with rather small concave thin buttresses; bole often branching low, crooked, sometimes tall and straight, stout. Crown dense, irregularly oblong to hemispherical. Bark surface tawny-brown, irregularly thinly flaking. Twigs, petioles, leaf bud, stipules, midrib above, panicles, parts of petals exposed in bud and ovary densely persistently greyish buff puberulent; sepals at first densely so, becoming sparse in fruit; lamina nervation below sparsely caducously so; petals within villous. Twig c. 2–3 mm diam. apically, at first ribbed, becoming terete, grey-brown. Leaf bud –4 × 3 mm, ovoid, subacute. Stipule –6 × 3 mm, oblong, subacute, fugaceous. Lamina 10–19 × 4–7 cm, oblong, coriaceous, drying pale mauve-brown above, tawny below or occasionally glaucous, with deeply cordate base, frequently subrevolute margin, and –2 cm long prominent tapering acumen; nerves 13–16 pairs, very prominent beneath, more or less shallowly depressed above; intercostals scalariform, evident and elevated beneath, obscure above; midrib very prominent beneath, more or less evident but depressed above; petiole 1–2 cm long, c. 2 mm diam. Panicle –13 cm long, c. 2 mm diam. at base, axillary to ramiflorous, singly branched, the –3 cm long branchlets bearing –6 flowers; flower buds –5 × 2 mm, fusiform; sepals ovate, subacute; petals cream with a pinkish base, lanceolate, narrowly obtuse; stamens c. 60, subequal; connectival appendage stout, shorter than anther, with c. 3 terminal bristles; ovary and stylopodium ovoid, surmounted by a short glabrous style. Fruit pedicel –2 mm long, short, stout; 3 longer fruit sepals –6 × 2 cm, broadly spatulate, obtuse, tapering to c. 6 mm broad above the –8 × 6 mm elliptic saccate thickened base; 2 shorter lobes –4 × 1 cm, otherwise similar. Fruit –2 × 1.4 cm, ovoid-ellipsoid, prominently apiculate. Seedling leaves with long slender geniculate petioles; sapling lamina –20 × 14 cm, less coriaceous than that of mature tree.

D i s t r. Common throughout the lowland hills of the wet zone in Mixed Dipterocarp forest –700 m altitude.

E c o l. Often abundant on moist lower slopes, particularly where rocky, and on river banks including alluvium; running up the hillsides and overlapping there with the ecological range of *S. dyeri*. Flowering in April–June, gregariously at irregular intervals.

U s e s. A useful potential construction timber.

S p e c i m e n s   E x a m i n e d. RATNAPURA DISTRICT: Sinharaja forest, Eknaligoda, *s. coll. C.P. 3005* (PDA); Kahawatte near Ratnapura, *Livera s.n.* (PDA); Gilimale forest, Ratnapura, *Miejer 432* (PDA), *Worthington 4833* (K); Sinharaja via Hiniduma, *Worthington 3671* (K); Weddagala, Sinharaja, *Meijer 519* (PDA, US); Kutapitiya jungle, Palmadulla, *Worthington 6444* (PDA). GALLE DISTRICT: Hinidoom, *s. coll. C.P. 3005* (PDA); Beraliya forest near Elpitiya, *R.F.O. Elpitiya, s.n.*, 19.8.1940 (PDA); Hinidoom, *s. coll. s.n.* (PDA); Hiniduma, Kunelli Ella, *Worthington 2326* (K), *Ashton 2098* (PDA, US); Ithandukita near Nellowe, *Ashton 2064* (PDA, US); Kanneliya forest reserve, *Ashton 2043* (PDA, US); Udugama Rest House, *Worthington 2336, 6613* (K), *Ashton 2040* (PDA, US), *Koelmeyer and de Rosayro 1426* (PDA), *Cramer 3082* (PDA US); Kottawe, *de Rosayro 2083, 2089* (PDA);

Nakiyadeniya, *de Rosayro 2020* (PDA). KANDY DISTRICT: Peradeniya Royal Botanical Gardens, cultivated, *Worthington 6835, 6363* (K), *de Silva 76, 253* (PDA, K). COLOMBO DISTRICT: Labugama kande, *Broun s.n.,* 18.2.90 (PDA); Puvakpitiya-Tummodera Road, *Jayawardena 9834* (PDA); Ingiriya, Padukka, *Livera s.n.* (PDA); Kalatuwawa catchment, *Worthington 3538* (K); Labugama F.R. *Worthington 3491, 3492* (K). KALUTARA DISTRICT: Hewesse, Pelawatte, *Worthington 6599* (K); Moragala, Pasdun Korale, *s. coll. s.n., 1883* (PDA); Haycock, *Meijer 573* (PDA, US), *Cramer 3088* (PDA, US). MATARA DISTRICT: Hulandawa Ganga, Morowaka, *Worthington 2233, 3666* (K); Taunahena, Hulandawa Ganga, Worthington *3663* (K). DISTRICT UNKNOWN: Mondeli Kande, *de Silva s.n.,* 25.4.28 (PDA). LOCALITY UNKNOWN: *s. coll. C.P. 3505* (K).

N o t e. Occasionally a form occurs with markedly white lepidote lamina under-surface; this is represented by *Meijer 423* and *Worthington 6444*, and occurs also at Kiribatgalla and elsewhere; without flowers its status remains obscure, but it may represent a hybrid between this and *S. pallescens.*

4. Shorea pallescens Ashton, Blumea 20 (2): 360. 1972. Holotype: *Worthington 4869* (K; dupl. in US, L).

Shorea dealbata Alston, nomen in herb., non Foxw.; de Rosayro, Ceylon Forester 1, 2: 80. 1953.

A large tree, –45 m tall, –3 m girth; crown large, emergent, hemispherical, pale from below, with large ascending branches; bole tall, straight, cylindrical; buttresses –3 m tall and long, large, concave, thin. Bark surface mauve-brown, becoming deeply persistently fissured, the intervening ridges coming away in irregular small flakes; outer bark thick, dark chocolate-brown with pale brown lacunae between fissures; inner bark pale brown, hard, homogeneous; sapwood straw yellow, hard, heartwood dark chocolate brown. Twigs, petioles and lamina undersurface cream lepidote, leaf buds, stipules, panicles and fruit densely persistently pale buff puberulent, fruit sepals densely so at base, sparsely so distally. Twig c. 1 mm diam. apically, slender but much branched, smooth, becoming chocolate-brown. Leaf bud c. 4 × 2 mm, lanceolate-falcate, acute. Stipules unknown. Lamina 7–13 × 3.4–8 cm, ovate-falcate, the apex twisting over on pressing; coriaceous, drying pale mauve-brown above, cream below with black nervation; base broadly cuneate, subequal, apex –1.3 cm long slender acuminate; nerves 8–9 pairs, slender and barely elevated below, applanate above, with minute axillary pore-like domatia; intercostals densely scalariform, set vertically to the midrib, unraised; midrib slender but elevated on both surfaces; petiole 15–20 mm long, slender, drying black. Whole panicles and flowers unknown. Fruit pedicel c. 1 mm long, short; 3 longer fruit sepals –7 × 2 cm, spatulate, obtuse, tapering to c. 6 mm broad above the –12 × 8 mm ovate saccate thick-

SHOREA 389

ened base; 2 shorter lobes –4 × 0.4 cm, lorate, acute, with similar base; fruit –15 × 10 mm, ovoid, tapering into a prominent stylopodium. Sapling and young tree lamina glabrous, not lepidote, lustrous below, with as few as 6 pairs of nerves and petiole as short as 12 mm.

D i s t r. Endemic. Locally frequent from Kegalle and the southern flanks of the Peak Sanctuary southwards, in Mixed Dipterocarp forest below 1000 m altitude.

E c o l. Usually on deep soils on ridges and well drained hillsides. Collected fruiting in July and September.

U s e s. Much-sought-after construction timber.

V e r n. Ratu Dun.

S p e c i m e n s E x a m i n e d. KANDY DISTRICT: Peradeniya Royal Botanical Gardens, cultivated, *Worthington 4869* (K), *de Silva 88* (PDA), *Meijer 288* (PDA, US). KEGALLE DISTRICT: Kegalle, Tetugalla Kande, *Ferguson s.n.* (PDA). KALUTARA DISTRICT: Yagirella F.R., *Ashton 2099* (PDA). RATNAPURA DISTRICT: Bambarabotuwa F.R., *Ashton 2012* (PDA). GALLE DISTRICT: Kanneliya F.R., *Ashton 2047* (PDA), *Ramalingam 1046* (PDA). COLOMBO DISTRICT: Indikada Mukalana, Waga, *Worthington 3548* (K); Ingiriya F.R., near Labugama, *Broun s.n.*, (PDA). DISTRICT UNKNOWN: Mondeleta Kande, *de Silva 254* (PDA); *Jayakody 435, 444* (PDA).

N o t e. A further collection, *Worthington 6444*, Kuttapitiya jungle, Pelmadulla, has the leaf shape of *S. oblongifolia* and could be a hybrid.

Section ANTHOSHOREAE

Heim, Rech. Dipt. 41. 1892; Ashton, Gard. Bull. Sing. 20 (3): 268. 1963. Type species: *S. harmandii* Lanessan.

Flowers relatively large, buds broadly lanceolate. Petals slender, prominently imbricate and contorted forming an urceolate base to the corolla, falling in a rosette with the stamens adhering. Stamens 15 (–30), in 3 verticils or indefinite; anthers narrowly oblong; connectival appendage prominent, unreflexed, usually at least half as long as anther, stout or slender, scabrous or glabrous. Ovary without distinct stylopodium; style longer than ovary, more or less trifid apically. Stipules often relatively large, caducous; bracts and bracteoles frequently large, somewhat persistent. Young leaves crimson. Bark surface with irregular-section fissures, frequently short and anastomosing; inner edge of outer bark ill defined; outer surface rotting off in old trees, rarely flaking regularly; periderms undulate or incomplete or absent; inner bark simply laminate.

D i s t r. c. 30 species, from Ceylon and southern India eastwards to Indo-China and the Moluccas. 1 species in Ceylon.

U s e s. The timber of this section is pale in colour, moderately hard and heavy, and siliceous; it is very suitable as a peeler for plywood manufacture.

5. Shorea stipularis Thw., Enum. Pl. Zeyl. 36. 1858; Dyer in Hook. f., Fl. Br. Ind. 1: 307. 1872; Thw. in Trimen, J. Bot. 23: 205. 1875; Trimen, Handb. Fl. Ceylon 1: 118. 1893; Alston in id. 6: 23. 1931; Lewis, Trees and Fl. Pl. of W. and Sab. Prov. 29. 1902; Worthington, Ceylon Trees 53. 1959; Ashton, Blumea 20 (2): 361. 1972. Type: *C.P. 3408.*

Large tree, –45 m tall, –4 m girth. Bole tall, straight, cylindrical, with low concave rounded buttresses; crown emergent, large, hemispherical, dense, the persistent stipules often conspicuous. Bark surface chocolate-brown, becoming irregular-section fissured at wide intervals, later becoming deeply fissured and coming away in chunky flakes; inner bark dark red-brown and pale yellow-brown laminated, fibrous; wood pale yellow, relatively soft, siliceous. Lamina undersurface, petiole, stipules and twig endings sometimes more or less persistently golden lepidote, otherwise all parts glabrous. Twig c. 5 × 3 mm diam. apically, stout, compressed, chocolate-brown, with conspicuous amplexicaul stipule scars. Leaf bud ovoid, compressed, enclosed within the –2.5 × 1.5 cm large persistent ovate subacute stipules. Young leaves red; lamina 6–15 × 3–11 cm, very variable in size, lanceolate to broadly oblong-ovate, thickly coriaceous, with more or less revolute margin, broadly cuneate to obtuse base and shortly acuminate to retuse apex; nerves 14–17 pairs, very slender but distinctly elevated beneath, applanate above, spreading; intercostals densely scalariform, hardly elevated on either surface; midrib stout and prominent below, obscurely depressed above; petiole 1.5–3 cm long, slender or stout. Panicles –12 cm long, –3 mm diam. at base, axillary, lax, with –7 cm long spreading branches bearing –5 more or less secund distant flowers; bracts subpersistent, as stipules but –12 × 10 mm, obtuse; floral sepals, ovary and style unknown; corolla c. 3 cm diam. at anthesis, large, the petals adhering in a rosette, prominently imbricate and contorted forming an urceolate base; stamens 15, connate with the petals in 3 subequal verticils; filaments applanate, broad at base, tapering and filiform below the narrowly oblong anthers; connectival appendage acicular, slender, c. 3 times as long as the anthers. Fruit pedicel –4 mm long, very stout; 3 larger fruit sepals –13.5 × 3.5 cm, broadly spatulate, obtuse, tapering to c. 1 cm wide above the –2 × 1.4 cm elliptic saccate thickened base; 2 shorter lobes –9 × 1.5 cm, otherwise similar; fruit –3 × 2 cm, ovoid, glabrous, typically resin-coated, tapering into a prominent slender apiculus. Seedling leaves with prominent long geniculate petiole; sapling lamina –20 × 8 cm, oblong to suborbicular, chartaceous.

D i s t r. Endemic. Frequent and widespread in Sabaragamuwa and Southern Provinces to the margin of the intermediate zone, and in Yagirella and Labugama forests in Western Province.

Ecol. In lowland Mixed Dipterocarp forest −1000 m altitude.

Vern. Nawadun, Nawada, Hulan-Idda.

Specimens Examined. RATNAPURA DISTRICT: Cassewitha Kanda, Sinharaja Forest, *s. coll. C.P. 3408* (PDA, K); Sinharaja Forest at Veddagalla, *Ashton 2030* (PDA); Bambarabotuwe F.R., *Ashton 2011* (PDA); Ratnapura, *Barnes 576* (PDA). KALUTARA DISTRICT: Pelanda, *Pereira 330* (PDA). KANDY DISTRICT: Peradeniya, Royal Botanical Gardens cultivated, *Worthington 4409* (K), *de Silva s.n.*, 20.3.29 (PDA). GALLE DISTRICT: Naunkita Elle, Kanneliya F.R. *Worthington 3674* (K); Nellowe, Sinharaja Forest, Hiniduma, *Ashton 2084* (PDA); Kanneliya Forest Reserve, *Mendis 1195* (PDA), *Cramer 3079* (PDA), *Meijer 554* (PDA, US), *Forest Department 1195* (PDA); Malariyana Reserve, *de Silva 1344* (PDA). MATARA DISTRICT: Near Anningkande, Morowak Korale, March 1881, *s. coll s.n.* (PDA); Morowaka below Captain Bayle's Estate, *s. coll. C.P. 3987* (PDA, K). DISTRICT UNKNOWN: Uluwindawa F.R., *Worthington 3658 3704, 3705* (K). Tutta Weraluwa Kothe, *s. coll. s.n.*, 27.3.1919 (PDA). LOCALITY UNKNOWN: *de Silva s.n.*, 20.3.29 (PDA).

Note. Thwaites (1875) described a var. *minor* to account for those specimens with very small leaves. Though trees from the eastern margin of its range, and also trees from high ridges, tend to have smaller leaves there is great variation in individual trees in the centre of the range, leaves tending to become small at the end of the flush. There appears to be continuous variation in the dimensions and the variety is consequently not maintained here.

Section DOONA

(Thw.) Ashton, Blumea 20 (2): 360. 1972. Type species: *S. zeylanica* (Thw.) Ashton.

Doona Thw., l.c.

Flower buds broadly lanceolate to ovoid or ellipsoid. Petals broadly oblong, hardly imbricate or contorted, falling in a loose rosette with the stament adhering. Stamens 15, in 3 subequal verticils; filaments short, applanate, tapering and filiform below the narrowly oblong apiculate anthers; connectival appendage shorter than anther, stout, clavate, glabrous. Ovary without distinct stylopodium; style at least twice as long as ovary, columnar, usually puberulent in the basal three-fourths; stigma obscure. Fruit sepals prominently twisted; fruit usually resinous, glabrous. Cotyledons much folded in seed, very unequal, the larger remaining within the fruit at germination and the smaller opening and photosynthesising. Stipules typically small, fugaceous. Young leaves deep magenta to purple. Bark anatomy as in Sect. Anthoshoreae but periderms more continuous; bark surface rotten but also scalloped and overall scaly; inner bark more or less distinctly laminated.

D i s t r. Endemic. 10 species, forming the commonest canopy trees in the wet zone primary forests from the Knuckles region southwards and –1800 m altitude; often gregarious.

U s e s. The timber appears to be variable in weight and durability; some are much valued for construction.

6. Shorea affinis (Thw.) Ashton, Blumea 20 (2): 361. 1972. Lectotype: *C.P. 3409* (PDA).

Doona affinis Thw., Enum. Pl. Zeyl. 35. 1858; Dyer in Hook. f., Fl. Br. Ind. 1: 311. 1872; Trimen, Handb. Fl. Ceylon 1: 120, 1893.

Medium sized main canopy tree, –35 m tall, –2 m girth, with low thin concave buttresses and dense umbrella-shaped crown with many small straight ascending branches; bole straight, cylindrical. Bark surface at first pale grey, becoming pale brown, longitudinally cracked and flaked; inner bark pale brown. Parts glabrous but for the densely puberulent outside of the petals. Twig c. 1 mm diam., slender, much branched; leaf bud minute; stipule minute, linear, fugaceous. Lamina 4.5–7.5 × 2–3.3 cm, lanceolate, subcoriaceous, drying purplish brown, with more or less broadly cuneate base, revolute margin, and –1 cm long slender tapering acumen; main nerves c. 9 pairs, very slender, arched, hardly elevated below, obscure above as also the scalariform intercostals; with many more or less shorter intermediates between each; midrib slender but sharply raised below, obscurely depressed above; petiole 7–8 mm long, c. 1 mm diam., slender, drying black. Panicles –4.5 cm long, –1 mm diam. at base, slender, axillary, ascending, with –1.5 cm long branchlets bearing –3 nodding flowers; corolla at anthesis –1 cm diam., otherwise typical; panicle and flower entirely white but for the yellow anthers. Fruit pedicel 1 cm long, slender; 3 longer sepals –4 × 0.8 cm, tapering to –5 mm broad above the –10 × 7 mm elliptic thickened saccate base; 2 shorter lobes –12 × 8 mm, ovate, acute, appressed to the base of the –18 × 9 mm ovoid apiculate fruit. Sapling lamina –12 × 4 cm, chartaceous, without revolute margin, with –1.5 cm long slender acumen; main nerves –12 pairs; otherwise as in mature tree.

D i s t r. Common in Mixed Dipterocarp forest on deep soils, especially on hillsides, below 1000 m altitude in Sabaragamuwa, Western and Southern Provinces.

E c o l. Flowering gregariously, apparently rather frequently, in March and April.

U s e s. Apparently too small, and with too light a wood, to be useful.

V e r n. Beraliya Dun.

S p e c i m e n s   E x a m i n e d. RATNAPURA DISTRICT: Sinharaja Forest, *s. coll. C.P. 3409* (PDA, K); Balangoda, *Lewis s.n.* (PDA); Sinharaja Forest at Veddagalla, *Ashton 2027, 2028* (PDA); Kiribatgalla near Pelmadulla, *Ashton 2120* (PDA); Bambarabotuwa F.R., *Meijer 433, 435* (PDA, US). MATARA DISTRICT: Deniyaya, *Worthington 2202* (K); Dediyagala, *s. coll. 295* (PDA). GALLE DISTRICT: Ilhandukita, Nellowe, *Ashton 2065* (PDA); Nellowe, borders of Sinharaja Forest, *Ashton 2072* (PDA); Kanneliya Forest Reserve, *Ashton 2088, 2089, 2091* (PDA), *Cramer, 3072* (PDA), *Meijer 541, 541a, 541b, 987, 988, 996, 1010, 1040* (PDA, US); Kottawe Natural Arboretum, *Ashton 2038, 2096* (PDA); Panangala, *s. coll. 102* (PDA), *de Rosayro 2079, 2080, 2082, 2087* (PDA); Udugama, *M. Walker s.n.* (PDA).

N o t e. Thwaites also quoted *C.P. 3712* in the original description; this specimen is more correctly *S. worthington* Ashton resembling *S. zeylanica*, but differing in the lamina base, tapering acumen in the mature tree, and erect twigs, as well as the smaller size of the tree.

7. Shorea congestiflora (Thw.) Ashton, Blumea 20(2): 362. 1972. Type: *C.P. 3411.*

Doona congestiflora Thw., Enum. Pl. Zeyl. 35. 1858; Dyer in Hook. f., Fl. Br. Ind. 1: 313. 1872; Trimen, Handb. Fl. Ceylon 1: 123. 1893; Alston in id. 6: 24. 1931; Lewis, Trees, and Fl. Pl. of W. and Sab. Prov. 32. 1902; Worthington, Ceylon Trees 54. 1959.

Medium sized to large tree, –40 m tall, –2 m girth, with low concave but thin rounded buttresses; bark surface purplish brown to greyish mottled, vertically fissured and becoming patchily flaked towards the base in old trees; inner bark rich meaty red, fibrous; wood pink, darkening to reddish brown. Young parts gold-brown pubescent, caducous except on leaf bud and stipule. Twig c. 1–2 mm diam., terete, becoming conspicuously lenticellate verruculose, pale brown. Leaf bud minute; stipule –12 × 6 mm, ovate, subacute, fugaceous. Lamina 6.5–12.5 × 2.5–6 cm, narrowly elliptic-ovate, coriaceous, drying purplish brown, with obtuse to narrowly subcordate base and –1.5 cm long slender tapering acumen; margin hardly or not revolute, nerves 11–15 pairs, slender, arched, elevated on both surfaces though more so below, frequently with short intermediates; intercostals densely scalariform, very slender, more or less equally elevated or obscure on both surfaces; midrib slender but prominent below, obscurely depressed above; petiole 8–12 mm long, c. 2 mm diam. Panicles –5 cm long, –3 mm diam. at base, relatively stout, with short branchlets; flower buds –6 × 5 mm, ellipsoid; corolla at anthesis –8 mm diam., pale pink; flowers otherwise typical. Fruit pedicel –6 mm long, broadening into the receptacle, or short; 3 longer fruit sepals –4.7 × 1 cm including the –10 × 7 mm elliptic saccate thickened base; 2 shorter lobes –17 × 8 mm, ovate, caudate; fruit –10 × 8 mm, narrowly ovoid, apiculate, resinous. Sapling lamina –16 × 6.5 cm, chartaceous, with shallowly cordate base, –2 cm long subcaudate acumen and 8–10 mm long, short, petiole; otherwise as in mature tree.

D i s t r. Western, Sabaragamuwa and Southern Provinces: Common in the lowland Mixed Dipterocarp forests –1000 m altitude.

E c o l. Typically found in gregarious groups in the heads of valleys and on moist hillsides, sometimes in extensive 'drifts' recognisable owing to their uniform canopy in aerial photographs. Flowering in August and September, gregariously at infrequent intervals.

U s e s. A useful plywood timber.

V e r n. Tiniya.

S p e c i m e n s E x a m i n e d. KALUTARA DISTRICT: Nellowe-Pella-watte Road, Pasdun Korale, *Ashton 2075* (PDA); Udugama, *Lewis s.n.* (PDA); Badureliya, 37th mile post, *Worthington 4604* (K); Homodola Estate, Udugama, *Worthington 4110, 4113* (K). GALLE DISTRICT: Kanneliya, road from Udugama, *Worthington 6024* (K); Hellepel, Hiniduma *s. coll. C.P. 3411* (PDA, B, K); Kunelli Mukalana, Hiniduma, *Worthington 2245* (K); Naunkita Ela in Kanneliya Forest, *Worthington 3694, 4138, 5257* (K); Naki-adeniya, *Worthington 5235* (K); Sinharaja Forest at Nellowe, *Ashton 2071* (PDA); Kanneliya Forest, *de Rosayro 293* (PDA), *Meijer 4035* (PDA); trail to Haycock Hill, Hiniduma, *Meijer 580* (PDA); Masmulla Kelle, *Jayawar-dena 324* (PDA). MATARA DISTRICT: Deniyaya, *Worthington 2202* (K); Uluwinduwa, Deniyaya, 59th mile post, *Worthington 3713* (K); Dediyagala Forest, *Worthington 2564* (K). RATNAPURA DISTRICT: Pelmadulla, *Norris 19* (PDA); Ratnapura, *Ashton 2022* (PDA); Kalawana Road, mile 15, culvert 19, *Ashton 2024, 2026* (PDA); *Meijer 453* (PDA); Sinharaja Forest, *Worthington 3667* (K); Gilimale Forest, *Meijer 430* (PDA); Sinharaja, *de Rosayro 423* (PDA).

N o t e. Differing from *S. worthingtoni* in the inner bark, the dry leaf colour, the tomentum, lenticellate twigs, short stout petiole, glabrous petals, and in the sapling characters.

8. Shorea cordifolia (Thw.) Ashton, Blumea 20 (2): 362. 1972. Type: *C.P. 3410.*

Doona nervosa Thw., Enum. Pl. Zeyl. 35. 1858; Dyer in Hook. f., Fl. Br. Ind. 1: 311. 1872; Trimen, Handb. Fl. Ceylon 1: 121. 1893; Alston in id. 6: 24. 1931; Lewis, Trees and Fl. Pl. of W. and Sab. Prov.: 31. 1902; Worthing-ton, Ceylon Trees 57. 1959.
Doona cordifolia Thw., l.c.; Dyer, id. 313; Trimen, id. 144; Alston, l.c. Type: *C.P. 3340.*

Medium-sized tree, –30 m tall, –2 m girth, with low concave rounded buttresses, straight bole frequently branching rather low, and dense oblong to hemispherical crown. Bark surface chocolate brown, becoming cracked and flaking in thin rectangular scales; inner bark pale brown; wood light, pale cream. Young parts fugaceous puberulent, petals outside persistently pubescent. Twig c. 1–2 mm diam., slender, much branched, pale brown. Leaf bud minute; stipules fugaceous. Lamina 8–15 × 3–6 cm, ovate-lanceolate to elliptic, chartaceous, drying purplish brown, with broadly cuneate to obtuse base and –1.8 cm long slender tapering acumen; margin undulate; nerves 8–11 pairs, very slender but prominent beneath, evident above, often with a few short slender intermediates; intercostals densely scalariform, very slender but elevated beneath, evident and distinctly elevated above; petiole 6–10 mm long, c. 2 mm diam. Panicle –5 cm long, –1 mm diam. at base, short, slender, with 1.5 cm long branchlets bearing –5 flowers; flower bud –5 × 4 mm, ellipsoid; corolla –11 mm diam. at anthesis, white as also the calyx, ovary, and panicle; anthers yellow. Fruit pedicel –6 mm long, broadening into the base of the fruit; 3 longer fruit sepals –3.8 × 1.2 cm, strongly twisted over, broadly spatulate, obtuse, tapering to c. 6 mm broad above the –8 × 6 mm elliptic saccate thickened base; 2 shorter sepals –12 × 8 mm, ovate, acute; nut –16 × 10 mm, ovoid, apiculate, resinous. Sapling lamina as in mature tree but –11 × 2.5 cm, lanceolate, caudate, with –5 mm long, short, petiole.

D i s t r. Sabaragamuwa and Southern Provinces.

E c o l. Locally common in Mixed Dipterocarp forests on hills below 1000 m altitude. A main canopy species, not noticeably gregarious. Flowering in March and April, gregariously at irregular intervals.

U s e s. The wood is apparently not durable, and the tree not often large enough to be economically important.

V e r n. Kotikan Beraliya.

S p e c i m e n s   E x a m i n e d. RATNAPURA DISTRICT: Eknaligoda near Ratnapura, *s. coll. C.P. 3410* (PDA, K, B); Gilimale Forest, Ratnapura, *Ashton 2018, 2020* (PDA), *Meijer 828, 418, 401* (PDA); Eknaligoda Kande, Kuruwita, *Ashton 2009* (PDA); Bambarabotuwa, *Ranawane s.n.* (PDA). GALLE DISTRICT: Naunkita Ela, Kanneliya Forest, *Worthington 3687, 4146* (K); Hiniduma, West of Gin Ganga, *Worthington 2299* (K); Kanneliya Forest Reserve, *Ashton 2045* (PDA), *Meijer 556, 972* (PDA); Ithandukita near Nellowe, *Ashton 2063* (PDA); Beraliya Forest Reserve, Elpitiya, *Illaperuma 506* (PDA); N.W. of Hiniduma, *Alston 2347* (K). KANDY DISTRICT: Peradeniya Royal Botanical Garden cultivated, *Alston 619, 814* (PDA); *de Silva 56* (K), *Worthington 6826, 5862, 4040, 3782, 1794* (K), *Ashton 2108* (PDA), *Meijer 383* (PDA, US). KALUTARA DISTRICT: Hewesse, Pasdun Korale, *s. coll. C.P. 3410* (PDA, B, K); Pasdun Korale, *s. coll. C.P. 334* (PDA, K). MATARA DISTRICT: Hulandawa, *Worthington 3702* (K); Taunahena, Hulandawa, mile 17, culvert 8, *Worthington 3664* (K); Deniyaya, Diyadawa Forest, *Worthington 2216* (K). LOCALITY UNKNOWN: *s. coll. C.P. 1355* (K); *Walker 1355* (E).

N o t e. One sheet of the type at Peradeniya has 3 twigs, one of which represents *S. worthingtoni*. The type of *Doona cordifolia* is a galled sapling of this species; that name was confused by Trimen and Lewis with *S. dyeri*. The collection of Walker cited by Trimen under *D. nervosa* belongs to *S. affinis*.

The name *Shorea nervosa* is preoccupied by *Shorea nervosa* Kurz, For. Fl. Br. Burma 1: 119. 1877, a synonym of *Anisoptera oblonga* Dyer.

9. Shorea disticha (Thw.) Ashton, Blumea 20, 2: 362. 1972.

Vateria disticha Thw., Enum. Pl. Zeyl. 404. 1864. Type: *C.P. 3707*.

Vatica disticha (Thw.) A. DC., Prod. 16 (2): 620. 1868; Dyer in Hook. f., Fl. Br. Ind. 1: 303. 1872.

Sunaptea disticha (Thw.) Trimen, Cat. 9. 1885; Trimen, Handb. Fl. Ceylon 1: 127. 1893; 5: 383. 1900.

Doona disticha (Thw.) Pierre, Fl. For. Cochinch. fasc. 15: t. 237. 1890; Heim, Bull. Soc. Bot. France 39. 1: 153. 1892; Rech. Dipt. 72. 1892.

Doona oblonga Thw., in Trimen, J. Bot. 23: 206. 1885; Trimen, Handb. Fl. Ceylon 1: 123. 1893; Alston in id. 6: 24. 1931. Type: *C.P. 3986*.

Stemonoporus distichus (Thw.) Heim, Rech. Dipt. 72. 1892.

Medium sized tree with pale brown inner bark; mature bark surface configuration unrecorded. Twigs conspicuously relatively persistently shortly densely evenly tawny pubescent; petiole puberulent. Twigs c. 3×2 mm apically, somewhat compressed and ribbed at first, becoming pale brown, with more or less prominent horizontal stipule scars. Leaf buds small, ovoid; stipules -12×5 mm, ovate-oblong. Lamina $9-17 \times 5-8$ cm, ovate-oblong to elliptic, coriaceous, drying pale brown to reddish, with obtuse to subcordate base and 1 cm long tapering acumen; margin frequently narrowly revolute; nerves 8–11 (–12) pairs, slender, arched, elevated on both surfaces though more so below, without distinct intermediates; intercostals densely scalariform, more or less elevated or obscure on both surfaces; midrib slender but prominent below, obscurely depressed above; petiole 8–12 mm long, c. 2 mm diam. Inflorescences and flowers unknown. Fruit pedicel -4 mm long; 3 longer fruit sepals -4×1 cm including the -10×7 mm saccate thickened base; 2 shorter lobes -20×8 mm, ovate-caudate, fruit -12×8 mm, narrowly ovoid, apiculate. Sapling lamina as in mature tree but somewhat larger and less thickly coriaceous, with applanate margin and caudate acumen.

D i s t r. Apparently rare but easily overlooked; known only from Lanegal Kande north of Nellowe, near Haycock and in Kanneliya forest, and at Gilimale, Ratnapura.

S p e c i m e n s   E x a m i n e d. GALLE DISTRICT: Kanneliya Forest Reserve, *Ashton 2090* (PDA); *Meijer 552, 604, 1015, 1038* (PDA), *Cramer 3078* (PDA); trail to Haycock, Hiniduma, *Meijer 570* (PDA), *Cramer 3086*, (PDA). RATNAPURA DISTRICT: Gilimale Forest, *Meijer 424* (PDA); Bambarabotuwa, *Ponnudurai s.n.*, 27.12.38 (PDA). KEGALLE DISTRICT: Lanegal

Kande, *s. coll. C.P. 3707* (PDA). LOCALITY UNKNOWN: *s. coll. C.P. 3986* (PDA, K).

N o t e. The sterile type of *Vateria disticha* is undoubtedly to be associated with *C.P. 3986* (with fruit), the type of *Doona oblonga*, as the dense short subpersistent ocherous velutinate indumentum is unique among Ceylon dipterocarps.

Trimen (1893) described the young expanding stipulate shoots of *C.P. 3707* as panicles. This species is imperfectly known and, especially when mature, is difficult to distinguish from *S. worthingtoni*, differing principally from it in the compressed tomentose twig. The *C.P.* numbers of these two species differ greatly for the type of *S. worthingtoni* possesses foliage typical of immature trees.

10. Shorea gardneri (Thw.) Ashton, Blumea 20 (2): 362. 1972. Type: *C.P. 1919.*

Doona gardneri Thw., Enum. Pl. Zeyl. 35. 1885; Dyer in Hook. f., Fl. Br. Ind. 1: 313. 1872; Trimen, Handb. Fl. Ceylon 1: 121. 1893; Alston in id. 6: 24. 1931; Lewis, Trees and Fl. Pl. of W. and Sab. Prov.: 30. 1802; Worthington, Ceylon Trees 55. 1959.

Magnificent tree, –45 m tall, –3 m girth, but usually smaller especially on exposed sites, with characteristic dense hemispherical dark olive-green crown fed by large twisting branches; bole often sinuate; buttresses –2 m tall and long, prominent, rounded, concave. Bark surface purplish brown, becoming cracked and flaky; inner bark thick, orange-brown when fresh, fibrous; sapwood dark yellow-brown, hard, heartwood orange-brown. Parts glabrescent but for the sparsely puberulent stipule and buff pubescent outside of petals. Twig c. 1 mm diam. apically, much branched, smooth, blackish. Stipule –15 × 4 mm, lanceolate, acute, fugaceous. Lamina 4–9 × 2–5 cm, ovate, coriaceous, drying dark chocolate-brown, with prominently revolute base obtuse to cordate on unfurling, subrevolute margin and –1 cm long tapering acumen; nerves c. 12 pairs with a few shorter to occasionally subequal intermediates, ascending, the basal pair sometimes with short lateral branchlets, very slender and hardly raised below, evident above; intercostals densely obscurely subscalariform; midrib slender, prominent below, obscurely depressed above; petiole 12–20 mm long, c. 1 mm diam., long, slender, hardly geniculate. Panicles –7.5 cm long, –2 mm diam. at base, terminal or subterminal-axillary, with –2.5 cm long branchlets. Flower buds –6 × 4 mm, ellipsoid, relatively large; corolla –11 mm diam. at anthesis, pale pink; flowers otherwise typical. Fruit pedicel –6 mm long, slender, broadening into the receptacle; 3 longer fruit sepals –4 × 1 cm, tapering to 5 mm broad above the –6 × 5 mm elliptic saccate thickened base; 2 shorter lobes –7 × 5 mm, ovate; fruit –12 × 8 mm, ovoid, apiculate. Sapling lamina chartaceous, with typically broadly cordate to obtuse, hardly revolute, base, –1.5 cm long slender subcaudate acumen, and as few as 8 pairs of nerves; otherwise as in mature tree.

D i s t r. Mid-mountain forests; from Raxawa, Dolosbage and Gampola southwards to the Handapan Ella plains, between 1000 and 1800 m altitude.

E c o l. Still forming majestic stands on hillsides and ridges in a few areas, the dense canopy of olive-green crowns a memorable sight, especially when in flower. Once their hemispherical crowns with twisted branches dominated the skyline in the hill country, but it prefers the deep soil sought after by the tea planters and is now very local. Flowering between November and February and sometimes into April, gregariously at irregular intervals.

U s e s. A beautiful red-brown durable hardwood popular for construction and for railway sleepers.

V e r n. Koongili Maram (T); Rata Dun (S).

S p e c i m e n s E x a m i n e d. RATNAPURA DISTRICT: Aigburth Estate, Rakwana, *Worthington 782, 3715, 3724, 2644* (K); Balangoda Estate, *Worthington 3242* (K), *Meijer 439, 962* (PDA); Rakwana, mile 64, *Worthington 2643* (K); Suriya Kande, Rakwana, *Worthington 2151* (K); Drumlarig Forest, Balangoda Group, *Worthington 6918* (K); Aberfoyle Estate, Rajakand Valley, Rakwana, *Worthington 2625* (K); Orange Field Estate, *Worthington 2144* (K); Kurulugala, Rakwana, *Ashton 2129, 2130* (PDA). KANDY DISTRICT: Brownlow Estate, Maskeliya, *Worthington 2758* (K); Kellie Estate, Dolosbage, *Worthington 1866, 1913* (K); Le Vallon, Galaha, *Worthington 6503* (K); Ginigathhena-Maskeliya Road, mile 4, culvert 23, *Ashton 2006* (PDA); Southern flanks of Adam's Peak, *Ashton 2113* (PDA); Aspawa and Hewahette, *s. coll. C.P. 1919* (PDA, B, K); Dikoya, *Alexander s.n.*, December 1889 (PDA); Delta Estate, Pusselawa, *Worthington 2890* (K); Queensberry, Upper Kotmale, *Worthington 6636* (K); Midford Estate, Hatton, *Worthington 5508* (K). BADULLA DISTRICT: Uva Highlands Estate, *Worthington 591* (K).

N o t e. *Worthington 5508* has a narrowly cuneate hardly revolute lamina base and in other respects also gives the appearance of being a hybrid with *S. trapezifolia*.

11. Shorea megistophylla Ashton, Blumea 20 (2): 362. 1972. Type: *C.P. 3713*.

Doona macrophylla Thw., Enum. Pl. Zeyl. 402. 1864; Dyer in Hook. f., Fl. Br. Ind. 1: 313. 1872; Trimen, Handb. Fl. Ceylon 1: 124. 1893; Alston in id. 6: 24. 1931; Lewis, Trees and Fl. Pl. of W. and Sab. Prov. 32. 1902; Worthington, Ceylon Trees 56. 1959.

Medium sized to large tree, –40 m tall, –3 m girth, with dense hemispherical crown. Bole tall, straight, cylindrical; buttresses –1 m tall and long, stout, concave but prominent. Bark surface tawny brown, coming away in conspicuous large oblong subpersistent pieces from above in patches, leaving

scalloped surfaces beneath; inner bark pale brown; wood pale yellow, hard.
Parts glabrous but for the pubescent outside of the petals. Twig c. 2–3 mm
diam. apically, stout, terete, pale buff-brown, with prominent stipule scars.
Leaf buds c. 6 × 5 mm, ellipsoid, obtuse. Stipules –5 × 1.5 cm, large, narrowly elliptic, fleshy, with a prominent median sinuate nerve, fugaceous. Lamina
(10.5–) 13–23 × (4–) 5–15 cm, large, oblong-elliptic, thickly coriaceous, drying chocolate to reddish brown, with shallowly subrevolute margin, obtuse
base and –1.5 cm long, usually short, broad tapering acumen; nerves 13–18
pairs, slender but distinctly raised beneath, obscurely elevated above, without or with a few distinct short intermediates; intercostals subscalariform,
evident beneath, obscure above; petiole 8–30 mm long, c. 2–3 mm diam.,
stout, not geniculate. Panicle –13 cm long, –3 mm diam. at base, with prominent bract scars, regularly alternately branched, erect, the branchlets –3 cm
long and bearing –6 flowers; flower bud –8 × 6 mm, ellipsoid; corolla –15 mm
diam., white as also the inflorescence, calyx and ovary; anthers yellow;
flowers otherwise typical. Fruit pedicel –8 mm long, stout, broadening into
the fruit; 3 longer sepals –6 × 2 cm, broadly spatulate, obtuse, tapering to
c. 8 mm broad above the –13 × 5 mm broadly elliptic saccate thickened base; 2
shorter lobes –15 × 12 mm, ovate, subacuminate; fruit 3 × 1.8 cm, ovoid, prominently apiculate. Sapling and young tree lamina –35 × 12 cm, with –28 pairs
of nerves; otherwise similar.

D i s t r. Sabaragamuwa and the western part of Southern Province.

E c o l. Locally common, occurring in semi-gregarious groups, particularly on undulating land and on ridge tops on deep soils in Mixed Dipterocarp
forest below 1000 m altitude. Flowering between February and April, gregariously at infrequent intervals.

U s e s. A useful medium hardwood, for light construction and for plywood. The yellowish-white resin is also used.

V e r n. Honda-beraliya, Kana-beraliya, Maha-beraliya (S).

S p e c i m e n s E x a m i n e d. KANDY DISTRICT: Peradeniya Royal
Botanical Gardens, cultivated, *Alston 620* (PDA, US), *Worthington 5502,
6251, 6837, 3403* (K), *Ashton 2107* (PDA), *de Silva 74, 85,* 12.4.23 (PDA, K),
Meijer 387 (PDA, US). KALUTARA DISTRICT: Mandegala Mukulana,
Hewesse, *s. coll. s.n.,* March 1887 (PDA); Udugama, Homodola Estate, *Worthington 4115, 6021* (K). GALLE DISTRICT: Kanneliya Forest, *Broun s.n.,*
11.1.90 (PDA), *Meijer 1013* (PDA), *Cramer 3073* (PDA); Naunkita Forest
Reserve, *Worthington 4144, 4145, 4151* (K); Udugama Road from Galle, mile
20, culvert 5, *Worthington 5269* (K); Kottawa, *Holmes 751* (PDA), *Weera-
ratne 1839* (PDA), *D.F.O. 123* (PDA), *de Rosayro 1421,* (PDA); Wellam-
bagala in Beraliya F.R., *Jayakody 442* (PDA); Habaragodde, *s. coll. C.P.
3713* (PDA, B, K). RATNAPURA DISTRICT: Gilimale Forest, Ratnapura,
Worthington 6462, 3178 (K), *Ashton 2016, 2017* (PDA), *Meijer 417, 425, 490*

(PDA), *de Rosayro 1421, 1427* (PDA); Ratnapura, Moropitiya road, *Meijer 1082* (PDA); Kukul Korale, *s. coll. C.P. 3717* (PDA).

12. Shorea ovalifolia (Thw.) Ashton, Blumea 20 (2): 363. 1972. Type: *C.P. 3711.*

Doona ovalifolia Thw., Enum. Pl. Zeyl. 404. 1864; Dyer in Hook. f., Fl. Br. Ind. 1: 313. 1872; Trimen, Handb. Fl. Ceylon 1: 123. 1893; Alston in id. 6: 24. 1931; Lewis, Trees and Fl. Pl. of W. and Sab. Prov. 32: 1902; Worthington, Ceylon Trees 59. 1959.

Medium sized to large tree, –35 m tall, –3 m girth, remaining at first monopodial, with tapering bole and many concave low buttresses ascending into ribs; crown feathery, becoming densely hemispherical. Bark surface dark tawny brown, irregularly thinly flaking leaving paler surfaces below; inner bark pale brown; wood pale yellow-brown, hard. Parts glabrous but for the pubescent outside of the petals. Twigs c. 1 mm diam. apically, slender, much branched; leaf buds minute; stipules linear, fugaceous. Lamina 4–6 × 2–3.5 cm, ovate, applanate, thinly coriaceous, drying chocolate brown, with broadly cuneate to subcordate base and –1 cm long subcaudate acumen; nerves 7–8 pairs, very slender but distinctly elevated below, obscure above, with a few short intermediates; intercostals densely subscalariform, evident below, obscure above; midrib very slender but prominent below, obscurely depressed above; petiole 4–8 mm long, c. 1 mm diam., slender, short. Panicle –7 cm long, c. 1 mm diam. at base, slender, subterminal axillary, lax, with –1.5 cm long branchlets bearing –2 flowers; flower buds –3 × 2 mm, ellipsoid; corolla –1 cm diam. at anthesis, white as also the calyx, ovary and panicle; anthers yellow. Fruit pedicel –1 cm long, slender, expanding at apex only; 3 longer fruit sepals –3.5 × 0.6 cm, relatively small, narrowly spatulate, tapering to c. 4 mm broad above the –10 × 7 mm elliptic saccate thickened base; 2 shorter sepals –15 × 10 mm, ovate, acute; fruit –13 × 10 mm, ovoid, apiculate. Sapling lamina –9 cm long, lanceolate, with –2.5 cm long very slender caudate acumen.

D i s t r. Western, Sabaragamuwa and Southern Provinces.

E c o l. Locally abundant in Mixed Dipterocarp forest, occasionally –1300 m, usually on ridges on skeletal soils and in rocky places; typically with dense thickets of saplings beneath. Flowering in April–May, and sometimes in December; gregariously at irregular intervals.

V e r n. Tiniya Dun.

S p e c i m e n s E x a m i n e d. KALUTARA DISTRICT: Hewesse, Pasdun Korale, *s. coll. C.P. 3711* (PDA, B, K); Lihinigala, Hewesse, *s. coll. s.n.*, March 1887 (PDA). KANDY DISTRICT: Peradeniya, Royal Botanical Gardens, cultivated, *de Silva s.n.*, 15.4.1926 (PDA), *s. coll. s.n.*, 4.5.23 (PDA), *s. coll. 59, 72* (PDA, K), *Worthington 4042, 5863* (K), *Ashton 2101* (PDA),

Meijer 821 (PDA). COLOMBO DISTRICT: Heneratgoda Gardens, *Worthington 3395* (K). GALLE DISTRICT: Ithandukita near Nellowe, *Ashton 2066* (PDA); N.W. of Hiniduma, *Alston 2437* (K).

13. Shorea trapezifolia (Thw.) Ashton, Blumea 20 (2): 363. 1972. Type: *C.P. 3341.*

Doona trapezifolia Thw., Enum. Pl. Zeyl 35. 1858; Dyer in Hook. f., Fl. Br. Ind. 1: 311. 1872; Trimen, Handb. Fl. Ceylon 1: 121. 1893; Alston, in id. 6: 24. 1931; Lewis, Trees and Fl. Pl. of W. and Sab. Prov. 31. 1902; Worthington, Ceylon Trees 60. 1959.

Enormous trees, –45 m tall, –5 m girth, with straight somewhat tapering bole often branching low, and large hemispherical cauliflower-shaped crown fed by large straight ascending branches; buttresses –3 m tall and long, stout, concave, prominent. Bark surface pale brown, becoming deeply vertically irregular-section fissured and coming away in rectangular flakes; inner bark pale brown; wood pale yellow, medium hard. Young twig and petiole caducous tawny puberulent, stipules outside and exposed margins of petals outside persistently pubescent, otherwise glabrous. Twig c. 1 mm diam. apically, very slender, dark brown, smooth. Leaf buds minute, stipules –16 × 10 mm, lanceolate, acute, fugaceous. Lamina 5–9 × 1.8–4 cm, lanceolate to elliptic-rhomboid, thinly coriaceous, drying dull dark purplish brown, with broadly cuneate to obtuse base and –12 mm long slender tapering acumen; nerves c. 11–14 pairs, with shorter intermediates, very slender and hardly elevated but evident on both surfaces as also the densely subreticulate intercostals; midrib slender but prominent beneath, narrowly depressed above; petiole 8–12 mm long, c. 0.5 mm diam., very slender, not geniculate. Panicles –6 cm long, c. 1 mm diam. at base, very slender, terminal or subterminal axillary, with –2.5 cm long branchlets bearing –5 flowers; flower buds –5 × 4 mm, ellipsoid; corolla 9 mm diam. at anthesis, white as also the calyx, ovary and panicles; anthers yellow. Fruit pedicel –6 mm long, stout, expanding into the base of the fruit; 3 longer fruit sepals –4.5 × 0.8 cm, spatulate, obtuse, tapering to c. 5 mm broad above the –11 × 8 mm elliptic saccate thickened base; 2 shorter sepals –13 × 8 mm, ovate, cuspidate; fruit –2 × 1 cm, ellipsoid-ovoid, apiculate. Sapling lamina –15 × 4 cm, lanceolate, chartaceous, with shallowly cordate base, –1.5 cm long caudate acumen, and scalariform intercostals; petiole –4 mm long, very short, prominently pubescent as also the twigs.

D i s t r. From Nawalapitiya in Central Province southwards to the eastern Sinharaja.

E c o l. Occurring in large 'drifts,' their majestic crowns dominating the canopy, in hill forests between 600 and 1200 m. Much destroyed now, but still persisting in particular in eastern Bambarabotuwe and on the southern flanks of the Peak Sanctuary. Found particularly on deep soils on gentle slopes. Flowering in April, heavily and gregariously at long intervals, but a little in most years.

U s e s. The wood is suitable for light construction and for plywood.

V e r n. Yakahalu Dun.

S p e c i m e n s   E x a m i n e d. KANDY DISTRICT: Ambagamuwa, *s. coll. C.P. 3541* (PDA, K, B); between Nawalapitiya and Watamula, Ambaga-muwa, *Alexander s.n.*, September 1891 (PDA); Kellie Estate, Dolosbage, *Worthington 1912* (K); Imboopitiya Estate, Nawalapitiya, *Worthington 3151, 4087* (K). RATNAPURA DISTRICT: Pelmadulla, Kuttapitiya Estate, *Norris 19* (PDA); Sinharaja Forest, *s. coll. C.P. 3341* (PDA, K, B); Walboda, 6 miles N.E. of Balangoda, *Worthington 991, 3286, 3288* (K); Orange Field Estate, Rakwana, *Worthington 3624* (K); Deepdene, Rakwana, *Worthington 3743, 3745* (K); Rassagalla, *Worthington 4860* (K); Ouvella, Balangoda, *Worthing-ton 3328* (K); Agar's Land, Rasagalla, *Ashton 2021* (PDA); Kurulugala, Rak-wana, *Ashton 2127, 2128* (PDA); Peak Wilderness bordering Carney Estate, *Worthington 6468* (K); Bambarabotuwa, *W. de Silva 82* (PDA), *Ponnudurai 135* (PDA); Weddagala, Sinharaja, *Meijer 521, 521a* (PDA). MATARA DIS-TRICT: Uluwinduwa, Deniyaya, *Worthington 3707* (K); Deniyaya, *Worthing-ton 2200* (K).

14. Shorea worthingtoni Ashton., Blumea 20(2): 363. 1972. Type: *C.P. 3675*.

Doona venulosa Thw., Enum. Pl. Zeyl. 402. 1864; Dyer in Hook. f., Fl. Br. Ind. 1: 123. 1872; Trimen, Handb. Fl. Ceylon 1: 123. 1893; Alston in id. 6: 24. 1931; Worthington, Ceylon Trees 61, 1959.

A medium sized tree, –30 m tall, –2 m girth, with low rounded concave buttresses. Bark surface pale brown, becoming cracked and thinly flaked; inner bark pale brown; wood pale yellow, hard. Parts glabrous but for the pubescent outer surface of the petals. Twigs c. 2 mm diam. apically, slender, rugulose, grey-brown, with short horizontal linear stipule scars. Leaf buds minute; stipules –16×3 mm, linear-lanceolate, acute, fugaceous. Lamina 4.3–9.5×1.5–4 cm, elliptic to ovate, coriaceous, drying coppery brown, with subrevolute margin, cuneate base, and –12 mm long slender subcaudate acumen; nerves 6–9 pairs, ascending, very slender and evident but hardly raised on either surface, with a few short intermediates, the basal pair fre-quently with a few lateral branchlets (immature trees); intercostals obscure, densely subscalariform (mature trees); midrib slender but prominent below, narrowly depressed above; petiole 6–12 mm long, c. 1.5 mm diam., slender, with adaxial furrow, not geniculate. Panicle –7 cm long, c. 2 mm diam. at base, terminal or subterminal axillary, slender, lax, with –5 cm long branch-lets bearing –4 flowers; flower bud –6×4 mm, broadly ellipsoid; corolla –13 mm diam. at anthesis, white as also the calyx, ovary and panicle; anthers yellow. Fruit unknown. Sapling lamina –15 × 6.5 cm but usually smaller, with obtuse to subcordate base, the basal pair of nerves obliquely ascending, with lateral branchlets; intercostals frequently distinctly elevated on both surfaces; petiole –16 mm long.

D i s t r. Sabaragamuwa and Southern Provinces.

E c o l. Locally common on well-drained soils on hillsides and ridges below 1000 m altitude in Mixed Dipterocarp forest. Flowering in April, gregariously at infrequent intervals.

S p e c i m e n s E x a m i n e d. KANDY DISTRICT: Peradeniya, Royal Botanical Gardens, cultivated, *de Silva 77* (PDA, K), *Livera s.n.*, April 1923 (PDA), *Alston 618* (PDA), *Ashton 2106*. KALUTARA DISTRICT: Homodola Estate, Udugama, *Worthington 4118* (K); Haycock, *Meijer 567* (PDA). GALLE DISTRICT: Kottawa Natural Arboretum, *Holmes 752* (PDA), *de Rosayro 2088* (PDA), *Ashton 2095* (PDA); Ithandukit near Nellowe, *Ashton 2062* (PDA); Kanneliya F.R., *Ashton 2086* (PDA), *Meijer 556, 969* (PDA), *Cramer 3081* (PDA). RATNAPURA DISTRICT: Gilimale Forest, *Worthington 3172* (K), *Ashton 2015, 2020* (PDA), *Meijer 422, 427, 428* (PDA). LOCALITY UNKNOWN: *s. coll. C.P. 3675, 3712* (PDA, K).

N o t e. The combination *Shorea venulosa* is preoccupied by *S. venulosa* Meijer, Act. Bot. Neerl. 12: 342. 1963.

15. Shorea zeylanica (Thw.) Ashton, Blumea 20 (2): 363. 1972. Type: *C.P. 2423.*

Doona zeylanica Thw., Hook. J. Bot. 4: 7. 1852; Enum. Pl. Zeyl. 34. 1858; Dyer in Hook. f., Fl. Br. Ind. 1: 311. 1872; Trimen, Handb. Fl. Ceylon 1: 119. 1893; Alston in id. 6: 23. 1931; Lewis, Trees and Fl. Pl. of W. and Sab. Prov. 30. 1902; Worthington, Ceylon Trees 62. 1959.

Medium sized to occasionally large tree, –45 m tall, –4 m girth, with tall frequently somewhat sinuate bole and low concave rounded buttresses; crown at first oblong, dense, with conspicuously pendant twigs especially in immature trees, becoming hemispherical and cauliflower-shaped with large almost horizontal branches. Bark surface tawny-brown, becoming thinly irregularly flaky; inner bark pale brown; wood pale yellow, relatively light. Parts glabrous but for the pubescent outside of the petals. Twigs c. 1 mm diam. apically, very slender. Leaf buds minute; stipules fugaceous. Lamina 3–9 × 1–2.8 cm, narrowly elliptic-lanceolate, coriaceous, with narrowly cuneate prominently revolute base and –12 mm long slender caudate acumen; nerves c. 8 pairs, with many more or less subequal intermediates, obscure, ascending, arched, with elongate pubescent pore-like axillary domatia; intercostals obscure, minutely reticulate; midrib slender but prominent, sharply acute below, depressed above; petiole 8–14 mm long, c. 0.5 mm diam., very slender, hardly geniculate. Panicles –5 cm long, c. 1 mm diam. at base, terminal or axillary, very slender, lax, pendant, with –3 cm long branchlets bearing –4 flowers; flower buds –5 × 4 mm, ellipsoid; corolla –9 mm diam. at anthesis, white as also the calyx, ovary and panicle, or sometimes rose-coloured; anthers yellow. Fruit pedicels –8 mm long, slender, broadening into the fruit; 3 longer fruit sepals –2.8 × 0.6 cm including the –6 × 5 mm elliptic saccate thickened base, spatulate, obtuse, prominently twisted; 2 shorter lobes –7 × 5 mm, ovate; nut –7 × 5 mm, ovoid, apiculate. Sapling lamina as in mature tree but somewhat larger.

D i s t r. From Gampola, Central Province, to the Sinha Raja Forest.

E c o l. In hill Mixed Dipterocarp forests between 300 and 1400 m altitude; once common, now very local, still a conspicuous ridge-top emergent in some areas. Flowering from March to May, sporadically in most years but gregariously and heavily at infrequent intervals.

U s e s. The timber is suitable for construction work.

V e r n. Dun (S); Koongili (T).

S p e c i m e n s E x a m i n e d. KANDY DISTRICT: Deltota, *s. coll. C.P. 2423* (PDA, B, K); Tembiligala Estate, Gampola, *Worthington 4090, 4089* (K); Peradeniya Royal, Botanical Gardens, cultivated, *Worthington 3408, 6481, 3836, 3785, 3611, 5711* (K), *s. coll. s.n.*, March 1889 (PDA), *Ashton 2101* (PDA); New Peacock Estate, Pussellawa, *Worthington 4963* (K); Adam's Peak Sanctuary, *Meijer 511* (PDA). RATNAPURA DISTRICT: Rakwana, Kurulugala, *Ashton 2131, 2132* (PDA); Rasagala, Balangoda, *Worthington 3322* (K); Borangamuwa res., *de Rosayro s.n.*, 24.5.58 (PDA). MATARA DISTRICT: Deniyaya, *Worthington 2606* (K).

Excluded species

Shorea reticulata Thw., in Hook. f., Fl. Br. Ind. 1: 307. 1872. Holotype: *C.P. 3884*, Morowak Korale, Sept. 1865 (PDA).

This, the only specimen, consists of the fallen fruit of a species of *Shorea* in the type section, possibly *S. dyeri*, that is unidentifiable, and a sterile leafy twig which does not belong to this family, and which I am unable to identify.

5. STEMONOPORUS

Thw., Hook., J. Bot. 6: 67. 1854. Lectotype species: *S. gardneri* Thw.

Monoporandra Thw., id. 69.
Vesquella Heim, Rech. Dipt. 90. 1892.
Sunapteopsis Heim, id. 92.
Kunckelia Heim, id. 92.

Small understorey, or main canopy, trees with smooth bark surface, no buttresses and clear resin; habit and crown variable; inner bark pale brown; wood pale yellow, even grained, hard. Young parts typically densely puberulent. Twigs smooth, with very small obscure stipule scars. Buds small, obtuse, typically depressed within the twig apex; lateral buds more or less supra-axillary, apical buds borne on a more or less prominent prolongation of the axis above the first leaf. Stipules minute, linear, fugaceous. Leaves spiral, usually elliptic to oblong, very variable, with reticulate intercostals (excl. *St. cordifolius*) and prominent geniculate petiole. Flowers in subterminal axillary racemes or panicles, or inflorescence more or less ramiflorous and reduced to a shortly pedunculate subcymose cluster or single flower. Flowers pale or dark lime yellow, or white with chrome yellow anthers, nodding, with patent perianth exposing the stamens closely appressed in a cone round the style; sepals imbricate, lanceolate, acuminate or acute; petals oblong, falling in a connate ring leaving the stamens attached to the receptacle; stamens 5 and equal or 10 or 15 and more or less unequal; filaments very short; anthers linear, tapering, the outer sacs longer than the inner pair, endporous, completely concealing the style; appendage shorter than, or only slightly exceeding, apex of outer anthers; ovary ovoid, densely pubescent, small, without stylopodium; style 2-3 times length of ovary, with obscure stigma. Fruit sepals short, equal, patent or reflexed; nut globose to ovoid, pale brown verrucose, with thick corky fibrous pericarp and distinct loculicidal sutures; germination hypogeal, the plumule becoming freed by elongation of the cotyledonary petioles; cotyledons subequal, ruminate, fleshy, reddish, eventually expanding and abscissing while the first 2 pairs of opposite true leaves are opening.

D i s t r. Endemic. 15 species. Confined to the wet zone, from the Knuckles region south and westwards, and eastwards to Rakwana, with the exception of *St. acuminatus*, which occurs in Badulla district in the intermediate zone.

E c o l. Growing especially as small or large gregarious groups, in the understorey or on river banks in the lowlands, or as frequently common to subdominant trees in the mid-mountain forests at 1000-1600 m. Each species has its own well-defined habit, geographical and ecological range. There is much allopatric variation and species definition can be difficult on this account. Flowering apparently at almost any time of the year; many appear to be found with a few individuals sporadically flowering in each population at all times. The flowers are seen to be visited by small bees, which alight upside down on the stigma and bite at the anther apices. Anthers have not been observed to dehisce in nature and this may explain their end-porous condition in some herbarium specimens. They are only faintly scented.

U s e . Not considered at present of any economic importance.

V e r n. Mendora.

KEY TO THE SPECIES

1 Stamens 5; ovary 2-celled

  2 Nerves prominent below, shallowly depressed above; intercostals very slender, densely scalariform; midrib obscurely depressed above.....................**5. St. cordifolius**

  2 Nerves very slender and hardly more elevated than the reticulate intercostals on either surface..**6. St. elegans**

1 Stamens (10–)15; ovary 3-celled

  3 Flowering inflorescence exceeding 5 cm long, axillary, bearing at least 6 flowers

    4 Nerves 20–23 pairs, prominent beneath; lamina large, oblong; fruit ovoid, acute, ribbed ....**4. St. ceylanicus**

    4 Nerves less than 15 pairs; lamina not as above; fruit globose, smooth

      5 Lamina broadly ovate, with subcordate base and obscure midrib above, in mature trees ....**7. St. gardneri**

      5 Lamina lanceolate, with obtuse base and midrib evident above in mature trees......
....**1. St. acuminatus**

  3 Flowering inflorescences not exeeding 4.5 cm long, bearing at most 5 flowers, generally ramiflorous at least in fruit

    6 Mature tree lamina acute to retuse

      7 Midrib narrowly keeled above..............................**11. St. oblongifolius**

      7 Midrib obscurely depressed above

        8 Nerves narrowly depressed above, prominent below...............**15. St. rigidus**

        8 Nerves hardly raised on either surface, though more so below.....**14. St. revolutus**

    6 Lamina prominently acuminate

      9 Lamina ovate, typically less than twice as long as broad..............**2. St. affinis**

      9 Lamina oblong to lanceolate

        10 Nerves and intercostals depressed above; nerves more or less anastomosing within margin

          11 Nerves not exceeding 9 pairs; midrib prominent above..........**8. St. lanceolatus**

          11 Nerves typically more than 12 pairs (saplings excluded)

            12 Midrib raised above; medium-sized tree.....................**12. St. petiolaris**

            12 Midrib depressed above; understorey tree.................**3. St. canaliculatus**

        10 Nerves elevated above, not anastomosing within the margin

          13 Fruit large, ovoid, acute, ribbed; nerves at least 9 pairs; lamina acuminate......
....**13. St. reticulatus**

          13 Fruit small, globose, obtuse, smooth; nerves c. 6 pairs; lamina caudate

            14 Large tree; intercostals densely reticulate, almost as prominent as nerves below
....**10. St. nitidus**

            14 Understorey shrub or small tree; intercostals very slender, laxly reticulate, hardly raised below.......................................**9. St. lancifolius**

1. Stemonoporus acuminatus (Thw.) Beddome, Fl. Sylv. 100. 1870; Trimen, Handb. Fl. Ceylon 1: 133. 1895; id. 5: 383; Alston in id. 6: 26. 1931; Lewis, Trees and Fl. Pl. of W. and Sab. Prov. 37. 1902. Lectotype: *C.P. 3687.* (PDA).

Vateria acuminata Thw., Enum. Pl. Zeyl. 403. 1864.

Vateria jucunda Thw. ex Trimen, Cat. 10. 1885; Dyer in Hook. f., Fl. Br. Ind. 1: 314. 1872, nomen.

Vesquella acuminata (Thw.) Heim, Rech. Dipt. 90. 1892.

Sunapteopsis jucunda (Thw. ex Trimen.) Heim, id. 92.

Small to large canopy tree, –30 m tall, –3 m girth. Young twig fugaceous buff puberulent, inflorescence and sepals outside persistently so, otherwise glabrous. Twig slender or stout, rugulose, drying red-brown distally, much branched. Lamina 6–16 × 1.7–7 cm, lanceolate, subcoriaceous to coriaceous, drying pale grey-brown, with broadly cuneate to obtuse base and –2 cm long slender, or short, tapering acumen; nerves 10–12 pairs, very slender but raised below and evident above; intercostals densely subreticulate, slightly elevated below, evident above; midrib slender but prominent below, narrowly elevated above; petiole 10–27 mm long, c. 2 mm diam., prominently geniculate. Inflorescence –6 cm long, c. 2 mm diam. at base, axillary, bearing –8 flowers, ascending, shortly branched or unbranched; pedicel –4 mm long; bud –6 × 5 mm, ovoid, acute; corolla at anthesis c. 12 mm diam.; stamens 15. Fruit unknown. Sapling lamina –18 × 5 cm, with –3 cm long caudate acumen, and –16 pairs of nerves.

D i s t r. Along the eastern margin of the wet zone, in the eastern Sinharaja and Kiribatgala northwards to Pelmadulla and in Ambagamuwa district north of Adam's Peak.

E c o l. Abundant there in mid-mountain forests between 900 and 1300 m, and down to 600 m on exposed knolls and spurs. Flowering sporadically at all times.

S p e c i m e n s E x a m i n e d. KANDY DISTRICT: Ambagamuwa *s. coll. C.P. 3687* (PDA, B, K); between Madmahanuwara and Alutnuwara, *s. coll. C.P. 3595* (PDA, K). BADULLA DISTRICT: Badulla, *s. coll. C.P. 3474, 3595* (in Part) (PDA). RATNAPURA DISTRICT: Lauderdale, Rakwana, *Worthington 6072* (K); Kurulugala, Rakwana, *Ashton 2125, 2126* (PDA); Kiribatgala, Pelmadulla, *Ashton 2121, 2122, 2123, 2124, 2133* (PDA).

N o t e. Trimen confused this species with *Vatica obscura* Thw.; *C.P. 3595* is a mixture with that species, and was wrongly cited by him as from Badulla. He correctly recognised two forms: *a* with prominent, oblique nerves, and *b* with hardly elevated spreading nerves, though his further distinguishing character, the number of nerves, merely reflects that one collection was from a sapling. *Ashton 2125, 2126* (form *b*) confirm that these forms are distinct, form *b* apparently occurring in the intermediate zone, and form *a* only in the wet zone part of the species range. Trimen described form *b* from *C.P. 3595*, annotated 'between Medamahanuwara and Alutnuwara', in other words somewhere along the main Kandy-East coast road as it crosses south of the Knuckles massif but before it finally crosses east of the Mahaweli Ganga at Mahayangana. Scrutiny of the maps suggested that the only forested site in that area, at least at present, is on the hill Kurulugala, which is 'by the Mahaweli' as Trimen describes the locality. Patient search failed to reveal any dipterocarps in this forest, indeed it appeared far too dry for *Stemonoporus*.

It seems extraordinary, that almost the only other locality for form *b* is a hill of exactly the same name east of the Sinharaja, and I suggest that the present annotations on *C.P. 3595* represent a misunderstanding of the collecting locality.

2. Stemonoporus affinis Thw., Kew. J. Bot. 6: 68. 1854; Enum. Pl. Zeyl. 38. 1858; Trimen, Handb. Fl. Ceylon 1: 134. 1895; Alston, id. 6: 26. 1931. Type: *C.P. 2430*.

Vateria affinis Thw., Enum. Pl. Zeyl. 403. 1864; Dyer in Hook. f., Fl. Br. Ind. 1: 314. 1872.
Vateria thwaitesii DC., Prod. 16 (2): 621. 1868.

Canopy tree, –15 m tall, –1 m girth, with irregular hemispherical crown and twisted branches. Inflorescence and base of calyx outside sparsely puberulent, ovary densely so, otherwise glabrous. Twig slender, ribbed, drying dark brown, much branched. Lamina 4.5–13 × 2.7–7 cm, more or less broadly ovate, with broadly cuneate to typically subcordate base and –2.5 cm long slender tapering acumen; nerves 9–11 pairs slender but prominent below, evident but more or less channelled above, arched; intercostals laxly subscalariform; midrib slender but prominent below, evident and elevated above; petiole 8–25 mm long, c. 1.5 mm diam., slender. Inflorescences –15 mm long, slender, few-flowered; flowers –15 mm diam. at anthesis, white with 15 slightly unequal yellow stamens. Fruit –2.5 cm diam., globose, subtended by the –8 × 4 mm subrevolute patent sepals. Sapling lamina lanceolate, with –3.5 cm long slender petiole.

D i s t r. Apparently confined to the Knuckles massif; Alston's records from elsewhere appear to be based on misidentifications.

E c o l. Common, even semigregarious, in the canopy and understorey of mid-mountain forests between 1100 and 1600 m. Flowering sporadically throughout the year.

S p e c i m e n s E x a m i n e d. KANDY DISTRICT: Hunasgiriya, *s. coll. C.P. 2430* (PDA, K); Rangala, *Lewis s.n.*, September 1888 (PDA); Corbett's Gap, Rangala Road, *Ashton 2055, 2056*, (PDA, US); *Worthington 5470* (K); Knuckles, *de Silva 18* (PDA).

3. Stemonoporus canaliculatus Thw., Enum. Pl. Zeyl. 38. 1858; Trimen, Handb. Fl. Ceylon 1: 135. 1895. Type: *C.P. 3413*.

Vateria canaliculata Thw., Enum. Pl. Zeyl. 403. 1864; Dyer in Hook. f., Fl. Br. Ind. 1: 315. 1872.

An extraordinary hardly branching or unbranched treelet, –15 m tall but –15 cm girth only; the stems later flopping over and then coppicing at the base. Twig, leaf bud, nervation below and petiole, pedicel and calyx outside more or less densely caducous yellow-brown puberulent, lamina undersurface sparsely so. Twig slender, ribbed, becoming dark grey-brown. Lamina 7 × 2 (on branches) –35 × 12 (on erect stems) cm, elliptic-lanceolate, coriaceous, with cuneate base and –13 mm long slender acumen; nerves 11–20 pairs, ascending, arched round and forming a more or less distinct looped intra-marginal nerve just within the margin, slender but prominent below, more or less prominently depressed above as also the midrib; intercostals distinctly raised below, more or less depressed above, laxly subreticulate; petiole 1.5–6 cm long, c. 2 mm diam., slender, prominently geniculate. Flowers solitary, axillary; pedicels very short; corolla –18 mm diam. at anthesis, white with 15 yellow subequal stamens. Fruit –3 cm diam., depressed globose to globose, smooth, with –8 × 4 mm subacute patent sepals.

D i s t r. Hiniduma Pattuwa, Reigam and Pasdun Korales, S.W. Ceylon; including Kanneliya F.R., Nellowe, Hewesse, and Hiniduma Kande.

E c o l. Locally common and gregarious in the understorey of Mixed Dipterocarp forest on yellow podsolic soils on low hills; often associated with *St. reticulatus.* Flowering in April; irregular and sporadic.

S p e c i m e n s E x a m i n e d. GALLE DISTRICT: Nellowe, *s. coll. C.P. 3413* (PDA, B, K); Hiniduma Kande, *Lewis s.n.*, 9.3.1881 (PDA); Kanneliya F.R., *Ashton 2046* (PDA), *Meijer 545* (PDA); Nellowe-Pellawatta Road, *Ashton 2073* (PDA). KALUTARA DISTRICT: Pasdun Korale, *s. coll. C.P. 3413* (PDA, B, K).

4. Stemonoporus ceylanicus (Wight) Alston in Trimen, Handb. Fl. Ceylon 6: 26. 1931 (as *St. zeylanicus*). Type: *C.P. 3415.*

Vateria ceylanica Wight. Ill. 1: 88. 1840; Dyer in Hook. f., Fl. Br. Ind. 1: 314. 1872.
Stemonoporus wightii Thw., Enum. Pl. Zeyl. 37. 1858; Trimen, Handb. Fl. Ceylon 1: 132. 1885; Lewis, Trees and Fl. Pl. of W. and Sab. Prov. 36. 1902.
Vateria wightii Thw., id. 403. 1864.

Medium-sized monopodial tree, –30 m tall, –1.5 m girth, with dense oblong crown; bole branching law. Twig, leaf bud, nervation below, and petiole at first densely pale ocherous-buff puberulent, leaf bud, stipule, inflo-rescence, calyx outside and ovary persistently so. Twig c. 5 mm diam. api-cally, smooth to ribbed, with prominent leaf scars, becoming pale brown. Lamina 10–25 × 8–14 cm, oblong-elliptic, coriaceous, drying pale brown, with obtuse base and obtuse to mucronate apex; nerves 14–24 pairs, arched, promi-nent below, narrowly depressed above as also the more or less evident midrib; intercostals densely subscalariform, elevated below, hardly so above; petiole

2–7 cm long, c. 3 mm diam., long, stout, prominently geniculate. Panicles –12 cm long, –3 mm diam. at base, axillary, white when fresh, with –4 cm long lax branchlets bearing –6 flowers; corolla –18 mm diam. at anthesis, white, with 15 unequal yellow anthers. Fruit (young) c. 1.8×1.6 cm, ovoid, subacute, prominently ribbed, with -9×3 mm reflexed sepals. Sapling lamina prominently caudate.

D i s t r. Ratnapura district and the western margin of the wet zone hills; Sinharaja Forest, Ellaboda Kande, Yatipora, Pelmadulla; Kuruwita, Nambapana, Labugama.

E c o l. Scattered at low altitudes on moist soils near streams in Mixed Dipterocarp forest. Flowering in April.

S p e c i m e n s   E x a m i n e d. RATNAPURA DISTRICT: Sinha Raja Forest, *s. coll. C.P. 3415* (PDA, B, K); Kalatuwawa Reservoir, *Ashton 2059* (PDA), *Meijer 397* (PDA). DISTRICT UNKNOWN: Ellaboda Kande, *Lewis s.n.*, 25.3.1891 (PDA).

5. Stemonoporus cordifolius (Thw.) Alston in Trimen, Handb. Fl. Ceylon 6: 27. 1931; Worthington, Ceylon Trees 71. 1959. Type: *C.P. 2647.*

Monoporandra cordifolia Thw., Kew J. Bot. 6: 70. 1854, Enum. Pl. Zeyl. 39. 1858; Dyer in Hook. f., Fl. Br. Ind. 1: 317. 1874; Beddome, Fl. Sylv., t. 101. 1870; Trimen, Handb. Fl. Ceylon 1: 137. 1893.
Vateria cordifolia Thw., Enum. Pl. Zeyl. 404. 1864.

Medium sized understorey tree, –15 m tall, –1 m girth, with feathery spreading crown branching low on bole. Young twigs, petioles, leaf nerves and midrib below, and panicles caducous buff puberulent, ovary persistently so. Twig c. 1 mm diam. apically, terete, slender but much branched and thickening, becoming pale cream-brown, smooth. Lamina $3.5–11 \times 2–6$ cm, ovate, coriaceous, lustrous, with obtuse to subcordate base and –1.5 cm long prominent slender caudate acumen; typically drying pale tawny; nerves 6–7 pairs, arched, slender but prominent below, obscurely elevated above; intercostals slender, densely subscalariform, hardly raised; midrib prominent below, shallowly depressed above as also the nerves; petiole 1.2–2.5 cm long, c. 0.5 mm diam., very long and slender, geniculate, drying black. Panicles –2 cm long, c. 1 mm diam. at base, short and slender, axillary, bearing –6 flowers on each short branchlet; flowers –7 mm diam. at anthesis, dark lemon yellow throughout; stamens 5; ovary 2-celled. Fruit –1.3 cm diam., globose, apiculate, with -5×2 mm slender patent sepals.

D i s t r. Ambagamuwa and Galboda in Central Province, the southern flanks of the Peak Sanctuary Massif, and eastern Bambarabotuwa.

E c o l. Between 700 and 1000 m alt. in hill Mixed Dipterocarp forest. Locally abundant there in the understorey. Flowering in April.

Specimens Examined. KANDY DISTRICT: Ambagamuwa, *s. coll. C.P. 2647* (PDA, B). RATNAPURA DISTRICT: Between Kuruwita and Eratne, *de Silva 114* (PDA); Balangoda Estate, *Worthington 770, 3228, 3232* (K); N.E. of Carney Estate in Peak Sanctuary, *Ashton 2114* (PDA); Balangoda-Bogawantalawa road in Peak Sanctuary, *Ashton 2139, 2140* (PDA), *Meijer 963* (PDA, US). DISTRICT UNKNOWN: Galboda, *Worthington 6546* (K).

Note. A further collection, *Lewis s.n.*, Medda Kande, Balangoda District, 2.3.1899, differs in having a revolute lamina margin, rufous puberulent young parts, anastomosing nerve endings, and distant intercostals. It has been identified as *St. affinis* by Alston, but has 5 stamens and may represent an undescribed species.

6. Stemonoporus elegans Thw. Alston in Trimen, Handb. Fl. Ceylon 6: 27. 1931. Type: *C.P. 371.*

Monoporandra elegans Thw., Kew J. Bot. 6: 69. 1854; Enum. Pl. Zeyl. 39. 1858; Dyer in Hook. f., Fl. Br. Ind. 1: 317. 1872; Trimen, Handb. Fl. Ceylon 138. 1893.
Vateria elegans Thw., Enum. Pl. Zeyl. 404. 1868.

Small to medium sized monopodial understorey tree, sometimes reaching 20 m tall, –0.7 m girth. Crown feathery, the branches descending and more or less pendant apically. Entirely glabrous. Twigs c. 1 mm diam. apically, very slender, much branched; leaf buds minute. Lamina 4–7 × 2–2.7 cm, ovate to lanceolate, thinly coriaceous, somewhat concave, lustrous, drying tawny-brown, with cuneate base and –1.6 cm long very slender caudate acumen; nerves 6–7 pairs, with shorter intermediates, very slender and hardly elevated on either surface, with almost equally elevated reticulate intercostals; midrib prominent below, obscure, shallowly depressed to applanate above; petiole 7–9 mm long, c. 0.5 mm diam., very slender. Flowers dark lemon yellow, in secund groups of –6 on reduced terminal or axillary –1.5 cm long racemes; pedicel –8 mm long, slender; corolla at anthesis –8 mm diam.; stamens 5; ovary 2-celled. Fruit –12 mm diam., globose, apiculate, verruculose, subtended by –4 mm long slender patent sepals.

Distr. Apparently confined to the southern slopes of the Adam's Peak range, between 700–1100 m alt., in hill Mixed Dipterocarp forest.

Ecol. Locally abundant in the understorey, often in association with *St. cordifolius*. Flowering in April.

Specimens Examined. KANDY DISTRICT: Adam's Peak, *Gardner, C.P. 371* (PDA), *Meijer 509* (PDA, US). RATNAPURA DISTRICT: N.E. of Carney Estate on the southern slopes of the Peak Sanctuary, *Ashton 2115* (PDA).

7. Stemonoporus gardneri Thw., Kew J. Bot. 6: 68. 1854; Enum. Pl. Zeyl. 38. 1858; Trimen, Handb. Fl. Ceylon 1: 133. 1893; Alston in id. 6: 26. 1931; Lewis, Trees and Fl. Pl. of W. and Sab. Prov. 36.1902. Type: *C.P. 1920.*

Vateria gardneri Thw., Enum. Pl. Zeyl. 403. 1864; Dyer in Hook. f., Fl. Br. Ind. 1: 314. 1874; Beddome, Fl. Sylv. t. 99. 1870.

Medium sized main canopy tree, –20 m tall, –2 m girth, with dense spreading hemispherical crown with many ascending twisted branches. Young parts sparsely pale tawny pubescent, fugaceous except at twig apex, leaf bud, and sometimes petiole and raceme. Twig c. 2 mm diam. apically, much branched, somewhat ribbed, with prominent leaf scars. Lamina 4.5–12 × 2–7 cm, ovate, subcoriaceous, somewhat lustrous, drying pale tawny, with obtuse to subcordate base and –1.5 cm long slender tapering acumen; nerves 9–13 pairs, slender but prominent beneath, applanate above as also the densely subreticulate intercostals; midrib prominent beneath, depressed above; petiole 6–28 mm long, c. 2 mm diam., slender, geniculate. Inflorescence –10 cm long, c. 2 mm diam. at base, paniculate, lax, with 3 cm long branchlets each bearing –5 flowers; buds –7 × 6 mm, ovoid, the calyx loosely enclosing the bud; pedicels c. 4 mm long, short; flowers pale lemon-yellow, stamens 15. Fruit –3.5 cm diam., globose, smooth, subtended by –8 × 4 mm long subovate sepals. Young tree lamina –23 × 8.5 cm, lanceolate, with 7 pairs of nerves, the nerves somewhat depressed above, the midrib prominently raised above; petiole –5 cm long.

D i s t r. From Ramboda southwards to the eastern Sinha Raja.

E c o l. Occurring in mid-mountain forests between 1200 and 1600 m alt., and often dominant in the upper parts of its altitudinal range. Flowering more or less gregariously most years between January and March.

S p e c i m e n s   E x a m i n e d. NUWARA ELIYA DISTRICT: Rambodde and Langalla, *s. coll. C.P. 1920* (PDA, K). KANDY DISTRICT: Adam's Peak, *s. coll. C.P. 1920* (PDA, K); Maskeliya, *Lewis s.n.*, March 1891 (PDA); Southern slopes of Adam's Peak, *Ashton 2109, 2110, 2112* (PDA). RATNAPURA DISTRICT: Aigburth Estate, Rakwana, *Worthington 2157* (K); Walankande, Sinharaja Forest, *Lewis s.n.*, December 1893 (PDA); Lauderdale, *Worthington 6072* (K).

8. Stemonoporus lanceolatus Thw., Kew J. Bot. 6: 68. 1854; Enum. Pl. Zeyl. 38. 1858; Trimen, Handb. Fl. Ceylon 1: 134. 1893. Type: *C.P. 2658.*

Vateria lanceolata Thw., Enum. Pl. Zeyl. 403. 1864; Dyer in Hook. f., Fl. Br. Ind. 1: 315. 1872.

Small treelet, –6 m tall, –20 cm girth. Twig, leaf bud, petiole and flower pedicel subpersistently densely buff puberulent, midrib below sparsely caducously so. Twig c. 3 mm diam. apically, terete, smooth. Lamina 7.5–19 ×

3.2–8 cm, lanceolate to narrowly elliptic, thinly coriaceous, with obtuse to broadly cuneate base and –1.5 cm long tapering to subcaudate acumen, drying lustrous, orange-brown; nerves 7–12 pairs, slender but prominent below, depressed above, arched; midrib prominent on both surfaces but more so below; intercostals laxly subreticulate; petiole 12–25 mm long, c. 2 mm diam., obscurely geniculate. Flowers solitary, axillary to ramiflorous on –5 mm long pedicels; corolla –14 mm diam. at anthesis; stamens 15. Fruit –2.5 cm diam., globose, verruculose, with –5 × 2 mm more or less reflexed sepals.

D i s t r. Rare: Kuruwita Korale, at Eratne and Demanhandiya.

E c o l. Locally common, in groups on steep rocky hillsides in Mixed Dipterocarp forest at low altitudes. Flowering in March.

S p e c i m e n s   E x a m i n e d. RATNAPURA DISTRICT: Kuruwita, *s. coll. C.P. 2658* (PDA, B, K); Eknaligoda Kande, Kuruwita, *Ashton 2010* (PDA, US).

9. Stemonoporus lancifolius (Thw.) Ashton, Blumea 20 (2): 365. 1972. Type: *C.P. 3412.*

Monoporandra lancifolia Thw., Enum. Pl. Zeyl. 39. 1858.
Vateria lancifolia Thw., Enum. Pl. Zeyl. 404. 1864.
Stemonoporus nitidus ssp. *lancifolius* Dyer in Hook. f., Fl. Br. Ind. 1: 316. 1874; Trimen, Handb. Fl. Ceylon, 1: 136. 1893.
Stemonoporus nervosus Thw. in Trimen, J. Bot. 23: 206, 1885; Handb. Fl. Ceylon l.c. Type: *C.P. 3885.*

Elegant treelet or shrub, with straight ascending stems arising from the base as coppices and later flopping over with pendant leafy twigs. Twigs c. 1 mm diam. apically, slender. Lamina 5–14 × 1.2–4.8 cm, lanceolate, somewhat chartaceous, with broadly cuneate to obtuse base and –2.5 cm long slender to subcaudate acumen; nerves 8–12 pairs, typically very slender and hardly raised below, sometimes more prominent; intercostals very slender, laxly reticulate, hardly elevated, midrib elevated or depressed above; petiole 5–9 mm long, c. 0.5 mm diam., very slender. Flowers borne in groups of –3 on –1 cm long hardly branched slender axillary peduncles; pedicel –12 mm long, slender; corolla –12 mm diam. at anthesis, white; stamens 15, chrome yellow. Nut –15 mm diam., globose, apiculate, with –8 × 2 mm slender patent sepals.

D i s t r. Western part of the wet zone hills: Kitulgala; Hewesse, Pasdun Korale.

E c o l. Occurring in large semigregarious groups on moist soils on hillsides and river banks in Mixed Dipterocarp forest. Flowering sporadically throughout the year.

Specimens Examined. KALUTARA DISTRICT: Hellepel, Pasdun Korale, *s. coll. C.P. 3412* (PDA, B, K); Hewesse, *s. coll. C.P. 3885* (PDA). KEGALLE DISTRICT: Kitulgala Forest, *Ashton 2003* (PDA), *Balakrishnan 343* (PDA).

Note. Apparently a variable species. The few collections all differ in certain leaf characters: *C.P. 3885* possesses relatively more prominent nerves on the undersurface, whereas the Kitulgala collection is the only one with a depressed midrib above.

10. Stemonoporus nitidus Thw., Enum. Pl. Zeyl. 39. 1858; Trimen, Handb. Fl. Ceylon 1: 136. 1893; id. 5: 383. 1900. Type: *C.P. 3483*.

Vateria nitida Thw., Enum. Pl. Zeyl. 403. 1864; Dyer in Hook. f., Fl. Br. Ind. 1: 316. 1872.

Medium sized to large main canopy tree, –30 m tall, –2.5 m girth, with oblong or compact hemispherical crown. Twigs c. 1 mm diam. apically, slender. Lamina 5.5–12×2.5–4 cm, lanceolate, coriaceous, with broadly cuneate base and –1.5 cm long subcaudate acumen; nerves 6–8 pairs, very slender and hardly more prominent than the densely reticulate intercostals on either surface; midrib prominent on both surfaces though more so below; petiole 5–16 mm long, c. 1 mm diam., very slender, geniculate. Flowers apparently borne singly; pedicel short; stamens 15. Fruit –1 cm diam., globose, apiculate, subtended by –5×3 mm patent sepals. Sapling lamina with –3 cm long slender caudate acumen.

Distr. Gilimale F.R. southwards through the lowland Mixed Dipterocarp forests of Sinharaja to Pasdun Korale.

Ecol. In small groups on ridges below 1000 m alt.; apparently the principal Mendora reaching timber sizes in the lower ridge forests of Sinharaja. Flowering in April, at irregular intervals.

Specimens Examined. GALLE DISTRICT: Hiniduma Korale, *s. coll. C.P. 3483* (PDA, K); Sinharaja, North of Nellowe, *Ashton 2082* (PDA). RATNAPURA DISTRICT: Sinharaja Forest, *Worthington 3668* (K).

11. Stemonoporus oblongifolius Thw., Kew J. Bot. 6: 68. 1854, Enum. Pl. Zeyl. 38. 1858; Trimen, Handb. Fl. Ceylon 1: 135. 1893. Type specimen: *C.P. 2646*.

Vateria oblongifolia Thw., Enum. Pl. Zeyl. 403. 1864; Dyer in Hook. f., Fl. Br. Ind. 1: 315. 1872.

Medium sized tree, –20 m tall, –1 m girth; crown irregular, with ascending twisted branches and ascending leaves; bole usually of irregular shape. Young twigs, buds, inflorescences, pedicels, petiole and midrib below persistently densely shortly buff puberulent, elsewhere glabrescent. Twig c. 4 mm diam., stout, much branched. Leaf buds –3 × 3 mm, subglobose, obtuse. Lamina 4–12 × 2.5–4.5 cm, elliptic to oblanceolate, thickly coriaceous, frequently somewhat concave to revolute, with broadly cuneate base and obtuse to subacute apex, drying pale tawny and lustrous below, dull grey-brown above; nerves 7–10 pairs, spreading, arched, slender, somewhat sinuate, elevated on both surfaces but more so below as also the subreticulate intercostals; midrib shortly prominent below, narrowly keeled above; petiole 7–22 mm long, c. 2 mm diam. Inflorescence –3 cm long, short, stout, terminal or axillary, bearing –5 flowers; pedicel –5 mm long; flower buds –7 × 5 mm, broadly ovoid; stamens 15. Fruit –2.8 cm diam., subglobose, with 3 shallow loculicidal grooves, subtended by –6 × 3 mm broad reflexed sepals. Young tree lamina –16 × 6 cm, shortly broadly acuminate.

D i s t r. Along both north and south sides of the Peak Sanctuary range; 'Ambagamuwa'.

E c o l. Locally common in the canopy of mid-mountain forests between 1200 and 1400 m. Flowering sporadically throughout the year.

S p e c i m e n s E x a m i n e d. KANDY DISTRICT: Ambagamuwa, *s. coll. C.P. 2646* (PDA, B, K); Maskeliya side of Adam's Peak, *Ashton 2007* (PDA), *Worthington 2739, 2744* (K), *Kostermans 24259, 24155, 24178* (PDA); Southern slopes of Adam's Peak, *Ashton 2111* (PDA).

12. Stemonoporus petiolaris Thw., Enum. Pl. Zeyl. 38. 1858; Trimen, Handb. Fl. Ceylon 1: 135. 1893; Alston in id. 6: 26. 1931. Type specimen: *C.P. 3151.*

Vateria petiolaris Thw., Enum. Pl. Zeyl. 403. 1864; Dyer in Hook. f., Fl. Br. Ind. 1: 365. 1874.

Medium sized tree, –20 m tall, –1 m girth. Young parts buff pubescent, glabrescent except on bud, twigs and petiole. Twig c. 3 mm diam. apically, terete, smooth. Lamina 8–30 × 3.5–10 cm, narrowly oblong, coriaceous, with obtuse to broadly cuneate base and –2 cm long subcaudate acumen; nerves 10–19 pairs with more or less distinct shorter intermediates, arched, slender but prominent below, applanate to shallowly depressed above, coalescing within the margin to form a looped intramarginal nerve; intercostals distantly subscalariform, slender but prominent below, applanate above; midrib slender but prominent on both surfaces, more so below than above; petiole 2.2–7 cm long, c. 2 mm diam., slender, prominently geniculate. Flowers pale yellow, in groups of –5 in –1 cm long constricted axillary to ramiflorous inflorescences; pedicels –3 mm long, short; corolla –14 mm diam. at anthesis; stamens 10–15. Fruit unknown.

D i s t r. Kitulgala in Central Province; Gilimale, Ratnapura District. Apparently now rare.

416 DIPTEROCARPACEAE

E c o l. In Mixed Dipterocarp forest on deep well-drained soils in the low-lands. Flowering in February (Trimen).

S p e c i m e n s E x a m i n e d. KEGALLE DISTRICT: Kitulgala, *s. coll. C.P. 3151* (PDA, B, K). RATNAPURA DISTRICT: Gilimale, F.R., *Ashton 2014, 2038* (PDA), *Meijer 404* (PDA).

N o t e. Resembling *St. canaliculatus*, but of very different habit, with entirely pale yellow flower, raised midrib and applanate intercostals above, and with more slender petiole. The specimen cited by Alston (l.c. 26) under this name should be referred to *St. gardneri*.

13. Stemonoporus reticulatus Thw., Enum. Pl. Zeyl. 38. 1858; Trimen, Handb. Fl. Ceylon 1: 136. 1893; 5: 383. 1900. Type: *C.P. 3414*.

Vateria reticulata Thw., Enum. Pl. Zeyl. 403. 1864; Dyer in Hook. f., Fl. Br. Ind. 1: 316. 1872.

Medium sized tree, –25 m tall, –1.5 m girth, with dense oblong crown, branching low on bole. Young parts buff to pale rufous puberulent, subper-sistent on ovary, pedicels and inflorescence, petiole and twigs, otherwise fugaceous. Twig c. 3 mm diam. apically, rather stout, much branched. Lamina 5–17 × 2.5–9 cm, ovate-lanceolate, thickly coriaceous, with broadly cuneate to obtuse base, subrevolute margin and –2 cm long slender acumen, drying pale orange-brown; nerves 8–12 pairs with short intermediates, very slender and hardly raised below, distinctly so above; intercostals scalariform, distinctly elevated below; midrib prominent below, depressed but more or less evident above. Petiole 1.1–5 cm long, c. 3 mm diam., prominently geni-culate. Flowers in groups of –5 in –5 cm long reduced axillary to ramiflorous inflorescences; corolla at anthesis –2 cm diam., white; anthers 15, chrome yellow. Fruit –5 × 4 cm, ovoid, subacute, prominently ribbed, with –10 × 4 mm reflexed sepals at the more or less impressed base. Sapling lamina with –3 cm long caudate acumen.

D i s t r. Apparently confined to Hiniduma Korale.

E c o l. Known from Nellowe and Kanneliya F.R. where it is a locally common main canopy tree on deep leached soils in Mixed Dipterocarp forest at low altitudes. Flowering sporadically throughout the year.

S p e c i m e n s E x a m i n e d. GALLE DISTRICT: Near Nellowe, *s. coll. C.P. 3414* (PDA, K); Nellowe-Pelawatte Road, *Ashton 2092* (PDA); Kan-neliya F.R., *Ashton 2041, 2048* (PDA), *Worthington 6036* (K), *Meijer 540, 990* (PDA), *Cramer 3071* (PDA).

14. Stemonoporus revolutus Trimen ex Hook. f., Handb. Fl. Ceylon 5: 384. 1900. Holotype: *Lewis s.n.*, Dec. 1893, Walankanda, Panilla (PDA).

Medium sized tree. Young parts fugaceous puberulent, otherwise glab-rous. Twig c. 4 mm diam., stout, much branched, drying dark brown.

Lamina 4–10 × 2–5 cm, more or less elliptic, thickly coriaceous, prominently revolute, more or less shallowly retuse, with broadly cuneate base, drying lustrous chocolate-brown; nerves 8–14 pairs, very slender, hardly elevated on either surface though more so below as also the reticulate intercostals; midrib prominent below, obscurely depressed above. Petiole 10–12 mm long, c. 3 mm diam., stout, hardly geniculate. Flowers borne in groups of –5 in –3 cm long axillary to ramiflorous inflorescences; buds –6 × 4 mm, ovoid; stamens 15. Fruit unknown. Sapling lamina –17 × 6 cm, subacute, with –19 pairs of nerves and –2.3 cm long geniculate petiole.

D i s t r. Sinharaja Forest: Kukul Korale and Walankande; Kiribatgala south-west of Pelmadulla.

E c o l. Apparently a very local canopy tree in ridge forests at 900–1300 m. Flowering apparently sporadically at all times.

S p e c i m e n s E x a m i n e d. RATNAPURA DISTRICT: Kiribatgala near Kahawatte, *Livera s.n.*, (PDA); Facing Sinharaja overlooking Kukul Korale, ridge 3000 ft., *Lewis s.n.*, January 1893 (PDA, K); Walankande, Panilla, *Lewis s.n.*, December 1893 (PDA).

15. Setmonoporus rigidus Thw., Kew J. Bot. 6: 69. 1854; Enum. Pl. Zeyl. 38. 1858; Trimen, Handb. Fl. Ceylon 1: 134. 1893. Type: *C.P. 2645.*

Vateria rigida Thw., Enum. Pl. Zeyl. 403. 1864; Dyer in Hook. f., Fl. Br. Ind. 1: 315. 1874.

Medium sized tree. Young parts buff puberulent, persistent on twig and petiole, inflorescence, sepals outside and ovary. Twig c. 4 mm diam., stout, much branched. Lamina 6–14 × 3.5–5.5 cm, narrowly elliptic to oblanceolate, thickly coriaceous, with connate base and subacute to retuse acumen, drying chocolate-brown with blackish nerves and midrib below; nerves 7–11 pairs, ascending, rather straight, prominent beneath, depressed above as also the midrib; intercostals subscalariform, more or less obscure, hardly elevated. Petiole 1–2.5 cm long, c. 2 mm diam., more or less obscurely geniculate, dry-ing black. Flowers in congested axillary to ramiflorous clusters; pedicels –2 mm long, very short; flower bud –5 × 4 mm; stamens 15. Fruit unknown. Sapling leaves narrowly oblanceolate, shortly acuminate; nerves slender, elevated on both surfaces; intercostals elevated below; petiole short, slender.

D i s t r. Rare, known only from Ambagamuwa. Apparently once replac-ing *St. oblongifolius* in the mid-mountain forests north of Maskeliya in Central Province, in an area now mostly under tea.

E c o l. Flowering in December (Trimen).

S p e c i m e n E x a m i n e d. KANDY DISTRICT: Ambagamuwa, *s. coll. C.P. 2645* (PDA, K).

Excluded Species

Stemonoporus moonii Thw., Enum. Pl. Zeyl. 39. 1858; Trimen, Handb. Fl. Ceylon 1: 137. 1893; Alston in id. 6: 27. 1931. Type: *C.P. 1792.*
Vateria mooni Thw., Enum. Pl. Zeyl. 403. 1864; Dyer in Hook. f., Fl. Br. Ind. 1: 316. 1872.

This extraordinary, now sterile, collection, with its persistent long linear stipules and narrowly oblanceolate leaves with relatively short geniculate petioles clustered round the stout twig apex, is unlikely to be a dipterocarp; the leaf arrangement, the terminal bud, and the stipules at once exclude it from this genus. Without fertile material it is impossible to identify, but could belong to *Tiliaceae, Bombacaceae* or *Sterculiaceae,* or even *Euphorbiaceae.*

6. VATERIA

L., Gen. Pl. 153. 1737; ed. 5. 231. 1754. Type species: *Vateria indica* L. *Hemiphractus* Turcz., Bull. Soc. Nat. Mosc. 1: 262. 1859.

Large trees. Bole usually somewhat crooked, frequently tapering, without true buttresses though bole sometimes ribbed towards the base. Crown at first oblong, dense, monopodial, becoming irregularly narrowly hemispherical if in closed forest, with a few large ascending twisted pale branches. Bark surface smooth, conspicuously very pale grey, hoop-marked, becoming thinly irregularly flaky leaving scalloped surfaces below as in *Cotylelobium;* outer bark thin; inner bark c. 8 mm thick, homogeneous pale yellow-brown; wood pale yellow, fine-grained, rather soft. Young parts rufous scabrid tomentose. Twigs stout, rugulose. Stipules hastate, subpersistent, leaving conspicuous pale horizontal scars. Lamina large, more or less oblong, coriaceous, with prominent nervation below and depressed nerves and midrib above; intercostals scalariform. Petiole long, stout, geniculate. Inflorescence subterminal axillary, paniculate, lax, ascending, twice branched, the branches long, bearing many secund pedicellate flowers and conspicuous ovate acute bracts; sepals slightly imbricate; petals oblong; stamens many, subequal, with very short filaments, long linear 2-celled anthers the abaxial sacs of which are prolonged apically into recurved awns, and short connectival appendages; ovary short, ovoid, tomentose, crowned by a slender columnar glabrous style many times its length. Fruit large, ovoid, acute, with short equal more or less reflexed sepals and thick corky pericarp with 3 loculicidal sutures along which it splits at germination. Germination hypogeal, the large ruminate pinkish unequal cotyledons eventually becoming released but not apparently photosynthesising.

D i s t r. 2 species: Southern India (1), Ceylon (1). Occurring both in forest and in cultivation.

Vateria copallifera (Retz.) Alston in Trimen, Handb. Fl. Ceylon 6: 26. 1931; Fischer, Kew Bull. 51. 1932; Worthington, Ceylon Trees 70. 1959. Holotype: *Koenig, s.n.* (LD).

Elaeocarpus copalliferus Retz., Obs. 4: 27. 1786.
Vateria acuminata Heyne, Arzneik., 11: 15. 1830; Dyer in Hook. f., Fl. Br. Ind. 1: 313. 1872; Trimen, Handb. Fl. Ceylon 1: 131. 1893; Lewis, Trees and Fl. Pl. of W. and Sab. Prov. 36. 1902; non Thw. 1864 (*Stemonoporus acuminatus*).
Vateria indica sensu Blume, Mus. Bot. 2: 29. 1852; Thw., Enum. Pl. Zeyl. 37. 1858; A. DC., Prod. 16 (2): 625. 1868; Moon, Cat. 42. 1824; non L.

Large tree, –40 m tall, –4 m girth under forest conditions, but never so large in cultivation; branches dense, ascending. Twigs and panicles densely persistently dark fulvous tufted tomentose; petiole, lamina nerves and midrib below sparsely so; outside of stipules and bracts, parts of perianth exposed in bud, ovary and fruit densely evenly fulvous pubescent (pinkish mauve when fresh). Twig c. 5 mm diam., stout, much branched; stipules –25 × 6 mm, narrowly hastate, not at first caducous, persistently loosely clustered around the hidden apical buds. Lamina 11–50 × 5–18 cm, large, broadly to narrowly oblong, thickly coriaceous, drying dull tawny-brown, with obtuse to cordate base and –8 mm long short abrupt tapering acute acumen; nerves 18–25 pairs, prominent below, spreading; intercostals distant, elevated beneath; nervation and midrib depressed above; petiole 1.8–5.5 cm long, usually long, c. 4 mm diam., stout, prominently geniculate. Panicles –25 cm long, –4 mm diam. at base, stout, with –12 cm long branches bearing –8 more or less secund flowers; bracts –10 × 6 mm, ovate, concave, acute; flower bud –12 × 8 mm, lanceolate, relatively large; sepals hastate, subequal, imbricate at base only, subacute; petals cream, oblong; stamens 45–55, anthers yellow. Fruit sepals –15 × 7 mm, lanceolate, subacute, reflexed, subequal; nut –11 × 7 cm, very large, ovoid, apiculate, with –2.5 cm thick fibrous spongy pericarp and deeply impressed base; cotyledons markedly unequal, the larger bilobed. Seedling lamina with c. 16 pairs of nerves, at first smaller than in mature tree, with c. 2 cm long relatively slender petiole; stipules –12 mm long, acicular.

D i s t r. Widespread in the wet zone, from Colombo to Matara and Kandy.

E c o l. Common both in lowland Mixed Dipterocarp forest and in cultivation, on moist hillsides and along river banks, below 1000 m altitude. Flowering in late April, apparently regularly.

U s e s. The wood is valueless but the bark is used for arresting fermentation; the fruit is ground into a flour, and the clear resin is tapped for varnish.

V e r n. Hal.

Specimens Examined. KANDY DISTRICT: Ambagamuwa, *s. coll. C.P. 1918* (PDA, K); Peradeniya Royal Botanical Gardens, *s. coll. s.n.*, 10.5.1923 (PDA); Hantane Estate, Kandy, *Worthington 6133* (K); Imboolpitiya, Nawalapitiya, *Worthington 112* (K); Nawalapitiya-Ginigathhena Road, mile 1, culvert 14, *Ashton 2001* (PDA), *Balakrishnan 1186* (PDA); Kolugala, Tumpane Valley, *Worthington 1474* (K); Nawalapitiya mile 24, *Kostermans 24049* (PDA). GALLE DISTRICT: Galle, *s. coll. C.P. 1918* (PDA, K); Kanneliya F.R., *Ashton 2044* (PDA), *Meijer 548* (PDA); Bentota, *Worthington 2476* (K). RATNAPURA DISTRICT: Induruwa in Gilimale, Ratnapura, *Worthington 6464* (K). COLOMBO DISTRICT: Labugama reservoir catchment, *Ashton 2058* (PDA), *Worthington 3474* (K); Wagga, Avissawella, *Ashton 2061* (PDA); Avissawella, *Meijer 394, 395* (PDA); Indikade, *Wijesinghe 50, 51* (PDA). KEGALLE DISTRICT: Ballahele, Kelani Valley, *Worthington 2102* (K). LOCALITY UNKNOWN: *C. Paulett, s.n.* (K).

N o t e. I have not examined the type, and rely on Alston and Fischer's identification.

7. VATICA

L., Mant. 2: 152. 1771. Type species: *V. chinensis* L. *Isauxis* Reichb., Nom. 210. 1841.

Small to medium sized, rarely large, trees. Bole frequently sinuate. Buttresses absent or small, thick. Crown irregular, oblong, sympodial, of the main canopy or understorey. Bark surface pale grey, smooth and hoop-marked; outer bark thin; inner bark pale brown to pink-brown, homogeneous, with narrow fingers of dark phloem fibres; cambium cream; sapwood pale yellow, hard and close textured. Resin clear. Young parts more or less shortly densely caducous pubescent. Leaves spiral, with reticulate intercostals and very small inconspicuous fugaceous stipules. Inflorescences somewhat irregularly paniculate; buds fusiform; sepals valvate, subequal; petals narrowly oblong, cream frequently with a purplish tinge, falling separately; stamens 15, in 3 verticils, single stamens alternating with pairs, short, the inner row slightly longer than the outer row; filaments short, dilated at base, more or less tapering and filiform below the anthers; anthers broadly oblong, the inner pollen sacs smaller than the outer; appendage to connective short, rarely as long as the anthers, more or less deltoid, stout; ovary ovoid, superior (Ceylon spp.), shortly densely pubescent; no stylopodium; style columnar, short, glabrous, somewhat expanded below the prominent conical 3-lobed stigma. Fruit (Ceylon spp.) relatively large, ovoid to globose, with thick corky pericarp, subtended by the subequal short thinly coriaceous more or less recurved lanceolate sepals; pedicel relatively long, slender. Fruit splitting along 3 loculicidal sutures at germination; hypogeal, the subequal lobed or

laciniate fleshy cotyledons later becoming released but hardly photosynthesising. Sapling leaves somewhat larger but otherwise similar to those of mature
trees.

D i s t r. c. 80 species: Southern India, Ceylon, Assam, Burma, Indo-
China, Hainan, south-eastwards to New Guinea and the Entrecasteaux
Islands. 3 species in Ceylon, each with a very distinct distribution.

U s e s. The wood is durable and hard. It can be used for construction
purposes, the resin is sometimes collected from *V. chinensis*.

V e r n. Mendora.

KEY TO THE SPECIES

1 Lamina with 6–8 pairs of nerves..**1. V. affinis**
1 Lamina with at least 11 pairs of nerves
  2 Petiole exceeding 2 cm long, stout; lamina ovate, nerves prominent beneath, frequently
    branched distally..**2. V. chinensis**
  2 Petiole –1.8 cm long, slender; lamina narrowly elliptic-lanceolate; nerves very slender,
    not branched..**3. V. obscura**

1. Vatica affinis Thw., Enum. Pl. Zeyl. 404. 1864., Dyer in Hook. f., Fl. Br.
Ind. 1: 303. 1872; Trimen, Handb. Fl. Ceylon 1: 128. 1893. Type: *C.P. 3416.*

Medium sized canopy tree, –35 m tall, –2 m girth, with compact hemispherical crown. Young parts pinkish puberulent, subpersistent only on leaf
bud, cyme, and calyx and corolla outside; fruit sparsely cream pubescent.
Twig c. 2 mm diam. apically, smooth. Bud –3 × 2 mm, ovoid, acute. Stipule
fugaceous. Lamina 6–16 × 2.5–6.5 cm, lanceolate to elliptic, subequal, coriaceous, drying tawny-brown with the nerves blackish below, with broadly
cuneate base and –1 cm long slender acumen; nerves 6–8 pairs, arched, ascending, bluntly raised on both surfaces as also the midrib; intercostals
elevated on both surfaces, reticulate; petiole 13–25 mm long, c. 2 mm diam.,
geniculate, drying blackish. Cyme –4 cm long, terminal or subterminal axillary, c. 2 mm diam. at base (in flower); flowers typical. Fruit –2.5 × 2 cm,
ovoid, obtuse, with 3 indistinct loculicidal grooves; sepals –10 × 8 mm, oblong,
obtuse, subequal, revolute but clasping the base of the nut; pedicel –11 mm
long, slender.

D i s t r. Local; S.W. wet zone: Kalutara; Hewesse and elsewhere in Pasdun Korale; Nellowe in Hiniduma Pattuwe.

E c o l. Scattered in Mixed Dipterocarp forest on deep soils on low hills
and sometimes by streams. Flowering in March, sporadically with infrequent
heavy years.

S p e c i m e n s E x a m i n e d. KALUTARA DISTRICT: Botaloogodda,
Pasdun Korale, *s. coll. C.P. 3416* (PDA, B, K); Nelunkeliya F.R., *Rajalingam
409* (PDA). GALLE DISTRICT: Nellowe-Pelawatte Road, *Ashton 2074*

(PDA); Nellowe, South East margin of Sinharaja Forest, *Ashton 2082* (PDA).

2. Vatica chinensis L., Mant. 2: 242. 1771; Alston in Trimen, Handb. Fl. Ceylon 6: 25. 1931; Worthington, Ceylon Trees 67. 1959. Holotype:? *Hermann, s.n.* (Linnean Herb.).

Vatica roxburghiana Blume, Mus. Bot. 2: 331. 1852; Thw., Enum. Pl. Zeyl. 404. 1864; Dyer in Hook. f., Fl. Br. Ind. 1: 302. 1874; Beddome, Fl. Sylv. t. 95. 1870; Trimen, Handb. Fl. Ceylon 1: 128. 1893; Lewis, Trees and Fl. Pl. of W. and Sab. Prov. 35. 1902.
Isauxis roxburgiana Thw., Enum. Pl. Zeyl. 37. 1858.

Medium sized tree, –30 m tall, –2 m girth, with irregular spreading dense oblong crown often branching low on bole. Twigs, buds, stipules outside, inflorescences, pedicels, parts of perianth exposed in bud, ovary and fruit densely persistently pinkish mauve puberulent; petiole caducously so. Twig c. 3–4 mm diam. apically, stout, smooth, with prominent horizontal stipule scars. Leaf bud –4 × 3 mm, lanceolate, acute. Lamina 9–25 × 3–11 cm, narrowly ovate, with subequal obtuse to broadly cuneate base, tapering distally gradually into an –1.5 cm long subacute acumen; nerves 11–13 pairs, arched, ascending, elevated on both surfaces but more prominent beneath as also the midrib, irregularly disposed along the midrib and frequently branching distally; intercostals very slender and hardly elevated on either surface, densely reticulate. Petiole 2–4.5 cm long, c. 2 mm diam., long, persistently geniculate. Panicle –30 cm long, –3 mm diam. at base, axillary, thrice branched, lax, spreading; flowers typical. Fruit –2.5 cm diam., subglobose, with 3 obscure loculicidal furrows; sepals –15 × 11 mm, ovate, subacute, recurved and more or less appressed to the base of the fruit; pedicel –1.5 cm long, slender.

D i s t r. S.W. India, Ceylon: Western plains of the wet zone from Colombo southwards to Kalutara.

E c o l. Locally common on alluvial river banks, and formerly forming pure stands in seasonal fresh water swamps. Flowering sporadically at any time of year, but mostly in early May.

V e r n. Mendora.

S p e c i m e n s E x a m i n e d. KANDY DISTRICT: Peradeniya Royal Botanical Garden, *Worthington 6836* (K), *Ashton 2100, 2104* (PDA), *de Silva s.n.*, 17.4.23 (PDA). COLOMBO DISTRICT: Heneratgoda Garden, *Simpson 9419* (PDA, K); Nuripitiya, Hanwella, *Ashton 2060* (PDA). RATNAPURA DISTRICT: Paraketiya Estate, Kiriella, Ratnapura, *Ashton 2135* (PDA); Banks of Kulu Ganga, Dambagas Forest, *Samarawickrema 20* (PDA); Galahitiya Forest, *Ramalingam 408* (PDA). LOCALITY UNKNOWN: *Walker 65* (K), *s. coll. C.P. 604* (PDA, K).

3. Vatica obscura Trimen, J. Bot. 23: 203. 1885, Handb. Fl. Ceylon 1: 129. 1893; Lewis, Trees and Fl. Pl. of W. and Sab. Prov. 35. 1902; Worthington, Ceylon Trees 68. 1959.

Small- to medium-sized tree, –30 m tall, –2 m girth, usually with leaning bole. Young parts densely evenly pale buff pubescent, caducous except on panicles, ovary and fruit. Twigs c. 1 mm diam. apically, very slender, much branched. Leaf bud minute. Lamina 7–15 × 1.5–3.5 cm, narrowly lanceolate, drying pale greyish green, thinly coriaceous, with broadly cuneate base, tapering distally into the –1.5 cm long subacute acumen; nerves 11–15 pairs, very slender and hardly raised on either surface, arched, spreading, with shorter intermediates; intercostals densely reticulate, elevated on both surfaces; midrib prominent on both surfaces though more so below. Petiole 7–18 mm long, c. 1 mm diam., very slender, drying black. Panicles –6 cm, long, slender, with –2 cm long many-flowered branchlets, copiously borne in axils and along twigs; flowers sweet-scented, typical. Fruit (immature?) –2.3 cm diam., globose to broadly ovoid, subacute; pericarp with 3 obscure loculicidal furrows; sepals –9 × 4 mm, oblong-elliptic, obtuse, clasping the base of the nut.

D i s t r. Endemic. Eastern and Uva Provinces.

E c o l. Locally abundant in gallery forest along permanent water courses, from Batticaloa southwards to Bintenne, including Galodai, Pulukanawa, and Divulane. Flowering in May, June or July.

V e r n. Tumpalai (T), apparently a corruption of Sinhala: Dunmala.

S p e c i m e n s E x a m i n e d. BADULLA DISTRICT: Bintenne, *Vincent s.n., 1882* (PDA). BATTICALOA DISTRICT: Batticaloa, *Walker 5* (PDA, K), *Livera s.n.* (PDA); Tiraka Odei Nursery, Batticaloa, *Holmes 438* (PDA), *Ramalingam 70* (PDA), *Worthington 5309* (K); Batticaloa-Kandy Road, mile 80, culvert 9, *Worthington 5302* (K); Nuwaragala Reserve, *Casipillai 323* (PDA), *Ramalingam 354* (PDA); Pulukanawa, *Walker s.n.* June 1884 (PDA). AMPARAI DISTRICT: Galodai, *Ashton 2137* (PDA). MONERAGALA DISTRICT: By the Gal Oya at Nigale, *Worthington 4690* (K).

ELATINACEAE

(by S.H. Sohmer*)

Annual or perennial herbs of aquatic habitats, often growing completely submerged, as in species of *Elatine*, more usually emergent, or on dry land as in *Bergia* sp.; leaves opposite or whorled, simple and stipulate; flowers bisexual, small, usually regular, solitary or in axillary dichasia; sepals 3–5, free or connate below; petals 3–4, distinct; stamens 3–5 (–6), biseriate, free, the inner whorl often abortive, with filaments broadened at the base, anthers introrse, dorsifixed, with longitudinal dehiscense; pistil 1, with ovary superior, 3–5 locules and carpels and as many styles with small capitate stigmas; placentation axile and ovules numerous and anatropus; fruit a septicidal capsule with small seeds without endosperm.

A family of only 2 genera and about 30 species, widely distributed throughout the world and of no known economic importance, *Elatine* being mostly aquatic in temperate and warm areas of the world and *Bergia* less often aquatic and mostly tropical and subtropical in distribution.

There are only 2 species indigenous to Ceylon and both are members of the genus *Bergia*. They may be found around the margins of tanks, along streams, and in other wet places in the Dry Zone. They can be locally very abundant but in general are infrequent in occurrence. Both are frequently confused with herbaceous members of the Lythraceae and have maintained these disguises successfully in the herbarium for many years.

BERGIA

L., Mant. 2: 152.1771.

Annual or perennial herbs, infrequently suffrutescent, of aquatic or terrestrial habitats, glabrous or pubescent; leaves opposite, simple, entire or serrate, stipulate; flowers small, in axillary dichasia or solitary, pentamerous, except for *B. ammannioides* which is usually trimerous in Ceylon, with sepals and petals free; pistil with ovate 5-celled ovary, short styles and generally capitate stigmas.

The genus contains approximately 20 species generally classified into 2

*La Crosse, Wisconsin, U.S.A.

424

sections (Niedenzu, 1925). Section *Monanthae* with species possessing axillary, solitary flowers with long pedicels generally without bracts, and distributed primarily in South America and South Africa and section *Dichasianthae* with species usually possessing several to many flowers disposed in axillary dichasia with bracts (with only one exception in which the dichasia have been reduced to one flower) and distributed mainly in the Old World tropics (Niedenzu, 1925).

KEY TO THE SPECIES

1 Glabrous annual herbs of aquatic habitats, generally emergent, with succulent stems and pentamerous flowers..**1. B. capensis**
1 Pubescent herbs, annual or perennial, often somewhat woody at base, generally terrestrial, without succulent stems and flowers in Ceylon, usually trimerous........
....**2. B. ammanioides**

1. Bergia capensis L., Mant. 2: 241. 1771; Cooke, Fl. Bombay 1: 74. 1901; Backer, Beknopt. Fl. Java 4 (1): 53. 1943; Milne-Redhead, Kew Bull. 1948: 450. 1949; Backer, in Fl. Mal. 4: 203. 1954; Backer, Fl. Java 1: 205. 1963.

Bergia verticillata Willd. in L., Sp. Pl. ed. 4, 2: 770. 1799; Roxb. Fl. Ind. 2: 456. 1832; Oliver, Fl. Trop. Africa 1: 152. 1868; W.T. Dyer in Hook. f., Fl. Br. Ind. 1: 252. 1874; Trimen, Handb. Fl. Ceylon 1: 92. 1893; Alston in Trimen, Handb. Fl. Ceylon 6: 19. 1931. Koorders, Exkursion Fl. Java 2: 623. 1912; Niedz., in Pflanzenfam. 21: 274. 1925.
Bergia aquatica Roxb., Pl. Corom. 2: 22, t. 142. 1798.

Aquatic, annual plants, generally emergent, with primary stems decumbent, generally submerged, rooting at nodes, vertical branches emergent, succulent, and with a pink or dark reddish coloration; leaves opposite, with a pair of ovate to deltoid stipules 1–3 mm long with irregularly serrate margins, sessile, or with the blade narrowed to a short, stout petiole 1–5 mm long; blades oblanceolate, narrowly elliptic or lanceolate, serrate, 0.5–4 cm long, and with acute to somewhat obtuse apices; flowers several to many, clustered in the leaf axils, 1.5–2.0 mm long at anthesis, with 5 nearly linear, truncate, acute to obtuse sepals 0.9–1.3 mm, and 5 linear to oblanceolate, obtuse, greenish-white petals 1.3–1.7 mm long; stamens 10, in 2 series, with filaments about 1.5 mm long at anthesis and with anthers about 0.2 mm long; pistil with a globose, 5 locular, ovary about 1 mm long at anthesis and with 5 separate styles about 0.3 mm long with minute stigmatic, glandular hairs at the top of each, with numerous ovules in each locule and with central placentation; capsule globose, septicidal, reddish, with numerous brown, reticulate, oblong seeds 0.4–0.6 mm long.

D i s t r. Found around the quiet waters of tanks, seepage areas, streams and in rice paddies mostly in the Dry Zone. It is found also in India and Malaysia.

Ecol. Flowering period variable as conditions permit growth, usually from November–December to March–April.

Specimens Examined. KANDY DISTRICT: Peradeniya, in paddy field, *Amaratunga 804* (PDA). MATALE DISTRICT: Dambulla, *Silva· s.n.* 29 Sept. 1926 (PDA). ANURADHAPURA DISTRICT: Anuradhapura, *Trimen s.n.* Sept. 1891 (PDA). AMPARAI DISTRICT: near Pottuvil, *Alston s.n.* 6 Mar. 1928 (PDA). HAMBANTOTA DISTRICT: Tissamaharama Road near mile 152, culvert 4, *Cramer 2824* (PDA, US), Uraniyawala, *Fosberg, Mueller-Dombois, Wirawan, Cooray* and *Balakrishnan 51019* (PDA, US), Palatupana Tank, *Sohmer, Jayasuriya* and *Waas 9001* (PDA, US). WITHOUT FURTHER DATA: *s. coll. s.n.* (PDA).

2. Bergia ammanioides Roxb. ex Roth, Nov. Pl. Sp. 219. 1821; DC., Prod. 1: 390. 1824; Roxb., Fl. Ind. 2: 457. 1832; Benth., Fl. Austral. 1: 180. 1863; Oliver, Fl. Trop. Africa 1: 152. 1868; Dyer in Hook. f., Fl. Br. Ind. 1: 251. 1874; Trimen, Handb. Fl. Ceylon 1: 92. 1893; Bailey, Queensl. Fl. 1: 100. 1899; Cooke, Fl. Bombay 1: 73. 1901; Koorders, Exkursion Fl. Java 2: 623. 1912; Merr., Enum. Philip. Fl. Pl. 3: 102. 1923; Backer, in Fl. Mal. 4: 205. 1951; Backer, Fl. Java 1: 205. 1963.

Elatine ammanioides Wight & Arn., Prod. 41. 1834; Spanoghe, Linnaea, 15: 167. 1841 (in part); Miq., Fl. Ned. India 1 (2): 119. 1859.
Bergia serrata Blanco, Fl. Filip. 387. 1837; Merr., Phillipp. J. Sci. (Bot.) 2: 431. 1907.
Bergia trimera Fisch. & Mey., Linnaea 10: 74. 1836.

Annual or perennial herbs, often becoming woody at base, erect but with lower branches often decumbent, stems thickly covered with capitate, glandular hairs throughout; leaves opposite, simple, with 2 narrowly triangular stipules 2.0–2.6 × 0.6–0.9 mm, with glandular hairs along the margins, blades oblanceolate, with serrate, gland-tipped teeth, acute, slightly pubescent, or glabrous above and below, 0.3–2 cm tapering to form short petioles or sessile; flowers numerous in axial dichasia, small, about 1 mm on pedicels 1.0–4.0 mm at anthesis and covered with glandular hairs, and multicellular trichomes, trimerous with 3 ovate, acute to acuminate somewhat keeled sepals 0.9–1.2 mm glabrous, or with a few trichomes, and 3 ovate, obtuse petals 0.9–1.2 mm, glabrous; stamens with filaments about 1.0 mm at anthesis with anthers about 0.2 mm; pistil of 3–5 clearly defined carpels with a superior, globose ovary 0.5–0.7 mm at anthesis with 3–5 locules, 3–5 separate styles less than 0.2 mm and terminal stigmata; ovules 0.1 mm or less, numerous in each locule, placentation axile. Capsule with 3–5 valves.

Distr. Suffrutescent herbs perennating along the borders of tanks, seepage areas, and marshes of the Dry Zone, becoming, by repeated branching at the base, decumbent with a relatively long tap root. This plant was considered by Trimen a variety of *Bergia ammanioides*. It is found relatively widespread in similar conditions in Africa, tropical Asia from Southern China and Malaysia, Indonesia, the Philippines through Iran as well as Ceylon. Until study is made of this species in order to determine how the variation fits into a general pattern so that the significance of the frequently trimerous individuals is understood, it would be best to continue to consider the Ceylonese representative as part of *Bergia ammanioides*.

E c o l. Flowers mostly December to April.

S p e c i m e n s E x a m i n e d. TRINCOMALEE DISTRICT: near Muttur, *Simpson 9716* (PDA). POLONNARUWA DISTRICT: near Tamankaduwa, *Townsend 73/248* (US). BADULLA DISTRICT: *Gunaratne s.n.* 1890 (PDA). MONARAGALA DISTRICT: Bibile, in paddy fields, *Hepper* and *G. de Silva 4721* (PDA). WITHOUT FURTHER DATA: *s. coll. C.P. 1543* (PDA).

FABACEAE

(by Velva E. Rudd*)

Juss., Gen. 345. 1789, nom. cons. Type: *Faba* Mill. (= *Vicia* L. p.p.).

Fabaceae Lindl., Nat. Syst. ed. 2, 148. 1836, nom. alt. Type: *Faba* Mill. (= *Vicia* L. p.p.).

Trees, shrubs, or herbs, the stems sometimes twining; leaves commonly alternate, rarely opposite, compound, sometimes simple, usually stipulate, sometimes stipellate; flowers commonly bisexual, 5-merous, solitary or in compound inflorescences, axillary or terminal; sepals free or united, 4 or 5, rarely 1, then spathaceous; petals free or united, 5 or sometimes fewer or lacking; stamens commonly 5-many, sometimes reduced to only one fertile member, the sterile members may be present or sometimes reduced to staminodes, the filaments free or united, the anthers 2-celled, dehiscing lengthwise or by terminal pores; pistil usually 1, the ovary superior, 1-locular, 1-many-ovulate; fruit a legume, dehiscent or indehiscent, 1-many-seeded, 2-valved, but may be modified as a drupe, samara, follicle, or loment; seed commonly with a coriaceous testa, reniform, lenticular, or spherical, sometimes alate, sometimes arilate, the hilum orbicular to linear, sometimes circumcinct, the endosperm little or none.

D i s t r. Worldwide.

KEY TO SUBFAMILIES OF LEGUMINOSAE

1 Flowers actinomorphic, radiate and regular; corolla and calyx valvate in bud (except calyx imbricate in Parkiëae); stamens 4-many; leaves commonly bipinnate, sometimes pinnate or reduced to phyllodes...................................**Mimosoideae**
1 Flowers generally zygomorphic, sometimes subactinomorphic; corolla and calyx imbricate in bud or, sometimes, valvate
  2 Uppermost (adaxial) petal enveloped by the other petals in bud; stamens (fertile) 1-many, commonly 10 or fewer; leaves usually pinnate, sometimes bipinnate, rarely simple...**Caesalpinioideae**
  2 Uppermost (adaxial) petal exterior in bud, enveloping the other petals; stamens 10, rarely fewer; leaves simple or pinnate, never bipinnate..................**Faboideae**

*Smithsonian Institution, Washington D.C., U.S.A.

Subfamily FABOIDEAE

Type: *Faba* Mill. (= *Vicia* L. p.p.).

Papilionaceae Giseke, Praelect. Ord. Nat. Pl. 415. 1792.
Fabaceae H.G.L. Reichenb., Consp. Regni Veg. 149. 1828.
Leguminosae fam. Papilionatae A. Braun in Aschers., Fl. Prov. Brandenb.
Einleit. 67. 1864.
Leguminosae subfam. Papilionoideae Robinson & Fernald, Gray's New Man.
Bot. ed. 7. 500. 1908.
Papilionaceae subfam. Lotoideae Luerssen, Grundzüge Bot. 379. 1877. Type:
Lotus L.
Leguminosae subfam. *Lotoideae* (Luerssen) Rehder, J. Arn. Arb. 26: 477. 1945.

Characters are those of the family except as noted in the key to subfamilies, viz., leaves simple or pinnate, never bipinnate; flowers with adaxial petal exterior in the bud, enveloping the other petals; stamens commonly 10.

The taxa listed above without typification were presumably based on *Faba* Mill.

KEY TO TRIBES OF FABOIDEAE IN CEYLON

1 Flowers with stamens free, the filaments separate to the base; plants woody........
....**Sophoreae**
1 Flowers with stamens monadelphous, the filaments all joined at the base, or diadelphous 5 : 5 with filaments joined in two fascicles of five stamens each, or 9 : 1, the vexillar stamen free, at least at the base, the others joined
  2 Fruit lomentaceous, the articles usually separating at maturity, sometimes 1-seeded; plants herbaceous or woody.......................................**Hedysareae**
  2 Fruit not articulated
    3 Leaves digitately 3- or 5-foliolate, sometimes simple or unifoliolate, or reduced to spinescent phyllodes
      4 Leaflets gland-dotted below
        5 Plants annual, herbaceous.................................**Galegeae** in part
        5 Plants perennial, woody or suffrutescent...................**Phaseoleae** in part
      4 Leaflets not gland-dotted below
        6 Stamens monadelphous; anthers often dimorphic; leaflets with entire margins, sometimes reduced to spinescent phyllodes; plants herbaceous or woody....**Genisteae**
        6 Stamens diadelphous 9 : 1; anthers usually uniform; plants herbaceous; leaflets with margins usually toothed...**Trifolieae**
    3 Leaves pinnate, 3-many-foliolate or sometimes simple or unifoliolate
      7 Fruit commonly samaroid or drupaceous, indehiscent; plants woody....**Dalbergieae**
      7 Fruit 2-valved, commonly dehiscent
        8 Leaflets 3, rarely 1
          9 Plants erect, herbaceous or suffrutescent; stipels absent........**Galegeae** in part
          9 Plants mostly twining, herbaceous or woody; stipels present..........**Phaseoleae**
        8 Leaflets 5 or more

10 Plants erect, herbaceous or woody; leaves paripinnate or imparipinnate..............
....Galegeae in part
10 Plants twining; leaves paripinnate
  11 Stamens 9, the vexillar stamen lacking; leaves terminating in a bristle; plants woody
    or suffrutescent..Abreae
  11 Stamens 10; leaves usually terminating in a tendril; plants herbaceous.......Vicieae

Tribe SOPHOREAE

Spreng., Anleit. 2, 2: 741. 1818. Type: *Sophora* L.

Trees, shrubs, or herbs, sometimes scandent; leaves pinnately 1-many-foliolate; stipules present or absent; stipels sometimes present; inflorescences racemose or paniculate; flowers with the corolla zygomorphic or subactinomorphic; calyx valvate or imbricate in bud; petals free or with keel petals joined; stamens 10 or rarely fewer, the filaments separate to the base, equal or alternately subequal in length, the anthers essentially uniform, dorsifixed, oblong to ellipsoid; ovary 1-many-ovulate, the style glabrous, at least toward the apex; fruit 2-valved, dehiscent or indehiscent, sometimes samaroid; seed with hilum apical, lateral, or rarely circumcinct.

KEY TO THE GENERA OF SOPHOREAE

1 Leaflets with resinous, pellucid lines and dots; fruits elongate-samaroid, 1-seeded at
  apex; flowers white...1. Myroxylon
1 Leaflets lacking pellucid lines and dots; fruits not elongate-samaroid as above; flowers
  white, yellow, violet, or purple
  2 Fruit compressed, narrowly winged or thickened along one or both sutures; flowers
    yellow or dark purple
    3 Flowers dark purple (in Ceylon); fruit usually narrowly alate or marginate along
      both sutures; leaflets alternate or sometimes subopposite..............2. Pericopsis
    3 Flowers yellow; fruit alate along only one suture; leaflets opposite or subopposite..
    ....5. Calpurnia
  2 Fruit terete or turgid; flowers white to yellow or violet
    4 Flowers orange-yellow, about 3.5–4 cm long; fruit subfalcate, about 5 cm wide, elas-
      tically dehiscent; leaflets predominantly 8–15 cm long..........3. Castanospermum
    4 Flowers white to yellow or violet, about 2.5 cm long or less; fruit straight, torulose
      or moniliform, usually not dehiscent; leaflets predominantly 5 cm long or less.......
    ....4. Sophora

1. MYROXYLON

L. f., Suppl. 34, 233. 1781, nom. cons., non Forster, 1776. Type species: *M. peruiferum* L. f.

Toluifera L., Sp. Pl. 384. 1753. Type species: *T. balsamum* L.

Trees; leaves alternate, imparipinnate, 5–15-foliolate; leaflets alternate, with resinous, pellucid lines and dots; stipules and stipels minute or lacking; inflorescences axillary or terminal, racemose; flowers small; calyx turbinate-campanulate with 5 subequal lobes, valvate in bud; corolla with 5 free petals, subequal except for a broader standard; stamens 10, the filaments free, essentially equal, the anthers uniform, oblong, acuminate, sagittate, dorsifixed; fruit indehiscent, samaroid, commonly with one apical seed; seeds reniform or subreniform, usually resinous, the hilum elliptic, lateral, subapical.

A genus of two or three species native to tropical America.

Myroxylon balsamum (L.) Harms, Notizbl. Bot. Gart. Berlin 5: 94. 1908; Worthington, Ceylon Trees 179. 1959. Based on *Toluifera balsamum* L.

Tree, to about 40 m tall; bark resiniferous; leaves 5–11-foliolate, the axis about 6–15 cm long, puberulent to subglabrous, the lateral leaflets alternate, the blades moderately coriaceous, with pellucid lines and dots, predominantly ovate, sometimes elliptic, 3–14 cm long, 1–7 cm broad, the apex obtuse to acuminate, sometimes retuse, the base rounded to subcordate, the surfaces essentially glabrous at maturity, the upper surface nitid or subnitid, the secondary venation relatively inconspicuous; inflorescences with axes puberulent, the bracts and bracteoles deltoid, the bracts 1–3 mm long, the bracteoles about 1 mm long; flowers 12–15 mm long; calyx minutely pubescent, suffarinose, 5–8 mm long, the lobes about 1 mm long, the tube 4–7 mm long; corolla white, the petals glabrous, spatulate, clawed, subequal except the standard 2–3 times as broad as the others; stamens 10, the filaments slightly longer than the calyx, the anthers oblong, resinous, acuminate, sagittate, about 4–4.5 mm long; ovary and style glabrous, the stigma terminal, truncate; fruit indehiscent, coriaceous, light brown or yellowish, glabrous, samaroid with 1, rarely 2, apical seeds, essentially straight or curved, 6–12 cm long exclusive of stipe 5–15 mm long, 2–3 cm broad and 1 cm thick at the seed, the basal portion sterile, alate, compressed, 4–7 cm long, 1–3 cm broad, 1 mm thick or less; seed reniform, light brown, resinous, about 15–20 mm long and 5–8 mm in diameter. Chromosome number 2n = 18.

D i s t r. Native of tropical America, introduced elsewhere.

U s e s. The trees are planted for shade along roadsides and in plantations. The wood has value for construction of buildings and for fine cabinet work. The balsam, or resin, is used pharmaceutically, as incense, and in the preparation of perfumes and confections.

V e r n. Balsam, Tolu balsam (var. *balsamum*), Peru balsam (var. *pereirae*) (E); kata-kamanchal (S); sambranee (T).

1. var. balsamum

Myroxylon balsamum (L.) Harms, Notzbl. Bot. Gart. Berlin 5: 94. 1908. Based on *Toluifera balsamum* L.

Toluifera balsamum L., Sp. Pl. 384. 1753. Type: Tolu, near Cartagena, Colombia. Type: L.

Myroxylon (as *Myroxylum*) *toluiferum* A. Rich., Ann. Sc. Nat. Paris 2: 171, 172. 1824. Nomen novum for *Toluifera balsamum* L.

The typical variety is characterized by relatively large fruit, about 8–11 cm long, straight or somewhat curved, 2–3 cm broad with the margins essentially parallel. The leaflets are glabrous, commonly acuminate at the apex.

I have seen no material from Ceylon that can be identified with certainty as referable to the typical variety although some of the collections cited below as var. *pereirae* have unusually long pods.

D i s t r. In forest, up to about 300 m elevation, Panama and northern South America.

2. var. pereirae (Royle) Harms, Notizbl. Bot. Gart. Berlin 5: 95. 1908.

Myrospermum pereirae Royle, Man. Mat. Med. ed. 2, 414. 1853. Type: El Salvador, *Pereira s.n.*

Myroxylon pereirae (Royle) Klotsch, Bonplandia 5: 275. 1857.

Toluifera pereirae (Royle) Baill., Hist. Pl. 2: 383. 1870.

The fruit of this variety tends to be smaller than that of the typical variety, usually 6–9 cm long, 1.5–2.5 cm wide, straight or sometimes strongly curved, the winged portion usually narrower toward the stipe. The leaflets commonly are smaller than those of the other two varieties, glabrous or with a trace of pubescence along the midvein, the apex acute to breviacuminate. In Ceylon, the fruits tend to be larger than average but much less resinous. The bark, also, appears to be less resinous.

D i s t r. Southern Mexico and Central America in moist or dry forest at elevations up to about 1000 m. Introduced elsewhere.

S p e c i m e n s   E x a m i n e d. MATALE DISTRICT: Matale, *Worthington 2386* (BM), *6362* (BM). KANDY DISTRICT: Kandy, *Thwaites s.n.*, April 1874 (K); *Worthington 2884* (BM), *6362* (BM), *6644* (K); *Rudd 3059* (PDA, US); Peradeniya, Royal Botanic Gardens, *Baker 123* (K, PDA, US); *J. M. de Silva*, 22 Dec. 1924 (PDA); *de Silva 93* (PDA). TRINCOMALEE DISTRICT: Trincomalee, Deadman's Cove, *Worthington 202* (K). BATTICALOA DISTRICT: Batticaloa, *Worthington 1233* (BM), *1234* (K).

N o t e s. Worthington, l.c., states that *Myroxylon* has been planted in Colombo but I have seen no specimens from there.

According to Stockdale, Petch, and Macmillan (The Royal Botanic Gardens, Peradeniya, Ceylon 49. 1922), "*Toluifera Pereirae*, the Balsam of Peru, was introduced in 1861. It grows and seeds prolifically in and near Kandy."

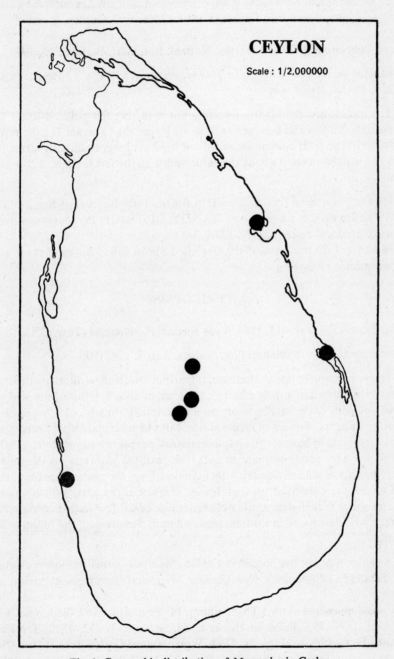

Fig. 1. Geographic distribution of *Myroxylon* in Ceylon.

In the herbarium at Kew there is a specimen sent by Thwaites with the notation "4/74, introduced into Ceylon in 1861, Governor's Garden, Kandy."

3. var. **punctatum** (Klotsch) Harms, Notizbl. Bot. Gart. Berlin 5: 97. 1908.

Myroxylon punctatum Klotsch in Hayne, Arzneigew. 14: t. 12. 1843. Type: Peru, *Ruiz & Pavon, s.n.*

The leaflets are abundantly punctate but with very few pellucid lines. In general, the leaflets and fruit are as large or larger than average for the typical variety. The pods commonly are about 8–12 cm long, essentially straight, with the winged portion about the same width as the fertile apex, 2.5–3 cm wide.

D i s t r. Northern Peru and western Brazil. Introduced elsewhere.

S p e c i m e n s E x a m i n e d. KANDY DISTRICT: Peradeniya, Royal Botanic Gardens, *Baker 122* (K, PDA, US).

N o t e s. I do not know if the tree cited above still exists or if there are any naturalized offspring.

2. PERICOPSIS

Thw., Enum. Pl. Zeyl. 413. 1864. Type species: *P. mooniana* (Thw.) Thw.

Afrormosia Harms, in Pflanzenfam. Nachtr. 3 zu 3: 158. 1906.

Trees and shrubs; leaves alternate, imparipinnate; leaflets alternate or subopposite; stipules and stipels minute, caducous, or absent; inflorescences racemose or paniculate, axillary or pseudo-terminal; bracts and bracteoles minute, caducous; flowers of medium size; calyx campanulate with 5 subequal lobes, imbricate in bud; corolla papilionaceous, purple to yellowish, the petals free or the keel petals connate in part, the vexillum glabrous on the outer face; stamens essentially equal with filaments free, the anthers small, ellipsoid to oblong, dorsifixed; style glabrous, involute at the apex; stigma terminal, truncate; fruit indehiscent, oblong, compressed, few-seeded, marginate or narrowly alate on both sutures; seeds elliptic, compressed, the hilum subapical.

A genus of about five species in Ceylon, Malaysia, Sumatra, Borneo, Celebes, Talaud Is., Philippines, New Guinea, Micronesia and tropical Africa.

Pericopsis mooniana (Thw.) Thw., Enum. Pl. Zeyl. 414. 1864; Beddome, Fl. Sylv., pl. 187. 1872; Baker in Hook. f., Fl. Br. Ind. 2: 252. 1878; Trimen, Handb. Fl. Ceylon 2: 97, pl. 31. 1894; Worthington, Ceylon Trees 178. 1959; van Meeuwen, Bull. Jard. Bot. Etat. Brux. 32: 218. 1962; Brummit, Kew Bull. 24: 233. 1970. Based on *Dalbergia mooniana* Thw.

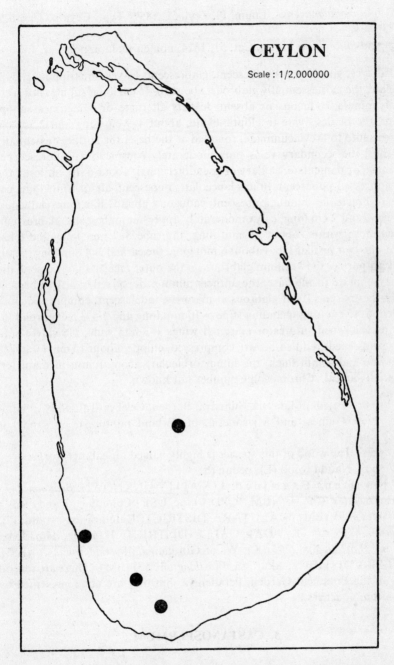

Fig. 2. Geographic distribution of *Pericopsis mooniana* in Ceylon.

Dalbergia mooniana Thw., Enum. Pl. Zeyl. 51. 1859. Type: Ceylon, *Thwaites, C.P. 439.*

Dalbergia lanceolaria Moon, Cat. 51. 1824, nomen nudum, non L. f. 1781.

Tall tree; young stems pubescent, glabrescent; leaves imparipinnate, 5–8-foliolate, the axis essentially glabrous, about 10–16 cm long; stipules not seen; stipels minute, caducous or absent; leaflets alternate or sometimes subopposite, the blades ovate to elliptic-ovate, about 4–9 cm long and 2.5–5 cm broad, acute to breviacuminate, rounded at the base, the surfaces essentially glabrous, the secondary veins only moderately conspicuous; inflorescences racemose or paniculate, axillary or pseudoterminal, about 6–10 cm long, the axis appressed-pubescent; bracts lanceolate, pubescent, about 1 mm long, caducous; bracteoles minute, pubescent, caducous, about 1 mm long, caducous; flowers about 2 cm long; calyx moderately appressed-pubescent, glabrescent, tomentulose within, about 15 mm long, the tube 8–9 mm long, the lobes acute, the two vexillar lobes about 6 mm long, the carinal 3–4 mm long; petals blackish-purple, the vexillum glabrous on the outer face; stamens essentially equal, separate to the base, the anthers minute, dorsifixed; ovary pubescent along the margins; fruit glabrous at maturity, indehiscent, compressed, 1–6-seeded, 6–15 cm long including stipe 5–10 mm long and 2.5–3.5 cm broad including thickened sutures or marginal wings 1–3 mm wide, the valves subcoriaceous; seeds reddish-brown, compressed, elliptic, about 15 mm long, 7–8 mm wide and 4 mm thick, the hilum orbicular, about 1 mm in diameter, essentially apical. Chromosome number not known.

D i s t r. Ceylon, Malaysia, Sumatra, Borneo, Celebes, Talaud Is., Philippines, New Guinea, and Micronesia, in lowland rainforest, on sandy or clayey soil.

U s e s. The wood of this species is highly valued for cabinet work.

V e r n. Nandu wood (E); nedun (S).

S p e c i m e n s E x a m i n e d. LOCALITY UNKNOWN: *Beddome 2475* (BM); *Thwaites, C.P. 439* (BM, P, PDA type, US); "Colombo—Kandy Rd.", *Worthington 99* (BM). KALUTARA DISTRICT: Kalutara (as "Caltura"), *Ferguson, C.P. 439* (K, PDA). GALLE DISTRICT: Haycock, Hinaduma Kanda, *Worthington 2295* (K), W. of Gin ganga, *Worthington 2316* (BM). MATARA DISTRICT: Akuressa, *Worthington 2525* (BM). [There are several trees in the Botanical Garden, Peradeniya, but they are not represented by herbarium vouchers.]

3. CASTANOSPERMUM

Cunningham ex W.J. Hook., Bot. Misc. 1: 241, t. 51, 52. 1830. Type species: *C. australe* Cunningham & Fraser ex W.J. Hooker.

Trees; leaves alternate, imparipinnate; leaflets alternate or subopposite; stipules and stipels apparently lacking; inflorescences racemose, often compact, lateral; bracts minute, caducous; bracteoles apparently lacking; flowers fairly large; calyx campanulate, shallowly 5-lobed; corolla papilionaceous, yellow, the petals free, glabrous, the standard usually longer than the wings and keel; stamens with filaments free, the anthers linear-oblong, about 4 mm long, dorsifixed; ovary stipitate, several-ovulate; style elongate, glabrous; stigma terminal, truncate; fruit turgid, dehiscent, oblong, subfalcate, few-seeded, the valves coriaceous; seeds subspherical, the hilum lateral, linear.

A genus of one or two species native to Australia, New Caledonia, and New Hebrides. Introduced elsewhere in tropical and warm temperate areas.

Castanospermum australe Cunningham & Fraser ex W.J. Hook., Bot. Misc. 1: 241, t. 51, 52. 1830. Worthington, Ceylon Trees 181. 1959. Type: Australia, *Fraser s.n.*

Trees, to about 25 m tall; young stems puberulent, glabrescent; leaves imparipinnate, about 11–15-foliolate, the axis glabrous, 10–30 cm long; stipules apparently lacking; leaflets alternate or subopposite, the blades elliptic to ovate-oblong, 4–15 cm long, 2–4.5 cm broad, breviacuminate, rounded at the base, glabrous, the secondary veins inconspicuous; inflorescences racemose, sometimes subfasciculate, lateral, about 4–10 cm long; bracts minute, caducous; bracteoles lacking; flowers 3.5–4 cm long; calyx minutely appressed-pubescent, glabrate, about 15 mm long, the lobes broad, scarcely 1 mm long; petals saffron or orange-yellow, glabrous, the vexillum about 3.5 cm long, slightly recurved, the wings and keel about 3 cm long; stamens separate to the base, the anthers linear-oblong, about 4 mm long, dorsifixed; ovary glabrous, stipitate, few-ovuled; fruit; elastically dehiscent, glabrous, lustrous, oblong, subfalcate, turgid, 3–5-seeded, about 8–15 cm long including stipe 1–1.5 cm long, 5 cm broad, 0.5–1 cm thick, the valves coriaceous; seeds brown, subspherical, about 3 cm in diameter, nitid, the hilum lateral, linear, about 2 cm long. Chromosome number 2n=26.

D i s t r. Australia, New Caledonia, New Hebrides. Introduced to Ceylon in 1874.

U s e s. The trees are planted as ornamentals. The timber is said to be termite-proof. The seeds are edible but astringent; they are roasted or made into a coarse flour by the Australian aborigines.

V e r n. Moreton Bay Chestnut; Australian Chestnut (E).

S p e c i m e n s E x a m i n e d. KANDY DISTRICT: Peradeniya, Royal Botanic Gardens, [*Trimen* ?], March 1888 *s.n.* (PDA), *Worthington 6828* (Worthington herb.), *Rudd 3339* (PDA, US); Murutalawa, *Ranasingha*, 12 March 1927 (PDA); Panwila, *Worthington 1048* (BM). NUWARA ELIYA DISTRICT: Lindula, *Worthington 5388* (K).

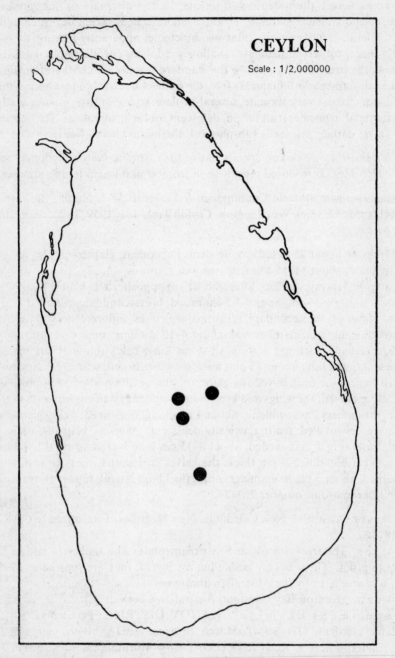

CEYLON

Scale : 1/2,000000

Fig. 3. Geographic distribution of *Castanospermum australe* in Ceylon.

4. SOPHORA

L., Sp. Pl. 373. 1753. Lectotype species: *S. alopecuroides* L. (Britton & Brown, Illustr. Flora No. U.S., ed. 2, 2: 342. 1913).

Trees, shrubs, or perennial herbs; leaves alternate, imparipinnate; leaflets alternate to subopposite; stipules commonly deltoid, sometimes lacking; stipels present or absent; inflorescences terminal or axillary, racemose or paniculate; flowers small to medium in size, about 1–4.5 cm long; calyx campanulate with 5 subequal lobes, sometimes subtruncate; corolla papilionaceous, white to yellow, bluish, or violet, glabrous, the keel petals commonly joined; stamens 10, free or the filaments united merely at the base, alternately subequal, the anthers ellipsoid, dorsifixed, about 1 mm long; stigma minutely capitate-penicillate; fruit commonly indehiscent, 1–6 (–15)-seeded, usually torulose; seeds spherical or subellipsoid, red or yellowish to light brown, the hilum lateral or subapical, elliptic or suborbicular.

A genus of about 75 species, worldwide in tropical and temperate regions.

KEY TO THE SPECIES

1 Leaves predominantly 11–25-foliolate; leaflets obtuse to acute; flowers 15–25 mm long, yellow or violet
  2 Flowers yellow, about 25 mm long; leaflets commonly suborbicular, about 2–6 cm long, 1–4 cm broad..**1. S. tomentosa**
  2 Flowers violet, about 13–15 mm long; leaflets elliptic, about 0.5–2 cm long, 0.5–1 cm broad..**2. S. violacea**
1 Leaves predominantly 7–11-foliolate; leaflets acute to acuminate; flowers 8–10 mm long, white..**3. S. zeylanica**

1. Sophora tomentosa L., Sp. Pl. 373. 1753. Burm., Fl. Ind. 93. 1768; Moon, Cat. 33. 1824; Roxb., Fl. Ind. ed. 2, 2: 343. 1832; Wight & Arn., Prod. 179. 1834; Thw., Enum. Pl. Zeyl. 94. 1859; Baker in Hook. f., Fl. Br. Ind. 2: 249. 1878; Trimen, Handb. Fl. Ceylon 2: 95. 1894. Lectotype: Ceylon, *Hermann* [herb. no.] 3: 13.

Shrub, to about 3 m high, sometimes sprawling; stipules linear-deltoid, tomentulose, about 3 mm long, caducous; leaves 13–21-foliolate, the axis about 12–25 cm long, puberulent, the lateral leaflets alternate to subopposite, the blades oblong, orbicular, ovate, or obovate, commonly suborbicular, about 2–6 cm long, 1–4 cm broad, the apex obtuse, the base cuneate to subcordate, the upper surface sericeous to glabrous, sometimes nitid, the lower surface sericeous or puberulent, the secondary venation inconspicuous; bracts linear, 3–5 mm long; bracteoles apparently lacking; flowers about 25 mm long; calyx pallid-sericeous, about 10 mm long, subtruncate; petals yellow, sometimes almost white, the standard a little longer than the other petals;

fruit coriaceous, cinereo-tomentulose, terete, torulose or moniliform, 1–15-seeded, 5–15 cm long and about 8 mm in diameter at the seeds; seeds sublustrous, brown, spherical to subellipsoid, 5–8 mm long, 5–6 mm in diameter, the hilum orbicular, about 1 mm in diameter, subapical. Chromosome number 2n = 18.

D i s t r. Pantropical, near the sea, on limestone or calcareous sand.

U s e s. This species could be used as an ornamental shrub where the edaphic conditions are suitable.

V e r n. Moodoomoroonga, mudu-murunga (S).

S p e c i m e n s E x a m i n e d. Without exact locality, *Hermann* [herb. no.] 1: 61 (BM), 3: 13 (BM lectotype); *Thunberg s.n.* (UPS); *Stothouder* [herb. page] 19 (P), 83 (P); *Moon s.n.* (PDA); *Viburg s.n.* (BM). JAFFNA DISTRICT: Jaffna, *Gardner C.P. 1487* (PDA). KANDY DISTRICT: Peradeniya, Royal Botanic Gardens, cultivated, *Senaratne 10042* (PDA). TRINCOMALEE DISTRICT: Trincomalee, Welcomb, *Worthington 1143* (BM); Trincomalee, Shell Bay, Foul Point, *Worthington 741* (K). BATTICALOA DISTRICT: Batticaloa, *Nevill*, Sept. 1884 (PDA); N.E. of Kalkudah, *Mueller-Dombois 68041905* (PDA, US), *Rudd & Balakrishnan 3153* (PDA, US). GALLE DISTRICT: s.loc. *Thwaites C.P. 1487* (BM); Bentota (as "Bentotte"), *Thwaites, C.P. 1487* (PDA); Galle, *Gardner 196* (BM, K). MATARA DISTRICT: Palalla, 2 mi. W. of Kottegoda, *Fosberg & Sachet 52846* (PDA, US).

2. Sophora violacea Thw., Enum. Pl. Zeyl. 94. 1859, non Zipp. in Span. 1841, nomen in synon.; Baker in Hook. f., Fl. Br. Ind. 2: 249. 1878; Trimen, Handb. Fl. Ceylon 2: 95. 1894. Type: Ceylon, *Thwaites, C.P. 3546.*

Shrubs, to about 1 m tall; young stems densely appressed-pubescent; leaves imparipinnate, 11–23-foliolate, the axis 4–15 cm long, appressed-pubescent; stipules minute or absent; stipels absent; leaflets alternate to suboppo-site, the blades elliptic, about 5–20 mm long, 5–10 mm wide, obtuse to acute, the base obtuse to cuneate, the surfaces appressed-pubescent, glabrescent, the secondary veins inconspicuous; inflorescences racemose, lateral or pseudo-terminal, about 8–15 cm long, the axis appressed-pubescent; bracts acicular, about 1 mm long, caducous; bracteoles lacking; flowers about 15 mm long; calyx gibbous, sparsely appressed-pubescent, 7–8 mm long including broad lobes about 1 mm long; petals violet, glabrous, about 13–15 mm long, the standard a little longer than the wings and keel; fruit indehiscent, moniliform, stipitate, long-beaked, 5–8 cm long, 1–4–seeded; seeds ovoid, compressed, red to brown. Chromosome number not known.

D i s t r. In low country of eastern and southern Ceylon.

U s e s. This ornamental shrub is planted in gardens in suitable areas.

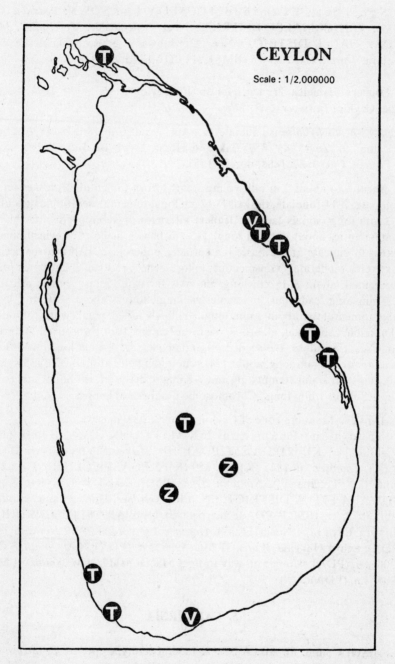

Fig. 4. Geographic distribution of *Sophora* in Ceylon. T—*S. tomentosa*;
V—*S. violacea*; Z—*S. zeylanica*.

Specimens Examined. LOCALITY UNKNOWN: *Beddome s.n.*
(BM). TRINCOMALEE DISTRICT: Near Trincomalee, *Morris C.P. 3456*
(PDA). GALLE DISTRICT: Near Dewinuwara, between Dickwella and
Matara, *Thwaites, C.P. 3456* (BM, K, P, PDA lectotype, US).

3. Sophora zeylanica Trimen, Handb. Fl. Ceylon 2: 96, pl. 30. 1894. Lectotype: Ceylon, *Thwaites, C.P. 570.*

Sophora heptaphylla sensu auct., Arn., Act. Acad. Cur. 18: 328. 1836; Thw.,
Enum. Pl. Zeyl. 94. 1859; Baker in Hook. f., Fl. Br. Ind. 2: 250. 1878;
Trimen, Cat. 9: 27. 1888, non L. 1753.

Shrubs, to about 2 m tall; young stems brown-tomentulose; leaves imparipinnate, 7–11-foliolate, the axis 8–12 cm long, tomentulose; stipules acicular,
1–3 mm long; stipels lacking; leaflets alternate or subopposite, the blades
ovate-elliptic, about 2–6 cm long, 1–3 cm broad, acute to breviacuminate,
obtuse to cuneate at the base, the surfaces puberulent, glabrate, the secondary veins moderately conspicuous; inflorescences racemose, lateral or pseudoterminal, about 8–18 cm long, the axis ferrugino-pilose; bracts acicular,
1–2 mm long, caducous; bracteoles lacking; flowers about 8–10 mm long;
calyx tomentulose, about 3 mm long, shallowly lobed; petals white, about 8–
10 mm long, subequal, glabrous; ovary pubescent; fruit glabrous at maturity,
indehiscent, torulose, 1–3-seeded, essentially sessile, 4–5 cm long including a
beak about 5–8 mm long, about 1–1.3 cm in diameter at the seeds; seeds dark
red, ellipsoid, about 10 mm long and 7–8 mm in diameter, the hilum subapical,
elliptic, about 1 mm long. Chromosome number not known.

Distr. Montane zone of Ceylon at 1000–2000 m elevation.
Specimens Examined. LOCALITY UNKNOWN: *Walker* [herb.
Wight no.] *41* (K), *52* (PDA), *54* (PDA); "*Dr. Maxwell*" *s.n.*, ex herb. Hook-
er (K); *Thomson*; in 1845 (K), in 1859 (K). KEGALLE DISTRICT: Laksa-
pana (as "Laxapana"), *Simpson 8998* (BM). KANDY DISTRICT and
NUWARA ELIYA DISTRICT: "N. Ellia, *Gardner*, Hunasgiria, [*Thwaites*],
Jan. 1885", *s.n.* (BM, P, PDA lectotype, US). NUWARA ELIYA DISTRICT:
Nuwara Eliya (as "Neuer Ellia"), *Gardner 197* (BM, K), *W. Nock*, in 1893
(PDA); Below Hakgala, *Willis*, 31 May 1906, *s.n.* (PDA); *A.M. Smith*, 8 Oct.
1906, *s.n.* (PDA); "Jungle on way to Fort MacDonald", *A.M. Smith*, 31 May
1906, *s.n.* (PDA).

5. CALPURNIA

E. Meyer, Comm. Pl. Afr. Austr. 2. 1836. Lectotype species: *C. intrusa* (R.
Br.) E. Meyer (*Virgilia intrusa* R. Br.) (E. P. Phillips, Gen. S. Afr. Fl. Pl. ed.
2. 400. 1951).

Trees or shrubs; leaves alternate, imparipinnate; leaflets opposite or sub-opposite; stipules minute; stipels lacking; inflorescences racemose or panicu-late, axillary; bracts minute, caducous; bracteoles lacking; flowers small to medium sized; calyx hypanthoid, campanulate with 5 subequal lobes, the vexillar lobes somewhat connate; corolla papilionaceous, yellow, the keel petals connate, the vexillum glabrous on the outer face; stamens with fila-ments free, the anthers small, ellipsoid, dorsifixed; style glabrous, slightly curved; stigma terminal, capitate or minutely penicillate; fruit indehiscent, oblong, compressed, few to many-seeded narrowly alate along the upper (vexillar) suture; seeds compressed, oval to oblong.

About seven species, native to Africa, with one extending to India.

Calpurnia aurea (Ait.) Benth., Leg. Gen. Comm. 26. 1837 (preprint); Ann. Wien Mus. 2: 90. 1838. Worthington, Ceylon Trees 180. 1959. Based on *Sophora aurea* Ait.

Sophora aurea Ait., Hort. Kew 2: 44. 1789. Lectotype: Kew, England, culti-vated, *Aiton*, 1778 (Brummitt, Kirkia 6: 123. 1967).
Robinia subdecandra L'Herit. Stirp. Nov. tab. 75. 1791, non 1784 nec 1789.
Calpurnia subdecandra (L'Herit.) Schweik. Bothalia 3: 237. 1937.

Shrubs or small trees, to about 3 m high; young stems puberulent, glabre-scent; leaves 13–21-foliolate, the axis 8–15 cm long, puberulent, glabrescent; stipules minute, linear, 1–2 mm long; stipels lacking; leaflets opposite or sub-opposite, the blades elliptic-oblong, 2–3 cm long, 0.5–1.5 cm wide, obtuse or emarginate at the apex, rounded at the base, the surfaces moderately to sparsely appressed-pubescent, the secondary veins inconspicuous; inflores-cences racemose, axillary, about 10–16 cm long; bracts deltoid to lanceolate, 1–3 mm long; bracteoles lacking; flowers 18–20 mm long; calyx puberulent, about 10 mm long with lobes 4–5 mm long, the two vexillar lobes obtuse, adnate, the other lobes acute; petals yellow, glabrous, essentially equal in length; fruit appressed-pubescent when young, glabrous at maturity, indehis-cent, oblong, compressed about 3–6-seeded, essentially sessile, 8–10 cm long, 1.5–1.8 cm wide including a wing about 2 mm wide along the upper suture; seeds dark brown, subreniform, sublustrous, about 5 mm long, 4 mm wide, 2 mm thick, the hilum elliptic, about 0.7 mm long, lateral, subapical. Chro-mosome number $2n = 18$.

D i s t r . Native to Africa and southern India. Introduced in Ceylon and elsewhere.

U s e s . Showy flowering shrubs or trees planted as ornamentals and as tea shade.

S p e c i m e n s   E x a m i n e d . MATALE DISTRICT: Hunugalla Elka-duwa, *Worthington 6641* (K). KANDY DISTRICT: Kandy, *Worthington*

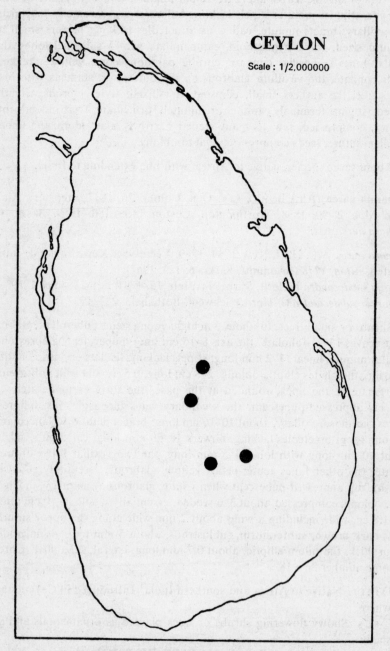

Fig. 5. Geographic distribution of *Calpurnia aurea* in Ceylon.

7012 (K); Deltota, *Worthington 6625* (K). NUWARA ELIYA DISTRICT: Nuwara Eliya, *Worthington 5631* (BM). BADULLA DISTRICT: Bandarawela, *Worthington 5833* (K), *3002* (BM); Hakgala, *J.M. de Silva*, 27 April 1926, *s.n.* (PDA); Badulla, *Richards* 3 June 1955, *s.n.* (PDA).

In addition to the native species and the few exotics described above there are several species of Sophoreae that have been introduced and planted as specimens in the botanical gardens of Ceylon, especially at Peradeniya and Hakgala. Otherwise, they seem not yet to have become a part of the flora of the country. Included in this category are *Baphia nitida* Lodd., *B. racemosa* (Hochst.) Baker, *Camoensia maxima* Welw. ex Benth., and *Virgilia oroboides* (Berg.) Salter (= *V. capensis* Lam.), from Africa, and *Ormosia monosperma* (Sw.) Urb. (= *O. dasycarpa* Jacks.), from the West Indies.

Tribe A B R E A E

Hutchinson, Gen. Fl. Pl. 1: 451. 1964. Type: *Abrus* Adans.

Subshrubs or lianas; leaves paripinnate with numerous, opposite leaflets, the rachis projecting slightly beyond the terminal pair of leaflets; stipules and stipels present, usually minute; inflorescences racemose or fasciculate, axillary or terminal; flowers papilionaceous; calyx campanulate with 5 short, subequal teeth or lobes; petals white or yellowish to pink, blue, or purple; stamens 9, the vexillar stamen absent, the filaments united to about midpoint, separate above, the anthers uniform or with 4 smaller; ovary many-ovuled, the style short, glabrous, somewhat curved, the stigma capitate; fruit 2-valved, dehiscent, lightly septate, somewhat compressed; seeds subglobose or compressed, the hilum small, excentric.

ABRUS

Adans., Fam. Pl. 2: 327. 1763. Type species: *A. precatorius* L.

Hoepfneria Vatke, Oesterr. Bot. Zeitschr. 29: 222. 1879.

Only one genus in the tribe, described as above, consisting about 17 species occurring in tropical areas.

KEY TO THE SPECIES

1 Inflorescences shorter than the leaves; pod oblong, slightly inflated, about 2–4 cm long, 1.5 cm wide; seeds commonly bicolored red and black, sometimes white and black, or whitish..**1. A. precatorius**

1 Inflorescences longer than the leaves; pod linear-oblong, compressed, about 5–7 cm long, 1 cm wide; seeds brown or mottled greyish-brown and black......**2. A. pulchellus**

446   FABACEAE

1. Abrus precatorius L. Syst. Nat., ed. 12, 2: 472. 1767. Moon, Cat. 52. 1824; Roxb., Fl. Ind. ed. 2 [Carey] 3: 258. 1832; Wight & Arn., Prod. 236. 1834; Thw., Enum. Pl. Zeyl. 91. 1859; Baker, Fl. Br. Ind. 2: 175. 1876; Trimen, Handb. Fl. Ceylon 2: 57. 1894; Gamble, Fl. Pres. Madras 1: 349. 1918; Verdcourt, Kew Bull. 24: 240. 1970. Based on *Glycine abrus* L.

Glycine abrus L. Sp. Pl. 753. 1753. Lectotype: *P. Hermann* [Herb. no.] 2: 6, Ceylon (BM).

Woody or suffrutescent, perennial vine, to about 5 m long; young stems puberulent, glabrescent; stipules linear, about 5 mm long, 1 mm wide or less, caducous; leaves about 16–40-foliolate; leaflets predominantly oblong to elliptic, 5–30 mm long, 3–10 mm wide, obtuse at apex and base, the upper surface glabrous, the lower surface sparsely pubescent with minute, appressed hairs, glabrescent, the venation reticulate, inconspicuous; inflorescences racemose, terminal or axillary, shorter than the leaves; bracts deltoid, minute, caducous; bracteoles suborbicular, about 1 mm in diameter; flowers 9–12 mm long; calyx sparsely pubescent, 2–4 mm long with teeth 1 mm long or less; petals pink to lavender or white, glabrous; fruit (1–) 3–7-seeded, oblong, slightly inflated, fulvo-puberulent, essentially sessile, (2–) 3–4 (–5) cm long, 1–1.5 cm wide; seeds subglobose, shining, 5–7 mm long, 4–5 mm in diameter, most commonly red with a black spot surrounding the hilum, or, sometimes completely black, black and white, or whitish, the hilum elliptic, about 1 mm in diameter or less.

D i s t r. Pantropical, usually climbing on bushes and trees.

U s e s. The seeds are used in many countries as rosaries, necklaces, and other ornaments. In India they have long been used as goldsmiths' weights. The seeds are poisonous to cattle and to humans unless boiled; they are said to have been used as famine food in Egypt and India. A paste made from the seeds has been used as an arrow poison. According to Chakravarthy (Science 166: 44. 1969) "The principal poisonous constituent is abrin which was formerly used as a remedy for granular eyelids, but a dangerous one, as it frequently proved.... A poultice of the seeds is said to bring about abortion... the roots and leaves of *A. precatorius* contain glycorrhizin, the active ingredient in licorice which accounts for its being known as Indian licorice. The leaves taste sweet and a decoction of the leaves and roots is widely used for coughs, colds, and colic." Macmillan states, "Juice of green lvs. taken for 'purifying the blood'; root taken for sore throat and rheumatism" (Tropical Planting and Gardening, ed. 5, 364. 1962).

V e r n. Olinda, olinda-wel (S); kundu-mani, kuntamani (T); rati (Hindi); bead-vine, crab's eyes, Indian-liquorice, jequirity beans (E).

N o t e s. According to the collectors, *Glenie, C.P. 1466* and *Crawford 149* are white-seeded specimens and *Alston 1454* is black-seeded. The other specimens have bicolored, black and red, seeds.

Specimens Examined. PROVINCE AND DISTRICT NOT KNOWN: Wetakeyapotta, *Alston 1454* (PDA). JAFFNA DISTRICT: Between Kayts and causeway to Jaffna, *Rudd 3270* (PDA, US); between Paranthan and Pooneryn, *Rudd 3300* (PDA, US). MANNAR DISTRICT: Mannar, *Crawford 149* (PDA). VAVUNIYA DISTRICT: Just S. of Mullaitivu, *Fosberg & Balakrishnan 53502* (PDA, US). PUTTALAM DISTRICT: Wilpattu National Park, between Salamba Motai and Periya Naga Villu, *Wirawan, Cooray & Balakrishnan 900* (PDA, US). MATALE DISTRICT: Dambulla, *Amaratunga 1493* (PDA). KANDY DISTRICT: Peradeniya, Royal Botanic Gardens, *O.F. Baker 110* (K, PDA). TRINCOMALEE DISTRICT: Trincomalee, *Glenie, C.P. 1466* (K, PDA). COLOMBO DISTRICT: Muturajawela, *Amaratunga 387* (PDA); Miriswatta, *Amaratunga 1636* (PDA). GALLE DISTRICT: Koggala, SE of Galle, near lake and abandoned RAF airfield, *Rudd 3085* (PDA, US). HAMBANTOTA DISTRICT: Main Yala road, near mile marker 7, *Comanor 825* (PDA, US); Ruhuna National Park, 200 meters W of Karaugaswala junction, *Mueller-Dombois & Cooray 67121084* (PDA, US); Karaugaswala, *Cooray 68053003*R (PDA, US).

2. Abrus pulchellus Wall. ex Thw., Enum. Pl. Zeyl. 91. 1859; Baker, Fl. Br. Ind. 2: 175. 1876; Trimen, Handb. Fl. Ceylon 2: 57. 1894; Gamble, Fl. Pres. Madras 1: 350. 1918; Verdcourt, Kew Bull. 24: 246. 1970. Type: *G. Gardner s.n.*, July 1848 and/or *G.H.K. Thwaites*, July 1853, *C.P. 1467*, Ceylon, Dambulla, Minneriya, Uma Oya, etc. (holotype PDA; isotypes K, P, PDA). [The sheet at PDA with notations of collectors and localities, presumably written by Thwaites, is designated as the holotype, and the other *C.P.* sheet, without such annotations, is selected as the isotype.]

Suffrutescent vine, to about 6 m long; young stems pubescent with appressed hairs, glabrescent; stipules linear, about 3 mm long, 1 mm wide at the base or less, caducous; leaves (10–) 14–34-foliolate; leaflets oblong or oblong-obovate, 0.7–2 cm long, 5–6 mm wide (in Ceylon), to 5 cm long, 2 cm wide in other areas; inflorescences racemose, terminal or axillary, longer than the leaves; bracts lanceolate to deltoid, 1–3 mm long, 1 mm broad at the base, or less; bracteoles ovate or suborbicular, about 1 mm in diameter; flowers 8–10 mm long; calyx 2–3 mm long, subtruncate, moderately pubescent with minute, appressed hairs; petals pale lavender or mauve; fruit oblong, fulvo-puberulent, essentially sessile, compressed, 5–7 cm long, about 1 cm wide; seeds lenticular, about 5 mm in diameter, 1.5–2 mm thick, mottled greyish-brown, the hilum elliptic, about 1 mm long, 0.5 mm wide.

Distr. Tropical Asia and Africa, climbing on bushes or trailing in grassy areas.

Vern. Ella olinda (S).

Notes. On the specimen designated as the holotype, in addition to the

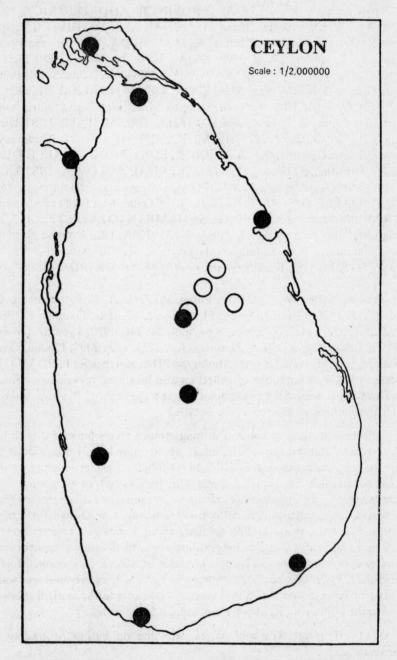

Fig. 6. *Abrus precatorius* (black dots); *A. pulchellus* (open dots).

readily decipherable localities, "Damboul", Minneriya, and "Ooma Oya", there are two that are not clear to me. One possibly is Jaffna, the other appears to be "Ukwitare."

This species is one of an imperfectly known complex. I am following Verdcourt (cited above) in maintaining *A. pulchellus*, rather than Breteler who placed it in synonymy under *A. fruticulosus* Wall. ex Wight & Arn. (Blumea 10: 614. 1960). In addition, I am treating *A. tenuiflorus* Benth. (*A. pulchellus* subsp. *tenuiflorus* (Benth. Verdcourt), from the Amazon basin of South America, as a separate species.

Although Thwaites validated Wallich's *nomen nudum*, he cited only the Ceylon collections, as "*C.P.* 1467", which, therefore must be taken as the type material of *A. pulchellus*. It is possible that the three collections cited by Wallich (Wall. Cat. 5819), from Nepal, Khasia, and Burma actually represent other taxa.

S p e c i m e n s E x a m i n e d. POLONNARUWA DISTRICT: Polonnaruwa, Government Farm, *J.E. Senaratna 3511* (PDA); between Habarane and Kantalai, *Rudd 3121* (PDA, US). MATALE DISTRICT: Dambulla, *N.D. Simpson 9789* (BM).

Tribe T R I F O L I E A E

(Bronn) Benth. in Benth. & Hook., Gen. Pl. 1: 442. 1865. Type: *Trifolium* L. Tribe Curvembryae decandrae subtribe Trifolieae Bronn, Diss. Legum. 132. 1822.

Herbs or rarely shrubs, erect or prostrate, sometimes twining; leaves digitately or pinnately 3-foliolate, rarely 5- or 7-foliolate; stipules present, more or less adnate to the petiole; stipels lacking; leaflets usually denticulate or lobed, sometimes entire, the secondary veins mostly extending to the marginal teeth; inflorescences capitate, spicate, racemose, umbellate, or the flowers sometimes solitary; flowers papilionaceous; calyx campanulate with 5 subequal teeth or lobes; petals white, yellow, blue, pink, red, or purple; stamens 10, monadelphous or diadelphous 9 : 1 with the vexillar stamen free, the filaments sometimes broadened at the apex, the anthers usually uniform; ovary 1-many-ovulate, the style glabrous, the stigma small, terminal or subterminal, capitate or subcapitate; fruit 2-valved, dehiscent or indehiscent, straight or coiled, sometimes rugose, sometimes armed with prickles; seeds small, reniform to subglobose, sometimes compressed-quadrate, the hilum lateral or sublateral.

With the exception of the genus *Parochetus*, the taxa of this tribe occurring in Ceylon are all introductions. A few species of *Trifolium* have been found as escapes or are naturalised. *Melilotus indica* escapes occasionally but *M. alba* and species of *Medicago* and *Trigonella* apparently occur only in cultivation.

KEY TO THE GENERA
(Based on species in Ceylon)

1 Petals deciduous after flowering, free from the staminal tube; stamens with filaments uniform, not dilated
  2 Fruit linear to linear-oblong, many-seeded, 2–10 cm long, 3–5 mm wide; flowers 13–23 mm long in 1–4-flowered umbels; leaves digitately or pinnately trifoliolate
    3 Leaves digitately trifoliolate; petals blue to purplish; fruit 2–2.5 cm long, 3–4 mm wide, glabrous, somewhat compressed...........................**1. Parochetus**
    3 Leaves pinnately trifoliolate; petals white, purplish-tinged at the base; fruit 6–10 cm long, 4–5 mm wide, glabrous or pubescent, terete......................**Trigonella**
  2 Fruit usually small, oblong or obovate, few-seeded or, if longer, with several seeds and spirally coiled; flowers 2–15 mm long, usually in many-flowered racemes; leaves pinnately trifoliolate
    4 Flowers 2–5 mm long; petals white or yellow; fruit ovoid or subglobose, 1.5–3.5 mm long, 1.5–2.5 mm in diameter..**Melilotus**
    4 Flowers 6–15 mm long; petals usually purplish; fruit spirally coiled, 3–9 mm in diameter.. **Medicago**
1 Petals persistent after flowering, the wings and keel usually adherent to the staminal tube; stamens with some or all filaments dilated at the apex..............**2. Trifolium**

1. PAROCHETUS

Buch.-Ham. ex D. Don, Prod. Fl. Nepal. 240. 1825. Lectotype species: *P. communis* Buch.-Ham. ex D. Don (vide J.G. Baker in J.D. Hook., Fl. Br. Ind. 2: 86. 1876).

Cosmiusa Alef. Bot. Zeit. (Berlin) 24: 146. 1866. Type species: *C. repens* Alef.

Prostrate herb, rooting at nodes; leaves digitately trifoliolate with long petioles; stipules present, free or somewhat adnate to the petiole; stipels lacking; leaflets obcordate, entire or shallowly lobed or shallowly dentate; flowers in 2–4-flowered, umbellate, axillary inflorescences or sometimes solitary; bracts stipule-like; bracteoles lacking; calyx campanulate, 5-lobed, the two vexillary lobes fused almost to the apex; petals blue or purplish, glabrous, deciduous; stamens free from the petals, diadelphous 9: 1, the vexillary filament free, the anthers essentially uniform; ovary glabrous, many-ovuled; style glabrous; stigma minute, capitate; fruit linear to linear-oblong, acute, somewhat compressed, many-seeded; seeds reniform, the hilum lateral.

A monotypic genus known from tropical upland areas of Asia and Africa.

1. Parochetus communis Buch.-Ham. ex D. Don, Fl. Nepal. 240. 1825; Wight & Arn., Prod. 252. 1834 (as *P. major*); Wight, Ic. Pl. Ind. Or. 483. 1840–43 (as *P. major*); Thw., Enum. Pl. Zeyl. 82. 1858; Baker in Hook., Fl. Br. Ind. 2: 86. 1876; Trimen, Handb. Fl. Ceylon 2: 20. 1894; Alston, in Trimen, Handb. Fl. Ceylon 6: 67. 1931; Macmillan, Trop. Pl. Gard. ed. 5. 28. 1962. Type: *Buchanan-Hamilton s.n.*, Nepal, Narainhetty (holotype BM).

Parochetus major D. Don, Fl. Nepal. 241. 1825. Type: *Buchanan-Hamilton s.n.*, Nepal (holotype BM).

Parochetus oxalidifolia Royle, Illustr. Bot. Himal. 201, tab. 35, fig. 1. 1834–35. Type: *Wallich 5972*, India (isotype BM).

Parochetus maculata Bennett & Brown, Pl. Jav. Rar. 1: 162, tab. 34. 1840. Type: *Horsefield s.n.* (holotype BM; isotype BM).

Cosmiusa repens Alef., Bot. Zeit. (Berlin) 24: 146. 1866. Type: *Schlagintweit s.n.*, Nepal, Kathmandu, 5000–7000 ft. elev., 4–8 March 1857 (holotype B destroyed).

Stems slender, creeping, rooted at the nodes, sometimes twining, glabrous or nearly so; stipules scarious, deltoid-ovate, acute, 4–10 mm long, glabrous, free or somewhat adnate to the petiole; leaves digitately 3-foliolate, the petiole glabrous or sparsely villous, about 2–7 (-25) cm long; leaflets 7–30 mm long, 5–30 mm wide, almost sessile, the petiolule 1 mm long or less, cuneate-obcordate, emarginate or truncate at the apex, the margin entire or shallowly lobed or toothed toward the apex, glabrous above, moderately appressed-puberulent below; inflorescences 1–4-flowered, axillary; bracts stipule-like but smaller, 2–4 mm long, somewhat laciniate with filiform tips; flowers about 13–23 mm long; calyx moderately puberulent, 6–7 mm long, 2.5 mm in diameter, the teeth acute, 2–3 mm long; petals blue to purplish, glabrous, deciduous; fruit glabrous, about 2–2.5 cm long, 3–4 mm wide, essentially sessile, about 8–12-seeded, dehiscent, sometimes tardily; seeds reniform, brown, sometimes mottled, 2 mm long, 1 mm thick or less, the hilum small, circular, lateral.

D i s t r. In damp or wet soil at high elevations, Ceylon, India, China, Southeast Asia, and Africa. In Ceylon fairly common in high, moist areas of the Central and Uva Provinces.

U s e s. Macmillan (l.c.) considered this species a promising ground cover for up-country. The plants are sometimes used in ornamental hanging baskets.

V e r n. Shamrock pea (E).

S p e c i m e n s   E x a m i n e d. LOCALITY UNKNOWN: *"Col. & Mrs. Walker" s.n.* (K); *"Dr. Maxwell" s.n.* (K); *"Col. Walker no. 11"* (PDA). NUWARA ELIYA DISTRICT; *"N. Ellia Gardner" Thwaites C.P. 2409* (BM, P, PDA); Rambodda Pass, roadside among rocks, *N.D. Simpson 8903* (BM); Horton Plains, at entrance from Pattipola, tussock, *Muller-Dombois & Cooray 68011319* (PDA); Horton Plains, near Farr Inn, open patana grassland, *Fosberg 53328* (PDA, US); Horton Plains, edge of woods in wet hummocks, *Rudd & Balakrishnan 3179* (PDA, US), at base of dirt bank, *Rudd & Balakrishnan 3182* (PDA, US); between Kandy and Nuwara Eliya, near milemarker 44/13, at base of wet wall, *Rudd & Balakrishnan 3161* (PDA, US).

BADULLA DISTRICT: Ambewela, cattle farm, *D. Rhind s.n.*, 16 April, 1968 (PDA).

2. TRIFOLIUM

L., Sp. Pl. 764. 1753; Gen. Pl. 337. 1754.* Lectotype species: *T. pratense* L. (vide Britton & Brown, Ill. Fl. No. U.S., ed. 2., 2: 353. 1913).

Herbs, annual or perennial; stems usually prostrate, sometimes erect, sometimes rooting at the nodes; stipules adnate to the petiole; stipels lacking; leaves digitately 3-, sometimes 4–9-foliolate, sometimes pinnately 3–5-foliolate; leaflets cuneate-obovate to oblanceolate, usually denticulate; inflorescences axillary or pseudoterminal, few- to many-flowered, capitate, spicate, or umbellate, rarely solitary; bracts small, persistent or caducous, sometimes connate, sometimes lacking; bracteoles absent; flowers papilionoid; calyx campanulate with 5 subequal teeth, the vexillary teeth sometimes connate; petals persistent, white, yellow, pink to purple or reddish, glabrous; stamens diadelphous 9 : 1, the vexillary filament free or, rarely, somewhat connate with the others, the alternate filaments, or all, dilated at the apex, the anthers uniform; ovary few-ovulate; style glabrous; stigma minutely capitate; fruit small, oblong or obovate, terete or compressed, enclosed by the persistent calyx and petals, commonly 1- or 2-, rarely 3-seeded; seeds subreniform to spheroid or ellipsoid.

A large genus of about 300 species chiefly in temperate areas of America and Eurasia. In Ceylon all species have been introduced; a few have become more or less naturalised.

KEY TO THE SPECIES

1 Flowers white, cream, rose, pink, or lavender; leaves digitately foliolate, the petiolules essentially equal in length
  2 Inflorescences oblong-cylindric at maturity; calyx villous, longer than the petals, the teeth plumose, longer than the tube...................................**1. T. arvense**
  2 Inflorescences globose or subglobose at maturity; calyx glabrous or sometimes puberulent, shorter than the petals, the teeth shorter than the tube
    3 Flowers 6–12 mm long in heads (1–) 1.5–2 (–2.5) cm in diameter; petals white, sometimes pinkish-tinged...**2. T. repens**
    3 Flowers 4–8 mm long in heads 0.5–1 cm in diameter; petals rose to pinkish-lavender
    ....**3. T. glomeratum**
1 Flowers yellow; leaves pinnately-foliolate, the terminal petiolule longer than the laterals
  4 Inflorescences spherical or hemispherical, 5–8 mm in diameter, axillary; flowers 2.5–4 mm long...**4. T. dubium**

*Hutchinson (Gen. Fl. Pl. 1: 457. 1964) lists 34 synonyms of *Trifolium*, which will not be repeated here.

4 Inflorescences globose to short-spicate, 5–15 cm long, 8–12 mm in diameter, axillary or pseudoterminal; flowers about 4–6 mm long.......................**5. T. campestre**

1. Trifolium arvense L., Sp. Pl. 769. 1753. Trimen, Handb. Fl. Ceylon 2: 20. 1894; Alston in Trimen, Handb. Fl. Ceylon 6: 71. 1931. Type: *Hort. Cliff. 374.13* (BM).

Annual; stems prostrate or erect, to about 4 dm long; stipules subcoriaceous, lanceolate to ovate, acuminate; leaves digitately 3-foliolate, the lower short-petiolate, the lower essentially sessile; leaflets linear-oblong to linear-lanceolate or oblanceolate, 10–25 mm long, 3–10 mm wide, cuneate at the base, truncate to acute at the apex, the margin shallowly denticulate, or entire, the surfaces puberulent; inflorescences oblong-cylindric at maturity, 10–40 mm long, 7–15 mm in diameter, many-flowered, axillary and pseudoterminal, short-pedunculate; flowers about 6–7 mm long, sessile; calyx 6–7 mm long, villous, the teeth setaceous, plumose, spreading, about twice the length of the tube; petals white or pinkish, about 4 mm long; fruit 1-seeded, broadly ovoid; seeds ellipsoid to obovoid, pale yellow or yellowish-green.

D i s t r. Native to Eurasia and North Africa but widely introduced elsewhere. In Ceylon known only from the Central Province.

V e r n. Rabbit-foot clover, Hare's foot trefoil (E).

S p e c i m e n s E x a m i n e d. NUWARA ELIYA DISTRICT: "Roadside between N. Ellia & Hakgalla." *s. coll. s.n.* (PDA).

N o t e s. Trimen suggests that this species, and other clovers, "no doubt were introduced with grass seed."

2. Trifolium repens L., Sp. Pl. 767. 1753. Thw., Enum. Pl. Zeyl. 82. 1858; J.G. Baker in Hook., Fl. Br. Ind. 2: 86. 1876; Trimen, Handb. Fl. Ceylon 2: 20. 1894; Alston in Trimen, Handb. Fl. Ceylon 6: 71. 1931. Type: *Hort. Cliff. 375.18.*

Perennial; stems prostrate, glabrous, rooting at the nodes, to about 4 dm long; stipules lanceolate, setaceous at the apex, about 8–15 mm long; leaves digitately 3-foliolate, rarely 4–6-foliolate, the petiole to about 30 cm long; leaflets glabrous, obovate to elliptic-oblong, 10–20 mm long, 7.5–25 mm wide, cuneate at the base, the apex emarginate or obtuse, the margin denticulate; inflorescences globose or subglobose, (1–) 1.5–2 (–2.5) cm in diameter, many-flowered, axillary; peduncles usually longer than the petioles; bracts small, scarious, lanceolate; flowers 6–12 mm long, fragrant; calyx glabrous or puberulent, 3–4 mm long, the teeth lanceolate-acuminate, shorter than the tube; petals white or sometimes pinkish-tinged; fruit linear-oblong, 4–5 mm long, 3- or 4-seeded; seeds ovoid-truncate, yellowish.

D i s t r. Native to Europe, Asia Minor, and northern Asia; cultivated and naturalised elsewhere. In Ceylon known from the Central Province.

V e r n. White Clover (E).

S p e c i m e n s E x a m i n e d. NUWARA ELIYA DISTRICT: "Naturalised in the neighborhood of Newera Ellia", *Thwaites C.P. 3087* (BM); "N. Ellia, introduced," *s. coll. s.n.* (PDA); Hakgala, *s. coll. 74*, "5.1.1900" (PDA).

N o t e s. There is a specimen of *T. repens* in the Hermann herbarium, 4: 25 (BM), but it is not cited by Linnaeus in Flora Zeylanica and, presumably, was not collected in Ceylon.

3. Trifolium glomeratum L., Sp. Pl. 770. 1753. Alston in Trimen, Handb. Fl. Ceylon 6: 71. 1931. Type: *Hort. Cliff. 373.3* (BM).

Perennial; stems glabrous, procumbent, rarely erect, to about 3 dm long; stipules scarious, lanceolate, long-acuminate; leaves digitately 3-foliolate, the lower leaves alternate with petioles to about 30 mm long, the upper leaves opposite with petioles 5 mm long; leaflets obovate, sometimes oblanceolate, 3–10 (–17) mm long, 3–10 (–14) mm wide, glabrous, the base cuneate, the apex truncate, obtuse, or emarginate, the margin setose-denticulate; inflorescences globose, 5–10 mm in diameter, many-flowered, axillary, sessile or nearly so; bracts lanceolate; flowers 4–8 mm long; calyx glabrous, 3–5 mm long, the teeth deltoid-ovate, aristate, subauriculate, subequal, about half as long as the tube, recurved at maturity; petals rose to pinkish-lavender; fruit glabrous, 1.5–3 mm long, 0.5 mm wide, obliquely mucronate, 1- or 2-seeded; seeds spherical to subreniform, minutely verrucose, dull yellow.

D i s t r. Native of western and southern Europe, Asia Minor, and northern Africa; introduced elsewhere. In Ceylon known only from the Central Province and the Province of Uva.

V e r n. Cluster clover (E).

S p e c i m e n s E x a m i n e d. NUWARA ELIYA DISTRICT: Nuwara Eliya, golf course, *T. Petch s.n.*, 26 July 1927 (PDA), *Rudd & Balakrishnan 3164* (PDA, US); Mahagastota Vegetable Farm, alt. 6000 ft., *D. Rhind s.n.*, 27 October 1948 (PDA). BADULLA DISTRICT: Ambewela Cattle Farm, *D. Rhind s.n.*, 16 October, 1948 (PDA).

4. Trifolium dubium Sibth., Fl. Oxon. 231. 1794. Trimen, Handb. Fl. Ceylon 2: 20. 1894 (as *T. minus*); Alston in Trimen, Handb. Fl. Ceylon 6: 71. 1931. Type: *Herb. Sherard* (OXF).

Trifolium procumbens L., Sp. Pl. 772. 1753, in part.
Trifolium minus Smith in Relhan, Fl. Cantabr., ed. 2, 290. 1802.

Annual or biennial; stems slender, to about 4 dm long, usually procumbent, sometimes erect; stipules obliquely ovate, acuminate, about 4–8 mm long, ciliate; leaves pinnately 3-foliolate, the petiole about 3–10 mm long; leaflets glabrous, obovate, 5–10 mm long, 2–4 mm wide, cuneate at the base, truncate, obtuse or emarginate at the apex, the margin denticulate toward the apex, the terminal petiolule 1–3 mm long, the laterals 0.5 mm long or less; inflorescences spherical or semispherical, relatively small, 5–8 mm in diameter, axillary; bracts minute, deltoid; flowers 2.5–4 mm long; calyx glabrous, 1.5–2 mm long, the upper teeth longer than the tube, the lower teeths horter; petals yellow, turning brown with age; fruit 1-seeded, lenticular or oblong, 1.5–3 mm long, 1.25–1.5 mm wide; seeds ovoid, nitid, yellowish-brown, 1.5 mm long, 1 mm wide, the hilum subapical.

D i s t r. Native to Europe; introduced elsewhere. In Ceylon known only from the Central Province and the Province of Uva.

V e r n. Small hop clover, least hop clover (E).

S p e c i m e n s E x a m i n e d. NUWARA ELIYA DISTRICT: Nuwara Eliya road to Hakgala, *A.M. Smith s.n.*, 3 March, 1906 (PDA); Nuwara Eliya, in golf course, *Rudd & Balakrishnan 3163* (PDA, US); Hakgala, *s. coll.*, August 1881 (PDA). BADULLA DISTRICT: Ambewela cattle farm, *D. Rhind s.n.*, 16 October 1948 (PDA).

I am indebted to Mr. F. White, Curator of the Herbaria, Oxford, who very kindly provided me with a photograph of the type specimen of *T. dubium*.

5. Trifolium campestre Schreb. in Sturm, Deutschl. Fl. heft 16, pl. 13. 1804.

Trifolium procumbens L., Fl. Suec. ed. 2, 261. 1755, non Sp. Pl. 772. 1753.
Trifolium agrarium L., Fl. Suec. ed. 2, 261. 1755, non Sp. Pl. 772. 1753.

Annual or biennial; stems procumbent or erect, to about 3 dm long, appressed-pubescent; stipules obliquely ovate or lanceolate-ovate, acuminate, ciliate, 5–8 (−10) mm long; leaves pinnately 3-foliolate with petiole about 1–2.5 cm long; leaflets obovate, sometimes subrhombic, 5–15 mm long, 5–8 mm wide, cuneate, the apex truncate, obtuse, or emarginate, the margin obscurely denticulate, the terminal petiolule 3–7 mm long, the lateral leaflets essentially sessile; inflorescences axillary and pseudoterminal, globose to brevispicate, 5–15 mm long, 8–12 mm in diameter; peduncles puberulent, 1–3 cm long; bracts minute; flowers about 4–6 mm long; calyx scarious, glabrous, 2 mm long, the tube 0.5 mm long, the two vexillary teeth acute, 0.5 mm long, the three carinal teeth filiform, 1.5 mm long; petals yellow becoming brown with age; fruit 1-seeded, oblong, 2.5–3 mm long including stipe 1 mm long or less; seeds narrowly ellipsoid.

D i s t r. Native to Europe, western Asia, and northern Africa; introduced elsewhere. In Ceylon known only in the Central Province and the Province of Uva.

V e r n. Low hop clover, large hop clover (E).

S p e c i m e n s   E x a m i n e d. NUWARA ELIYA DISTRICT: Nuwara Eliya, in the park among weeds, *K.J.H. de Sylva s.n.*, 24 April 1950 (PDA); Mahagastota, *E.J. Livera* 1011 (PDA). BADULLA DISTRICT: Ambewela cattle farm, alt. 6000 ft., *D. Rhind s.n.*, 16 October, 1948 (PDA).

N o t e s. In addition to the species cited above, other clovers such as *Trifolium alexandrinum* L. (Berseem or Egyptian clover), *T. hybridum* L. (Alsike clover), and *T. pratense* L. (Red clover), have been introduced into Ceylon with varying degrees of success but are not known to have escaped or become naturalised.

Trigonella foenum-graecum L. (Sp. Pl. 777. 1753) known as ulu-hal, asumo-dhagam (S), uluvaarisi, mathai, vendayum (T), fennugreek (E), is cultivated for use as a condiment, in medicine, and as a yellow dye according to Mac-millan (Tropical Planting and Gardening, ed. 5. 333. 1962). There is one voucher specimen from Ceylon, presumably collected during the decade 1830–1840: "Col. Walker; no. 65, Ceylon" ex Herb. R. Wight (PDA). Apparently there have been no recent collections.

Trigonella indica L. (Sp. Pl. 778. 1753), based chiefly on Hermann collections from Ceylon (Fl. Zeyl. 285. 1747) is now referred to *Rothia indica* (L.) Druce.

Medicago sativa L. (Sp. Pl. 778. 1753), alfalfa or lucerne (E) has been intro-duced into Ceylon but apparently has not become naturalised. Two voucher specimens are known: "Trincomalee, seeds from Mr. C. Drieberg 14/8/13" (PDA); "Lucerne (Broad leaf), Experiment station, Peradeniya, 15/1/25" (PDA).

Melilotus indica (L.) All. (Fl. Ped. 1: 308. 1785), known commonly as Indian clover, yellow annual sweet clover, or sour clover, must have been introduc-ed into Ceylon very early. It was collected by P. Hermann during his stay in Ceylon, in about 1672–1677 and cited in his catalog (Herm. Zeyl. 64). Linnaeus included it in his Flora Zeylanica (224. 1747) as species no. 552 and in Species Plantarum (765. 1753) as *Trifolium indica*. It was also cited by J. Burman (Thesaurus Zeylanicus 157. 1737) and by subsequent authors, in-cluding N.L. Burman (Fl. Indica 172. 1768), Moon (Catalogue no. 444. 1824) from Trincomalee, Trimen (Handb. Fl. Ceylon 2: 21. 1894) as *Melilotus par-viflora* Desf., and Alston in Trimen (Handb. Fl. Ceylon 6: 72. 1931). A collection by *W. Ferguson s.n.* (PDA) made, probably, about 1850–1858 is annotated, "Road beyond Wilson's Bungalow, introduced by cooly lines." There apparently have been no recent collections.

The Habam variety of *Melilotus alba* Desr., white sweet clover, or white melilot, was planted at the Experiment Station, Peradeniya and a collection was made by *de Silva s.n.*, 23 March 1925 (PDA) but no plants have been observed recently.

Tribe VICIEAE

(Adans.) Bronn, Diss. Legum. 133. 1822. Type: *Vicia* L.
Viciae Adans., Fam. 2: 329. 1763, as "section" of Leguminosae.

Herbs, erect or twining: leaves imparipinnate with the rachis terminating in a tendril or bristle, sometimes imparipinnate or reduced to a phyllode; stipules present, often foliaceous; stipels lacking; leaflets entire or dentate; inflorescences axillary, racemose, or the flowers solitary; flowers papilionaceous; calyx campanulate with 5 subequal lobes or the vexillar lobes shorter, the base sometimes gibbous; petals blue or violet to yellowish or white; stamens 10, usually diadelphous 9: 1 with the vexillar stamen free or sometimes essentially monadelphous, the filaments uniform or sometimes broadened toward the apex, the anthers uniform, dorsifixed; ovary 2- many-ovulate, the style filiform or compressed dorsally, usually curved, glabrous or bearded, the stigma terminal or subterminal, capitate; fruit 2-valved, usually dehiscent, compressed or terete; seeds globose or compressed, the hilum small or sometimes circumcinct, sometimes covered by the expanded funicle.

Apparently no taxa of the Vicieae are native to Ceylon but the following are, or have been, cultivated. They are included in Macmillan's "Tropical Planting and Gardening," ed. 5, 1962 and some are represented by herbarium specimens at Peradeniya. Two species were cited by Moon in his "Catalogue of Ceylon Plants", 1824.

Cicer arietinum L. (Sp. Pl. 738. 1753), konda-kadala (S); chick pea, Bengal gram (E). According to Macmillan (pp. 280, 300) the "seeds are largely imported into Ceylon." There is one voucher specimen, "R.B.G. Peradeniya, kitchen garden," 23 March 1900, *collector not known* (PDA).

Lathyrus latifolius L. (Sp. Pl. 733. 1753), everlasting pea, perennial pea (E) was cited by Macmillan (p. 181) as *L. latiflorus*, in his list of ornamental climbers and creepers but no voucher specimens have been seen.

Lathyrus odoratus L. (Sp. Pl. 732. 1753), sweet pea (E) was included in Moon's catalogue, no. 433, and by Macmillan (p. 192). No voucher specimens have been seen. Linnaeus, followed by N.L. Burman in Flora Indica, 162. 1768, recognized a var. *zeylanicus* based on a taxon cited by J. Burman Thesaurus Zeylanicus 138. 1737.

Lathyrus sativus L. (Sp. Pl. 730. 1753), vetchling, grass pea (E); khessari (India) is listed in Macmillan (p. 300) and is represented by one herbarium specimen, "Peradeniya, cultivated, flowers dull slate blue, poisonous to goats, from seed adulterant of gram imported from India, 22–I–40," *J.E. Senaratne 3014* (PDA).

Lens culinaris Medic. (Vorles. Churpf. Phys.-Okon. Ges. 2: 361. 1787), *Lens esculenta* Moench (Meth. 136. 1794), *Ervum lens* L. (Sp. Pl. 738, 1753), lentil (E), misurupur (T) was cited by Macmillan but with no especial mention of cultivation in Ceylon. No herbarium vouchers from Ceylon are known.

Pisum sativum L. (Sp. Pl. 727. 1753) peas (E), bola-kadala (S), pairu (T) was included by Moon (no. 432). Two of the four varieties listed, Early Charlton (Bála) and Dwarf Spanish (Kuru) were cited as "Kandy, cult. gard." Macmillan (p. 312) gives cultural data. There is one voucher specimen from Ceylon, Peradeniya, "kitchen garden 1900," *s. coll., s.n.* (PDA).

Vicia faba L. (Sp. Pl. 737. 1753) broad bean, fava bean, horse bean, windsor bean (E) was included by Macmillan (p. 305), and three herbarium specimens have been seen, Hakgala, 19 October, 1917, *s. coll. s.n.* (PDA); "R.B.G.," date and *s. coll. s.n.* (P); July 1896, *s. coll. s.n.* (PDA).

Vicia gracilis Lois. (Fl. Gall. 2: 148. 1806) is a weedy species represented by two voucher collections, Mahagastota, 1 April, 1947, *E.J. Lewon 1012* (PDA), and Mahagastota, vegetable farm, alt. 6000 ft., 27 October, 1948, *D. Rhind s.n.* (PDA).

MIMOSACEAE

(by A.J.G.H. Kostermans*)

Trees, shrubs, lianes or rarely herbs, often prickly or spiny. Leaves bipinnate, often provided with glands. Inflorescences spikes, racemes or heads of sessile or shortly pedicelled, small, regular, 4- or 5-merous flowers. Sepals valvate in bud, usually gamosepalous with small lobes. Petals valvate in bud, free or connate below into a tube. Stamens as many or twice as many as the petals or numerous, free, or adnate below to the corolla, or the filaments connate below into a tube, free part of filaments usually exserted. Anthers small, versatile, sometimes with a minute, apical, stalked fugaceous gland. Pollen grains simple or often compound or united. Pods and seeds various. Seeds often marked with an areole.

The family is represented in Sri Lanka by 16 genera, comprising 35 species. Of these, five genera are alien, their species more or less naturalized, whereas five genera comprise each one endemic species (*Abarema* 2 species).

KEY TO THE GENERA

1 Free-floating aquatic herbs with thick, white, spongy floating tissue (cf. also the terrestrial *N. plena*)..**1. Neptunia**
1 Climbers, trees, shrubs or woody herbs
  2 Flowers 4-merous. Stamens 4–8. The one-seeded segments of the moniliformous pods detaching from the persistent, spiny frame of sutures.....................**2. Mimosa**
  2 Flowers 5-merous. Stamens 10 or indefinite
   3 Stamens 10
    4 Flowers in spikes or racemes
     5 Woody, unarmed large climber. Leaves ending in a forked tendril. The one-seeded segments of the pod detaching from the persistent frame of the sutures and the exocarp detaching as a flap from each segment.....................**3. Entada**
     5 Woody herbs, shrubs or trees, when climbers without tendrils. Pods dehiscent along both sutures
      6 Spikes biformous and bicoloured, the upper, yellow flowers bisexual, the lower pink or violet ones barren with large staminodes..............**4. Dichrostachys**
      6 Spikes concolorous, usually all flowers bisexual
       7 Armed trees. Pod pulpy, indehiscent............................**5. Prosopis**
       7 Unarmed trees. Pods without pulp, dehiscent along both sutures..**6. Adenanthera**

*Krukoff Botanist, Rijksherbarium, Leiden, Netherlands.

4 Flowers in umbels
  8 Tree. Stigma small, capitullate......................................**7. Leucaena**
  8 Woody herb. Stigma clavate, tubular.............................**8. Desmanthus**
3 Stamens indefinite, more than 10
  9 Pod indehiscent
    10 Pod moniliformous, without pulp, breaking into one-seeded segments. Thorny
       tree...**9. Cathormion**
    10 Pod straight, pulpy, septate, not breaking up into segments. Unarmed trees......
       ....**10. Samanea**
  9 Pods dehiscent
    11 Filaments free
      12 Pods cylindrical, slightly pulpy...................................**11. Vachellia**
      12 Pods strap-shaped, flattened, without pulp.........................**12. Acacia**
    11 Filaments connate at the base into a tube
      13 Spiny trees
        14 Seed funicle filiform..**13. Painteria**
        14 Seed funicle fleshy, aril-like..............................**14. Pithecellobium**
      13 Unarmed trees
        15 Pods with thin, flat valves, satiny white inside.....................**15. Albizia**
        15 Valves after dehiscence twisted, without satiny white layer..........**16. Abarema**

1. NEPTUNIA

Lour., Fl. Cochinch. 2: 653. 1790; Windler in Austral. J. Bot. 14: 379. 1966.

Spineless herbs, often aquatic. Leaves bipinnate. Stipules persistent. Inflorescences axillary, the flowers arranged in heads on long peduncles, with basal bracts. Flowers 5-merous, polygamous, the lower ones of the heads barren or male, with protruding flattened staminodes; upper flowers bisexual. Calyx tube small with 5 small teeth. Petals 5, valvate, coherent at the base, later free. Stamens 10 (Ceylon), unequal, exserted; anthers with apical gland or glandless. Ovary sessile or stipitate, style slender, stigma club-shaped, tubular. Pod ligulate, flattened, sub-septate between the seeds, without pulp, dehiscent along both sutures.

A genus of 11 species in America, Asia and Australia. In Sri Lanka one species, and another (doubtfully) introduced one.

KEY TO THE SPECIES

1 Stems rarely branched, usually free floating. Pinnae 2–6, rachis glandless. Leaflets 8–20
  pairs. Pod up to 2.5 cm long. Seeds 4–10.............................**1. N. oleracea**
1 Stems branched, usually erect and ascending, terrestrial. Pinnae 4–10 pairs, rachis with
  a sessile gland below the lowest pair of pinnae. Leaflets 9–40 pairs. Pod up to 6 cm
  long. Seeds 5–20...**2. N. plena**

1. Neptunia oleracea Lour., Fl. Cochinch. 564. 1790; Benth. in Hook. Lond. J. Bot. 4: 354.1805; Thw., Enum. Pl. Zeyl. 99. 1859; Baker in Hook. f., Fl. Br. Ind. 2: 285. 1878; Trimen, Handb. Fl. Ceylon 2: 118. 1894; Prain ex King in J. As. Soc. Beng. 66 (2): 244. 1897; Gagnep. in Lecomte, Fl. Indoch. 2: 59, f.

89 (1–5). 1913; Alston in Trimen, Handb. Fl. Ceylon 6: 95. 1931; Brenan in Fl. trop. Afr., Leg.-Mimos. 40, f. 12. 1959; Windler in Austral. J. Bot. 14: 401, f. 10. 1966; Anon., Wealth of India 7: 15. 1966; Ross, Fl. S. Afr. 16 (1): 121, f. 14. 1975; Kostermans in Ceylon J. Sci. (Biol. Sci.) 13 (1 & 2): 257, Sept. 1979. Type: *Loureiro*.

Mimosa natans auct. non L., Vahl, Symbol. 3: 102. 1794; Roxb., Pl. Corom. 2: 11, t. 119. 1799; Fl. Ind. 2: 553. 1832.

Desmanthus natans Willd., Sp. Pl. 4 (2): 1044. 1806, p.p. Type: *Koenig* in herb. Vahl (LUND).

Aeschynomene herbacea Aubl., Hist. Pl. Gui. fr. 2: 775. 1775, p.p., quoad cit. Niti-todda-vaddi.

Neptunia prostrata (Lam.) Baill. in Bull. Soc. Linn. Paris 1: 356. 1883; Macbride in Contr. Gray Herb. 59: 15. 1919; Merr. in Trans. Amer. phil. Soc. N.S. 24: 187. 1935; Windler, l.c. 379.

Mimosa prostrata Lam., Enc. 1: 10. 1783. Type: *Lamarck s.n.* (P).

[Niti-toddavaddi, Rheede, Hort. Ind. Malab. 9: 35, t. 20. 1689].

Annual, glabrous herb. Stem terete, horizontal, purplish, hardly branched, thick, fistular, floating freely in warm, stagnant or slowly moving water, often provided with thick, spongy white floater tissue at the internodes. The nodes with numerous, feathery rootlets, leaves and sometimes branches. Pinnae 2–6, 5–8 cm long. Stipules obliquely ovate-cordate, thin, persistent, 5–9 mm long. Petioles at right angles to stem, glandless, folioles sessile, glabrous, sensitive, 8–20 pairs, narrowly oblong, obtuse or acutish, 2 × 5–4 × 20 mm, the lower ones smaller, midrib obscure. Inflorescence peduncles erect, very acrescent, 6–25 cm long, the oblong heads up to 1.5 cm long. Flowers minute, sessile, yellow, glabrous. Bracts obovate, trapezoid, subobtuse, 2 × 1 mm. Calyx 2 mm long. Corolla 12 mm long. Stamens 10 with acrescent filaments; anthers hardly 1 mm long, glandless (Windler). Ovary glabrous. Staminodes in the barren flowers strap-shaped, 10 mm long, yellow. Pod long-stalked, deflexed, broadly oblong, falcate, beaked, up to 25 × 6 mm, 9 mm wide, dehiscent early by the upper suture. Pedicel thin, 5 mm. Seeds 6–10, elliptic, 5 × 3–4 mm, slightly attenuate at the base, smooth, flat; funicle filiform, short. Chromosome number 2n = 56.

Distr. Pantropical.

Ecol. Tanks and other places with stagnant water in the dry zone. When the water level falls, the plant perishes. The rooted landform has smaller leaves and flowers.

Uses. Young ends of stem are eaten as a pot herb and the pods sometimes as a vegetable. In Malaya the juice of the stem is squeezed into the ear to cure ear-ache. The root is used in late stages of syphillis.

Vern. Diya (= water) nidi kumba (= sensitive plant = sleep) (S).

Note. *Mimosa natans* L. f. was considered to be a mixture of *M. tri-*

quetra (the description) and of *M. natans* (the specimen) in our sense, by Vahl, who named the described plant *Mimosa triquetra* and described another plant as *Mimosa natans* Vahl, which is our *Neptunia natans*. Macbride thought, that it would be impossible to disentangle this confusion and this viewpoint was accepted by Windler. However, following the type method conception, the Linnaeus f. plant was typified by the specimen, now in the Smith Herbarium of the Linnean Society, disregarding the Linnaeus f. description. But, the description is so poor, that it can as well completely refer to our plant, as the only discriminating word: "prostrata" may be also interpreted as alluding to the floating, horizontal position of our plant. The same reasoning was accepted by Backer and Bakhuizen (Fl. Java 3: 650. 1968).

S p e c i m e n s   E x a m i n e d. MANNAR DISTRICT: Mannar, shallow waters of Thaladikulam, March, fl., *Cramer 2891* (PDA); Minniniraindan, marsh, Jan., fl., *Jayasuriya 613* (PDA). PUTTALAM DISTRICT: Muneswaram, Chilaw, tank, terrestrial form on banks without swollen nodes, June, ster., *Maxwell et al. 832* (PDA). TRINCOMALEE DISTRICT: Kuchchaveli, N. of Trincomalee, in tank, May, fl., *Kostermans 24828* (L). HAMBANTOTA DISTRICT: Tissamaharama Rd., Febr., fl., *Cramer 2831* (PDA); Yala, tank, June, fl., *Meyer 231* (PDA).

2. Neptunia plena (L.) Benth. in Hook. Lond. J. Bot. 4: 355. 1842; Baker in Hook. f., Fl. Br. Ind. 2: 286. 1878; Trimen, Handb. Fl. Ceylon 2: 119. 1894; Alston in id. 6: 95. 1931; Windler in Austral. J. Bot. 14: 398, f. 9. 1966.

Mimosa plena L., Sp. Pl. 519. 1753. Type: Vera Cruz (LINN).
Mimosa adenanthera Roxb., Fl. Ind. 2: 554. 1832.

Perennial, terrestrial or sub-aquatic erect or ascending (rarely prostrate) herb, up to 2 m high, glabrous, forming spongy, floating tissue in water. Stipules lanceolate with obliquely cordate base, acuminate. Pinnae 4–10. Petiole 1–4 cm with a gland just below the lowest pinnae, the rachis ending in a soft, short stipe. Rachis of pinnae winged, sometimes slightly pubescent. Leaflets 9–40 pairs, 4–18 × 1.5–3 mm, oblong, obtuse or broadly acute or mucronulate, oblique, glabrous or margins sparingly ciliate, lateral nerves obscure. Flowers as in *N. natans*. Pod oblong-ligulate, up to 6 cm long, 5–20-seeded. Chromosome number 2n = 78.

D i s t r. Coastal regions of southern N. America, Central America and northern S. America, found in Bengal in India.

N o t e. There is only one specimen known: *Walker 1417* (K), labelled Ceylon.

2. MIMOSA

L., Sp. Pl. 516. 1753; Gen. Pl., ed. 5. 233. 1754.

Shrubs, herbs or trees with or without spines. Leaves bipinnate, or palmate-bipinnate. Stipules small, stipels small, usually 2 to each pinna. Leaflets small, sensitive. Flowers in globose heads, sometimes forming a terminal raceme, polygamous, usually 4-merous. Calyx campanulate with short teeth. Petals 4, adnate at the base. Stamens 4 or 8; filaments hardly connate at the base; anthers glandless. Ovary stipitate, many-ovuled; style filiform; stigma indistinct. Pod flat, membranous, made up of one-seeded joints, which at maturity separate from the persistent sutures.

A genus of about 400 species, mostly south American, one introduced and naturalized in Sri Lanka (*M. pudica*); one (*M. invisa*) introduced as green manure.

KEY TO THE SPECIES

1 Pinnae arranged palmately...**1. M. pudica**
1 Pinnae arranged pinnately...**2. M. invisa**

1. Mimosa pudica L., Sp. Pl. 518. 1753, p.p.; Willd., Sp. Pl. 4 (2): 1031. 1806; Moon, Cat. 75. 1824; Roxb., Fl. Ind. 2: 364. 1832; Baker in Hook. f., Fl. Br. Ind. 2: 291. 1878; Trimen, Handb. Fl. Ceylon 2: 122. 1894; Alston in id. 6: 96. 1931; Brenan in Kew Bull. 1955: 184; in Fl. trop. Afr., Leg.-Mim. 46. 1959; Anon., Wealth of India 6: 382. 1962. Type: Linn., Herb. Cliffort. (BM).

A diffuse undershrub or woody herb, up to 1 m high, often flattened by trampling. Stems and branches sparingly prickly and with long, weak, deflexed bristles from bulbous base (those of the rachises ascendant). Leaves sensitive, digitate. Petiole 2–5 cm, bristly. Stipules linear-lanceolate, acute, bristly, up to 8 mm long. Pinnae 1–4 pairs, 5–8 cm long, sessile or nearly so. Leaflets 12–20 pairs, sessile, sub-coriaceous, linear-oblong, acute, base truncate, 8–15 × 2–4 mm, above glabrous, with apressed bristles underneath and on margins. Flowers 4-merous. Peduncles slender, hispid, 2–2.5 cm long. Flowers pink. Bracteoles linear, carinate, up to 1.5 mm, denticulate at margin, ending in a short mucro. Calyx campanulate, very short, almost invisible, hardly toothed. Petals 4, 1.2 mm long, adnate in the lower half; lobes ovate-oblong, obtuse, pilose. Stamens 4, much exserted. Ovary with 4 ovules. Pods arranged in a star, flat, slightly recurved, 10–20 × 3–4 mm, consisting of 3–5 one-seeded joints which fall away from the persistent sutures. Sutures with patent, weak, up to 3 mm long bristles, the pods glabrous. Seeds obovate, 2 × 1.5 mm.

D i s t r. Originally from S. America, said to be introduced by Moon, but it must have been introduced much earlier.

E c o l. Waste places, lawns, etc. in the wetter zones.

U s e s. It is said to improve milk production in cattle. Pods cause intestinal trouble in cattle. Fed to chickens the leaf meal causes stunted growth and death, the toxic agent is mimosine, identical with leucenine of *Leucaena*.

It has been used as green manure. A decoction of the root is used in urinary complaints; a paste of the leaves is applied to glandular swellings and the juice of the leaves in dressing for application on sores, sinus trouble, etc. For chemistry cf. Wealth of India.

V e r n. Nidi kumba (S), a name used for all sensitive plants; Tottal-vadi (T).

N o t e. Brenan recognizes four varieties.

2. Mimosa invisa Mart. I have once found the variety *inermis* Adelbert of this species along the road outside the Agricultural Station in Peradeniya. The plant was imported as a green manure.

3. ENTADA

Adans., Fam. Pl. 2: 318. 1763 (nom. cons.).

Pusaetha [L. ex] O. Kuntze, Rev. Gen. Pl. 1: 204. 1891.
Entadopsis Britton in N. Amer. Fl. 23: 191. 1928.

Usually large woody climbers, unarmed (Ceylon). Leaves bipinnate, the apical pair of pinnae transformed into tendrils, which are caducous, when they find no support. Flowers 5-merous, polygamous, arranged in pedunculate spikes and these often in panicles. Calyx gamosepalous, shortly toothed. Petals free or shortly connate at the base. Stamens 10, shortly connate at the base and adnate to the petals, much exserted; anthers with an apical, stalked, fugaceous gland. Ovary many-ovuled; style slender, stigma minute. Pod straight, rarely curved, strap-shaped, very large (Ceylon), compressed, bullate over the seeds, the sutures indented between the seed bearing parts, at maturity the segments fall away from the persistent, thick sutures and the exocarp of the pod wall detaches as a flap, the endocarp remaining as an envelope around the seeds. Seeds many, large, exalbuminous, usually orbicular.

A genus of about 30 species, pantropical, in Sri Lanka on species.

Entada pusaetha DC., Prod. 2: 425. 1825 (pursaetha, sphalm.); Mém. Lég. 421. 1826; Alston in Trimen, Handb. Fl. Ceylon 6: 95. 1931 (excl. synon.); Brenan in Kew Bull. 1955: 164. Lectotype: Mauritius, Delessert, 1822 (DC).

Mimosa entada L., Sp. Pl. 518. 1753. Type: Plate 77, Rheede, Hort. Ind. Malab. 9: 151. 1689.
Entada rheedii Spreng., Syst. 2: 325. 1825.
Entada scandens auct. (non Benth.), Baker in Hook. f., Fl. Br. Ind. 2: 187. 1878; Trimen, Handb. Fl. Ceylon 2: 119. 1894.
Acacia scandens auct. non Willd., Moon, Cat. 73. 1824; Thw., Enum. Pl. Zeyl. 98. 1959.
Entada monostachya DC., Prod. 2: 425. 1825; Alston, l.c.; Brenan, l.c.

[*Perim-kaku-valli*, Rheede, Hort. Ind. mal. 8: 59, t. 32–34. 1688.
Entada Rheede, l.c. 9: 151, t. 77. 1689.
Pusaetha, Puswael, Phaseolus zeylanicus maximus folio lentisci, Hermann, Mus. Zeyl. 44. 1717.
Lens phaseoloides foliis subrotundo oppositis, flore spicato pentapetalo, lobis latissimis, fructu orbiculato fusco Burman, Thes. Zeyl. 138. 1737.
Mimosa foliis duplicato-pinnatis, cirrho terminatis L., Fl. Zeyl. 98, no. 219. 1748 (excl. cit. Plumier), based on tab. 77 of Rheede.
Pusaetha, L., Fl. Zeyl. 236. 1748 (Barbarae. Annihilatae), based on Rheede, tab. 32–44. Pus = name of the liana; aetha = etta = seed.]

Large, woody climber, up to 30 m long. Branchlets glabrous. Rachis thick, stiff with (1–) 2–3 pairs of pinnae, up to 25 cm long, glabrous. Pinnae up to 10 cm long, the apical part transformed into a forked, at last rather woody tendril. Leaflets 3–4 (–5) pairs, chartaceous, glabrous, elliptic to obovate-elliptic to obovate-oblong, 2.5–9 × 1–4 cm, obtuse, rounded or emarginate, base acute, sometimes slightly pilose on midrib and near the base underneath. Spikes axillary or on lateral branches, which are sometimes arrested and leafless, the spikes arranged in a panicle. Peduncle 1–9 cm long. Pedicels 0–0.5 mm long. Flowers creamy or yellowish. Calyx glabrous, ca 1 mm with short teeth. Petals ca 2.5 mm. Stamens ca 6 mm. Pods very large, straight or slightly curved, never twisted, strap-shaped, at last (dry) sub-woody, 50–200 × 7–15 cm. Seeds flattened, circular, very hard, glossy, brown, ca 5 cm diam.

D i s t r. Low country, wet zone.

U s e s. The juice of the wood and bark is used externally on ulcers. The plant is said to be a fish poison.

V e r n. Pus wael (sometimes maha = large or heen = small, is added).

N o t e s. There are usually only 4 leaflets per pinna, I have found sterile specimens over rocks (not high climbing) which had 5 leaflets. This might be a youth form. Alston thought this to represent *E. monostachya*.

S p e c i m e n s E x a m i n e d. MATALE DISTRICT: Ramamure, off Pallegama, Oct., fr. *Jayasuriya 345* (PDA). KANDY DISTRICT: Teldeniya Road, near Kandy, along ravine, July, fl., fr., *Kostermans 25269* (A, BO, G, K, L, P, PDA, US). RATNAPURA DISTRICT: Ratnapura, one mile S. of Karney, June, fr., *Maxwell 955* (PDA). BADULLA DISTRICT: Uma Oya, Sept., fr., *Balakrishnan s.n.* (PDA). AMPARAI DISTRICT: Senanayake Samudra, *Jayasuriya s.n.* (PDA). GALLE DISTRICT: Weerakande, on rock, ster., *Kostermans 25570* (id.).

4. DICHROSTACHYS

Wight & Arn., Prod. 1: 271. 1834 (nom. conserv.).
Desmanthus, sect. *Dichrostachys* DC., Mém. Légum. 12: 428. 1825.

Spinous trees or shrubs. Leaves bipinnate, gland-bearing. Stipules small. Flowers 5-merous in biformous, bicoloured spikes, the lower barren, the upper bisexual, the spikes on reduced axillary branches. Calyx minute, with short teeth. Corolla with petals valvate, coherent at the basal part. Stamens 10, free, in the barren flowers represented by long staminodes. Anthers with a small, stalked, apical gland. Pod linear, flattened, indehiscent or slightly dehiscent at the sutures, somewhat jointed, much twisted at maturity, unilocular, without pulp, 6–10 seeded.

A genus of ca 5 species in Asia, Africa and Australia, Malesia; in Ceylon one species.

Dichrostachys cinerea (L.) W. & A. subspec. **cinerea**, var. **cinerea**, Brenan & Brumitt in Bolet. Soc. Broter., Ser. 2, 39: 110. 1965.

Dichrostachys cinerea (L.) Wight & Arn., Prod. 1: 271. 1834 (cum syn.); Benth. in Hook. Lond. J. Bot. 4: 353. 1842; Wight, Ic. Pl. Ind. Or. 1: 357, text (4). 1843; Thw., Enum. Pl. Zeyl. 99. 1859; Bedd., Fl. Sylv. t. 184. 1869; Baker in Hook. f., Fl. Br. Ind. 2: 288. 1878; Trimen, Handb. Fl. Ceylon 2: 121. 1894; Gamble, Fl. Pres. Madras 419. 1935; Anon., Wealth of India 3: 56, f. 25. 1952; Brenan in Kew Bull. 1957: 357. In Fl. trop. E. Afr., Leg.-Mimos. 36, f. 11. 1959; Bhattacharyya & Maheshwari in J. Ind. bot. Soc. 52: 283. 1973; Nasir & Ali, Fl. W. Pakistan 36: 37. 1973; Ross, Fl. S. Africa 16 (1): 123. 1975.

Mimosa cinerea L., Sp. Pl. 520, no. 25. 1753; ed. 2, 2: 1505. 1762; Roxb., Fl. Ind. 2: 561. 1832.

Desmanthus cinereus (L.) Willd., Sp. Pl. 4 (2): 1048. 1806; Moon, Cat. 73. 1824.

Acacia cinerea (L.) Spreng., Syst. 3: 143. 1826.

Cailliea cinerea (L.) Macbride in Contr. Gray Herb., N.S. 59: 16. 1919. Type: *Hermann*, Mus. Zeyl. no. 215 (BM).

Acacia dalea Desv., J. Bot. 3: 69. 1814. Type: India, Herb. Desvaux (P).

[*Acacia zeylanica flore spicato, papposo, colore ex albo-luteo et rubicundo, eleganter variegato, Andara, Kukulughas*, Hermann, Mus. Zeyl. 24. 1717. Type: folium 46, Herb. Hermann (L).

Acacia spinosa ex alis spicata, foliis pennaé avium referrentis Burm., Thes. Zeyl. 3, t. 2. 1737.

Mimosa spinis solitariis, foliis duplicato-pinnatis, floribus spicatis L., Fl. Zeyl. 96, no. 215. 1748].

Shrub or tree, up to 6 m high and 15 cm diam. with numerous, stiff, spreading branches. Bark yellowish grey, fibrous, longitudinally fissured, strips 5–10 mm wide, 2 mm thick. Live bark 3 mm, light brown. Ultimate twigs sharply spinous at end, many reduced to short, woody, axillary spines. Wood dark red, very hard and tough with disagreeable smell. Young branchlets with dense appressed, minute indumentum. Leaves paripinnate, usually from suppressed branchlets. Rachis 2.5–4 cm, slender, pilose with erect, shortly stipitate, cylindrical, concave glands between the bases of the pinnae. Pinnae 8–16 pairs, 1–1.5 cm long. Leaflets 12–20 pairs, sessile, closely packed, oblique, linear to lanceolate, ciliate, 1.5–3.5 × 0.5–1 mm, subacute, base truncate. Stipules subulate from triangular base, small. Spikes solitary or 2–3 together on the arrested branches. Calyx thin, pubescent, hardly 1 mm long with short teeth. Corolla up to 2.5 mm, of the barren, lower flowers pink to violet-pink, becoming white after anthesis, of the fertile upper flowers yellow. Stamens exserted. Staminodes of barren flowers filiform, red, 1.25 mm. Ovary pilose, style long, flexuous, exserted; stigma minute, truncate. Pod linear, 5–10 mm wide, glabrous, dark brown, sub-articulate, swollen over the 6–10 ellipsoid seeds, indehiscent.

D i s t r. India, Ceylon (var. *cinerea*), the species also in Asia, Australia and Africa (the varieties).

E c o l. Dry and arid zones, common, forming thickets.

U s e s. A host of the lac insect in India. Tender shoots bruised and applied to the eyes in cases of ophthalmia. The astringent root used in rheumatism, urinary calculi and renal troubles. Leaves used as fodder. Bark yields a yellowish white fibre.

V e r n. Andara (S); Vindatallai (T).

N o t e s. Very drought-resisting and reproducing freely by root suckers, often in considerable distance from the main stem, owing to the long and spreading roots, and thickets, many metres in diameter are formed in this way. Also comparatively immune against grazing. Flowers and fruit at various times, according to localities.

Bhattacharyya & Maheshwari proved that the glands have a secretorial and a non-secretorial part and that they have taxonomic importance.

Linnaeus (Sp. Pl., l.c.) named two species *Mimosa cinerea*, one on page 517, no. 10, based on a Plukenet plant (Cf. Brenan in Kew Bull. 1956: 188), the other on page 520, no. 25, is the base of *D. cinerea*. In Systema Naturae, ed. 10, vol. 2: 312. 1759 and in his Sp. Pl., ed. 2, 2: 1505. 1762 he retained *Mimosa cinerea* for species no. 25 and substituted *M. cineraria* for species No. 10.

Brenan & Brumitt, studying the variability, based their subspecific classification on the indumentum of the peduncles, the maximum number of pinnae, the limits of leaflet width and the shape of the glands. Flower characters could not be used and the fruit only in so far, that the broader pods are usually more strongly coiled. The Indian and Ceylon var. *cinerea* has the young branches and peduncles with appressed indumentum.

Specimens Examined. MANNAR DISTRICT: Mannar Road, dry scrub, common, May, fl., *Kostermans 24873* (A, BO, G, K, L, P, PDA, US). VAVUNIYA DISTRICT: near Vavunia, dry zone, low, July, fl., *Kostermans 25215* (id.). ANURADHAPURA DISTRICT: S. of Anuradhapura, June, fl., fr., *Maxwell et al., 789* (PDA). POLONNARUWA DISTRICT: Polonnaruwa, Oct., fr., *Kundu et al., 236* (PDA). HAMBANTOTA DISTRICT: Yala, Aug., fr., *Kostermans 25444* (A, BO, G, K, L, P, PDA, US); ibid., Jan., fl., *Cramer 3334* (PDA).

5. PROSOPIS

L., Mant. Pl. 1: 10. 1767; Burkhart in J. Arn. Arb. 57: 219–249. 1976.

Trees or shrubs with scattered thorns. Leaves pari-bipinnate with small, narrow leaflets. Stipules small or none, sometimes spinescent. Flowers bisexual, minute in narrow spikes or subspicate racemes. Calyx minute, campanulate, subentire or faintly 5-toothed. Petals 5, ligulate, subcoherent at the base. Stamens 10, free, slightly exserted; anthers with apical gland. Ovary stipitate, many-ovuled, style filiform, stigma minute. Pod fleshy, indehiscent, cylindrical or slightly flattened with thick, spongy mesocarp, septate between the seeds.

A genus of about 40 species, mainly American, some in S.W. Asia and in Africa. In Sri Lanka one cultivated and (a variety of it) naturalized in the coastal area near Hambantota.

Prosopis juliflora (Sw.) DC., Prod. 2: 447. 1825; Burkhart in Darwiniana 4: 103, t. 22. 1940; in J. Arn. Arb. 57: 499–503. 1976; Svenson in Amer. J. Bot. 33: 451, t. 11 (1,4,5). 1946; Anon., Wealth of India 8: 245. 1969 (as a syn. of *P. chilensis*).

Mimosa juliflora Swartz, Prod. 85. 1788; Fl. Ind. Occ. 2: 986. 1800 (*piliflora*).
Algaroba juliflora (Sw.) Benth. ex Heyne, Nomencl. 2: 18. 1840.
Neltuma juliflora (Sw.) Rafin., Sylv. Tellur. 119. 1838; Britton & Killip in Ann. N. York Acad. Sci. 35: 154. 1936. Type: Jamaica, Swartz.

Tree or shrub, up to 12 m high. Bark deeply, wavily fissured, the ridges 5 mm thick, 1–2 cm wide, brown. Live bark 5 mm, yellowish-brown. Spines straight, ca 5 mm long, solitary or paired, divergent, up to 5 cm long on older branches. Leaves glabrous with 2 or 4 pinnae. Petiole slender, 1–5 cm long with a small, circular gland near the bases of the lower pinnae. Pinnae 3–11 cm long with slender rachillae, flattened and somewhat channelled above, ending in a short stipe. Leaflets opposite, sessile, chartaceous, 6–29 (usually 11–15) pairs, oblong-linear, 6–23 × 1.5–5 mm, both ends obtuse or apex emarginate or mucronulate, the midrib slightly excentric, rather few lateral nerves, conspicuous below. Racemes or spikes axillary, many-flowered, up to 15 cm long, rachis microscopically, sparsely pubescent. Flowers greenish-yellow, subsessile. Calyx campanulate, glabrous, 1.5 mm long with small, triangular teeth. Corolla twice as long, the slender lobes inside densely tomentose. Pod coriaceous, pale yellow, glossy, smooth, flattened, up to 20 (–30) cm long and 1.5 cm wide, 4–10 mm thick, with straight parallel sutures or irregularly submoniliformous; segments up to 25, rectangular, mostly broader than long. Pedicel up to 2 cm long. Seeds oval, brown, transverse.

Distr. Originally from S. America (coastal areas) and West Indies, planted in gardens (Hambantota) and elsewhere.

Notes. Near the sea coast in Hambantota a form of this is naturalized; it has falcate to curved, smaller pods. The trees are low with spreading crowns and branches and bole are overgrown with masses of lichens.

The variety in Sri Lanka is var. **horrida** (Kunth) Burkhart (l.c. 502), based on *Prosopis horrida* Kunth, Mimos. et autres Pl. légum. 106, t. 33. 1822, characterized by its thorns.

Specimens Examined. HAMBANTOTA DISTRICT: Near Hambantota, salterns near Station, Aug., fl., fr., *Kostermans 25455* (A, BO, G, K, L, P, PDA, US); in garden in Hambantota, Aug., fr., *Kostermans 25456* (id.). seacoast, Hambantota, Aug., fl., fr., *Kostermans 25451* and *25452* (id.).

6. ADENANTHERA

L., Sp. Pl. 384. 1753; Gen. Pl. ed. 5. 181. 1754.

Unarmed trees. Leaves bipinnate, spirally arranged, without glands. Stipules small, caducous. Leaflets alternate. Inflorescences axillary or terminal, racemes or panicles of racemes, the racemes peduncled. Flowers bisexual, 5-merous, pedicelled, the pedicel with a persistent or caducous bract at the base and articulate slightly above its base. Calyx gamosepalous, campanulate with 5 small teeth. Petals 5, valvate in bud, hardly adnate at the base. Stamens 10, all free, slightly longer than the petals; anthers with a small, ovoid, stalked caducous gland at the apex. Ovary many-ovuled, slightly stipitate or sessile; style long, stigma inconspicuous. Pod narrow, slightly flattened, fleshy, straight, falcate or slightly twisted, unilocular, without pulp; endocarp a whitish satiny, fibrous layer. Seeds several, hard, subglobose, slightly compressed, either dark glossy red or half red, partly black, rarely yellowish; funicle short, thin.

A genus of eight species in S.E. Asia, Malesia and the Pacific area, one (*A. pavonina*) cultivated in all tropics. In Sri Lanka two species, one endemic.

KEY TO THE SPECIES

1 Flush of the leaves pale green. Flowers white or yellow. Raceme bracts deciduous. Seeds evenly dark red . . . .**1. A. pavonina**
1 Flush of the leaves dark wine-red with violet tinge. Flowers dark pink. Bracts of the racemes persistent. Seeds dark red with black spot . . . .**2. A. bicolor**

1. **Adenanthera pavonina** L., Sp. Pl. 384. 1753; ed. 2: 550. 1763; Wight, Ill. Ind. Bot. t. 80 (84). 1820; Moon, Cat. 34. 1824; Roxb., Fl. Ind. 2: 370. 1832; Wight & Arn., Prod. 1: 271. 1834; Thw., Enum. Pl. Zeyl. 98. 1859; Beddome, Fl. Sylv. t. 46. 1869; Benth. in Trans. Linn. Soc. Lond. 30: 375. 1875; Baker in Hook. f., Fl. Br. Ind. 2: 287. 1878; Trimen, Handb. Fl. Ceylon 2: 120. 1894; Troup, Silvicult. Ind. Trees 2: 485. 1921; Worthington, Ceylon Trees t. 201. 1959. Type: Linn., Hort. Cliffort. (BM).

[*Mandsjadi*, Rheede. Hort. Ind. Malab. 6: 25, t. 14. 1686.
Mandathiya. Mangili. Mara, Arbor indica, pisa rotunda compressa coccinea, etc., Hermann, Mus. Zeyl. 21. 1717.
Crista pavonis arbor, foliis subrotundis alternis, etc., Burm., Thes. Zeyl. 79. 1737.
Poinciana foliis duplicato-pinnatis, foliolis alternis L., Hort. Cliffort. 158. 1737.
Adenanthera foliis decompositis L., Fl. Zeyl. 70, no. 160. 1747.]

Tree, up to 20 m high and 40 cm diam. Bark grey, smooth, in older trees darker exfoliating. Live bark 3 mm, straw coloured. Wood hard, close grained, red. Branchlets sparsely to densely, minutely tomentellous to glabrous. Stipules hardly 0.5 mm long. Rachis up to 40 cm long, not produced beyond the apical foliole, glabrous to pubescent. Pinnae 2–6 pairs, opposite, 6–20 cm long. Leaflets chartaceous, 3–9 pairs, alternate, elliptic to ovate- or obovate-elliptic or oblong, 1.5–5.5 × 0.5–3.5 cm, rounded or emarginate, base slightly oblique, rounded or broadly cuneate, above smooth, glabrous, below sparsely, microscopically sericeous, nerves visible. Petiolules ca 1 mm long. Racemes solitary or in panicles, up to 30 cm long, the peduncular, bare part 2–5 cm. Pedicels 2–4 mm. Flowers white, then yellowish. Calyx usually glabrous, ca 1 mm long. Petals glabrous, linear-lanceolate, acute, up to 4.5 mm long. Filaments 2.5–4 mm. Pod straight to falcate to slightly twisted, narrow, rather fleshy, 10–25 × 1.5 cm, glabrous, tapered at the base, apex acute; after dehiscence the rather thin valves twisted spirally showing the satiny white inner surface. Seeds 6–15, elliptic-lenticular, with blunt keel, glossy red, 8–10 × 7–9 mm.

D i s t r. India, Burma, Thailand, Malesia, China; rare, usually planted.
E c o l. Low country, up to 1300 m alt., rather common, but usually planted.
U s e s. The hard, red wood for furniture, building purposes, but in Sri Lanka too rare. The wood yields a red dye, used by Brahmins to mark their

forehead. A cement is made of the seeds by beating them with borax and water. The pulp is used medicinally. The seeds are used for jewellers' weights and as necklaces.

V e r n. Madathiya (S); Anaikuntamani, Anikundamani (T).

S p e c i m e n s E x a m i n e d. KANDY DISTRICT: Deltota Tea Estate Group, alt. 1000 m, Sept., fr., *Kostermans 25679* (K, L, P, PDA, US). BADULLA DISTRICT: Bibile, dry zone, along rivulet, Jan., fl., *Kostermans 24383* (id.). KALUTARA DISTRICT: Morapitiya, mile 32, July, fr., *Meyer 458* (PDA). RATNAPURA DISTRICT: Ratnapura, rd. to Tiruwanaketiya, June, fr., *Maxwell 975* (PDA); Ratnapura, Udakarawita, May, fr., *Balakrishnan 328* (PDA).

2. Adenanthera bicolor Moon. Cat. 34. 1824 (nomen, excl. cit. Rumphius) et ex Thw., Enum. Pl. Zeyl. 98. 1859; Baker in Hook. f., Fl. Br. Ind. 2: 287. 1878; Trimen, Handb. Fl. Ceylon 2: 120. 1894, Kosterm. in Ceylon J.Sci., Biol. Sci. 13 (1 & 2): 254. Sept. 1979. Type *C.P. 324* (PDA).

Adenanthera aglaosperma Alston in Ann. R. Bot. Gard. Perad. 11: 204. 1929; in Trimen, Handb. Fl. Ceylon 6: 95. 1931; Worthington, Ceylon Trees t. 200. 1959.

Tree, up to 15 m high. Bark rough, dark grey, deeply fissured, strips 5 cm wide, 2 cm thick, peeling off in thin, rather large pieces. Live bark 3 mm, straw-coloured. Wood straw-coloured. Branchlets smooth, cylindrical. Leaves numerous, glabrous, the flush wine-red with violet tinge. Rachis slender, 4–20 cm long, hardly swollen at the base, ending in a short stipe. Pinnae usually 2 pairs, slender, 3–8 cm long. Folioles chartaceous, rather widely separated, 4–10, elliptic to subovate-elliptic, 1.5 × 3 cm (apical one), base acute, lateral nerves erect-patent, prominulous, arcuately united at some distance from the margin. Petiolules 1–2.5 mm, folded. Racemes axillary, slender, minutely, rather stiffly, sparsely pubescent, many-flowered, up to 6 cm long. Flowers vieux rose to dark pink. Pedicel c. 3 mm with a basal, small, slender, acute, persistent bract. Calyx shallowly campanulate, stiff with triangular, acute, rather patent lobes. Petals narrowly oblong, acute, explanate, 2 mm. Stamens slightly exserted. Ovary hardly stipitate, style slender, stigma inconspicuous. Pod narrow, torulose, slightly flattened, 6–12 cm long, 1–2 cm wide over the seeds, black, falcate or twisted after dehiscence. Seeds subglobose, slightly flattened with rather sharp margins, hard, glossy, part black, part dark red.

D i s t r. Endemic. Wet, Southwest area (Sinharaja), low alt.

V e r n. Mas mora (S).

N o t e s. Moon's name was a nomen nudum and not typified by the Rumphian quotation, as assumed by Alston, and hence Thwaites was right in taking up the name *bicolor*.

The tree does not occur outside Sri Lanka; the Malayan one, quoted by Baker, represents *A. malayana* Kosterm.
Specimens Examined. RATNAPURA DISTRICT: Moropitiya Rd., W. of Matugama, along rivulet, June, fr., *Kostermans 24952* (A, BO, G, K, L, P, PDA, US); Rakwana, 600 m alt., May, fr., *Kostermans 23636* (id.); mile 31, culvert 10 near Moropitiya, June, fl., *Meijer 457* (PDA, US).

7. LEUCAENA

Benth. in Hook. Lond. J. Bot. 4: 416. 1842.

Unarmed shrubs and trees. Leaves bipinnate with large gland on petiole. Stipules small, setaceous. Flowers in a globose, pedunculate head, axillary or the heads arranged in a terminal raceme. Flowers sessile, 5-merous, mostly bisexual; bracts usually 2. Calyx campanulate, shortly toothed. Petals 5, valvate, free or nearly so. Stamens 10, free or almost so, much exserted. Anthers without gland. Ovary stipitate, many-ovuled; stigma minute. The stalked pods flat, strap-shaped, unilocular, without pulp, dehiscent along both sutures, arranged in a head; funicle filiform. Seeds flat.

A genus of 6 species, all American, one introduced and planted in Sri Lanka.

Leucaena leucocephala (Lam.) de Wit in Taxon 10: 54. 1961; ibid. 24: 352. 1975; Gillis & Stearn in Taxon 23: 185–191. 1974; Shaw & Schubert in J. Arn. Arb. 57: 113–118. 1976.

Acacia leucocephala (Lam.) Link, Enum. Hort. Berol. 2: 444. 1822.
Mimosa leucocephala Lam., Enc. 1: 12. 1783. Type: Herb. Lamarck *s.n.* (P).
Leucaena glauca ("Willd.") Benth. l.c. 416; Baker in Hook. f., Fl. Br. Ind. 2: 290. 1878; Prain in King, J. As. Soc. Bengal 66 (2): 245. 1897; Trimen, Handb. Fl. Ceylon 2: 122. 1894; Alston in id. 6: 94. 1931; Gagnep. in Lecomte, Fl. Indoch. 2: 74, f. 11 (1–5). 1913; Troup, Silvicult. Ind. Trees 2: 486. 1921; Anon., Wealth of India 6: 77–79, f. 34. 1962; Bhattacharyya & Maheshwari in J. Ind. Bot. Soc. 52: table 5. 1973.
Mimosa glauca L., Sp. Pl. 520. 1753 (quoad nomen); ed. 2. 2: 1504. 1763.
Acacia glauca (L.) Moench, Meth. Pl. 466. 1794. Type: Herb. van Royen (L).
Acacia frondosa Willd., Sp. Pl. 4 (2): 1076. 1806; Wight & Arn., Prod. 1: 275. 1834.
Acacia biceps Willd., l.c. 1075.

Unarmed tree or shrub, up to 9 m high. Branchlets subangular, finely pubescent. Stipules very small, caducous. Rachis up to 20 cm long, petiole up to 7.5 cm, swollen at the base with above the base a large, oval, concave gland, pubescent (hairs short). Pinnae c. 6 pairs, 2–10 cm long. Leaflets 10–20 pairs, thin, finely downy, linear-oblong, subsessile, oblique and attenuate at base, apex acute or acuminate, ciliate, above glabrous, below pubescent, glaucous, 10–15 × 3–4 mm, the lowest and apical ones the smallest. The pedruncled heads solitary or in pairs. Peduncle pubescent, 4–6 cm, slender. Bracteoles ovate, as long as calyx. Flowers numerous, white, usually all perfect. Calyx funnel-shaped, teeth 3 mm, triangular, acute, ciliate. Petals 3–4 mm, finely pubescent. Stamens inserted very low on the stipe of the ovary, exserted; anthers with a few, long hairs; connective granular on the back. Ovary shortly stipitate, sparsely pubescent; style glabrous, as long as the ovary; stigma minute. Pod strap-shaped, straight, flat, coriaceous, up to 20 × 1.5 cm, ending in an acute hard beak, attenuate at the base into the up to 3 cm long pedicel; the valves inside with transverse ridges. Seeds 15–20, narrowly oval, flat, apex obtuse, base cuneate, brown, glossy, up to 8 × 4 mm.

D i s t r. Originally from tropical America, now pantropical, cultivated as green manure, fodder and for afforestation.

U s e s. Wood very hard, used us pestles, handles, etc. Young pods and seeds edible, also as fodder. Causes hair fall (leucine acid). It spreads readily from self sown seeds, but natural viability of seeds is low. For planting the soil is often inoculated with nodule bacteria by mixing soil of old plantations. Used for reafforestation of grass lands, wind break and for checking soil erosion; cover plant of tea, rubber, cinchona, teak, etc. Green manure; the leaves are rich in nitrogen. Excellent fodder but in excessive quantities toxic to monogastric animals (loss of hair), but reversible after stoppage (leucein or leucenol, alkaloid). Seeds concentrate selenium. Seeds as worm repellent and a fish poison. The wood is good, but too small.

V e r n. Tagavai, Nattucavundal (T).

N o t e s. *Leucaena glauca* ("Willd.") Bentham is based on *Acacia glauca* Willd., the description of which is that of *Mimosa glauca* of the second edition of Linn., Sp. Pl. 2: 1504. 1763 (non L., ed. 1: 520. 1753), but nomenclaturally the combination is based on *Mimosa glauca* (L., of the first edition) (= *Acacia glauca* (L.) Moench).

8. DESMANTHUS

Willd., Sp. Pl. 4 (2): 1047. 1806; Benth. in Lond. J. Bot. 4: 356. 1842.

Spineless shrubs or woody herbs. Leaves bipinnate with bristle-like persistent stipules. Flowers mostly bisexual, 5-merous, in peduncled heads. Calyx thin, campanulate with 5 teeth. Petals slightly coherent, valvate in bud, almost free. Stamens 10, free, much exserted; anthers without glands. Ovary sessile, many-ovuled; style long, filiform; stigma clavate-tubular. Pod flattened, straight, narrow, dehiscent along both sutures, without pulp, usually uni-locular; seeds numerous, albuminous; funicle filiform.

A tropical American genus with c. eight species; one introduced and natu-ralized in Sri Lanka.

Desmanthus virgatus (L.) Willd., Sp. Pl. 4 (2): 1047. 1806 (exc. cit. Plukenet); Moon, Cat. 73. 1824; Wight & Arn., Prod. 1: 270. 1834 (cum syn.); Benth., l.c. 357; Thw., Enum. Pl. Zeyl. 98. 1859; Baker in Hook. f., Fl. Br. Ind. 2: 290. 1878; Trimen, Handb. Fl. Ceylon 2: 122. 1894; Alston in id. 6: 96. 1931; Gagnep. in Lecomte, Fl. Indoch. 2: 75, f. 11 (6–11). 1913; Bhattacharyya & Maheshwari in J. Ind. Bot. Soc. 52: tab. 5. 1973.

Mimosa virgata L., Sp. Pl. 519. 1753; ed. 2, 2: 1502. 1762; Jacquin, Hort. Vin-dobon. 1: t. 80. 1770.
Acacia virgata (L.) Gaertn., de Fruct. 2: 317, t. 148, f. 3.1791. Type: India, Linnaeus, Hort. Cliffort. (BM).
Desmanthus strictus DC., Prod. 2: 445. 1825.
Desmanthus leptophyllus DC., l.c. 444.
Desmanthus pernambucensis (L.) Thellung in Mèm. Soc. Nat. Cherb., Sér. 1, 118: 296. 1911.
Mimosa pernambucensis L., Sp. Pl. 519. 1753.
[*Mimosa herba zeylanica, siliquus angustis, glabris media* Hermann, Mus. Zeyl. 66. 1717; Burman, Thes. Zeyl. 160. 1737 (ecl. cit. Plukenet); L., Fl. Zeyl. 505. 1747].

Shrub or semi-woody herb with virgate branches, up to 2 m high, mostly glabrous. Branchlets angular. Pinnae 3–8 pairs, up to 6 cm long. Rachis glabrous or with few, minute hairs, terminating in a thin stipe. Stipules thin, subulate, 5–8 mm, with few hairs. A large, oblong, subpeltate gland just be-low the bases of the lowermost pinnae. Leaflets thin, glabrous (margin often ciliate), 10–20 pairs, subimbricate, oblong-linear, 3–7 × 1–3 mm, very un-equal-sided with truncate base, apex mucronulate. Flower heads axillary, soli-tary, few-flowered on filiform, glabrous, up to 6 cm long peduncles. Flowers creamy white, glabrous, c. 3 mm long. Floral bracts setaceous (acumen 1 mm long), the base triangular and auricled. Calyx thin, sessile, tubular-campanu-late with triangular teeth. Stamens (sometimes staminodes in barren flowers) long exserted. Pod coriaceous flattened, straight, up to 10 cm long, 3–4 mm wide, in groups of 1–5. Seeds 20–30, ovoid-polygonal, brown, 2 × 1.5 mm. Valves thin.

D i s t r. and E c o l. Waste places, rather abundant, introduced from tropical America.

9. CATHORMION

Hassk., Retzia 1: 231. 1855 (reprint in Natuurk. Tijdschr. Ned. Ind. 10: 231. 1856); Kosterm. in Bull. 20, Organ. sci. Res. Indon. 11. 1954; Burkhart in Darwiniana 13: 443–48. 1964.

Trees or shrubs. Leaves bipinnate, gland-bearing. Stipules spinescent. Flowers as in *Pithecellobium* and *Abarema* in peduncled globose pseudo-umbels. Staminal tube as long as the corolla tube. Anthers glandless. Ovary sessile. Pods compressed, moniliform, indehiscent, more or less curved, without pulp, breaking at the joints. Seeds flattened, funicle filiform.

A genus of seven species, mostly American, one in Asia and Ceylon.

Cathormion umbellatum (Vahl) Kosterm. l.c. 12, f. 9 C and 10. 1954.

Mimosa umbellata Vahl, Symbol. Bot. 2: 103. 1790; Willd· Sp. Pl. 4 (2): 1027.1806; Wight & Arn., Prod. 1: 270. 1834.
Inga umbellata (Vahl) Willd., l.c. 1027; Moon, Cat. 73. 1824.
Feuilleea umbellata (Vahl) O. Kuntze, Rev. Gen. Pl. 1: 188. 1891.
Pithecolobium umbellatum (Vahl) Benth. in Hook. Lond. J. Bot. 3: 202. 1844; Thw., Enum. Pl. Zeyl. 100.1859; Baker in Hook. f., Fl. Br. Ind. 2: 303. 1878; Trimen, Handb. Fl. Ceylon 2: 132. 1894; Gamble, Fl. Pres. Madras 434. 1919.
subsp. *umbellatum* Brumitt in Kew Bull. 1924: 232. Type: Ceylon, *Koenig s.n.* (C).
Inga monilifera Decne., Herb. Timor. 131. 1835.
Cathormion moniliferum (DC) Hassk., 11. cc.
Pithecolobium moniliferum (Decne.) Benth., l.c. 211.
Feuilleea monilifera (Decne.) O. Kuntze, l.c. 188.
Albizzia monilifera (Decne.) F.v. Mueller in Trimen, J. Bot. 10: 10. 1872.
Pithecolobium umbellatum var. *moniliferum* Miquel, Fl. Ind. Bat. 1 (1): 38. 1855. Type: Timor, *s. coll.* (P).
Inga moniliformis DC., Prod. 2: 440. 1825.
Pithecolobium moniliforme (DC.) Benth. ex S. Blake in Austral. J. Bot. 2 (1): 115. 1954.
Cathormion moniliforme ("Hasskarl") Merrill in J. Wash. Acad. Sci. 6 (2): 43. 1916. Type: Timor, *s. coll.* (G, L, P).
Mimosa concordiana Roxb., Hort. Bengal. 40. 1814 (nomen); Fl. Ind. 2: 556. 1832.
Inga concordiana Wight & Arn., l.c. 269. Type: India, Roxburgh.
Inga corcondiana DC., Prod., l.c. 441.
Mimosa corcondiana DC., l.c.
Pithecolobium malayanum Pierre, Fl. for. Cochinch., fasc. 25: Pl. 394 B. 1889. Type: *Pierre* 5974, Siam (P).

Low, thick tree, up to 15 m tall, usually smaller, with a gnarled bole, up to 60 cm diam., branched lowly with spreading numerous spiny branches forming a dense crown. Bark greyish, deeply fissured, corky, 5 mm thick. Live bark 3 mm, pinkish to light brown. Branchlets glabrous, glossy, striate with large, scattered lenticels. Leaves with one or two pairs of pinnae, young ones microscopically pilose. Petiolar part slender, 1.5–2 cm with a small gland with raised margins near the bases of the pinnae; rachis up to 2 cm long; rachillae sulcate, up to 10 cm long (lower pair shorter), glandless or with minute, circular glands between the bases of the folioles. Folioles sessile, chartaceous, glabrescent, opposite, 4–7 pairs, the distal (largest) one obliquely obovate, up to 3.5 × 2 cm, the proximal ones trapezoid, wing like, 1 × 0.5 cm, midrib diagonal, obtuse or emarginate, base obtuse. Stipular thorns straight, long, sometimes absent, sometimes branchlets turned into spines. The peduncled globose heads erect on the plagiotropous branches. Peduncles slender, microscopically pilose, up to 4 cm. The peduncles fascicled on very short branchlets (sometimes they are longer and the fascicles bracteate). Pedicel filiform, up to 5 mm, sparsely pubescent. Calyx tubular funnel-shaped, glabrous, 2 mm, hardly more than 1 mm diam. with small, triangular acute teeth. Corolla tube narrowly funnel-shaped, slightly pubescent, 3 mm long, lobes narrowly ovate, 1.5 mm. Staminal tube as long as the corolla tube, free part 5 mm. Ovary glabrous, sessile. Pod straight or more or less curved, thickish, compressed, up to 20 × 3.5 cm, glossy black or dull rusty. Seeds circular, black.

D i s t r. Coastal areas in Malesia, in adequate places also further inland.
E c o l. In N.W. Ceylon in the arid zone.
N o t e s. It takes a very long time before the segments of the pod fall apart and still longer before they deteriorate to liberate the seeds. When the glossy exocarp wears away a rusty indument like appearance becomes visible.

Brumitt, l.c., recognizes subsp. *moniliforme*, which I consider a mere form with narrower leaflets, *P. malayanum* Pierre has similar narrow and smaller leaflets.

S p e c i m e n s E x a m i n e d. MANNAR DISTRICT: Madhu Road, 2.5 miles from Mannar Isl., July fl., *Kostermans 25228* (A, BO, G, K, L, P, PDA, US); Road Madhu to Vavuniya July, fl., *Kostermans 25236* (id.); Mannar-Parayananalkulam, ster., *Worthington 4470* (PDA); ibid., Murungan, Jan., fr., *Worthington 4470* (PDA).

10. SAMANEA

Merr. in J. Wash. Acad. Sci. 6: 46. 1916.

Pithecolobium Mart., sect. *Samanea* Benth. in Hook. Lond. J. Bot. 3: 197. 1844.

Unarmed trees. Leaves bipinnate, gland-bearing. Flowers in pedunculate, globose heads (pseudo-umbels), bisexual, 5-merous. Calyx tube-like to campanulate with 5 short teeth. Corolla with funnel-shaped tube, the lobes connate to the middle. Stamens indefinite, monadelphous, much exserted; anthers glandless. Ovary sessile, many-ovuled, style filiform, stigma minute. Pod strap-shaped, straight or slightly curved, thick, fleshy, indehiscent, flattened; mesocarp pulpy, fleshy, septate; endocarp firm, forming septa between the seeds. Sutures slightly thickened.

A monotypic genus from South America. The species widely planted in all tropics as avenue tree.

Samanea saman (Jacq.) Merr. in J. Wash. Acad. Sci. 6: 47. 1916. Britton & Killip in N. York Ac. Sci. 35: 129. 1936.

Mimosa saman Jacq., Fragm. 15, t. 9. 1800.
Pithecolobium saman Willd., Benth. in Hook. Lond. J. Bot. 3: 101. 1844; Trimen, Handb. Fl. Ceylon 2: 132. 1894.
Inga saman Willd., Sp. Pl. 4 (2): 1024. 1806.
Enterolobium saman (Jacq.) Prain in King in J. Asiat. Soc. Beng. 66 (2): 252. 1897; Gagnep. in Lecomte, Fl. Indoch. 2: 84, f. 12 (1–9). 1913; Troup, Silvicult. Ind. Trees 2: 483. 1921; Alston in Trimen, Handb. Fl. Ceylon 6: 100. 1931; Anon., Wealth of India 3: 175, f. 113. 1952; Worthington, Ceylon Trees t. 221. 1959.
Calliandra saman Griseb., Fl. Br. W. Ind. Isl. 225. 1864.
Albizzia saman F. v. Mueller, Select. Pl. 27. 1891. Type: Caracas, Venezuela.
Pithecolobium cinereum Benth., l.c.
Calliandra tubulosa Benth., l.c.

Tree, up to 25 m high and 1.5 m in diam. Bark rough, deeply fissured in a wavy pattern, yellowish brown, thick. Sapwood dirty white, heartwood black, streaked with yellow. Crown very large, spreading. Branchlets pubescent. Stipules small, lanceolate, densely pubescent, caducous. Petiolar part of leaf 1–1.5 cm, without gland, swollen at the base; glands between the bases of the pinnae. Pinnae c. 4 pairs, 3.5–15 cm long or longer, rachilla pubescent. Leaflets sessile, coriaceous, 12–16 pairs in the upper, 6–10 pairs in the lower pinnae, trapezoid to ovate-oblong (the lower smaller), 2–5 × 1–3 cm, both ends truncate or attenuate, above glossy, glabrous, softly pubescent underneath, midrib excentric, often diagonal, ending in a mucro, nerves c. 7 pairs forming with the veins a conspicuous network below. Flowers in dense heads on 6–10 cm long, pubescent peduncles, solitary or 2–3 together in the axils of the upper leaves. Flowers subsessile, each with a lanceolate, pilose bract, 2.5 mm long. Calyx slender, funnel-shaped, densely pilose, 3–5 mm long, teeth short, broadly triangular. Corolla pinkish, funnel-shaped, 8–13 mm long, puberulous, lobes ovate, half as long as the tube. Filaments pink, 3 cm long, connate at the base in a tube one-third as long as the corolla tube. Ovary glabrous, sessile. Pod sessile, fleshy, straight, indehiscent, 12–20 × 1–2.5 cm, slightly flattened, slightly depressed between the seeds, sutures thickened; epicarp thin, crustaceous, glossy brown, mesocarp pulpy, light brown, sticky, very sweet; endocarp firmly crustaceous and forming continuous septa between the seeds; seeds 16–20, transversally ovate, 1 × 0.6 cm, 5 mm thick, smooth, brown, glossy, funicle thin.

D i s t r. Originally from S. America, in Sri Lanka planted as an avenue tree.

U s e s. Leaves and pods are fodder (protein content 3–10%). Pod can be dried and stored. A full grown tree may yield 200 kg of pods annually. The pods contain 12% of protein and 55% carbohydrates. The wood is light and soft, the heartwood is a beautiful black and could be used for furniture, but it is not used in Sri Lanka.

V e r n. Rain tree (E); Mara (S).

N o t e s. The main roots are superficial and the tree should not be planted near buildings.

The tree was introduced in Ceylon in 1851.

The central flower of the head is much larger than the others, 7–8-merous and contains more stamens, a phenomenon also found in *Pithecellobium*, *Abarema* and *Albizia*.

11. VACHELLIA

Wight & Arn., Prod. 1: 272. 1834; Britton & Killip in Ann. N. York Acad. Sci. 35: 138. 1936.

Trees or shrubs. Leaves bipinnate with a small gland on the petiolar part of the rachis below the bases of the lowermost pinnae. The paired, stipular thorns thin, setaceous to slender, straight. The bisexual, 5-merous flowers arranged in pedunculate globose heads with bracts near the apex of the peduncle. Flowers sessile, as in *Acacia*. Pod turgid, subcylindrical, dehiscent along both sutures, straight or slightly curved, ending in a strong hook; mesocarp pulpy. Seeds subglobose, lenticulate, rather few.

A monotypic American genus, the species introduced and naturalized in Ceylon.

Vachellia farnesiana Wight & Arn., Prod. 1: 272. 1834; Wight, Ic. Pl. Ind. Or. 7: t. 300. 1840; Britton & Killip, l.c.

Mimosa farnesiana L., Sp. Pl. 521. 1753; Roxb., Fl. Ind. 2: 557. 1832.
Acacia farnesiana (L.) Willd., Sp. Pl. 4 (2): 1083. 1806; Benth. in Hook. Lond. J. Bot. 1: 494. 1842, Fl. Austral. 2: 419. 1864; in Trans. Linn. Soc. Lond. 30:

502. 1875; Beddome, Fl. Sylv. t. 52. 1869; Baker in Hook. f., Fl. Br. Ind. 2:
292. 1878; Troup, Silvicult. Ind. Trees 2: 462. 1921; Alston in Trimen,
Handb. Fl. Ceylon 6: 96. 1931; Anon., Wealth of India 1: 14. 1948. Type:
Santo Domingo (LINN).
Acacia pedunculata Willd., l.c. 1084.

Shrub or small tree, up to 4 m high. Branchlets zig-zag, smooth, red
brown (dried), often with numerous small, round lenticels. Young branchlets,
rachis and rachillae laxly, minutely tomentellous. Thorns very slender, white,
setaceous, 5 mm long, the longest up to 2 cm long, very slender. Leaf rachis
slender, flat above, up to 7 cm long with a tiny, circular, concave gland below
the bases of the lowermost pinnae. Pinnae 3–8 pairs, glabrescent, as a rule
glandless, 2–4 cm long. Leaflets sessile, coriaceous, glabrous, 10–20 pairs, oblong-linear, 3–4 × 1–1.5 mm, obtuse or mucronulate, the midrib almost
central. The sessile, very fragrant, dark yellow flowers in peduncled globose
heads on arrested, axillary branches (which also bear the leaves). Peduncles
filiform, slightly pilose, up to 4 cm long, the bracts near the apex. Calyx
campanulate-funnel shaped, 1 mm long with small teeth, glabrous; corolla
0.5 mm longer with short lobes. Stamens exserted. Pod thick, turgid, subcylindrical, up to 7 cm long and 1.5 cm diam., straight or slightly bent, ending in a sharp point or hook or obtuse; pedicellar part thick, short; sutures
entire or with a few constrictions, swollen over the rather few, lenticular
seeds; mesocarp pulpy; tardily completely dehiscent.

D i s t r. Originally from Central and South America, introduced in
Europe, where it flowered in the Farnesian Garden in 1611. Introduced and
naturalized in many tropical countries, usally near sandy sea shores.
E c o l. Cultivated in Ceylon. Thus far not found wild.
U s e s. The fragrant flowers are the source of the valued cassie perfume.
It is grown extensively around Cannes in southern France. The perfume is
mainly extracted by the so-called effleurage method, by placing the macer-
ated flowers on natural, purified fat for several hours and replacing them
by fresh flowers until the fat is saturated with the perfume, which is then
melted, strained and cooled. This pomade has the odour of violets,
but much stronger. The pomade can be extracted with alcohol, which is
distilled and yields a fine olive green liquid strongly smelling of the cassie
flowers.
The ripe pods contain 23 % tannin and are used for tanning. The bark
yields a gum, which is not entirely soluble in water and is said to be suitable
for confectionary. The leaves are said to be used as a substitute for tamarind
in chutneys.
N o t e s. As the fruit is quite different from that found in other species of
Acacia, I have followed Britton and Killip in keeping this separate.

12. ACACIA

Willd., Sp. Pl. 4 (2): 1049. 1806.

Spiny trees or shrubs, or woody climbers. Stipules fugaceous or transformed into spines. Other spines scattered, straight or hooked, variable on the same plant. Leaves bipinnate, petiolar part usually with gland and smaller glands between the bases of the two upper pinnae. Leaflets small, oblique, numerous, usually sessile. Flowers in peduncled spikes or globose heads, sometimes arrang in a large panicle. Flower bracts below the umbels or in the middle of the peduncle. Flowers 5-merous, bisexual (or some in the heads male). Calyx gamosepalous with 5 small teeth. Corolla gamopetalous with 5 lobes shorter than the tube. Stamens indefinite, free or slightly fascicled at the base; anthers minute, without glands. Ovary stipitate or sessile, often glabrous in bud, at anthesis pubescent, ovules many in 2 rows, style long, filiform, stigma inconspicuous. Pod straight or curved, flattened, not twisted, not articulate, unilocular, without pulp, dehiscent along the entire or irregularly indented sutures; seeds many, flat.

A genus of c. 400 species, mostly Australian, in dry and arid zones. In Ceylon 11 species, all in the dry zone. Introduced and cultivated are: *A. dealbata*, *A. decurrens* and *A. mearnsii*.

KEY TO THE SPECIES

1 Trees or shrubs
  2 Flowers in globose heads
    3 Stipular thorns very large and thick
      4 Thorns spindle-shaped, blackish. Rachis and rachillae densely, minutely tomentellous. Flowers white...**10. A. tomentosa**
      4 Thorns broadly conical, white. Rachis and rachillae glabrous or with a few hairs. Flowers dark yellow...**3. A. eburnea**
    3 Thorns, if long, very slender
      5 Pods as a rule very deeply indented between the seedbearing parts (submoniliform), densely, minutely grey-pubescent.....................**7. A. nilotica**, subsp. **indica**
      5 Sutures of pod not or not deeply indented; pods glabrous or pubescent
        6 Pods sub-terete, glabrous, curved into a ring-like spiral..........**9. A. planifrons**
        6 Pods flat, slightly curved, densely, minutely pubescent...........**6. A. leucophloea**
  2 Flowers in spikes
    7 Pinnae with linear, 20–30 pairs of leaflets, 1 × 3 mm..................**2. A. chundra**
    7 Pinnae with linear-oblong, up to 20 pairs of leaflets, 7–10 × 2–3 mm...............
    ....**4. A. ferruginea**
1 Climbers
  8 Leaf rachis with hooked thorns
    9 Pinnae with 15–17 pairs of oblong-linear to trapezoid, 3–10 × 2–7 mm leaflets; petiolar gland large, flat, at the proximal side narrowed into a usually upright or ascendent column...**1. A. caesia**
    9 Pinnae with 30–50 pairs of linear, 2–3 × 0.5–1 mm leaflets; petiolar gland without upturned part..**8. A. pennata**
  8 Leaf rachis without thorns...**5. A. lankaensis**

1. **Acacia caesia** (L.) Willd., Sp. Pl. 4 (2): 1090. 1806; Moon, Cat. 73. 1824; Trimen, Handb. Fl. Ceylon 2: 127. 1894, p.p.; Alston in id. 6: 98. 1931; Anon., Wealth of India 1: 9. 1948.

Mimosa caesia L., Sp. Pl. 522. 1753, p.p.
Acacia intsia, var. *caesia* Baker in Hook. f., Fl. Br. Ind. 2: 297. 1878. Type: *Hermann s.n.*, Ceylon (BM).
Acacia intsia auct. non Willd., Wight & Arn., Prod. 1: 278. 1834; Baker, l.c.; Thw., Enum. Pl. Zeyl. 99. 1859.
Acacia concinna auct. non DC., Alston in Trimen, Handb. Fl. Ceylon 6: 97. 1931.
Acacia columnaris Craib in Kew Bull. 1915: 410; Alston, l.c. 99; Gamble, Fl. Pres. Madras 429. 1935.
[*Acacia zeylanica sarmentosa flore luteo globoso*, Hermann, Mus. Zeyl. 34 (fol. 27). 1717; Burm., Thes. Zeyl. 3. 1737. Type: Ceylon, Hermann (BM), in Leiden fol. 137 (*A. zeylanica inodora*).
Mimosa aculeata, foliis duplicato-pinnatis, foliolis ovali-oblongis oblique acuminatis, L., Fl. Zeyl. 57, no. 217. 1748. Type: Ceylon, *Hermann s.n.* (BM, L)].

A large, woody climber, up to 6 cm diam. with grey-brown, rough bark, many-branched, the branches glabrous with leaf spurs and with numerous, up to 1–2 mm long, hooked, very sharp thorns. Young branchlets and leaves densely to sparsely, minutely tomentellous. Stipules ovate, acute with very broad base, 5–7 mm long, caducous. Rachis rather slender, 5–10 cm long with rather widely spaced, small, hooked, decurved thorns, near its base with a large, oval, disk-like gland, which at the distal end narrows into a usually upcurved or ascendent, slender column, up to 1 mm long, at one side buttressed. Pinnae 5–6 pairs, c. 5 cm long with ring like glands between the bases of the upper pinnae. Leaflets 15–17 pairs, chartaceous, oblong-linear to trapezoid, mucronate, base truncate, unequal, 2×7–3×10 mm, midrib excentric, c. 1 mm from the upper margin, another basal nerve, almost as strong as the midrib near the lower margin and a short one in the lobe of the leaf base, above glabrous, glossy, blue green, below glabrescent. The peduncled umbels usually 3 together widely spaced on slender racemes and these arranged in a large, terminal panicle with numerous small, hooked thorns. Peduncles slender, up to 1.5 cm long, the caducous bracts at the base. Buds brown-red. Flowers sessile, greenish white in globose heads, c. 1 cm diam. Calyx funnel shaped, pubescent, 1.5 mm with distinct lobes. Corolla hardly twice as long as the calyx with narrow, white lobes. Stamens much exserted. Pod glabrous, flat, strap-shaped, dark red-brown, stalked, apex shortly acute, c. 2.5×12 cm, dehiscent along both, rather thin, entire or irregularly and sparingly lobed sutures. Seeds flat, widely apart, 5–7.

Distr. India, Thailand, Malesia.
Ecol. The most common climbing *Acacia* in Sri Lanka, occurring

mainly in the dry zone, but also in the intermediate and wet zone in waste places, often along rivers, near bridges, etc. in the low country.

V e r n. Heenguru vel (S).

N o t e. Between the columnar glands of *A. columnaris* and the ones found in *A. caesia* there are all transitions, even in the same specimen. The petiolar gland consists of an oval, slightly raised, disk-like part, which at one end narrows abruptly into a cylindrical part, which is either horizontal or curved up, at one side buttressed. If the basal plate is absent only the slender upright column remains. Even glands with two columns were observed. The calyx is either completely green or its teeth are brown-red. The completely green calyces are correlated with the columnar glands.

S p e c i m e n s E x a m i n e d. KANDY DISTRICT: Ganuruwa Hill, Kandy, Oct., fl., *Kundu & al.* 164 (PDA); Haragama, 500 m, Dec., fl., *Jayasuriya & al.* 459 A (PDA); Akuranna, near bridge, Aug., fl., *Kostermans 25402* (A, BO, G, K, L, P, PDA, US); Teldeniya Road, 200 m July, fl., *Kostermans 25267* (id.); KURUNEGALA DISTRICT: Kurunegale, ster., *Kostermans s.n.* (L); ibid., foot of hill, low, Sept., fl., *Kostermans 25543* (A, BO, G, K, L, P, PDA, US); road Kandy-Kurunegale, near bridge, ster., *Kostermans 24239 A* (id.); Bulupitiya, Sept., fl., *Cramer 3197* (PDA); RATNAPURA DISTRICT: road Balangoda to Belihuloya, June, fr., *Kostermans 25010* (id.). BADULLA DISTRICT: Badulla road to Bibile 200 m, Aug., fl., *Kostermans 25324, 25325* (id.). HAMBANTOTA DISTRICT: Kataragama-Tissa Rd., Sept., fl. fr., *Cooray s.n.* (PDA). POLONNARUWA DISTRICT: Polonnaruwa Sacred area, near tank, fl., *Ripley 319* (PDA). GALLE DISTRICT: near Hiniduma, ster., *Kostermans 25379* (A, BO, G, K, L, P, PDA, US).

2. **Acacia chundra** Willd., Sp. Pl. 4 (2): 1078. 1806. Type: India, Roxburgh.

Acacia sundra (Roxb.) DC. Prod. 2: 458. 1825; Wight & Arn., Prod. 1: 273. 1834; Beddome. Fl. Sylv. t. 150. 1869 (*sundra*); Baker in Hook, f., Fl. Br. Ind. 2: 295. 1878, p.p.; Trimen, Handb. Fl. Ceylon 2: 125. 1894; Alston in id. 6: 97. 1931; Gamble. Fl. Pres. Madras 428. 1935; Anon., Wealth of India 1: 20. 1948; Worthington, Ceylon Trees t. 213. 1959.

Mimosa sundra Roxb., Pl. Corom. 3: 19, t. 225. 1819; Fl. Ind. 2: 562. 1832. Type: Roxburgh.

Acacia catechu auct. non Willd., Thw., Enum. Pl. Zeyl. 99. 1859 (*C.P. 3547*).

Tree, up to 8 m high. Bark dark brown, rough, peeling off profusely. Live bark 3 mm, pink and white. Branchlets smooth, glabrous, pale purplish brown. Thorns solitary below the stipules, small, hooked, c. 3–4 mm long on a very large, elongate, thick base, or lacking. Rachis slender, glabrous or very sparsely, minutely pilose, up to 13 cm long, the petiolar part 3–4 cm with a large, oval, flat gland with variable position (near the base, or middle or apex) and small, circular, concave glands between the bases of the two terminal pinnae, prickles absent. Pinnae 9–18 pairs, c. 3–4 cm long, sparsely pilose. Leaflets subsessile, 20–30 pairs, overlapping, small, linear, c. 3 × 1 mm, obtuse, glabrous, the midrib slightly excentric, base oblique. Flowers sessile, glabrous, white in rather lax, axillary, shortly stalked, erect spikes, up to 10 cm long. Calyx campanulate, 1 mm long with short teeth. Corolla three times as long as the calyx, lobes linear-lanceolate. Pod strap-shaped, flat, thin, almost straight, tapering at both ends, stalked, sometimes with few indents between seeds, veiny, dark reddish-brown. Seeds 3–6, flat, greenish-brown, broadly oval.

D i s t r. Peninsular India, Burma.

E c o l. Dry zone, not common, Bintenne below Balangoda, Pomparipu (Wilpattu Nat. Park), Haldumulla, Tissamaharama, between Vavuniya and Mannar, Ruhuna National Park.

U s e s. The red, extremely hard and heavy heartwood is used for making axe handles, etc. From the wood drinking cups are made, the wood tastes slightly bitter. Cutch and katha can be extracted from the heartwood. The timber is substitute for *Guiaiacum officinale* for motor shaft bearings. There seems to be a trade in red cutch in Bombay (Wealth of India).

V e r n. Red cutch (E); Karangali (T, ex Gamble).

N o t e. Very close to *A. catechu* and Baker thought it to be a mere variety. It differs by having fewer leaflets and pinnae (30–40 versus 40–80 pairs of pinnae and 40–80 versus 60–100 pairs of leaflets) and having glabrous leaves, calyces and rachises. But *A. cathechuoides* seems to be intermediate.

The thorns are infra-stipular, as indicated by Bentham.

S p e c i m e n s E x a m i n e d. HAMBANTOTA DISTRICT: Ruhuna Nat. Park, road to Yala Bungalow, Nov., fl., *Wirawan 702* (L, PDA); ibid., Aug., fr., *Kostermans 25448* (L).

3. **Acacia eburnea** (L. f.) Willd., Sp. Pl. 4 (2): 1081. 1806; Wight & Arn., Prod. 1: 276. 1834; Benth. in Hook. Lond. J. Bot. 1: 501. 1842; Thw., Enum. Pl. Zeyl. 99. 1859; Baker in Hook. f., Fl. Br. Ind. 2: 293. 1878; Trimen, Handb. Fl. Ceylon 2: 124. 1894; Troup, Silvicult. Ind. Trees 2: 462. 1921; Gamble, Fl. Pres. Madras 426. 1935; Worthington, Ceylon Trees t. 204. 1959.

Mimosa eburnea L. f., Suppl. Pl. 437. 1781; Roxb., Pl. Corom. 2: 54, t. 199. 1798; Benth. in Trans. Linn. Soc. Lond. 30: 512. 1875.
Acacia roxburghii Wight & Arn., l.c. 276. Type: India, *Koenig 77*, Smith Herb. 1228/24 (LINN).

Large or small bush or treelet, up to 3 m tall. Bark grey, superficially fissured, strips 5 mm wide, 1 mm thick. Live bark 3 mm, white, outside green. Wood white. Branches horizontal, glabrous to slightly, microscopically pilose. Stipular thorns straight, glossy, white, varying considerably in shape and size, the lower, enormous ones up to 8 cm long, at base 1 cm diam.

(sometimes fused at the base), gradually tapering to a very sharp, usually darker point. On the shoots the thorns are only 5–10 mm long and very slender. Leaves on arrested branches on the nodes with many bracts, up to 3 cm long, usually glabrous. Petiolar part short with a large, oval, slightly raised gland about the middle or higher up or lower down. Pinnae 2–8 pairs, opposite and sub-opposite 5–10 mm long, usually glabrous. Leaflets sessile, glabrous or minutely fimbriate, 5–8 pairs, stiffly coriaceous, oblong to ovate-oblong, obtuse or mucronulate, base truncate, oblique, veins invisible, 2–3 × 1.5 mm with round, raised glands between the bases of the two upper pairs of leaflets. Flowers dark yellow, sessile, smell disagreeable, in small, globose stalked heads, 5–10 mm diam. Peduncle slender, glabrous or pilose, 2 cm long, with the thin, tiny ovate bracts about the middle. Calyx campanulate, thin, 1 mm, teeth very small. Corolla c. 2.5 mm. Pod straight or falcate, narrow, flattened, glabrous, veiny, 3–10 cm long, 5–8 mm wide, margins entire or obscurely, irregularly lobed, the apex acute, the pedicellar part 5 mm long, dehiscent along both sutures. Seeds 5–9, oblong-elliptic, smooth, grey, flat.

D i s t r. India, Afghanistan, Arabia, dry and desert areas, especially near the coast.

V e r n. Udai vel, Kaludai (T).

N o t e s. Bentham described a very hairy plant, which might be something else. Wight & Arnott distinguished two forms, one with about 4, the other with 2 pinnae. These I found on the same plant. The flowers turn a reddish-brown after anthesis. Sometimes the large thorns have a small, round, lateral hole and are inhabited by black, tiny, very slow moving ants. There are no elaiosomes on the leaflets as in some African Acacias, the ants feed perhaps on the leaf glands and sometimes the pulvinus is very sticky and might provide some food.

S p e c i m e n s E x a m i n e d. MANNAR DISTRICT: Mannar Isl., near tank, May, fr., *Kostermans 24903* (A, BO, G, K, L, P, PDA, US); July, fl., *Kostermans 25233* (id.); July fr., *Kostermans 25234* (id.); N. of Vallankulam, road Pooneryn to Mannar, March, fl., *Robyns 6968* (L, PDA); ibid., fr., *Rudd 3302* (PDA); coastal highway near Mannar, saltflat, Jan., fl., *Theobald & al. 2859* (PDA). PUTTALAM DISTRICT: 8 miles E. of Putallam, July, fl., *Meyer 360* (PDA). HAMBANTOTA DISTRICT: Ruhuna Nat. Park, tank near entrance, Aug., fr., *Kostermans 25441 & 25445* (A, BO, G, K, L, P, PDA, US); ibid., Jan., fl., *Comanor 842* (PDA).

4. Acacia ferruginea DC., Prod. 2: 458. 1825; Wight & Arn., Prod. 1: 273. 1834; Benth. in Hook. Lond. J. Bot. 1: 508. 1842; Trans. Linn. Soc. Lond. 30: 518. 1875; Beddome, Fl. sylv. t. 51. 1869; Baker in Hook. f., Fl. Br. Ind. 2: 295. 1878; Trimen in J. of Bot. 23: 145. 1885; Handb. Fl. Ceylon 2: 126. 1895;

Alston in id. 6: 97. 1931; Gamble, Fl. Pres. Madras 428. 1935; Anon., Wealth of India 1: 15. 1948.

Mimosa ferruginea Roxb., Hort. Beng. 41. 1814; Fl. Ind. 2: 561. 1832. Type: Hort. Calcut., Roxburgh.

Tree, up to 8 m high and 25 cm diam. Bark rough, deeply fissured, dark rusty brown, strips 2–3 cm wide, 4 mm thick. Live bark 5–10 mm thick, pink. Branchlets glabrous, smooth, light purplish-brown. Thorns stipular, paired, hooked, sharp, 3–6 mm long, decurved, base broad, large. Leaves glabrous, up to 10 cm long, rachis slender with a circular or oval gland about the middle of the petiolar part or lower down and small glands between the bases of one or two apical pinnae. Pinnae 3–6 pairs, c. 4 cm long, rachis slender. Leaflets up to 20 pairs, glabrous, linear-oblong, chartaceous, 2–3 × 7–10 mm, subsessile, obtuse, the base oblique, the midrib slightly off the centre. Flowers glabrous, pale yellow (after anthesis darker yellow), sessile, arranged in spikes up to 10 cm long and these arranged in a loose panicle of up to 4 spikes. Calyx thin, campanulate, 1.5 mm long with 0.75 mm long teeth. Corolla 2–3 times as long as the calyx with oblong lobes. Pod strap-shaped, thin, flat, up to 12 cm long and 3 cm wide, scutish, distinctly pedicellate, dark brown. Seeds oval, flat, 1–6.

D i s t r. Western Indian Peninsula.

E c o l. Only known from a restricted area near Anamaduwa on flat, sandy land in the dry zone, near a monastery. The tree was perhaps introduced.

U s e s. The heartwood is olive brown, turning darker with age, very heavy, straight grained and coarsely textured, with much care it can be seasoned well. It is used for cart wheels, posts and beams, agricultural implements, but is too scarce in Sri Lanka. The bark and pods have astringent properties.

V e r n. Velvelam (T, ex Gamble).

N o t e s. There are some discrepancies in the description of the spines of different authors. De Candolle calls them rather straight; Wight & Arnott conical. Bentham calls them infra-stipular and sub-recurved; Baker: short hooked in pairs, small and straight. In our specimens they are well developed, stipular, paired, hooked. They are similar to those in *A. chundra*, but here they are single.

The only difference with *A. chundra* is in the size and the width of the leaflets: being much smaller and narrower in *A. chundra*. Also the description of the pod differs with different authors, Gamble describes it in the same way as we do, calling them Albizia—like pods.

The position of the petiolar gland is variable, as may even be observed in Beddome's plate.

Specimens Examined. PUTTALAM DISTRICT: Puttalam area, Anamaduwa, Diulwewa Temple near Paramakande, dry zone, July, fl., fallen pods, *Kostermans 25260* (A, BO, G, K, L, P, PDA, US).

5. Acacia lankaensis Kosterm. in Ceylon J. Sci. (Biol. Sci.) 13 (1): 253. Sept. 1979. Type: *Kostermans 25426* (L).

Acacia pennata auct. non Willd., Alston in Trimen, Handb. Fl. Ceylon 6: 98. 1931.

Large climber, stem 4 cm diam., grey. The younger branches brown, lenticellate with many, very thin horizontal lines and glossy, longitudinal narrow bands on which the few thorns are implanted. Thorns few, scattered, hooked, up to 1 mm long. Rachis 7–12 cm long without thorns, densely, minutely light brown tomentellous, glabrescent, with a flattish, large, oval gland about the middle of the 2–4 cm long petiolar part and small, round, sessile glands between the bases of the 2–3 upper pinnae. Pinnae 6–10 pairs, 3–8 cm long. Folioles sessile, 20–44 pairs, chartaceous, glabrous, small, linear, c. 1.5 × 5 mm, overlapping, acutish, base truncate, oblique, midrib very excentric, partly diagonal. Flowers in axillary pedunculate globose heads. Peduncles densely, minutely light brown pubescent, 1–2 cm long. Corolla glabrous, 1.5–2 mm long. Pod flat, strap-shaped, thin with slender 1 cm long pedicel, with a sparse indumentum of very short, minute hairs and numerous dark red tiny glandular hairs, glabrescent, up to 2 × 10 cm, both ends obtuse. Seeds flat, oval, about 3–5.

Distr. Endemic. So far known only from two places, the intermediate zone on the road from Madhugoda to Mahyangane and near the Dialuma waterfall.

Notes. Close to *Acacia pennata*, but differing by the few, very small thorns, the thornless leaves and the gland-bearing pods. This represents probably what Alston described as *A. pennata* based on a specimen from Haragama near Kandy.

Specimens Examined. KANDY DISTRICT: Roadside Madhugoda to Mahyangane, intermediate zone, alt. c. 400 m, Aug., young fr., *Kostermans 25426* (A, BO, G, K, L, P, PDA, US); ibid., May, fl., Maxwell et al. 722 (PDA); ibid., Oct., fr., Sohmer et al. 8272 (PDA); ibid., June, fl., *Kostermans 26623* (PDA, US). BADULLA DISTRICT: road Bibile to Badulla, Dialuma waterfall, below falls on rock, Aug., fr., *Kostermans 25239* (L).

6. Acacia leucophloea (Roxb.) Willd., Sp. Pl. 4 (2): 1083. 1806; DC., Prod. 2: 462. 1825; Wight & Arn., Prod. 1: 277. 1834; Benth. in Hook. Lond. J. Bot. 1: 503. 1842; in Trans. Linn. Soc. Lond. 30: 513. 1875; Thw., Enum. Pl. Zeyl. 99. 1859; Beddome, Fl. sylv. t. 48. 1869; Baker in Hook. f., Fl. Br. Ind.

2: 294. 1878 (cum var. *microcephala*); Trimen. Handb. Fl. Ceylon 2: 125. 1894; Anon., Wealth of India 1: 15, t. 4, f. 7. 1948; Worthington, Ceylon trees t. 207. 1959.

Mimosa leucophloea Roxb., Pl. Corom. 2: 27, t. 150. 1798; Fl. Ind. 2: 558. 1832
Type: India, Roxburgh.
Mimosa alba Rottler in Nov. Act. Berol. 1803: 208; Willd., l.c. 469.

Tree, up to 10 m high and 30 cm diam. Bark smooth, pale yellowish with white areas, exfoliating in irregular scales. Live bark dirty pale yellowish, outside green. Stipular thorns paired, straight, pilose and connate at the base, c. 1 cm long, rather slender, on the lower part of the branches and trunk black, glossy thorns up to 4 cm long. Rachis minutely, sparsely tomentellous, flat above, 6–11 cm; petiolar part short with a large, round, subsessile gland between the bases of the lower pinnae and smaller, similar glands between 2–3 pairs of apical pinnae. Pinnae 5–12 pairs, 2.5–6 cm long, rachillae slender, sparsely pilose. Leaflets sessile, chartaceous, 15–30 pairs, oblong-linear, up to 1.5 × 4 mm, rounded and mucronulate, the base truncate, oblique, midrib slightly excentric, glabrous or glabrescent. The peduncled globose flower heads arranged in an ample, terminal panicle up to 30 cm long and 30 cm in diam., densely, minutely yellow-brown tomentellous. Peduncles slender, 5–10 cm long, pilose, the bracts in the middle or lower down. Flowers white, sessile, pubescent, 1–1.5 mm long. Calyx funnel-shaped, 3/4 mm long; only the 1/3 mm long corolla lobes exserted from the calyx. Stamens long exserted. Pods strap-shaped, somewhat fleshy, 7–15 cm long, 5–8 mm wide, straight or slightly curved, flattened, shortly pedicelled, the apex rounded and mucronulate, densely, very minutely brown tomentellous, dehiscent along both sutures. Seeds numerous, oval, flat.

D i s t r. N.W. Provinces of India, Burma, drier parts of E. Java, Lesser Sunda islands.

E c o l. Dry areas. Common.

U s e s. The thick yellowish white bark, known as Velam bark is exported to India for arrack distillers acting as a clarifier and flavouring agent. It yields a coarse fibre. In Ceylon it is used for dyeing sails, mats, ropes and for tanning. The heartwood is very hard, tough, heavy, brownish red. The pods are edible and used as fodder, even the bark is ground and mixed with flour in India in times of scarcity.

V e r n. Maha Andara, Katu Andara (S); Velvel, Velvalayam (T).

S p e c i m e n s E x a m i n e d. MANNAR DISTRICT: Madhu-Mannar road, dry, May, fl., *Kostermans 24906* (A, BO, G, K, L, P, PDA, US); ibid., July, fl., *Kostermans 25231* (id.). KURUNEGALA DISTRICT: Puttalam-Kurunegala road, July, fl. *Meyer 341* (PDA). VAVUNIYA DISTRICT: Cheddikulam, July, buds, *Hepper et al. 4647* (PDA).

7. Acacia nilotica subsp. *indica* (Benth.) Brenan in Kew Bull. 84. 1957.

Acacia nilotica var. *indica* (Benth.) A.F. Hill in Bot. Mus. Leafl. Harvard Univ. 8: 99. 1940.

Acacia arabica (Lam.) Willd. var. *indica* Benth. in Hook. Lond. J. Bot. 1: 500. 1842.

Acacia arabica (Lam.) Willd., Sp. Pl. 4 (2): 1085. 1806, p.p.; Wight & Arn., Prod. 1: 277. 1834; Thw., Enum. Pl. Zeyl. 455. 1859; Beddome, Fl. sylv. t. 47. 1869; Benth. in Trans. Linn. Soc. Lond. 30: 506. 1875; Baker in Hook. f., Fl. Br. Ind. 2: 293. 1878; Trimen, Hand. Fl. Ceylon 2: 122. 1895; Gagnep. in Lecomte, Fl. Indoch. 2: 78. 1913; Alston in Trimen, Handb. Fl. Ceylon 6: 96. 1931; Troup, Silvicult. Ind. Trees 2: 410–444. 1921; Gamble, Fl. Pres. Madras 425. 1935; Anon., Wealth of India 1: 5–9. 1948.

Mimosa arabica Lam., Enc. 1: 19. 1783; Roxb., Pl. Corom. 1: 26, t. 149. 1795; Fl. Ind. 2: 557. 1832.

Acacia vera Willd., l.c. 1085; Moon, Cat. 73. 1824.

Mimosa nilotica L., Sp. Pl. 521. 1753.

Acacia nilotica (L.) Delile, Fl. Aegypt. Ill. 31. 1813, p.p.

Tree up to 8 m high and 80 cm diam. with short bole. Bark dark brown, deeply, wavily fissured, strips 2 cm wide, 1–1.5 cm thick. Live bark up to 1 cm thick, outside orange-yellow. Branchlets smooth, the young ones densely grey pubescent with short stiff, patent hairs. Stipular spines variable, from small to 5 cm long, slender, spreading, slightly conical, white, sometimes absent. Rachis 3–10 cm long, pubescent, glandless or with a small gland at the petiolar part and between the bases of the terminal pinnae. Pinnae 3–6 pairs, 2–5 cm long. Leaflets subsessile, 10–15 pairs, usually glabrous, chartaceous, narrowly oblong, 3–6 × 1–2 mm, obtuse at both ends, base oblique, the midrib almost central. Flowers dark yellow, strongly fragrant, in peduncled globose heads, 2–6 in each axil. Peduncles 1–3 cm long, densely grey puberulous with bracts above or below the middle. Flowers sessile, glabrous. Calyx campanulate, 1 mm long. Corolla twice as long. Pod initially greygreen, densely, minutely grey tomentellous, later black, the hairs more or less persistent, strap-shaped, straight, flattened but thickish, dehiscent along both sutures, bullate over the seeds, the sutures almost entire to usually deeply indented between the seeds, ending in a stipe, distinctly pedicelled, up to 15 × 2 cm. Seeds 8–12, black, flat, c. 5 × 4 mm.

D i s t r. Egypt, Arabia, India, cultivated and naturalized in many countries.

E c o l. Introduced in Ceylon, where it is slowly spreading in the dry and very dry areas, mainly near the coast.

U s e s. *Acacia nilotica*, the Babul of India, yields three major products: tannin, gum and timber. The bark is the most important tanning material of northern India, it is obtained mainly as a by-product when trees are felled for fuel. The leather tanned with babul is firm and durable but harsh and dark coloured, but in combination with myrobalans, an excellent, finished leather can be produced. The tannin content is not very high.

The pods contain up to 20% of tannin, but are seldom used, the main use, when green, is as fodder.

Babul does not yield much gum; it is not the true gum arabic which is produced by *Acacia senegal*. In India it is used in calico printing and dyeing and as a sizing material for silks and cotton and in the manufacture of paper.

The timber is strong and tough, as hard as teak, but available only in small sizes (Cf. Wealth of India, l.c.).

V e r n. Karuvel (T).

N o t e s. In Lanka some old trees were observed south of Puttalam, whereas younger ones were seen on the coast near Puttalam. As Trimen in 1895 called it very rare, it must have been spreading since that time.

Wight & Arnott described the leaves as glabrous and so did Bentham. Trimen, however, called them pubescent, which fits the Ceylonese material.

The pods dehisce along both sutures. The latter are as a rule strongly constricted between the seed-bearing parts, but pods with hardly indented sutures occur also.

S p e c i m e n s E x a m i n e d. PUTTALAM DISTRICT: Road from Kurunegale to Puttalam near Anamaduwa, July, fl., *Kostermans 25243 25245, 25247* (A, BO, G, K, L, P, PDA, US).

8. Acacia pennata (L.) Willd., Sp. Pl. 4 (2): 1090. 1806; Moon, Cat. 73. 1824; DC., Prod. 2: 464. 1825 (excl. Madagascar); Wight & Arn., Prod. 1: 277. 1834 (excl. *A. megaladena*); Benth. in Hook. Lond. J. Bot. 1: 516. 1842; Thw., Enum. Pl. Zeyl. 99. 1859 (quoad nomen tantum); Baker in Hook. f., Fl. Br., Ind. 2: 297. 1878 (excl. *A. megaladena*); Trimen, Handb. Fl. Ceylon 2: 127. 1894; Gagnep. in Lecomte, Fl. Indoch. 2: 83. 1915; Alston in Trimen, Handb. Fl. Ceylon 6: 97. 1931 (quoad nomen tantum); Gamble, Fl. Pres. Madras 429. 1935; Anon., Wealth of India 1: 19. 1948; Brenan & Exell in Bol. Soc. Broter., Ser. 2, 31: 102. 1957.

Mimosa pennata L., Sp. Pl. 522, no. 33. 1753; ed. 2. 1507. 1762 (excl. var.); Roxb., Fl. Ind. 2: 565. 1832. Type: *Hermann s.n.*, Ceylon (BM).
Acacia pennata Dalz. & Gibs., Bombay Fl. 87. 1861.
Mimosa torta Roxb., Fl. Ind. 2: 566. 1832.
Acacia tomentella Zippel ex Spanoghe in Linnaea 15: 190. 1841; Miquel, Fl. Ind. bat. 1: 13. 1855; Alston, l.c.; van Steenis in Blumea 17: 271. 1976.
Acacia prensans Lowe in Bot. Mag. 62: t. 3408. 1835.
Acacia pluricapitata Steud., Nomencl., ed. 2, 1: 7. 1840.
Acacia polycephala Graham in Wall., Cat. 5255. 1830 (non DC).

[*Acacia zeylanica floribus rotundis albis papposis in summitatis e ramulorum racematim dispositis, Hinghuruwael, Tsjawael*, Hermann, Mus. Zeyl. 24, fol. 50. 1717.

Acacia aculeata, multiflora, foliis pennas avium referentibus, Burm., Thes. Zeyl. 2, t. 1. 1737. Typus: Hermann *s.n.* (Paris, Académie des Sciences).

Mimosa aculeata, foliis duplicato-pinnatis numerosissimus lineari-acerosis, paniculis aculeato capitulis globosis, L., Fl. Zeyl. 96, no. 216. 1748.]

Woody climber, stem 4 cm diam., smooth. Branchlets, rachises and inflorescences densely, minutely, light brown tomentellous; the branches and the underside of the rachises with recurved, hooked, smooth prickles, those on the branchlets 2–4 mm long, their base broad. Rachis up to 15 cm long with 4 cm petiolar part which has scattered c. 1 mm long prickles and a large, flattish, oval gland near its base; smaller, more rounded flattened glands are found between the bases of the upper 1–3 pairs of pinnae. Pinnae 7–18 pairs, up to 4 cm long with slender, sparsely tomentellous rachillae without thorns. Leaflets sessile, chartaceous, overlapping, usually glabrous with fimbriate margins, very small, 30–50 pairs, very narrow, linear, base oblique, midrib diagonal, running along and very near the margin, 2–3 × 0.5–1 mm, mucronate. The pedunculate globose flower heads 1–3 together in leaf axils and these combined into a terminal, loose, many-umbelled, up to 20 cm long, terminal, leafy panicle (upper part without leaves). Peduncles 1–2 cm long, densely pale brown tomentellous. Heads 1–2 cm diam. Flowers subsessile in the axils of tiny spathulate bracts, of which the apical part is fimbriate. Buds brown red. Calyx thin, campanulate, 1.5–2 mm long, glabrous or very minutely and shortly pilose, the teeth distinct, 1 mm long, brown red. Corolla hardly 1 mm longer than the calyx, light green, the tips of the lobes green or red brown. Pod strap-shaped, flat with slightly raised sutures, smooth, reddish brown, thin, the sutures straight with few or no indents, 15–20 × 2–3 cm, dehiscent along both sutures, distinctly stalked, apex acute. Seeds 6–12, flat, round; the pod slightly bullate over the seeds.

D i s t r. India, Malesia.

E c o l. In Ceylon restricted to the dry and intermediate zone, common in waste places, near bridges, etc.

U s e s. The bark contains 9% of tannin and is used for tanning leather in Bombay, the leather becomes rather harsh.

V e r n. Hinguru, Goda hinguru (S).

N o t e s. Brenan and Exell have discussed the typification of *A. pennata*; they excluded *A. arophula* D. Don and considered this conspecific with *A. megaladena* Desv. They accept *A. pluricapitata* as a separate species, but this I have not been able to confirm.

What Alston calls *A. pennata* is described here as *A. lankaensis*.

The reduction of *A. tomentella* of the eastern part of Malesia was already published by Miquel and Alston; van Steenis, apparently unaquainted with this, reduced it again.

The variation in the number of pinnae is great. The midrib follows closely the margin, but its apical part is diagonal. The petiolar gland is sometimes smaller and more rounded.

When collected in alcohol (wet method), the pickled plant has a strong smell of hydrogen sulphide.

The colours of calyx and corolla match exactly those given by Lowe for *A. prensans*.

Specimens Examined. PUTTALAM DISTRICT: N. of Putallam, low, dry zone, July, fl., *Kostermans 25250, 25257* (A, BO, G, K, L, P, PDA, US); Wilpattu Nat. Park, July, fr., *Wirawan et al. 1108* (PDA). KURUNEGALA DISTRICT: Kurunegala, base of hill, intermediate zone, low, Sept., fl., *Kostermans 25542* (A, BO, G, K, L, P, PDA, US). KANDY DISTRICT: road Kandy-Teldeniya, ravine near river, alt. 200 m, July, fl., *Kostermans 25270, 25271* (id.); between Hunasgiriya and Weragantota, May, fl., *Maxwell et al. 722* (PDA).

9. Acacia planifrons Wight & Arn., Prod. 1: 276. 1834; Benth. in Hook. Lond. J. Bot. 1: 498. 1842; in Trans. Linn. Soc. Lond. 30: 512. 1875; Baker in Hook. f., Fl. Br. Ind. 2: 293. 1878; Trimen in J. of Bot. 23: 144, t. 35. 1885; Handb. Fl. Ceylon 2: 123. 1894; Troup, Silvicult. Ind. Trees 2: 461. 1921; Fischer in Kew Bull. 1932: 56; Gamble, Fl. Pres. Madras 426. 1935; Anon., Wealth of India 1: 19. 1948; Worthington, Ceylon Trees t. 211. 1959.

Mimosa planifrons Koenig ex W. & A., l.c. Type: Ceylon, Koenig *s.n.* (LUND).

Tree, up to 6 m high, bole 1 m, diam. 30 cm. Bark deeply fissured, strips 2-3 cm wide, 3 mm thick, grey. Live bark almost white, outside green. Crown very flat, the long, not or hardly branched, branches spreading in one plane, glabrous. The paired stipular spines dimorphic, one hooked, conical, rather thick, up to 5 mm long, the other slender, white, hardly tapered, straight, 4-5 cm long, 1-2 mm in diam. at the base. Leaves in fascicles from arrested, axillary branches, which bear also the flower peduncles, glabrous. Rachis 2-5 cm long, flattened above, glandless (rarely slightly pilose). Pinnae 3-4 pairs, 1-1.5 cm long, glandless. Leaflets coriaceous, 5-10 pairs, very shortly petioled, strap shaped, 2×1 mm, obtuse, base rounded-truncate, midrib invisible. Flowers white in dense pedunculate heads, before anthesis 5 mm in diam. Peduncles glabrous, filiform, 1-2 cm long, the thin bracts below the middle. Calyx broadly funnel shaped, thin, glabrous, 1 mm long with short teeth. Corolla twice as long as the calyx. Stamens exserted. Pod rather fleshy, flattened, shortly stalked, ligulate-linear, 5-9 cm long, curved into a ring-like spiral, 6 mm wide with 6-9 seeds.

D i s t r. S. India.

E c o l. In Ceylon restricted to Mannar Island and the opposite part of the main land, on Mannar abundant in arid, sandy area.

U s e s. The tree is so abundant in Mannar that the hard and heavy wood (which has a faint onion smell when freshly cut), is exported as firewood to neighbouring India. The stand of *A. planifrons* which I saw in 1973, consisted of even-aged trees, which were still young with green, smooth bark, as described by Trimen; the impression was, that these were planted. A much older tree on the road to Mannar had a rough, very deeply fissured bole.

V e r n. Odai, Udai (T).

N o t e. Trimen mentioned in synonymy *Mimosa eburnea* (non L.) Roxburgh, Pl. Corom., although he had remarked in 1885 (l.c.) that Bentham had said that Roxburgh had depicted a young shoot of *A. eburnea*. The fruit could be that of *A. eburnea* as well as that of *A. planifrons*.

The number of pinnae given by Bentham and Baker is higher than I have observed. Trimen suspected that Baker had another species before him, as also the colour of the flower is wrongly given as yellow.

S p e c i m e n s E x a m i n e d. MANNAR DISTRICT: Mannar Island., arid zone on sand, low, May, fr., *Kostermans 24696* (A, BO, G, K, L, P, PDA, US); road Madhu to Mannar, July, fl., *Kostermans 25230* (id.).

10. Acacia tomentosa Willd., Sp. Pl. 4 (2): 1087. 1806; DC., Prod. 2: 462. 1825; Wight & Arn., Prod. 1: 276. 1834; Thw., Enum. Pl. Zeyl. 99. 1859; Benth. in Trans. Linn. Soc. Lond. 30: 508. 1875; Baker in Hook. f., Fl. Br. Ind. 2: 294. 1878; Trimen, Handb. Fl. Ceylon 2: 124. 1894; Gagnep. in Lecomte, Fl. Indoch. 2: 79. 1913; Gamble, Fl. Pres. Madras 426. 1935.

Mimosa tomentosa Roxb., Hort. Beng. 41. 1814; Fl. Ind. 2: 558. 1832. Type: Klein in Herb. Willdenow (B).
Mimosa kleinii Poir., Dict., Suppl. 1: 82. 1810.
Mimosa tomentosa Rottler in Nov. Act. Nat. Cur. 1813: 208.
Acacia chrysocoma Miquel, Fl. Ind. bat. 1 (1): 6. 1858.

Tree, 3–5 m high with short bole, usually bushy, and open crown. Bark grey-black, cracked into quadrangular pieces, 2 mm thick. Live bark 3 mm, reddish. Young branches and leaves densely, minutely, yellowish brown tomentellous. Thorns straight, blackish brown, the apical ones 5 mm long; completely developed ones paired at the nodes (one often arrested in growth) spindle-shaped, up to 9 cm long, 1.5 cm diam. at the fused bases with rather short, sharp point, pubescent at base when young. Leaves crowded on arrested axillary branches, up to 10 cm long. Rachis and rachillae rather thick, flat above, densely, minutely tomentellous with a large, oval, disk-shaped gland below the bases of the lowest pair of pinnae. Pinnae 5–10 pairs, 2.5–5 cm long, ending in a small, thorny stipe. Leaflets 8–16 pairs, sessile, subcoriaceous, glabrescent, oblong-linear, 3–4 × 1.5–2 mm, obtuse, with a small round gland between the bases of the two upper pairs of leaflets, base truncate, oblique; midrib almost central. Flowers white in axillary pedunculate heads, the bracts about the middle or higher or lower down the rather thick, densely pubescent, 1–3 cm long peduncle. Calyx 1 mm long, funnel-shaped or campanulate, densely pilose with short teeth. Corolla 2–3 times as long as the calyx, pubescent, subcylindrical, lobes narrowly oblong. Stamens long-exserted. Pod ligulate, thin, flat, slightly falcate, 10–15 cm long, 1–1.5 cm wide, dehiscent along both sutures, shortly stalked. Seeds 6–10, oval, flat, brownish-green, areolate.

D i s t r. Southern India, Bengal, East Java.

E c o l. Dry arid areas. Rare. Kalpitiya, Mannar, Jaffna District and Vavuniya District. Locally gregarious.

N o t e s. The Javanese specimens have more pinnae and more slender leaflets and lack the enormous thorns.

S p e c i m e n s E x a m i n e d. VAVUNIYA DISTRICT: Road Vavuniya to Madhu, dry zone, low, July, fl., *Kostermans 25227* (A, BO, G, K, L, P, PDA, US); ibid., *25129* (id.).

There is a specimen of *Acacia suma* of Macrae in Kew Herb., which is perhaps of a tree formerly in the Botanic Garden in Peradeniya. It has a white, papery bark.

Planted species

Acacia decurrens Willd., Black wattle, planted as a green manure amongst tea and as a windbreak. Worthington, Ceylon Trees t. 203. 1959.

A. elata A. Cunn., Mountain Hickory, planted in Nuwara Eliya near the Racing Stables and on Liddesdale Estate, Kandapola. Worthington, l.c. t. 205.

A. floribunda Willd., Weeping Acacia, planted as an avenue tree north of the Grand Hotel, Nuwara Eliya; also at Hakgala Botanic Garden. Worthington, l.c. t. 206.

A. longifolia Willd., Sydney Golden Wattle. Planted in Hakgala and in Moray Estate (Maskeliya) at 1500 m alt. Worthington, l.c. t. 208.

A. mearnsii De Wild. Roadside tree Pattipola, Badulla Distr., alt. 1800 m.

A. melanoxylon R. Br. Australian Blackwood. Planted in Nuwara Eliya at 2000 m alt.

A. podaliriifolia A. Cunn. Silver Wattle. Planted at Adisham (Haputale), Diyatalawa at 1300 m alt.

A. pruinosa A. Cunn. Planted at Nuwara Eliya as ornamental. At lower elevation amongst tea, e.g. Dikoya, Castlereagh Estate. Worthington, l.c. t. 212.

13. PAINTERIA

Britton & Rose, N. Amer. Fl. 23 (1): 35. 1928.

Shrubs or small trees with small, stipular spines. Leaves bipinnate. Flowers sessile in heads. Calyx minute. Flowers as in *Pithecellobium*. Stamens numerous, the filaments united below; anthers glandless. Pod coriaceous, flattened, dehiscent along ventral suture, unilocular, without pulp. Seeds flattened, lenticular, funicle filiform.

A genus of four species in America, one (endemic) in Sri Lanka.

Painteria nitida (Vahl) Kosterm. in Public. 20, Organiz. Sci. Research Indon. 14. 1954.

Mimosa nitida Vahl, Symb. 2: 103. 1790; Roxb., Fl. Ind. 2: 557. 1832.

Acacia nitida (Vahl) Willd., Sp. Pl. 4 (2): 1086. 1806.

Pithecolobium nitidum (Vahl) Benth. in Hook. Lond. J. Bot. 3: 202. 1844.
Type: *Koenig s.n.*, Ceylon (C, LINN).

Inga koenigii Wight & Arn., Prod. 1: 269. 1834.

Inga geminata Wight & Arn., l.c.

Mimosa geminata Koenig ex W. & A., l.c.

Pithecolobium geminatum (W. & A.) Benth., l.c.; Thw., Enum. Pl. Zeyl. 100. 1859; Baker in Hook. f., Fl. Br. Ind. 2: 303. 1878, Trimen, Handb. Fl. Ceylon 2: 131. 1894; Hook., l.c. t. 1510. 1886.

Calliandra geminata (W. & A.) Benth. in Trans. Linn. Soc. Lond. 30: 585. 1875. Type: *Koenig s.n.*, Herb. Smith (LINN), para type: *Wight 591*.

Inga flexuosa Graham ex Wight & Arn., l.c.

Feuilleea flexuosa O. Kuntze, Rev. Gen. Pl. 1: 185. 1891.

Small, bushy tree. Bark smooth, grey. Branchlets smooth with small leaf buttresses, pubescent, sometimes zig-zag. Leaves with one pair of pinnae, with spinous stipules, ultimately 2 cm long, very sharp, the younger ones slender, pubescent, 5 mm long. Leaves on main branches usually two together on arrested, densely puberulous branches. Petiole very short, 2–10 mm with a long-stalked, trumpet-shaped gland between the bases of the pinnae. Pinnae 1–2 cm long, slender, puberulous with minute, slightly raised, circular glands between the bases of the petiolules and ending in a pilose, conspicuous stipe. Leaflets 1–5 pairs, opposite, the proximal pair consisting usually of one leaflet at the outside and a slender stipe at the inside, glabrous, chartaceous, subtrapezoid to obovate, oblique, the distal ones largest, up to 1.5 × 1 cm, the proximal ones often less than 5 × 3 mm, mucronate, laxly reticulate, the base obtuse, lateral nerves usually 4, usually ascendent, looped at some distance from the margin. Petiolules inconspicuous, densely pilose. Inflorescences axillary and terminal, consisting of fascicles of 1–3 peduncled umbels of white, sessile, glabrous flowers. Peduncles slightly pubescent, slender, up to 2 cm long. Calyx campanulate, 2–3 mm high, teeth 1 mm, triangular. Corolla tube trumpet-shaped, c. 4 mm, lobes 2 mm long. Staminal tube as long as corolla tube, free part of filaments 1.5–2 cm. Ovary sessile, glabrous. Pod curved, often twisted, shortly stalked, flattened, sub-moniliform, brown, glabrous, 5–12 mm long. Seeds 3–10.

D i s t r. Endemic. Dry and intermediate areas.

S p e c i m e n s E x a m i n e d. TRINCOMALEE DISTRICT: Trincomalee Club, Orrs Hill, Aug., fl. *Worthington 1127* (PDA); Trincomalee road, mile 99, Aug., fr., *Worthington 569* (PDA). KURUNEGALA DISTRICT: Dunkanda, Arankele, low, ster., *Jayasuriya 526* (PDA). ANURADHAPURA DISTRICT: west side of Ritigala, alt. 500 m, Nov., fl., *Balakrishnan et al.*, *11174* (PDA). LOCALITY UNKNOWN: fl., *Koenig s.n.* (C); fl., *s. coll. C.P. 1531* (PDA).

14. PITHECELLOBIUM

Mart., Hort. reg. Monac. 188. 1829 (nom. conserv.); Britton & Killip in Ann. N. York Acad. Sci. 35: 124. 1936; Kosterm. in Bull. 20, Organiz. Sci. Research Indon. 8. 1954.

Trees or shrubs. Stipules spinescent. Leaves bipinnate. Flowers in pseudo-umbels each with a minute bract at the base; the heads arranged in a panicle. Calyx campanulate, with 5 teeth. Corolla tubular with 5 patent lobes. Stamens numerous, the basal part of the filaments connate into a tube, about as long as the corolla tube, free part much exserted; anthers glandless. Ovary sessile or stipitate; style slender with minute, peltate stigma. Pod unilocular, falcate or circinate, flattened, dehiscent along ventral suture. Funicle much swollen, forming an aril.

A South American genus with numerous species, one introduced and naturalized in Sri Lanka.

Pithecellobium dulce (Roxb.) Benth. in Hook. Lond. J. Bot. 3: 199. 1844; Beddome, Fl. sylv. t. 188. 1869; Baker in Hook. f., Fl. Br. Ind. 2: 302. 1878; Trimen, Handb. Fl. Ceylon 2: 131. 1894; Prain in King in J. As. Soc. Beng. 66 (2): 263. 1879; Brown, Minor Prod. Phil. For. 2: 110. 1921; 292, f. 32; 3: 93; Kosterm., l.c.; Worthington, Ceylon Trees t. 219. 1959; Anon., Wealth of India 8: 140, f. 47. 1969.

Mimosa dulcis Roxb., Corom. Pl. 1: 67, t. 99. 1795; Fl. Ind. 2: 556. 1832.
Inga dulcis (Roxb.) Willd., Sp. Pl. 4 (2): 1005. 1806; Moon, Cat. 73. 1824; Wight, Ic. 1: t. 198. 1840.
Albizzia dulcis (Roxb.) F. v. Mueller, Select. Pl. 12. 1876.
Feuilleea dulcis (Roxb.) O. Kuntze, Rev. Gen. Pl. 1: 184, 187. 1891.
Mimosa edulis Gagnep. (sphalm.) in Lecomte, Fl. Indoch. 2: 105. 1913. Type: Roxburgh.
Inga javana DC., Prod. 2: 436. 1825.
Inga camatchili Perr. in Mém. Soc. Linn. Nord Paris 3: 122. 1824.

Inga pungens H.B.K. ex Willd., Sp. Pl. 4 (2): 1004. 1806.
Mimosa pungens Poir. in Lam., Enc., Suppl. 1: 36. 1810.

Tree, up to 10 m high with grey, smooth or lenticellate, hoopringed bark; in old trees of 45 cm diam. the bark becomes very rough, wavily fissured and peeling off profusely. Live bark 5–10 mm, brown to pink, white-marbled. Ultimate branchlets with stipular thorns. Rachis 0.5–2 cm long, glabrous, glandless. One pair of pinnae with a small, cupped gland between the bases of the pinnae, which are up to 1 cm long with a similar gland between the bases of the petiolules. Leaflets one-jugate, glabrous, oblique, obovate-oblong, coriaceous, 2–5 × 1–2 cm, obtuse to sub-acute. Stipular thorns conical, 5–10 mm long, rachis and rachillae usually produced into an acute point. Flowers in dense heads on puberulous, up to 5 mm long, slender peduncles, solitary or 2–3 together in the axils of small, lanceolate bracts, 1–2 mm long, along slender, nodiform branchlets, slightly zig-zag or straight towards their tips, puberulous or rarely glabrescent, from 7–15 cm long, the bracts of the lower two-thirds accompanied by minute, stipular thorns, those of the lowest fourth often replaced by reduced leaves; the raceme-like branches arranged in terminal panicles, 10–30 cm long, up to 20 cm diam., extending into the upper axils. Calyx subcampanulate, 1 mm long, grey downy, shortly toothed. Corolla white, 2 mm long, densely puberulous, tube wide, funnel-shaped, rather longer than the ovate, acute lobes. Staminal tube slightly longer than corolla tube or as long. Ovary puberulous, shortly stipitate. Pod turgid, sometimes curled into a circle, 5 cm in diam., sometimes falcate, dehiscent along lower suture and part of the upper, slightly lobed between the seed-bearing parts, 10–15 × 1 cm, glabrous, wide-reticulate or smooth, the valves coriaceous, claret-red. Seeds obovate-oblong, 12 × 8 mm, 1–2 mm thick with smooth, glossy testa, enveloped in a firm, edible, sweet, pink to white aril.

D i s t r. Originally from Mexico, naturalized in dry areas of all tropics.

U s e s. In the Philippines the bark is used for tanning (30% tannin), the kind of leather produced, is of poor quality. The bark has irritating properties, causing eye-infection and swelling of the eyelids. The seeds (eaten in Indochina, according to Gagnepain) contain 17% of proteins and 40% of carbohydrates. The bark is used as a febrifuge and a decoction is given as an enema (Kirtikar, Ind. med. Pl. 2: 946).

The tree is very hardy, grows in pure sandy soil and with its roots even in brackish water. Easily propagated by seeds or cuttings. Grown for hedges and as fuel, can stand any amount of pruning. Sometimes grown as an ornamental. Pods are used as fodder. In Mexico the swollen funicle (aril) is used to make a lemonade. The seed oil is edible and the remaining meal has a 30% protein content and may be used as fodder. For chemical constituents cf. Wealth of India.

V e r n. Madras thorn, Manila tamarind (E); Kodaikaapulli (T).

N o t e. The species, which is called Quamochitl in Mexico, was first introduced in the Philippines, where it is still known as Camonchilles or Camonsilles, a corruption of the original name. From there it went to India, where it is still called Manila tamarind. Roxburgh, who described it, thought it to be an Indian plant. An enumeration of Indian vernacular names is found in Watt, Dict. Ec., Prod. Ind. 6: 281. 1892. From India it came to the Malay Peninsula, where it is known as Madras thorn. In Java it was imported from the Philippines.

S p e c i m e n s E x a m i n e d. PUTTALAM DISTRICT: Coast near Anemaduwa, low, dry zone, July, fl., *Kostermans 25244* (A, BO, G, K, L, P, PDA, US). TRINCOMALEE DISTRICT: roadside Kuchchavelli, N. of Trincomalee, low, dry, May, fl., *Kostermans 24833* (id.).

15. ALBIZIA

Durazz. in Mag. Tosc. 3: 11. 1772; Little in Amer. Midland Natur. 33: 510. 1945.

Unarmed (in Ceylon) trees. Leaves bipinnate with usually a gland on the petiolar part of the rachillus and smaller ones between the bases of at least the apical pinnae. Stipules usually small, rarely large, early caducous. Flowers arranged in pedunculate, globose heads (Ceylon) or in spikes (the introduced *A. falcataria*) and these arranged racemosely into a usually terminal panicle, the peduncles aggregate and serial at nodes. Flowers small, bisexual, actinomorphous, 5-merous, sessile or shortly pedicelled with tiny bracts at the base. Calyx gamosepalous with campanulate or funnel-shaped tube with 5 tiny teeth. Corolla gamopetalous with long tube and 5 lobes distinct at anthesis, reflexed. Stamens indefinite, connate at the base into a long or short tube, free part of filaments long-exserted; anthers small, without apical gland. The central flower(s) of the heads with broader calyx and much longer filament-tube. Ovary flattened, stipitate or sessile; style long, slender, stigma minute. Pod thin, flat, linear-oblong, dehiscent along both sutures, unilocular, without pulp, the inner layer of the valves white, silky glossy. Seeds flat, ovate or orbicular, funicle filiform.

A genus of about 150 species in the tropics and subtropics of the world.

KEY TO THE SPECIES

1 Flowers in globose heads
 2 Rachis and rachillae very densely pubescent
  3 Below the pinnae a paired appendage............................6. A. lankaensis
  3 No appendages...1. A. amara
 2 Rachis and rachillae sparsely tomentellous or glabrous
  4 Flowers sessile..2. A. odoratissima
  4 Flowers pedicelled

5 Stipules very large. Pinnae 6–20 pairs; leaflets 20–45 pairs, small, 6–10 × 2–2.5 mm..
....3. A. chinensis
5 Stipules minute. Pinnae 1–4 pairs; leaflets 4–9 pairs, large, 25–40 × 10–25 mm....
....4. A. lebbeck
1 Flowers in spikes..5. A. falcataria

1. Albizia amara (Roxb.) Boivin in Enc. XIX e Siècle 2: 34. 1834; Benth. in Hook. Lond. J. Bot. 3: 90. 1844; Thw., Enum. Pl. Zeyl. 100. 1859; Beddome, Fl. sylv. t. 61. 1869; Baker in Hook. f., Fl. Br. Ind. 2: 301. 1878; Trimen, Handb. Fl. Ceylon 2: 130. 1894; Troup, Silvic. Ind. Trees 2: 483. 1921; Alston in Trimen, Handb. Fl. Ceylon 6: 100. 1931; Gamble, Fl. Pres. Madras 432. 1935; Brenan in Kew Bull. 1955: 189; Worthington, Ceylon Trees t. 214. 1959; Anon., Wealth of India 1: 42. 1948; Bhattacharyya & Maheshwari, J. Ind., bot. Soc. 52: 283. f. 6 B. 1973.

Acacia amara Willd., Sp. Pl. 4 (2): 1077. 1806; DC., Prod. 2: 469. 1825; Wight & Arn., Prod. 1: 274. 1834.
Mimosa amara Roxb., Pl. Corom. 2: 13, t. 122. 1798; Fl. Ind. 2: 548. 1832. Type: Roxburgh.
Acacia wightii Garham ex Wight & Arn., l.c. 274.
Mimosa pulchella Roxb., Fl. Ind. 2: 548. 1832.
Acacia nellyrenza Graham ex Wight & Arn., l.c. 274 (ought to be nella-renga).

A rather small tree, (in Mannar) up to 5 m high and 60 cm diam., much branched. Bark scaly, grey to greenish, rather smooth. Live bark 4 mm thick, outside green, inside yellowish. Branchlets densely, minutely yellowish brown pubescent. Stipules minute, lanceolate, caducous. Rachis 4–11 cm, densely yellow brown pubescent (the hairs short, patent, straight) with a small, round gland in the middle of the petiolar part and a similar one between the bases of the upper pinnae, or glands absent. Pinnae 6–16 pairs, densely pubescent, 2–4 cm long. Leaflets 10–30 pairs, sessile, slightly overlapping, very small, linear, 1–2.5 × 3–6 mm, rounded at both ends, base oblique, glabrescent, except the ciliate margins. Flowers white in peduncled, axillary umbels. Peduncles 1–3 per axil, densely pubescent, slender, up to 4 cm long. Pedicel slender, 1–1.5 mm long, puberulous. Calyx funnel-shaped, 1–1.5 mm long with short teeth, puberulous. Corolla funnel-shaped, 3–4 mm long, puberulous, the lobes lanceolate. Pod thin, flat, oblong, 12–22 × 2.5–3.5 cm, shortly stalked, apiculate, veiny, pubescent. Seeds ovate-orbicular, 3–8.

D i s t r. Peninsular India, Abyssinia and East tropical Africa in dry and arid zone.

U s e s. The purplish brown heartwood is very hard and used for building material, agricultural implements, but chiefly as fuel. In Sri Lanka it is too scarce to be of any use.

V e r n. Thuringi, Wienja, Ujil, Usil (T).

N o t e s. Brenan, l.c. recognizes two subspecies, one (subsp. *amara*), occuring in Asia but also in Kenya and Tanganyika, the other (subsp. *sericocephala* (Benth.) Brenan) restricted to the eastern part of Africa. They are connected by intermediate forms.

S'p e c i m e n s E x a m i n e d. MATALE DISTRICT: Nalanda, 36 mile, alt. 900 m, ster., *Worthington 670* (PDA). TRINCOMALEE DISTRICT: RAF Officers' Mess, China Bay, ster., *Worthington 4379* (PDA). MANNAR DISTRICT: Murungan, Madhu, Jan., fr., *Worthington 4466* (PDA); Madhu road to Mannar Isl., June, fl., *Kostermans 25133* (A, BO, G, K, L, P, PDA, US); Mannar Isl., May, fl., *Kostermans 24897* (id.); fr., *Kostermans 24897, 24898* (id.); fl., fr., *Kostermans 24898* (id.).

2. **Albizia odoratissima** (L. f.) Benth. in Hook. Lond. J. Bot. 3: 88. 1844; Bedd., Fl. sylv. t. 54. 1869; Baker in Hook. f., Fl. Br. Ind. 2: 299. 1878; Trimen, Handb. fl. Ceylon 2: 129. 1894; Prain in King in J. As. Soc. Beng. 66 (2): 259. 1897; Troup, Silv. Ind. Trees 2: 479. 1921; Gamble, Fl. trees Madras 431. 1935; Worthington, Ceylon Trees t. 218. 1959; Anon., Wealth of India 1: 44. 1948; Bhattacharyya & Maheshwari in J. Ind. bot. Soc. 52: 283, f. 6 C. 1973.

Mimosa odoratissima L. f., Suppl. Sp. Pl. 437. 1781; Roxb., Pl. Corom. 2: 12, t. 120. 1798; Fl. Ind. 2: 546. 1832; Wight & Arn., Prod. 1: 275. 1834 (*adoratissima*).
Acacia odoratissima Willd., Sp. Pl. 4 (2): 1063. 1806; Moon, Cat. 73. 1824; DC., Prod. 2: 466. 1825. Type: Ceylon, Koenig *s.n.* (LINN).
Acacia lomatocarpa DC., Prod., l.c. 467.
Mimosa marginata Lam., Enc. 1: 12. 1793.
Albizzia micrantha Boivin, Enc. XIX e Siècle 2: 34. 1834.
[*Waga* Rheede, Hort. Ind. Malab. 6: 9, t. 5. 1686.]

Unarmed tree, up to 30 m high and 80 cm diam. Bark rather smooth, yellowish-grey, soft, 2 mm thick. Live bark 10–15 mm, light red, marbled with white, outside green in young trees. Branchlets, when very young densely, minutely yellow-brown tomentellous, soon glabrous. Stipules very small, caducous. Rachis finely downy to glabrous, 10–30 cm long with a large, oval gland near its base and a small, round gland between the bases of the apical one or two pinnae. Pinnae 2–8 pairs, puberulent or glabrous, 5–20 cm long. Folioles 6–24 pairs, obliquely oblong, sessile, subcoriaceous, 3 × 15–5 × 20–10 × 30 mm, obtuse, base oblique, the midrib at 1/3 the width of the lamina along the margin, accompanied by some other basal, conspicuous nerves (one long), reticulate on both surfaces, initially sericeous both sides, adult ones above glabrous, below very sparsely, microscopically appressed pilose (on the midrib patent), glabrescent. Flowers sessile, greenish white with white stamens, arranged in peduncled, globose heads, in fascicles of 3–6 on the bracteate nodes of numerous small, corymbose branchlets and these forming terminal, lax panicles, up to 30 cm long. Peduncles slender, puberulous, c. 2 cm long. Flower heads 2–2.5 cm diam. Calyx minute, campanulate, densely to sparingly appressed pilose, 1 mm long, teeth very small. Corolla broadly funnel shaped, minutely puberulous, 4 mm long, lobes ovate-lanceolate, 2 mm long. Ovary glabrous or pilose. Filament tube half as long as corolla tube, 2–2.5 mm. Pod strap-shaped, flat, thin, oblong, red brown, microscopically pilose, 15–22 × 3–4 cm, very shortly pedicelled, apex obtuse or mucronate, margins thickish, faintly reticulate, slightly thickened over the 6–12 flat, oblong-orbicular, c. 8 × 6 mm, faintly areolate seeds.

D i s t r. India, Burma, Thailand, Indochina and western Malesia.

E c o l. Low country in both moist and dry areas, mostly in the latter. Common.

U s e s. Quick-growing tree with blackish-brown heartwood, used for building, carts, furniture, etc.

N o t e s. The leaflets vary considerably in size, the largest ones resembling strongly the smallest ones of *A. lebbeck*, the smaller ones more like those of *A. lebbekoides* of the Malesian area.

S p e c i m e n s E x a m i n e d. BADULLA DISTRICT: Ella, alt. 1000 m, Aug., fl., *Worthington 2954* (PDA). RATNAPURA DISTRICT: Rajavahanda, 10 miles S.E. of Balangoda, March, fr., *Worthington 3765* (PDA); Belihuloya, low, June, fl., *Kostermans 25011* (A, BO, G, K, L, P, PDA, US). KANDY DISTRICT: Kadugannawa near Kandy, alt. 500 m, Apr., fl., *Worthington 885* (PDA); Gannoruwa Jungle, Peradeniya, alt. 450 m, May, fl., *Kostermans 24032* (id.); Road Kandy-Allagala near Menikdiwalla, alt. 400 m, May, fl., *Kostermans 24043* (id.). MONERAGALA DISTRICT: Bibile, June, fl., *Kostermans 24397* (id.). KURUNEGALA DISTRICT: base of hill, low, Sept., fr., *Kostermans 25541* (id.). VAVUNIYA DISTRICT: Nanthikadul lagoon, July, fl., *Meyer 767* (L, PDA).

3. Albizia chinensis (Osbeck) Merr., Interpret. Rumph. Herb. Amboin. 49. 1917; Alston in Trimen, Handb. Fl. Ceylon 6: 100. 1913.

Mimosa chinensis Osbeck, Dagbok Ostind. Resa 233. 1757. Type: Osbeck (S).
Albizia stipulata (Roxb.) Boivin in Enc. XIX e Siècle 2: 33. 1834; Benth. in Hook. Lond. J. Bot. 3: 92. 1844; Thw., Enum. Pl. Zeyl. 100. 1859; Beddome, Fl. sylv. t. 55. 1869; Baker in Hook. f., Fl. Br. Ind. 2: 300. 1878; Trimen, Handb. Fl. Ceylon 2: 129. 1894; Prain in King in J. As. Soc. Beng. 66 (2): 255. 1875; Gagnep. in Lecomte, Fl. Indoch. 2: 87. 1913; Troup, Silvicult. Ind. Trees 2: 473, f. 181. 1921; Anon., Wealth of India 1: 44. 1948; Bhattacharyya & Maheshwari in J. Ind. bot. Soc. 52: 283, f. 6 E. 1973.
Mimosa stipulata Roxb., Hort. Beng. 40. 1814; Fl. Ind. 2: 549. 1832 (*stipulacea*).
Acacia stipulata DC., Prod. 2: 469. 1825; Wight & Arn., Prod. 1: 274. 1834.

Arthrospermum stipulatum Hassk., Retzia 1: 212. 1855. Type: Bot. Gard.
Calcutta, Roxburgh.
Albizzia marginata in Wall., Cat. 5243. 1830; Merr. in Philipp. J. Sci. 5: 25.
1910; Gamble, Fl. Pres. Madras 433. 1935.

Unarmed, deciduous or evergreen tree with flat crown, up to 40 m high
and 120 cm diam. Bark dark grey, rather smooth, densely hoop-ringed,
lenticellate, thin. Live bark 5 mm, pinkish. Sapwood white. Heartwood light
to dark brown. Branchlets densely, minutely tomentellous. Stipules very
large, caducous, obliquely cordate, crisped, pinkish-orange, pubescent, with
filiform tail, base much dilated at one side, 2.5–4 × 1 cm. Rachis stout, lenticellate, sparsely, minutely tomentellous, glabrescent, 6–40 cm long, with a
large, protruding more or less circular gland near the base and similar smaller
ones between the bases of most pinnae. Pinnae 6–20 pairs, slightly puberulous, 4–12 cm long. Leaflets 20–45 pairs, sessile, coriaceous, falcate-lanceolate, 6–10 × 2–2.5 mm, acute, base obtuse, oblique, midrib close to the upper
margin, above glabrous, beneath glaucous, sparsely tomentellous, the surface
microscopically pitted. Flowers white, the upper half of the filaments light
red, arranged in pedunculate, globose heads, solitary or in fascicles of 2–4 on
nodes in the upper half of pubescent racemes, 7–10 cm long with large, caducous ovate, acuminate, ca 1 cm long bracts, the branches arranged in a terminal or axillary panicle, up to 20 cm long. Peduncles slender, pubescent, 2–4
cm. Pedicels 0.5–1 mm, pubescent. Calyx funnel-shaped, pubescent, 5 mm,
with very short teeth. Corolla funnel-shaped, pubescent, 5 mm, the ovate-
lanceolate lobes half the tube length. Staminal tube yellowish, longer than
the corolla tube, hard, glossy, free part of filaments up to 4 times the corolla
length. Pod thin, flat, strap-shaped, reddish-brown, glossy, 6–20 × 2–3 cm,
very shortly stalked, usually obtuse, obscurely, widely reticulate, the round,
slightly bullate part over the seeds darker. Seeds 8–12, ovate, ca 8–10 × 5–6
mm, flat, dull dark brown, not areolate.

D i s t r. India, Burma, Thailand, Indochina, S. China, Malesia.
E c o l. Moist lowland, up to 1000 m alt.
U s e s. Sometimes used as a shade tree in tea. The wood is soft, not very
durable, used for house building, etc. and for tea boxes, also for veneer.
The wood contains a chemical substance, protecting it somewhat against
insect attack.
V e r n. Pili vagai (T); Kabal-mara, Hulan-mara (S).
N o t e s. The pods remain very long on the tree and are sometimes blown
away by the wind before dehiscence, which they do then on the ground, part-
ly they dehisce on the tree. The germination is epigeous. The growth of the
tree is very rapid.
S p e c i m e n s   E x a m i n e d. KANDY DISTRICT: Kandy Hillcrest,
Oct., fl., *Worthington 5494* (PDA); Kadugannawa near Peradeniya, Febr., fl.,

Worthington 747 (PDA); March, fl., *Worthington 856* (PDA); along river, Botan. Gard. Peradeniya, alt. 450 m, May, fl., *Kostermans 24919* (A, BO, G, K, L, P, PDA, US); Gampola Temilyola Estate, Aug., fr., *Worthington 4095* (PDA); along Puselawa road near Kandy, 500 m alt., Apr., fl., *Kostermans 24559* (A, BO, G, K, L, P, PDA, US); road Laxapana to Maskeliya, above Double cutting, alt. 900 m, Aug., fr., *Kostermans 25405* (id.).

4. Albizia lebbeck (L.) Benth. in Hook. Lond. J. Bot. 3: 87. 1844 (*lebbek*); Thw., Enum. Pl. Zeyl. 99. 1859 (*lebbek*); Beddome, Fl. sylv. t. 53. 1869; Baker in Hook. f., Fl. Br. Ind. 2: 298. 1878; Trimen, Handb. Fl. Ceylon 2: 128. 1894 (*lebbek*); Prain in King in J. As. Soc. Beng. 66 (2): 257. 1897; Troup, Silvicult. Ind. Trees 2: 466, pl. 177, f. 178. 1921; Alston in Trimen, Handb. Fl. Ceylon 6: 99. 1931 (*lebbek*); Gamble, Fl. Pres. Madras 432. 1935 (*lebbeck*); Worthington, Ceylon Trees t. 217. 1959; Anon., Wealth of India 1: 43. 1948; Bhattacharyya & Maheshwari in J. Ind. bot. Soc. 52: 283, f. 6 D. 1973.

Mimosa lebbeck L., Sp. Pl. 516. 1753; ed. 2: 1505. 1762, p.p.
Acacia lebbeck Willd., Sp. Pl. 4 (2): 1066. 1806; DC., Prod. 2: 466. 1825. Type: Egypt, Herb. Linn. (LINN).
Acacia speciosa Willd., l.c. 1066; Wight & Arn., Prod. 1: 275. 1834 (cum var.).
Mimosa speciosa Jacq., l.c. 1: 19, t. 198. 1781.
Acacia sirissa Hamilton in Wall., Cat. 5262 ex Prain, l.c.
Mimosa serissa Roxb., Hort. Beng. 40. 1814; Fl. Ind. 2: 544. 1832. Type: Hort. Calc., Roxburgh.
Albizzia latifolia Boivin, Enc. XIX e Siècle 2: 33. 1834.

Unarmed, deciduous tree, up to 25 m high and 50 cm diam. Bark dark yellowish-brown, rough, deeply fissured, 1–1.5 cm thick. Live bark reddish, 1 cm. Sapwood white, heartwood dark brown, streaked. Branchlets minutely puberulous to glabrous. Stipules small, caducous. Rachis up to 20 cm long, sparsely minutely pilose with an oval, disk-like gland near its base and smaller ones between the bases of the one or two apical pinnae, or glands absent. Petiolar part long. Pinnae (1–) 2–3 (–4) pairs, slightly pubescent, 5–10 cm long. Leaflets subsessile, chartaceous, often with tiny glands between their bases, 4–9 pairs, varying from elliptic to oblong, the apical ones much larger, often obovate-elliptic, 1–2.5 × 2.5–4 cm, obtuse or retuse, base oblique, rounded or one-half cuneate, the other rounded, both sides reticulate, midrib above glabrous, beneath sparsely finely pubescent (denser near the petiole) or glabrous. Flowers in pedunculate sub-globose heads, white, fragrant, up to 4 cm diam. Peduncles rather thick, puberulous or glabrous, 5–10 cm long, 1–4 together or sometimes forming a corymb at the end of short, leafless branches. Pedicels 3–4 mm, puberulous. Calyx funnel-shaped, 2–3 mm long, puberulous or glabrous with short teeth. Corolla 5–7 mm, infundibuliform, puberulous, lobes ovate-lanceolate. Filament tube shorter than corolla tube.

Pod glabrous, glossy, pale straw coloured, flat, thin, oblong, 10–30 × 2.5–5 cm, obtuse at both ends, the orbicular, slightly bullate part over the seeds darker and reticulate. Seeds 4–12, transversally oval, flat, 1.5 × 0.75 mm, testa smooth, pale brown.

D i s t r. Throughout tropical Asia and Africa, usually planted.

E c o l. Dry areas, not very common, mostly planted.

U s e s. A fast growing timber tree, reaching rather large dimensions when grown in stands, used for building and furniture, especially the burrs are valuable.

V e r n. Mara, Suriya-mara (S); Vakei, Vagei, Kona (T).

N o t e. The ripe pods remain very long on the (leafless) tree and produce a rattling sound in the wind. They dehisce when they reach the ground and then often only partially.

S p e c i m e n s E x a m i n e d. MATALE DISTRICT: Nalanda, alt. 300 m, July, fr., *Worthington 6357* (PDA); ibid., Jan., fr., *Worthington 3423* (PDA); Dambulla roadside, May, fl., *Kostermans 24283* (A, BO, G, K, L, P, PDA, US). KANDY DISTRICT: Kadugannawa, 600 m, May, fl., *Worthington 1157* (PDA); Jungle behind Peradeniya Garden, Apr., fl., *Kostermans 23134* (A, BO, G, K, L, P, PDA, US). BADULLA DISTRICT: Lunugala, 600 m, Aug., fr., *Worthington 2972* (PDA). VAVUNIYA DISTRICT: Mankulam, 60 m, May, fl., fr., *Worthington 4567* (PDA). JAFFNA DISTRICT: Jaffna, roadside, June, fr., *Kostermans 25120* (A, BO, G, K, L, P, PDA, US). MONERAGALA DISTRICT: Bibile, June, fl., *Kostermans 24388* (A, BO, G, K, L, P, PDA, US). ANURADHAPURA DISTRICT: Jan., fr., *Jayasuriya 370* (PDA). LOCALITY UNKNOWN: Jaffna Road, July, fl., *Meyer 780* (PDA).

5. Albizia falcataria (L.) Fosberg in Reinwardtia 7: 88. 1965 (excl. syn. *Albizzia falcata* (L.) Backer); Kostermans in Cylon J. Sci., (Biol. Sci.) 13 (1 & 2): 256. Sept. 1979.

Adenanthera falcataria L., Sp. Pl., ed. 2: 550. 1762. Type: *Clypearia alba,* Rumph., Herb. Amboin. 3: 176, t. 111. 1743 (the plate).

Albizzia falcata (L.) Backer, Voorl. School fl. Java 100. 1908; School fl. Java 437. 1911; Merr., Interpret. Rumph. Herb. Amboin. 249. 1917; Alston in Trimen, Handb. Fl. Ceylon 6: 100. 1931; Worthington, Ceylon Trees t. 216. 1959. sensu Backer and subsequent authors, non-sensu basionym Linn.

Albizzia ? *moluccana* Miq., Fl. Ind. bat. 1 (1): 26–27. 1855; Trimen, Handb. Fl. Ceylon 2: 131. 1894; Troup, Silvicult. Ind. Trees 2: 484. 1921. Type: Isl. Banda (U).

Large tree. Branchlets minutely pubescent with many, tiny, pale lenticels. Stipules small, caducous. Rachis up to 40 cm long usually with a large, oval, disk-shaped gland near its base. Pinnae minutely, densely rusty tomentellous,

c. 8–10 pairs, up to 10 cm long. Leaflets 15–25 pairs or less, obliquely oblong, slightly falcate, midrib at about 1/4 the lamina width along the distal
margin, with conspicuous other basal nerves, glabrous above, sparsely (denser on nerves) puberulous beneath, 3–13 × 3–8 mm, acutish. Panicles densely,
minutely pubescent, glabrescent, up to 15 cm long, ultimate branches rather
slender, spicate, the spikes elongating as flowers mature, 1–2 cm and more.
Calyx broadly campanulate-turbinate, sericeous, 1–2 mm long with small
teeth. Corolla sericeous, 3–5 mm, lobes long, oblong-ovate, acute. Stamens
1 cm long. Flowers greenish-yellow to cream. Pods straight, strap-shaped,
flat, up to 12 × 2.5 cm, with a narrow wing on the ventral margin, shortly
stipitate, shortly beaked, the seed-bearing parts marked as narrow rectangles.
Seeds c. 15.

D i s t r. Moluccas, New Guinea, New Britain and the Solomon Isl.,
widely planted in tropical countries as a fast-growing timber tree.

U s e s. In Sri Lanka sometimes used as a shade tree in coffee. It has soil-
improving properties. The soft, light wood is used for tea boxes and
planking. The tree may attain a height of 15 m and a diam. of 30 cm after
4 years.

6. Albizia lankaensis Kosterm. in Ceylon J. Sci. (Biol. Sci.) 13 (1 & 2): 255.
Sept. 1979.

Tree, branchlets densely, minutely pale brown tomentellous. Stipules
small, lanceolate, densely pubescent, caducous. Rachis 8–13 cm long, densely
tomentellous with a small gland about the middle of the petiolar part. Pinnae
10–16 pairs, 3–5 cm long, densely tomentellous (hairs erect), opposite and subopposite. Leaflets small, sessile, chartaceous, 10–31 pairs, linear, 4–6 × 1–1.5
mm, slightly overlapping, obtuse, base oblique, midrib slightly off the centre,
above glabrous, glossy, beneath very sparsely pilose (denser on the midrib).
Below the lower pinnae two small appendages. Flowers unknown. Pod strap-
shaped, thin, flat, reddish brown, slightly glossy, very minutely puberulous,
rounded both ends, distinctly, shortly, articulately pedicelled, up to 13 × 2.5
cm. Seeds 5–8, flat, oblong-elliptic, c. 7 × 4 mm with elliptic areole, brown,
glossy.

D i s t r. Only found above Frotoft Estate in mountain forest at c. 1500
m alt. In 1978 the forest was destroyed and the new species cut down.

N o t e. Resembling *A. amara*, but the indumentum different, the seeds
with a large areole and especially by the paired appendages below the lower
pinnae.

S p e c i m e n s E x a m i n e d. NUWARA ELIYA DISTRICT: Above
Frotoft Tea Estate, Ramboda, alt. c. 1500 m, wet mountain forest, trees low,
June, fr., *Kostermans s.n.* (L).

16. ABAREMA

Pittier, Arboles arbustos Legum. 56. 1927; Britton & Killip in Ann. N. York Acad. Sci. 35: 126. 1930; Kosterm. in Bull. 20, Organiz. Sci. Research Indon. 31. 1954.

Unarmed trees or shrubs. Leaves bipinnate, gland-bearing. Inflorescences apical and axillary, the flowers as those of *Pithecellobium*, arranged in pedunculate pseudo-umbels. Pod flattened, unilocular, falcate or circinate, slightly or not lobed at the ventral suture and here dehiscent, without pulp. Valves thin, twisted after dehiscence. Seeds lens-shaped, attached to a slender funicle usually with thin, brittle seed coat.

D i s t r. About 40 species, of which more than 20 in tropical S. America, 25 in Malesia, the others from India, Thailand, Burma, Indochina, Formosa. In Sri Lanka three species, two of which are endemic.

KEY TO THE SPECIES

```
1 Leaflets coriaceous or sub-coriaceous
  2 Rachillae densely rusty pubescent............................1. A. subcoriacea
  2 Rachillae glabrous.........................................2. A. abeywickramae
1 Leaflets thinly chartaceous to chartaceous.....................3. A. bigemina
```

1. **Abarema subcoriacea** (Thw.) Kosterm., Bull. 20, Organiz. Sci. Research Indon. 41. 1954.

Pithecolobium subcoriaceum Thw., Enum. Pl. Zeyl. 100. 1859; Benth., Trans. Linn. Soc. Lond. 30: 579. 1875; Beddome, Fl. sylv. 96. 1869; Baker in Hook. f., Fl. Br. Ind. 2: 305. 1878; Trimen, Cat. 30. 1885; Handb. Fl. Ceylon 2: 133. 1894; Bourdillon, Trees Travancore 163. 1908; Alston in Trimen, Handb. Fl. Ceylon 6: 100. 1931; Gamble, Fl. Pres. Madras 434. 1919; Worthington, Ceylon Trees t. 220. 1959.
Albizzia subcoriacea (Thw.) F. v. Mueller, Select. extratrop. Pl. 20. 1885.
Feuilleea subcoriacea (Thw.) O. Kuntze, Rev. Gen. Pl. 1: 189. 1891. Type: *Thwaites C.P. 337* (PDA, K).
Albizzia coriacea (sphalm.) ex Jackson, Index Kewensis 1: 71. 1895.
Pithecolobium anamallayanum Beddome, l.c. 189; Benth., l.c.; Trimen, l.c. Type: *Beddome 43* (CAL).

Small trees, up to 6 m high and 35 cm diam. Bole often twisted and gnarled. Bark dark brown to grey, roughish, peeling off in hard, quadrangular pieces. Live bark 4 mm, dark red to pink, outside green. Branchlets angular, rather thick, densely rusty pubescent. Pinnae up to 12 pairs (near the inflorescence sometimes only 2 pairs), petiolar part 1–6 cm long, with a large, circular cup or disk-like, almost sessile, gland a little above its base; rachis 2–14 cm long with similar glands a little below the bases of the pinnae. Pinnae diminishing in size from apex to base, the distal ones 4–10 cm long with similar glands between the base of the folioles, or glands, except the apical one, absent. Folioles up to 18 pairs, sessile, coriaceous, trapezoid, 4×10–2×5 mm, above glossy, midrib and lateral nerves prominulous, below laxly pubescent, rusty, the few lateral nerves rather patent, margins strongly incurved, apex acute, obtuse or sub-mucronulate. Inflorescences terminal, consisting of short (up to 12 cm), lax, densely rusty pubescent panicles, which are composed of fascicles of smaller panicles, which in turn consist of fascicles of peduncled flower heads. Peduncles up to 2 cm long. Flowers white, sessile, densely, minutely rusty tomentellous; bracts minute, lanceolate. Calyx campanulate, 3 mm long with ca 0.5 mm long, triangular, acute teeth. Corolla tube 5 mm long funnel-shaped, lobes lanceolate, 3 mm long, sericeous outside. Staminal tube as long as the corolla tube, free part of the filaments ca 7 mm long. Ovary glabrous. Pod circinate, flattened, minutely densely rusty pubescent, slightly undulate at the thinner ventral suture, up to 8 cm long and 1 cm wide, bullate over the seeds.

D i s t r.   Sri Lanka and S. India, above 1500 m alt.

S p e c i m e n s   E x a m i n e d.   KANDY DISTRICT: Knuckles, Corbets Gap, 1000 m alt., May, fr., *Kostermans 23519* (A, BO, G, K, L, P, PDA, US); Adam's Peak, May, fr., *Worthington 2731* (PDA). RATNAPURA DISTRICT: Balangoda Range, Debedde, Namunukula forest, 1000 m alt., June, fl., *Kostermans 24456* (A, BO, G, K, L, P, PDA, US), ibid., Aug., fr., *Worthington 5417* (PDA). NUWARA ELIYA DISTRICT: Hakgalle Jungle, 2000 m, May, fl., *Kostermans 24192* (A, BO, G, K, L, P, PDA, US). BADULLA DISTRICT: Adisham, Haputale, 1300 m alt., ster., *Worthington 5393* (PDA); Hope Estate, fl., *Worthington 6948* (PDA). LOCALITY UNKNOWN: buds, *Thwaites 337* (A, BO, CAL, K, L).

2. Abarema abeywickramae Kosterm. in Ceylon J. Sci. (Biol. Sci.) 9: 61, f. 1. 1971. Type: *Kostermans 23437* (PDA).

Tree, 4–7 m tall, 20 cm diam. Bark smooth, light brown or reddish-brown, 0.5 mm thick. Live bark 5 mm thick, dark or pale red. Wood white, without odour. Branchlets slender, glossy, at apex microscopically pilose. Leaves glabrous; rachis 1.5–7 cm long, bearing 2 pairs (rarely one) of pinnae; petiolar part with a small, disk-like, sessile, apically concave gland in the middle and a similar one between the bases of the upper pinnae. Pinnae 3–4 cm and more long (the lower shorter), slender, with tiny, sessile, disk-like glands between the bases of the 1–2 mm long petiolules. Leaflets lanceolate, the apical one largest, 0.5×2—3×9—3×10—3.5×10 cm, sub-coriaceous, acuminate with blunt point, conspicuously reticulate on both surfaces, lateral nerves c. 9–12 pairs. Panicles pseudo-terminal, lax, microscopically, laxly pilose, the

main peduncle 3–13 cm with few, widely separate branches with widely separate fascicles of stalked umbels. Peduncles filiform. Calyx sessile, tube less
than 0.5 mm long with minute teeth. Corolla tube broadly funnel-shaped,
1.5–2 mm long, lobes 1 mm, reflexed. Filament tube 1 mm, free part 5 mm
long. Ovary slender, hardly stipitate. Pod flat, circinate, or curved into a
circle, sometimes with a few constrictions between the seed-bearing parts,
ca 1.5 cm wide, rusty brown. Seeds black, small.

D i s t r. Endemic.

N o t e s. Close to *A. bigemina*, but the leaflets much smaller, thicker with
prominent reticulation and more lateral nerves. The seeds are smaller.

S p e c i m e n s E x a m i n e d. RATNAPURA DISTRICT: Belihuloya,
dirt road to Horton Plains, dry valley, alt. 600 m, rather common, May, fl.,
Kostermans 23437 (BO, PDA, US); ibid., May, fl., *Kostermans 23454 A* (id.);
ibid., dry fr., *Kostermans 23454* (id.); Hagele, above and west of Belihuloya,
alt. ca 1000 m, May, fl., *Kostermans 23619* (id.). KANDY DISTRICT: Nitre
Cave, Sept. 1888, *s. coll. s.n.*, fr. (PDA). LOCALITY UNKNOWN: fl. *s.
coll. C.P. 644* (PDA).

3. **Abarema bigemina** (L.) Kosterm. Bull. 20, Organiz. Sci. Research Indon.
51, fig. 34, 35. 1954.

Mimosa bigemina L., Sp. Pl. 517. 1753; ed. 2, 2: 1499. 1763; Burm. f., Fl. Ind.
222. 1768; Willd., Sp. Pl. 4 (2): 1007. 1806; Trimen, Handb. Fl. Ceylon 2:
132. 1894.
Inga bigemina (L.) Willd., l.c.; Wight & Arn., Prod., 1: 269. 1834 (excl. *Inga
lucida* Wall. & *Mimosa lucida* Roxb.); Moon, Cat. 73. 1824.
Pithecolobium bigeminum (L.) Mart., Herb. Fl. Brasil. in Flora 20, Beibl. 2:
115. 1837 (in observ.); Benth. in Hook. Lond. J. Bot. 3: 206. 1844; Thw.,
Enum. Pl. Zeyl. 100. 1859; Baker in Hook. f., Fl. Br. Ind. 2: 303. 1878; Als-
ton in Trimen, Handb. Fl. Ceylon 6: 100. 1931.
Spirolobus bigemina (L.) Raf., Sylv. Tell. 119. 1838; Merr., Index Rafinesq.
148. 1949.
Feuilleea bigemina (L.) O. Kuntze, Rev. Gen. Pl. 1: 187. 1891.
Albizzia bigemina (L.) F. v. Mueller, Sel. extratrop. Pl. 264. 1876. Type: *Her-
mann s.n.* (BM).
[*Ulhaenda* Hermann, Mus. Zeyl. 25. 1717; Burm., Thes. Zeyl. 231. 1737.
Mimosa foliis bigeminis (*acuminatis*), L., Fl. Zeyl. 97, no. 218. 1748 (excl.
Rheede)].

Tree, up to 10 m high and 30 cm diam. Bark dark brown, smooth, pustular, 0.5 mm thick. Live bark 5 mm, reddish. Wood white, soft with slight gar-
lic smell. Branchlets slender, glabrous. Leaves glabrous, petiolar part 4–6
cm and more long with large ovate or crater-shaped gland about the middle

or lower down. Pinnae 2–3 pairs, 5–9 cm long (proximal ones much shorter) with obscure, large, hardly raised glands between the petiolules. Folioles 2–4 pairs (lower pinnae usually 2 pairs), chartaceous, lanceolate to sub-oblanceolate, distal pair up to 8 × 16 cm, proximal ones sometimes only 1 × 2 cm, acuminate or bluntly caudate-acuminate, base acute, reticulation faint, the slender midrib and c. 7–9 pairs of slender, lateral nerves prominulous on both sides. Petiolules 1–5 mm long. Flowers cream, sessile in pseudo umbels on short peduncles arranged in a terminal, minutely pubescent panicle. Calyx broadly campanulate, about 1 mm long, minutely pubescent, teeth short. Corolla tube 2 mm long, lobes 2 mm long, ovate-lanceolate, slightly puberulous outside. Staminal tube as long as corolla tube, free part of filaments 3 mm. Ovary stipitate, puberulous. Pod circinate, 7–13 × 2 cm, flattened, glabrous, roughish, not indented between the seed-bearing parts, dirty brownred, bright brownish red inside. Seeds 5–8, dark blue, glossy, sub-globose, 1 cm diam, slightly flattened; funicle thin.

Distr. Ceylon, endemic (doubtfully in the Nicobars). Moist low country, up to 1300 m alt.

Specimens Examined. KANDY DISTRICT: Hunasgiriya, road to Mahyangane, 1000 m alt., June, fl. *Kostermans 24420, 24429, 25153* (A, BO, G, K, L, P, PDA, US); Nawalapitiya, roadside, Jan., fr., *Worthington 387* (PDA); Febr., fl., *Worthington 748* (PDA); Madulkelle, 700 m alt., July, fr., *Worthington 1992* (PDA); road Laxapana to Maskeliya near Doublecutting, 700 m alt., May, fl., *Kostermans 24063, 24077 A* (A, BO, G, K, L, P, PDA, US). BADULLA DISTRICT: Madawellagama, alt. 1000 m, June, fl., *Kostermans 24430* (A, BO, G, K, L, P, PDA, US). RATNAPURA DISTRICT: Kalawana-Morapitiya Rd., alt. 100 m, May, fr., *Kostermans 24703, 24704* (A, BO, G, K, L, P, PDA, US); above Carney's Estate, trail to Adam's Peak, July, fr., *Meyer 495* (PDA); id., June, fr., *Maxwell 951* (PDA); N. of Carney, June, fr., *Maxwell 950* (PDA); Gilimale, Dec., fl., *Tirvengadum 168* (PDA); ibid., July, fr., *Meyer 932* (PDA) GALLE DISTRICT: Udugama, Dolama. watte, 200 m, March, fl., *Cramer 3719* (PDA); Hinidumgoda, Hiniduma, March, fl. *Cramer 3714* (PDA); Hiniduma, Godakande, Sept., fl., *Kostermans* s.n. (A, BO, G, K, L, P, PDA, US). KALUTARA DISTRICT: Atweltota, West of Morapitiya, Aug., fr., *Meyer 1081* (PDA). LOCALITY UNKNOWN: fl., *Thwaites 644* (BO, CAL, K, P); ster., *Koenig s.n.* (C).

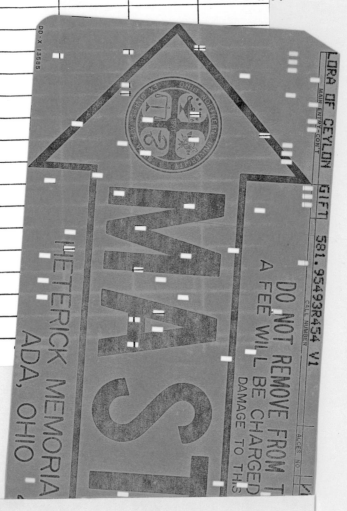